James W. Orr

599-3473

728

C10

C11

C12

C1279899-91

forest management:
regulation and valuation

THE AMERICAN FORESTRY SERIES

HENRY J. VAUX *Consulting Editor*

ALLEN AND SHARPE · *An Introduction to American Forestry*
BAKER · *Principles of Silviculture*
BOYCE · *Forest Pathology*
BROCKMAN · *Recreational Use of Wild Lands*
BROWN, PANSHIN, AND FORSAITH · *Textbook of Wood Technology*
  Volume II—*The Physical, Mechanical, and Chemical Properties of the Commercial Woods of the United States*
BRUCE AND SCHUMACHER · *Forest Mensuration*
CHAPMAN AND MEYER · *Forest Mensuration*
CHAPMAN AND MEYER · *Forest Valuation*
DANA · *Forest and Range Policy*
DAVIS · *Forest Management: Regulation and Valuation*
DAVIS · *Forest Fire: Control and Use*
DUERR · *Fundamentals of Forestry Economics*
GRAHAM AND KNIGHT · *Principles of Forest Entomology*
GUISE · *The Management of Farm Woodlands*
HARLOW AND HARRAR · *Textbook of Dendrology*
HUNT AND GARRATT · *Wood Preservation*
PANSHIN, DE ZEEUW, AND BROWN · *Textbook of Wood Technology*
  Volume I—*Structure, Identification, Uses, and Properties of the Commercial Woods of the United States*
PANSHIN, HARRAR, AND BETHEL · *Forest Products*
PRESTON · *Farm Wood Crops*
SHIRLEY · *Forestry and Its Career Opportunities*
STODDART AND SMITH · *Range Management*
TRIPPENSEE · *Wildlife Management*
  Volume I—*Upland Game and General Principles*
  Volume II—*Fur Bearers, Waterfowl, and Fish*
WACKERMAN, HAGENSTEIN AND MICHELL · *Harvesting Timber Crops*

Walter Mulford was consulting editor of this series from its inception in 1931 until January 1, 1952.

forest management: regulation and valuation

SECOND EDITION

Kenneth P. Davis

Professor of Forest Management
School of Natural Resources
The University of Michigan

McGRAW-HILL BOOK COMPANY

New York   St. Louis   San Francisco
Toronto   London   Sydney

to my wife
 Mary Shope Davis

preface

This book reflects over a decade of study, teaching, and participation in forest management since publication of its predecessor, "American Forest Management," in 1954. It follows the same general structure but has been rewritten in major part, strengthened, and enlarged through addition of new and deletion of old material. The subject matter has been broadened and balanced to meet developments. Illustrative material is drawn mainly from the United States—a country of very wide diversity in forest and practices and the country where my major experience lies—but much effort has been made to widen the applicability and usefulness of treatment. The hope is that wherever he may be or whatever he may be doing, a person interested in forest management will find that most of this book is written for him, at least in principle.

The central viewpoint is managerial. The book is written to and for the forest manager, since it is at this level that technological and economic problems must be resolved and decisions made. In large degree, successful forest management is the art of effective integration. This book treats primarily timber production, but clear recognition is maintained that the central core of the forester's concern is management for all resources. There is, consequently, a certain duality of purpose: to maintain a managerial outlook and to deal specifically with timber production as a major segment of forest land management. The purpose of the book is to be thorough in fundamentals and practical in their application. There is no necessary gap between theory and practice; applications can and do vary widely but rest on principles and techniques of wide applicability.

After an introductory chapter on the nature, purposes, development, and status of forest management, the book is organized into three parts. Part I gives methods and techniques of forest regulation for continued timber production. Part II deals with organization of a forest property as a whole. It includes forest administrative organization, timber management planning and plans, and, to obtain the continuing flow of forest information necessary for effective management, an entirely new chapter on inventory control.

The purpose of Part III is to give a concise and useful treatment of valuation principles and techniques applied to forest problems. There is much advantage in considering valuation in close relation to the biological and physical aspects of forest management. Sound knowledge of the forest is necessary to know what it is possible to do, but economic considerations largely control what can be done in a particular situation. The forest manager is continually confronted with choices, many of which necessitate value judgments. Valuation is regarded as an indispensable tool of management—a guide to making the best decision among alternatives.

The book is intended as a teaching instrument and as a useful reference; there should be no basic conflict between these aims. The teacher will find both opportunity and need to use illustrations and problems of his choosing. The forest practitioner will need to complement the treatment given here with experience and specific literature in meeting local problems.

It is impossible to name all those who have contributed ideas, materials, and help to this book and its predecessor. I will not try here. Looking back now on over 35 years of forestry experience, it is hard fairly to place labels on the who, when, where, and how of things. I express my sincere thanks to my many colleagues and students who have helped more than they know and absolve them from responsibility for errors of commission and omission which must remain mine. I shall, however, be deeply grateful to readers for bringing any of these matters to my attention. The dedication of this book reflects, among many other things, appreciation to my wife for typing of the manuscript.

KENNETH P. DAVIS

contents

appraisal problems. Appraisal when cutting to different diameter limits.

Importance and general methods of individual tree valuation. Development of a sample case from product values to value in the standing tree. Application of tree values; tree classes.

Purposes, uses, and conditioning factors. Application of single-factor analyses. Marginal analysis applied to an uneven-aged stand. Timber production schedule analyses. Guides to profitable utilization.

Nature, kinds, and purposes of damage appraisal. Legal aspects. Timberland damage.

1

introduction to forest management: nature, purposes, development, status

The Society of American Foresters (1958)[1] defines forest management as "The application of business methods and technical forestry principles to the operation of a forest property." This definition well brings out its many-sided nature. The task of forest management, as Roth (1925) stated many years ago, is "To build up, put in order, and keep in order a forest business." The arts, skills, and knowledge of forestry in its many branches achieve their full value only as they are integrated and applied in terms of successfully operated forest businesses.

Forest management is consequently the core, the mainline, of forestry. The forest manager is concerned with anything that affects the operation of the area in his charge. He needs to have the earthy and intimate forest understanding of the silviculturist, the long-range viewpoint of the planner, the skills of the administrator, and the alertness, flexibility, and all-around resourcefulness of a successful businessman.

The following indicates the wide range of subject material with which forest management is concerned.

[1] References cited are grouped by chapters or related groups of chapters in the Bibliography.

1

forest management

BUSINESS AND SOCIAL ASPECTS	TECHNOLOGICAL ASPECTS
Economics	Silvics and silviculture
Organization and administration	Mensuration
Finance	Logging and milling
Accounting	Wood technology
Statistics	Pathology
Marketing	Entomology
Business law	Fire control and use
Labor relations	Wildlife
Real estate	Recreation
Social and political science	Grazing
	Water
	Civil engineering

No individual can master all these subjects; yet forest management draws severally and collectively on all of them in its application. A well-rounded forest manager needs to have a general knowledge and appreciation of most of them and training in as many as possible. Above all, he must have a genuine sense and feeling for the forest as an entity. The following, written by a French forester, Charles Broilliard in 1860 (Trevor and Smythies, 1923), well states this and is equally applicable today:

> Forest management is also necessarily varied according to the forest concerned. All points of difference have therefore to be noted and indicated after the general rules applicable have been laid down. Every forest offers a real and living individuality. It differs from every other forest by its situation, its aspect and configuration; by its soil, by its component crops, and also by the character of the surrounding country. There are no two forests any more than two towns exactly alike, and it would be a great mistake to suppose that the management of forests adjoining each other or situated in the same region can be built up on the same framework or pattern. The forester labouring under so erroneous an impression would lack the very fundamental idea that should guide him, and instead of adapting himself to circumstances, would vainly endeavour to force circumstances to suit his silly imaginings.
>
> The great dangers to be avoided in forest management are preconceived ideas and foregone conclusions. Every rigid system refusing to yield to the varying requirements of different forests and localities must be equally vicious, and more than this, it must infallibly result in its staves [prescriptions] over-looking some important facts and indispensable conditions. Indeed, it is this very danger of carrying into effect preconceived opinions that justifies us in warning the forester against seeking any perfect solution of the

problem before him, the realization of any impossible ideal, and in advising him to confine himself to doing his best to obtain the results required. . . .

Although the general field of forest management is extremely broad in scope, its treatment as a specific subject necessarily must be limited. In addition to timber, well-defined fields of wildlife, range, recreation, and watershed management are also recognized. Each has important forestry relations, and each has a body of knowledge characteristic to it. In this book, the overall interest of the manager in all aspects of forest land management is maintained; but specific treatment is confined to the techniques and methods of management for timber production.

The book has, consequently, a certain duality of purpose that is necessitated by its subject material. Timber production is a major application of forest land management. The techniques of timber production, which are concerned with the establishment, measurement, control, and use of trees and other forest vegetation, apply in large degree to other forest land uses. These uses are, in fact, often exercised in relation to timber production through modification of cutting practice and related forest land treatment. Similarly, the managerial skills and integrative judgment requisite in timber production are no less important or useful in management for other forest land uses.

purposes of management

Forested lands are managed for a multiplicity of purposes, with usually one use, frequently timber production, dominant on a particular area. Forest lands can often be managed for several uses, sometimes on the same area and sometimes with different dominant uses assigned to separate areas. Management of the whole is directed to achieve the greatest total net benefit. A forest managed primarily for timber production can frequently, and with comparatively small adjustment, serve watershed, wildlife, or recreational purposes. In fact, a major use, well administered, often ensures others. In some situations, however, land uses are incompatible, one with another, and priority decision must be made. Grazing, for example, often does not fit in with timber or recreational use. Recreation is sometimes so strongly the dominant use that timber cutting, grazing, and hunting must be entirely suppressed.

Watershed management, to ensure that forest and other vegetative cover serve to protect and maintain water supplies to the fullest extent possible, is a consideration in most kinds of forest land management. It is frequently a dominant consideration; so much so, as in the case of municipal watersheds, that all other forms of use must be subordinated to it and often completely eliminated. Fortunately, however, watershed protection requirements are rather generally susceptible to harmonization with other forest land uses.

The dominant purpose for which a particular tract of forested land is managed is determined by the purposes of ownership and the general economic situation within which it must be operated. Indeed, it is a prime responsibility of the forest manager so to handle the tract that it best serves the purpose or purposes of management, whatever they may be. Beyond a definite and ingrained desire to see that the area in his charge is as efficiently and productively managed as possible and that the basic soil resource is maintained, he should avoid preconceived ideas or prejudices.

On lands in public ownership, whether municipal, county, state, or Federal, most forest uses and benefits are involved, and, in general, the larger the political unit, the broader its interest. This interest is frequently not measurable, at least directly, in monetary terms. The public is vitally concerned with water and will pay a survival price to ensure an adequate supply. It recognizes that recreation and wildlife are of major importance even though they are only partially measurable in dollar units. Questions of multiple use are usually important and frequently perplexing in the determination of the use of public lands. Decision concerning which lands should be used for what, and in what balance and proportion, is often one of the principal management problems on public lands, and the forester in public employment can expect to be deeply concerned with such questions. No formula can be given; decisions must be made in terms of particular situations, and each case requires careful and rational appraisal of alternatives.

Forest lands in private ownership produce the same general goods and services, whether monetary or not, as do public forest lands. Fish and game, for example, may be as abundant, even more so, on private as on public lands, and water is no respecter of property lines. But the interest of the private owner is limited, not because he is lacking in vision and public interest, but because he is usually concerned with only a portion of the total benefits and products that may be obtained from forest lands. If his measure is monetary, as is frequently the case, his interest is correspondingly focused on products from which direct monetary returns can be obtained. Industrial owners not only grow, sell, and buy stumpage, but must process and merchandise its products competitively. They are, consequently, concerned with both supply and demand as expressed in the market. Public ownership, in contrast, supplies only unprocessed forest goods and services to the market and is in a less competitive position. Management objectives on privately owned lands are consequently usually specific, often narrow in comparison with public interests, and focused on dollar revenue. A forester in such employment must understand and accept this situation. It is perfectly natural, normal, and proper.

It can happen, however, that private interests in forest management do not adequately protect public interests, which ultimately must be paramount. The public has an interest in all forest lands and expresses it in many ways through assistance to and cooperation with private owners. Protection against fire is an outstanding example. As a general principle, the public should expect to pay for clearly public interests in forest lands. Good management through private ownership will in large degree also protect public interests. Where this is possible the net benefit to the total economy is, in general, greater than through public ownership. Where the economic interests of private ownership do not suffice, the public must make up the difference in one way or another. A dominant problem of forest policy in many countries is to achieve a balance between private and public ownership-management of forest lands that is equitable to both and that ensures the protection of essential public interests. It must also be recognized that private business is part and parcel of public interest.

While the fundamental differences between forest management objectives on private and public lands must be recognized, it is easy to give them undue emphasis. It is more constructive and helpful to recognize and build upon the large area of common interest. Forest management is a business and this must be grasped in all its implications. Whether public or private, it demands much the same skill, technical knowledge, and general managerial ability. Any owner is concerned with managing his forest lands in a thoroughly businesslike manner to obtain the maximum benefits or returns whatever they may be or however measured. Forest management should be so approached. In fundamentals, a forest business is no different from any other business; the differences arise in application.

management for sustained yield

The basic aim of management is to keep forest lands productive. The idea of maintaining forest productivity distinguishes forestry as a profession from forest liquidation, no matter how skillfully the latter may be accomplished. Much has been written about sustained yield as a major objective of timber management, and it has been regarded as something of a general panacea. It is consequently important to understand what the term does and does not mean and its implications regarding timber production.

Sustained productivity may be thought of in two senses: as continuity of growth and continuity of yield or harvest. Confusion arises because the two often do not mean the same thing. For example, a tract of immature but currently unmerchantable even-aged timber may be well cared for and making excellent growth. The land is certainly productively employed and in this sense is being managed for sustained productivity. But since the timber is immature, its major harvest is in the future and the tract is not currently yielding a sustained cut or harvest related to its growth. In contrast, a forest area including a range of age or size classes may be managed as a unit to yield a sustained flow of harvested products as well as maintained in a state of continuous productivity from a growth standpoint.

Sustained-yield management, as the term is most accurately and commonly employed, means continuity of harvest.[1] Whether reckoned by years or by longer periods, the purpose is to obtain a sustained flow of products, a flow that may be currently increased or diminished in accordance with the purposes of management and the condition of the forest, but which may be continued indefinitely even though often at variable levels. The whole body of forest regulatory techniques is aimed at organization of a forest to bring about this sustained yield of harvested products in an efficient and orderly manner. Current harvest does not necessarily equal current growth, although in the long run and on the average it must.

The term "sustained yield" is sometimes rather broadly used separately from the word "management" to mean maintenance of forest productivity generally, whether of growth, harvest, or both. To use it so robs the term of its more specific meaning as applied to the management of a property. In this book, sustained yield is applied in its literal sense of meaning continuity of harvest from a forest area.

A full appreciation of the meaning and application of sustained yield necessitates that it be analyzed from several angles. In the following, it is considered regarding individual ownerships; economic production units, regionwide and nationwide; method of cutting; and intensity of management practice applied.

BY INDIVIDUAL OWNERSHIPS

Sustained yield by every forest owner is neither necessary, practicable, nor even desirable in many instances. Large public owners in most instances either are on a sustained-yield basis or aim to achieve it at the earliest possible time, usually in terms of rather sizable forest land units. Some public owners do not, however, press for strict sustained yield, being more concerned with protection, improving forest productivity, or other objectives. Most of the large private owners productively manage their lands for continued but not necessarily strictly sustained yield.

This situation is well illustrated by the pulp and paper industry, which has every reason and incentive to get and stay on a sustained-yield basis. Processing units are large and immobile and represent extremely heavy capital investments, yet few companies own sufficient timberlands fully to supply

---

[1] Sustained-yield management is defined by the Society of American Foresters (1958) as follows:

"Management of a forest property for continuous production with the aim of achieving, at the earliest practicable time, an approximate balance between net growth and harvest, either by annual or somewhat longer periods."

their mills. Most definitely plan to get a major part of their wood by purchase from other lands and regard it as sound business to do so. They naturally have a keen interest in seeing to it that a continued supply is available from lands other than their own. They expect to stay in business, own, and productively manage timberlands but are not on a sustained-yield basis so far as supplying their needs for forest products is concerned. Production from their own lands may or may not be organized on a strictly sustained-yield basis; much depends on current needs for wood and the procurement situation. The degree to which they practice sustained yield is not so important; what is important is the continued stability and prosperity of the forest economy of which they are a part and the productive management of forest lands they own or buy timber from.

The situation with small owners is complex. In the United States, there are about 3.8 million of them (U.S. Forest Service, 1958) in ownerships of less than 500 acres. Their actions and interests are extremely diverse. For a variety of reasons few practice sustained yield. The species, composition, age, and stocking of the stand and the size and situation of the ownership unit may not be suitable for sustained yield. Markets may be considered too unstable. Many owners do not have the technical knowledge or the necessary equipment to appreciate or practice continued production. Some hold forest land for speculative reasons and are not interested in managing it. Others regard their timberland essentially as a reserve for special needs and expect and desire harvest at irregular or periodic intervals only. Still others use timberlands primarily for grazing or other purposes and have only a secondary interest in organizing them for continuous timber production. Purposes of ownership are many, and often they do not include any particular incentive for sustained yield, even though good cutting practices may be employed.

BY ECONOMIC PRODUCTION UNITS

It is physically possible to get sustained yield from almost any size of ownership, but, as has been pointed out, it is often not practicable to do so. A more useful application of the sustained-yield concept is in terms of effective and economic operating units from the standpoint of both forest production and utilization. This is much more important than the size of the unit or its ownership.

Traditionally, sustained timber production has been sought through the organization of what are termed "working circles," which are operating forest land units of sufficient size to be managed effectively for continued production and to support a dependent local industry or community. Such units are most efficiently managed under a single ownership. There are many instances of intermingled ownerships in which consolidated management would be desirable at least from a managerial operating standpoint.

In the case of Federal and private lands in the United States, a legislative remedy is provided by the Federal Cooperative Sustained Yield Act,[1] which authorizes the Secretaries of Agriculture and Interior to enter into long-term contracts with private forest owners in establishing joint management on forest lands of intermingled Federal and private ownership when they can best be operated as a unit. Only one unit has been established (by 1966); long-term contracts of this nature have not been attractive to either public or private owners. A substantial area of forest land in the smaller ownerships is managed by large owners through a variety of leasing and other arrangements in some parts of the United States, notably the South. The major means of augmenting industrial control of forest lands is through mergers and consolidation of larger ownerships, or by direct purchase of smaller tracts.

Another approach is through cooperatives. For example, a number of small owners in an area may individually be unable to manage their lands effectively and market the products therefrom. Through a cooperative organization they may be able to get good timber-marking and harvesting service on the ground and, through pooling their production, market it much more effectively. Marketing may be in terms of rough products, such as logs or pulpwood, or of finished or semifinished articles resulting from operation of a cooperative processing plant, or it may be self-marketing for home use through group ownership of a small sawmill. Many such enterprises have been attempted, and they offer possibilities. Relatively few, however, have operated successfully for substantial periods of time in the United States. The reasons are the availability both of better markets and market information and of considerable technical assistance to small owners from both public and private sources. Industry procurement organizations in particular have well-established market outlets and offer marketing services and often management services as well. They perform some of the functions of cooperatives.

Considerations of utilization and economic welfare often demand that the approach to and concept of sustained yield be broadened to a community basis. The significant unit may be a single community, or it may be a large geographic trade area including several communities with allied economic interests. Good utilization requires more than a mill. It requires a group of processing plants collectively able to use and market the entire timber crop. This calls for a community or trade area of considerable size and a wide network of marketing outlets. Even large forest management production units such as a working circle are seldom self-sufficient from a utilization viewpoint.

Many sawmills, pulp mills, and other wood-using plants operate year after year with every prospect of continuing, but own little if any forest land. They are a part of community sustained yield. They are concerned

[1] Public Law 273, 78th Cong., 2d Sess., chap. 146, approved Mar. 29, 1944.

that reasonably good cutting practices are followed on the timberlands accessible from their mill for the cogent reason that their livelihood depends on the continued productivity of these lands.

Stability of employment and all the many related advantages and benefits that stem from sustained forest production can best be considered on a community or trade area basis. It is for this reason that public agencies sometimes place restrictions on where timber cut from their lands may be milled, at least so far as manufacture into lumber and other primary products is concerned. From the standpoint of the community, a continuing supply of available timber is what counts and not whether individual owners are or are not operating on a sustained-yield basis. Along with this, it must also be recognized that availability of a continued supply of raw material does not of itself necessarily ensure community stability. A forest industry is often as dependent upon markets for stability of employment as upon the source of raw material. A community may have an adequate timber supply but from a competitive standpoint may lack sufficient market outlets.

The fundamental need is that forest lands be kept productive. If this is done over any area of considerable size that includes a reasonable diversity of timber age classes, as is usually the case, then there will be a continued yield from that area, even though it may not be evenly distributed tract by tract or year by year. The difference between yields resulting from application of consistently productive forest practices and from a specific sustained-yield plan employing equally productive practices is one of timing and not of quantity or quality. There are strong self-adjusting forces of market outlets and the like that tend to even out the cut year by year. This explains why it is that forest production has continued on a comparatively stable basis year after year in many forest communities of the United States despite the fact that comparatively few forest owners in the area individually operate on a sustained-yield basis.

BY REGIONS AND NATIONWIDE

The general concept of sustained yield has been applied to major forest regions and to the country as a whole. Used in this way, forest growth is related to forest drain (by cutting and other agencies). If they are in approximate balance, either in total or in terms of certain classes of products, such as sawlogs, it can be said in a general sense that the area involved is on a sustained-yield basis for the particular class or classes of products being considered. The concept can be applied only to total area involved without respect to ownership, and it gives no information on size and character of individual or economic operating units. Comparisons and analyses of growth and drain are valuable in appraising the overall forest situation and in formulating national policies and programs.

It is not particularly helpful to apply the term "sustained yield" in this connection, as it loses its management significance. Sustained yield can best be considered in terms of the size and character of units for which it can be successfully organized on an operating basis.

Overall growth and drain data tell nothing about this. Growth and drain may be in approximate balance for a region as a whole and yet for particular communities and areas within the region be in poor balance and the forest economy of the region as a whole in undesirable condition because of these intraregional imbalances. This is even more true on a national basis. Much confusion and misunderstanding can be occasioned through lack of discrimination and care in interpreting and applying overall growth and drain statistics and in making inferences about sustained yield based on them.

RELATION TO METHOD OF CUTTING

It must be clearly recognized that application of forestry measures, even though they may keep the land productive, does not necessarily mean management for sustained yield. While application of the "technical forestry principles" included in the definition of forest management implies that some kind of positive forestry is practiced, nothing is specified, nor can be, about its character or effectiveness. There is a persistent popular notion, sometimes nurtured by foresters, that achievement of sustained yield requires application of a particular method of cutting. This is not true. Sustained yield can be brought about through the use of any of the standard regeneration systems. In fact, it is an actively debated question whether even- or uneven-aged forms of management are the more productive in certain forest types. What is true is that the method of cutting has much to do with the size of area upon which sustained yield can be applied successfully. A small woodlot composed of well-stocked, uneven-aged hardwoods can be managed to produce a harvest at annual or somewhat longer intervals under a selection or group-selection method. Sustained-yield management of even-aged stands requires larger areas for effective management. In extensively managed even-aged types, a minimum of several thousand acres is often necessary to organize and operate an economic sustained-yield unit.

Selection cutting is the method par excellence for the small woodlot owner, since it can readily be applied to small areas and ensures that a good growing stock is maintained at all times. Its use is consequently encouraged wherever possible. To put it another way, the selection method, by its nature, tends to ensure sustained yield and is often favored for this reason. But there are many forests, large and small, that cannot successfully be handled under a selection form of management. Basically, choice of cutting method is a matter of economic and silvicultural desirability and has no direct relation to sustained yield.

RELATION TO INTENSITY OF MANAGEMENT

Another popular idea is that sustained yield implies or requires fairly intensive forest practice. Reference to the definition of the term will show that there is no such implication. It is perfectly possible to organize for sustained yield on the basis of either extensive or intensive forestry. Which to adopt depends on economic circumstances and the wishes of management. In a number of areas in the United States there is sustained yield of a sort, but at an undesirably low level. The natural aim of a forester is to achieve the highest level of physical productivity possible, but this level must be consistent with sound business management. It is economics, not silviculture, that dictates the level of management possible. Except for practices resulting in actual site deterioration, like soil loss, there is little good or bad about silvicultural practices except as economic considerations make them so. Applied without qualification, the term "good silviculture" is meaningless.

The most significant thing about the relation of sustained yield to intensity of management is that organization for continued production is a powerful stimulus toward good forest practices. One tends to follow the other. If there is economic opportunity to manage lands for sustained production, a fairly good level of forest practice is usually most profitable and economic interest will ensure that the best possible practices are applied.

development of management in the United States

With a concept of the purposes of management and sustained production in mind, it will be helpful to give in broad outline the historical development of forest management in the United States.

Organized management has been slow to develop in the United States. The reasons have been many, mostly bound in with the unparalleled abundance of forest land and of commercially valuable timber with which this country was originally endowed and related to its general pattern of economic and political development. The establishment of the national forests in 1905, almost 300 years after the first permanent English settlement in America (Jamestown, Va., 1607), marked the first formal attempt to extend management to large forest areas. There were examples of effective and planned management before then by both private and public agencies, but the sum total was negligible. Even in 1905, protection against fire on any appreciable scale did not exist, protection against insects and diseases was practically unheard of, and the first few forest schools of the country, established at the turn of the century, had produced only a handful of technical trained foresters.

Nevertheless, inspired by their own zeal, these early foresters approached the staggering job of extending some form of management to immense forest areas with enthusiasm if not with adequate knowledge and facilities. Timber was of primary concern and the tendency that has persisted for many years to equate forest management with timber production has strong historical origin. There was much initial emphasis on silviculture. An intensity of practice was attempted in some of the earliest national forest timber sales that has scarcely been equaled since. The influence of intensive European forestry was strong, as brought to this country by early leaders like Pinchot, Fernow, Roth, and Schenck. For about three decades, the national forests set the forestry pace of the country and employed the majority of the professional foresters available.

It was early recognized that silviculture could not come first. The initial job was one of taming wild lands, opening up the country, building fire organizations, and establishing forest administration generally. Widespread and disastrous forest fires made it abundantly clear that fire control was an indispensable prerequisite to forest management of any sort (Davis, 1959). For many years, the tremendous job of extending some degree of protection against fire to the nation's forests crowded out any appreciable application of silvicultural measures. While management, some of it rather intensive, was practiced from the beginning mostly on the national forests, it developed slowly and large-scale application dates since the early 1930s.

As would be expected, development of lumbering considerably antedated timber growing as a business. Large-scale lumbering began about 1850; it was made possible by the development of the steam engine, circular saw, and the railroad and was given impetus by the great westward expansion of the country. Lumbering increased rapidly for the next half century, reaching a peak of annual lumber production of 46 billion board feet in 1906 and 1907 that has not been equaled since. This was a harvest of virgin timber of which there seemed to be a superabundance. The management problem of the industry in those days was to convert cheap standing timber into marketable forest products, mostly lumber, and plans were framed accordingly with timber regarded as a store. Such plans were successful as long as the store of timber was ample, and the investment in processing plants needed in its conversion was kept in balance both with the supply of timber and the consumer demand for forest products.

But the very nature of these plans, which treated the forest as a wasting asset, made stable continuation of a forest business impossible without continued purchase of more timber. As the national supply of readily available timber declined—that there was a limit to the supply became increasingly apparent after the turn of the century—additional stumpage became more expensive and difficult to acquire. A major part of the forest industry entering the twentieth century had a definitely limited operating life ahead of it, as measured by the store of existing timber available to it for cutting. At the same time, competition and the increased costs of carrying large tracts of virgin timber tended to encourage excess investments in conversion plants and in rapid cutting of timber stands in excess of normal demand. "Cut out and get out" became an increasingly common expression, and imbalance in the industry between available timber and operating capacity became an almost classic illustration of unsound investment. Continued operation of the timber industry on a wasting-asset basis became impossible. To stay in business, an operator's timber harvest must be related to growth, which measures the productive capacity of the forest in the long run.

This situation and fact was increasingly evident and was recognized during the first part of the present century. That action to meet it came slowly was probably inevitable. The existing timber industry was a product of its times and for many business reasons could not change its basic operating plans quickly. In fact, so long as the markets of the country were dominated by relatively cheap and high-quality virgin timber there was little incentive or reason for growing new timber crops.

Another large factor was that protection against fire during the early part of the century was not, in general, up to a level sufficient to make large investment in timberlands for permanent production a good business risk. For example, the advent during the thirties and forties of reasonably good fire control over much of the South had an almost miraculous effect on the forestry landscape. No other thing even approaches it as a force demonstrating and capitalizing on the great recuperative and growth capacity of southern forests and their possibilities for profitable management.

Still another factor was that the system of timberland taxation was not conducive to permanent production by those having large investments in mature timber. These and other reasons made the time not ripe for profitable commercial timber growing during the first part of the century except in comparatively few instances. Timber growing could not become practicable until it was also profitable.

Organized management of privately owned timberlands for continued production based on growth began to develop in appreciable volume during the late 1920s, primarily among the larger ownerships. It was halted by the depression during much of the 1930s but increased rapidly the following decade as a part of the intense industrial activity accompanying and following the Second World War. It was during this latter period that commercial management for sustained production became an accepted business practice. It can be said that by the mid-century point commercial private forestry, particularly among the larger owners, had definitely turned the corner and become a fact. The degree to which enlightened self-interest on privately owned lands will protect the wide public interest in forested lands is an actively debated question of American forest policy that is not the purpose of this book to answer.

In the early years of American forestry, timber was of major concern; there was plenty of forest land. But with an expanding population, pressures for other forest land uses have mounted along with that for timber. As timber growing became an established fact of large proportions at about the mid-century point, so have needs for forest land for other uses; there is not plenty of forest land. Forest managers are becoming acutely aware of these needs; everybody seems to want forest land for something—for recreation, game areas, reservoirs, rights-of-way, etc. Pressures of this kind necessitate searching analysis and application of integrated or, as commonly termed, multiple land use. In 1960, the U.S. Forest Service received specific legislative policy direction to so manage the national forests.[1] As the twentieth century progresses, mounting population pressure will accentuate this trend on both public and private lands. Management for timber production must be recognized as only a part, albeit of major area and economic importance, of forest land management.

status of timber management

What is the management status of American forests? In a country of the length, breadth, and diversity of the United States this question cannot be answered specifically; no one knows with precision. Forestry is on the march and far from being static; it changes every day. Nevertheless, there are some overall facts and statistics of significance and comparative stability that permit giving a general answer to the question and that must be grasped to understand the general situation in quantitative terms.

AREA AND OWNERSHIP

Both area and ownership appear to have come to comparative equilibrium and stability in the United States. The overall status is shown in Table 1.1 (U.S. Forest Service, 1965). Several facts stand out. Seventy-two percent of the commercial forest area is in private ownership. These lands include a larger share of the total timber growing capacity of the country than the acreages indicate, because Federal lands average lower in site quality than do lands in private ownership. Private lands are, therefore, of key importance in supplying the nation's timber needs.

Another item of large management significance is that 73 percent of the total commercial area is east of the Rocky Mountains, which virtually means east of the prairie states since the forest area of this region is small. Forty percent is in the South and over nine-tenths of this area is in private

[1] Public law 86–517, 86th Cong., June 12, 1960 .

TABLE 1.1. OWNERSHIP OF COMMERCIAL LANDS IN THE
UNITED STATES BY MAJOR REGIONS
(IN MILLIONS OF ACRES)

Ownership	East		West		Total
	North[a]	South[b]	Rocky Moun-tains[c]	Pacific Coast[d]	
Private:					
Forest industries...........	14.3	37.5	2.5	12.4	66.7
Farm.....................	55.5	78.9	8.8	7.8	151.0
Other...................	70.0	67.8	3.6	7.9	149.3
Total private...,........	139.8	184.2	14.9	28.1	367.0
Public:					
National forest...........	10.2	10.5	43.4	32.6	96.7
Other Federal............	2.3	3.6	4.9	5.6	16.4
State and local..............	19.5	2.8	2.4	4.0	28.7
Total public............	32.0	16.9	50.7	42.2	141.8
All ownerships...........	171.8	201.1	65.6	70.3	508.8

    [a] Central, Middle Atlantic, and Lake States, New England.
    [b] South Atlantic, East Gulf, Central Gulf, and West Gulf regions.
    [c] Northern and Southern Rocky Mountain regions.
    [d] Pacific Northwest (including Alaska), Pacific Southwest (including Hawaii)
regions.

ownership. While the bulk of the present standing sawtimber is in the West
(about 70 percent) and the current annual cut is much higher in the West
than in the East in relation to forest area, this is not a permanent thing.
As the virgin timber remaining in the West is cut over, the annual cut
will become more nearly proportional to the total commercial area. Forest
lands of the East (North and South) average somewhat higher in site quality than do lands in the West and hence in potential productivity. In the
long run this will count increasingly in commercial forest management.

CHARACTER OF MANAGEMENT PRACTICE

The character of management practiced is difficult to determine and
appraise since many things are involved, some almost impossible to measure
quantitatively. Intent of ownership is often an intangible thing; yet it may
be tremendously important in determining whether a given area is or will
be well managed, and also good intentions and even practices following
the best current knowledge do not always give good results on the ground.
Management must also be considered in relation to its economic setting;
it is a relative rather than an absolute matter. Existence of management

plans and provision for sustained yield is indicative of applied management but not conclusive evidence, as has been brought out.

In its reappraisal of the forest situation of the United States based on field work done mostly in 1953, the U.S. Forest Service (1958) developed a timber productivity index to classify recently cut areas into groups. The ratings are based on and combine four major elements: (1) existing stocking of desirable trees; (2) prospects for desirable stocking where present stocking is deficient; (3) composition of desirable species; (4) felling age rated in relation to the maximum average mean annual increment for the species or type. The ratings are based on "a standard or level considered reasonably attainable for the particular locality, site, and forest type under current and average operating situations" (U.S. Forest Service, 1958). Much judgment was necessary in making the ratings; they are relative to time and circumstances, and standards employed could have been higher or lower. They do, however, give a significant measure of total productivity. Summarized results are given in Table 1.2.

Productivity on industrial and public lands is the best, as might be expected. These are the largest owners with the most reason and facilities to apply productive cutting methods. Within industry, the pulp and paper group leads with an average of 84 percent in the upper level—96 percent for the South.

For the same reasons, only reversed, productivity is lowest on farm and "other private" lands. Further, within these two groups the smaller the ownership, the lower the level of productivity. The national importance of small ownerships is underlined by the fact that 83 percent of the total area of privately owned commercial forest lands, and 61 percent of the total area of all ownerships, is in these farm and smaller private lands.

TABLE 1.2. PRODUCTIVITY OF RECENTLY CUT
COMMERCIAL FOREST LAND IN THE
UNITED STATES, INCLUDING COASTAL ALASKA

Type of ownership	Total commercial forest land, million acres	Operating area,[a] million acres	Operating area by productivity classes, percent		
			Upper level	Middle level	Lower level
Forest industries...........	62	44	77	19	4
Farm.....................	165	53	41	37	22
Other private..............	131	42	52	28	20
Public....................	131	96	80	17	3
All ownerships...........	489	235	65	24	11

[a] Field examinations limited to operating units in which cutting had taken place from Jan. 1, 1947, through 1953.

What can be done to increase productivity on these lands is a major concern in American forestry. For many reasons, high productivity cannot be expected on a substantial proportion; the questions are: How much reasonably can be expected, and how can it be brought about?

A high level of timber management on all forest lands is not a necessary or even a desirable objective. The total forest growth potential of the United States is tremendous. The country does not need to grow timber intensively on all forest lands. What is important, nationally, is that there be a timber supply adequate to meet real needs however they may be determined or measured. It is the particular task of timber management to produce this timber where it can be most cheaply and efficiently grown and utilized. Some lands, because of low quality and remote situation, should receive only extensive management for timber production. These same lands may, however, have other important forest values requiring and justifying good management to perpetuate these values. Some forest lands of high site quality and easy accessibility should receive intensive management for timber production. Timber and other forest products should be grown where they can be grown best and most cheaply, other land uses considered, taking full advantage of the great opportunity for discriminating choice which the forest lands of the country offer. One of the most stimulating aspects of American forestry is the large scope for managerial initiative offered by this opportunity for wide choice.

CHARACTER OF THE FOREST AS AFFECTING MANAGEMENT

Another approach to a general grasp of the management situation is through appraisal of the character and condition of the forests of the country and appraisal of the nature of the problems they offer. To a considerable degree, the forests themselves set the general pattern of management.

In the West, where large areas of old-growth timber remain, practically all of softwood species, a major problem is to devise ways and means of harvesting these stands and putting the land on a producing basis. Virgin stands, while often of high commercial value, make little net growth, are usually irregularly stocked, and contain large volumes of low-value and often defective timber. Treatment of old-growth stands has dominated the western management picture in the past, and their cutting, regeneration, and utilization will continue to be important for years to come.

Depletion of old-growth timber is also placing increasing emphasis on the treatment of second-growth stands upon which management of the future must be based. Two general problems are involved. The first is the specific treatment of cutover areas. Some are poorly stocked or nonstocked. Others support plenty of good young trees and highly variable assortments of older trees. The need is primarily to restock, improve, and protect the stand. The second is the treatment of natural second-growth stands, many of which are approaching or have reached merchantable size. The need here, in addition to general stand improvement, is to determine a desirable level of growing stock under management and to apply cutting methods that will achieve it and also capture maximum growth possible in terms of usable products.

An overall problem is to coordinate cutting of old-growth and second-growth stands so that the transition from old to young and more productive timber can be accomplished with minimum disruption and shock to forest industries and dependent forest communities. A large owner planning for sustained production faces some difficult problems in scheduling the cutting of available old-growth timber. Such stands are very expensive, productivity is low, and likelihood of loss by insects, fire, and other agents is often high. A natural desire to cut these stands rapidly to liquidate the timber investment and to put the land to growing rather than storing timber must, however, be balanced against the need to maintain a reasonably stable cut during the transition period necessary for younger stands to reach merchantable size and to develop a more even proportion of all age classes on the property. Because most cutting in the West has been comparatively recent, there is often a good representation of the younger age classes. There is an oversupply of old-growth timber in many areas. But there is an almost chronic shortage of timber of intermediate age. Bridging this gap in an orderly way is a dominant management problem of the region. A major national trend toward fiber production to supply developing pulp and paper needs in relation to sawtimber production for lumber facilitates transition from old-growth to productive young stands.

The major management problems of the East differ considerably from those of the West. For all practical purposes, the virgin timber is gone and has been for some time, and the character of the forest has been profoundly changed by human actions. Timber is cut from young forests that were naturally or artificially established after cutting, forest fires, or agricultural use. Pulpwood production is dominant and becoming increasingly so. Large areas of plantations, especially in the Lake States and South, will become an increasingly important source of harvested products beginning in the latter 1960s. Particularly in the South, intensified timber-growing practice aimed primarily for pulpwood production has led to large-scale site improvement, preparation and planting work substantially enlarging the effective commercial area and increasing productivity.

The large amount of hardwoods in the East is another basic difference from the West where hardwoods are negligible in total significance. Hardwoods offer management and utilization problems greatly different from those offered by softwoods, and the many and variable hardwood-softwood mixtures extant make these problems particularly complex. In the northern part of the East, hardwoods predominate, comprising 83 percent of the total cubic foot timber volume. In the South, the corresponding proportion is 63 percent, which may be a surprise to those who consider the South predominantly a pine region. This is true regarding total value of products cut, but the hardwoods are there and they create problems. In fact, what to do with low-value hardwoods, often occupying or encroaching on pine types, is a major management and utilization problem. Much more study and attention needs to be given to hardwood management.

Natural stands tend to be understocked and of undesirable condition and species composition in both the North and South. Timber of sawtimber size and quality is in short supply. The principal commercial management problem of the East as a whole is how to build up stocking and quality and yet maintain a financially acceptable level of cutting. Private owners cannot wait until stands grow up; they must cut and sell products to stay in business. The problem of distributing the cut of old timber over a period of time sufficient to let the young timber reach merchantable size is almost entirely a western phenomenon.

As the results of better management and protection against fire, insects, and disease become more and more evident in the East, the supply of young timber of pulpwood size is increasing substantially, although such timber is frequently not of desirable species or quality. In hardwoods this is particularly true. The supply of pulpwood-sized timber is plentiful, though much of it is not currently merchantable. Hardwoods that can produce veneer-grade logs and furniture stock are, and will continue to be, very valuable; small and low-grade hardwood trees have relatively low value. A dominant management need is to bring about a desirable balance between size, quality, stocking, and species composition for pulpwood and sawtimber production. What this balance should be cannot be determined or measured by past history. Changing demands for timber and technological developments in utilization have had and will have profound influence. The trend is obviously toward production of pulpwood-sized timber although sawtimber will continue to be important.

forest management is a business

Another and probably most penetrating way of comprehending the status of forest management in a country is to recognize it as a business, as a segment of the total business community. This is particularly true in the United States where commercial forest lands are dominantly in private ownership and the owners must operate in a competitive economy. Many of the same forces apply to the management of publicly owned lands; raw materials from these lands also must be sold and processed and the final products distributed to the same markets. These considerations apply to other than timber forest uses too. Needs for recreation, wildlife, water, etc., also stem from the general economy and are a part of it. There is often a tendency to think that forestry affairs are somehow different or separate from others in the economy. They are in some particulars, but the large area of similarity is more important. In many respects one will learn more about the guiding forces of United States forestry by reading the general business journals and other material relating to the operation of the economy than by study of specific forestry literature.

While all business in a given area does not operate under the same conditions, there is much in common, particularly among certain business groups. Federal and state income and other tax laws tend to affect everybody alike. The same is true of social security, workman's compensation, and other social and industrial legislation. All businesses are served by the same general financial system and have more or less equal access to investment opportunities and financing services. Equipment and supplies are, for the most part, bought in general markets, and the products of forests are manufactured, distributed, and sold in competition with many others. Forest businessmen tend to have about the same general attitudes toward social problems, public controls, and such things as do other businessmen. They belong to the same service clubs and fraternal groups. The same general forces that operate to encourage or impede large or small business also affect forestry, which is both large and small business. Similarly, periods of general prosperity and depression affect forest businesses like others. Stripped to essentials, all business deals with the same managerial problems. Good administration is important in any business.

Some things are either peculiar to or of particular importance to forestry. The extreme length of the productive period is one of them. Few if any other businesses normally deal with a product that takes decades, or even a century or more, to grow. Another is the necessary identification of the "factory" (the tree) with the marketable product. In a shoe factory, for example, one cannot use up part of the factory itself to make more shoes. This can be done in forestry. There is no clear demarcation between growing stock, which for the most part is also marketable inventory, and the product that should be currently harvested. Also, the ratio between marketable inventory and products currently cut is very high, often 15 or 25 or more to 1. That is, there may be 15 to 25 merchantable volume units available in a forest to every 1 that should be harvested annually. There is a constant temptation to cut down trees that should be left standing for growing stock. Raw material supply and inventory control are consequently particularly critical and difficult problems in forestry and in part peculiar to it. But other businesses have supply and inventory problems too. Cyclic variations in demand for forest products are often wide, but this is scarcely peculiar to the timber business.

Capital requirements for forest production are extremely high. A 25,000-acre unit of well-stocked productive land in the charge of a unit forester can easily represent a total capital value of between 2 and 3 million dollars, including land, growing stock, and improvements. Counting all regular personnel and including overhead, the investment per employee is in the magnitude of several hundred thousand dollars. Few other industrial groups even compare with commercial forestry in per capita investment required.

While it is easy to see, to multiply, and sometimes to magnify differences, it is equally important to perceive and recognize a large area of similarity and common interest between forestry and many other businesses. The need is for balance and discrimination in recognizing both similarities and differences for what they are.

The United States is noted for the development of, high level of, and great importance attached to the arts of management. This is true of both public and private enterprises. Forestry is only one application. One will never understand the forces actuating forestry without at the same time understanding business and management in general.

part **1** *foundations of*
forest management

Part I deals with methods and techniques of forest regulation for continued timber production. It begins with the basic working tools of forest stocking, yield, and growth. These are applied in organizing even- and uneven-aged forest structures for continued production and in methods of determining the forest rotation and the volume of timber to be cut.

2
site, stocking, and spacing

The basic physical resources with which a forest manager works are the land and the timber growing upon it. "Site" expresses the capacity of a given area of land to grow timber or other vegetation. "Stocking" expresses the density of tree growth on the land, and "spacing" refers to its areal distribution. Site and stocking together determine growth and yield. The practicing forester has almost daily contact with matters of site and stocking; the technique of their determination are among his most frequently used working tools. A good knowledge of how to use them effectively is essential, and full advantage should be taken of the knowledge, skills, and arts of silviculture and mensuration. Detailed consideration of site and stocking measurement is given in the literature of these fields. The purpose here is to bring out their importance and application in forest management.

site quality in management

Site is defined by the Society of American Foresters (1958) as: "An area, considered as to its ecological factors with reference to capacity to produce forests or other vegetation; the combination of biotic, climatic, and soil conditions of an area." To put it more bluntly: How good is the land; how much timber can it grow? It is widely recognized that forest lands, even within a limited area, vary tremendously in their capacity to produce timber.

MEASUREMENT OF SITE

A first question about site is how to measure it and in what terms. It is theoretically possible to determine site directly by individually measuring the many factors affecting forest land productivity and integrating them into a single index of some sort. While attempts at direct site measurement have been made and are valuable in basic research on site factors, such an approach is not useful to the practicing forester. Indirect measures that integrate factors affecting site in terms of some readily definable and measurable indicator are necessary. Several such measures are employed.

Volume.   Since the payoff in timber production is the end product, nothing would seem more logical than to measure site in volume of desired materials produced, thus expressing in terms of the product itself the integrated net effect of all site factors. The capacity of a given area to produce timber as measured in volume per acre at a given age, or in the number of board feet, cubic feet, cords, or other units it can produce per acre per year, is indeed an ultimate aim in forest-site evaluation that should always be kept in mind. For a given area, and assuming a reasonably constant level of management, volume measure can be applied in the same way that farmers evaluate land quality by the number of bushels of wheat or corn it can produce per acre per year. As the business of timber growing becomes better established and more experience data are accumulated, volume (and quality) productivity can increasingly be applied as a final measure of site. In practice, however, the volume of timber on an area at a particular time and its growth during a specified period are affected by too many factors other than site, such as stocking, character of past cutting and partial yields that may have been obtained, species composition, and various agencies that have caused or may cause damage. Furthermore, measurement of volume and growth on an area are time-consuming and expensive jobs, particularly if done only to measure site.

Although volume or growth per unit of area is often an unsatisfactory measure of site, volume per tree in relation to age is a useful indicator. In a study of growth and yield of balsam fir in the Lake States (Gevorkiantz and Olsen, 1950), average cubic volume per tree was found to be a more sensitive and indicative measure of site quality than the height of dominant and codominant trees. Volume per tree reflects the effect of site on both height and diameter growth in terms of the usable product. The entire stand or the dominant and codominant trees only may be included in the volume measurements.

Soil.   The soil is basic, comparatively stable, and has a large and often controlling influence on tree growth. Site determination in terms of measurable soil factors offers many advantages. A principal advantage is that soil measures are independent of the timber stand and can be applied not only where well-developed stands of timber are present but also where they are absent, as in cutover, deforested, or nonforested areas where other than tree measures of site must be applied. Many studies relating measurable soil properties to site quality have been made in the United States (Lutz and Chandler, 1946; Coile, 1948, 1952; Coile and Schumacher, 1953; Zahner, 1958).

The correlation of site with soil survey types is often not close since site quality depends more on the thickness, structure, texture, and moisture characteristics of the soil, which soil survey types often do not describe. The correlation of soil with site quality improves "as the classification criteria are broadened to reflect as completely as possible the entire complex of ecologically important soil characteristics" (Lutz and Chandler, 1946). A number of useful and practical field methods of classifying soils in relation to site quality have been developed based on readily measurable soil properties. The "Manual for Forest Soils Evaluation" used by the Crown Zellerbach Corporation (Austin and Baisinger, 1950) and a field procedure manual for soil-site classification of pine land in south Arkansas and north Louisiana by Zahner (1957) are examples. Such manuals are of particular value in land acquisition and in guiding forestation work to get the right tree in the right place.

Lutz and Chandler give the following classification as including the most important soil characteristics from the standpoint of forest production:

1. Characters which are relatively permanent
   a. Thickness and texture of the *A* horizon
   b. Thickness, texture, structure, and consistency of the *B* horizon
   c. Texture and structure of the *C* horizon
   d. Nature of the underlying strata with respect to permeability to water and roots
   e. Nature of the parent material with respect to content of calcium (calcareous, noncalcareous)
   f. Position of the water table
   g. Content of rock in the soil
   h. Slope (degree and topographic position)
   i. Aspect
2. Characters which are subject to appreciable change during relatively short periods of time
   a. Humus-layer type
   b. Nitrogen content of the surface soil layers
   c. Structure of the surface soil layers

It must be recognized that site quality cannot be measured in terms of soil properties only. At best they can give no more than an indirect and cumulative indication of vegetative, biotic, climatic, and topographic factors which also may be very important. Different species often react differently to the same soil. Some are more exacting in their requirements than others and correspondingly more sensitive to soil differences. Trees of the same species may react differently to a given soil at different ages.

Lesser Vegetation. Considerable attention has been given, particularly in Scandinavia and Canada, to the use of plants among the lesser vegetation as indicators of site quality and as a basis for site classification. Under undisturbed natural conditions, in northern forests particularly, certain plants are characteristically associated with certain forest types and to a less specific degree with site quality within types. A forester should be aware of these relationships, since they can be of much practical usefulness in appraising forest land potentialities. A forester well grounded in ecology and plant indicators should be able to go into a forest area with which he is generally familiar and by looking only at the lower vegetation form a good judgment of what forest type the area does or could support and approximate the site quality.

Height Growth. Of all the indirect measures that have been investigated, tree height growth has been found to be the most practical, consistent, and generally useful indicator of forest-site quality. It is not a perfect measure by any means, but it is a good one and remains the standard by which other measures, such as soil properties, are compared. Height growth of trees in the dominant canopy is very sensitive to differences in site, strongly correlated with volume growth, and weakly related to stocking and species composition. Diameter growth, in contrast, is strongly correlated with stocking as would be expected.

The usual practice is to relate total height to age, both of which are, in temperate forests, relatively definite and measurable items. The assumption behind this is that measuring total height and age averages out climatic and other factors affecting growth, giving a stable indication of site quality. This has some limitations, however. Juvenile height growth is affected by factors other than site, for example, early competition. Total age is often not easy to determine and subject to some error as are height measurements. Also, beginning with early maturity, most species slow down in height growth, though they may be vigorous and growing rapidly in volume. Height growth consequently becomes less indicative of site quality. For these reasons, there is virtue in measuring height growth in relation to time for some intermediate portion of the bole. This eliminates early competition effects, and, for older trees, avoids including a period for which height growth is slow and often not a good measure of growth.

This idea of using an intercept distance on the middle bole as a measure of site is not new but is receiving renewed attention. It is most applicable where there are well-defined and visible annual branch whorls to measure. Wakeley and Marrero, 1958, for example, suggest starting at a fixed point on the bole, say the first whorl above the dbh point, and measuring 5 or more years of growth. An average annual height growth obtained in this way is certainly expressive of the capacity of the site to grow timber and is particularly significant under intensive practice as in plantations, for which the practice was proposed. Some difficulties are: (1) Measurement is not easy, and there are many species on which branch whorls are not consistently visible. (2) An intercept measurement does not necessarily indicate productivity throughout the significant life of a tree or of a stand from a management standpoint. Nevertheless, where the concept can be employed, it is useful in giving an indication of site growth potential not obscured by juvenile or older-age effects.

Heiberg and White (1956) propose a concept of current site evaluation and emphasize the dynamic rather than static nature of site. As has been emphasized, trees often do not grow consistently throughout their life (presumably on the same site) because of soil and other reasons. "What a stand is most likely to produce during the next five, ten, or twenty years is often of far greater importance to forest management than what it may produce throughout its life" (Heiberg and White, 1956). Current site quality can be estimated by measuring average height growth of dominant trees for the past few years. This can be related to total height-over-age curves.

Standard practice in the United States is to define site in terms of the total height in feet of trees that consistently have been in a dominant position in well-stocked stands (the dominant and codominant crown classes averaged together) at specified key ages, usually 50 and 100 years. Twenty to thirty years is the base age for stands maturing and/or primarily utilized at younger ages. Aspen, for example, commercially matures at around 40 years, and a 20-year base is appropriate. Site is expressed as a site-index number. For example, site index 60 on a 50-year base means that dominant trees will average 60 ft in total height at 50 years. Similarly, site index 140 on a 100-year base means that dominant trees will be 140 ft tall at 100 years. Site-index curves showing the average height of dominant and codominant trees of various ages have been prepared for most species by regions or more specific localities. Curves based on height for typical eastern and western species are given in Fig. 2.1. Note that in each case the curves pass through the height at the base age.

Site-index values on 50- or 100-year bases are commonly grouped in 5-ft, 10-ft, 20-ft, or sometimes broader classes. When expressed in broader classes, as 30 or 40 ft, they are sometimes denoted by Roman numerals and used to describe site quality in a general qualitative way as excellent, good, etc. This follows and is a carry-over from the older and more traditional practice of designating site in terms of four or five general productivity groups, based mainly on yield. Site I is the best site, Site II the next best, and so on. The difficulty with general qualitative groups is in identifying them specifically on the ground.

Site-index classes group all sites falling within the class interval. For example, when 10-ft classes are used, site-index class 120 on a 100-year base includes all sites that fall between 116 and 125 ft at the key age. In the United States, a 50-year base is generally used for eastern species and a 100-year base for the taller and longer-lived western conifers.

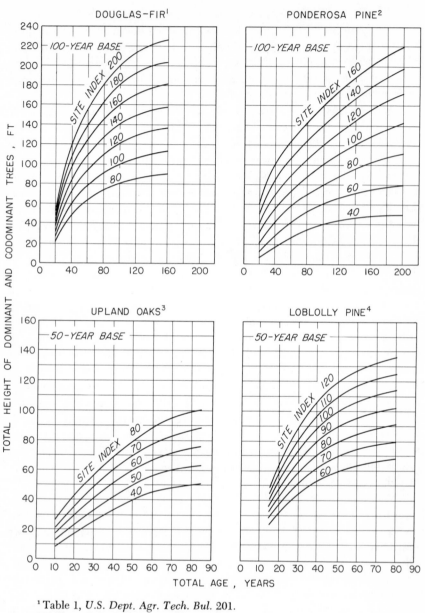

[1] Table 1, *U.S. Dept. Agr. Tech. Bul.* 201.
[2] Table 1, *U.S. Dept. Agr. Tech. Bul.* 630.
[3] Table 5, *U.S. Dept. Agr. Tech. Bul.* 560.
[4] Table 33, *U.S. Dept. Agr. Misc. Pub.* 50.

FIG. 2.1. SITE-INDEX CURVES FOR REPRESENTATIVE TIMBER SPECIES.

Height can also be expressed in number of logs, usually in units of 16 ft. This measure comes closer than total height to expressing site directly in terms of the usable product, which is the end objective. Timbermen often describe the general site quality of a stand in terms of the average number of logs per tree. While a good woodsman's practice, log heights are not sufficiently definite and consistent for general use in defining site.

Site determinations can be made for individual species in a stand or for the stand as a whole, although in the latter instance they are usually based on one or more key species in the stand. In even-aged stands, it is comparatively easy to identify dominant or codominant trees and to establish an average height. In uneven-aged stands, the process is not so simple, since ages are mixed and the crown canopy uneven. The best practice is usually to select a number of representative-appearing trees in the upper crown canopy that have grown evenly and at a moderately rapid rate, relative to the stand, throughout their lives. The heights of these trees in relation to their ages gives a measure of site index. Younger trees can also be measured if they have grown freely and normally.

IMPORTANCE OF SITE QUALITY IN MANAGEMENT

Productivity of timberlands varies tremendously by site quality. The practical importance of this fact is often given inadequate attention in the buying and selling of forest lands and in forest management generally. Studies of yields attainable from fully stocked natural stands at various ages give an excellent measure of relative differentials. Yields of such stands by site index for several United States species are shown in Fig. 2.2. Table 2.1 lists comparative yields for a number of eastern and western United States species for selected ages. The physical magnitude of the volume figures is not significant in this connection; attention should be directed to the comparative picture they give, particularly within species. The variation in yield on sites of different quality is truly astounding. Among the western conifers, for example, Douglas-fir site index 100 is a little less than a quarter as productive as site index 200. In western white pine, site index 80 is only half as productive as site index 100. The eastern species included show the same general picture. Even a 10-ft difference in site index may make 25 to 75 percent difference in possible yield at a given age.

These relative differences are persistent under management. Site quality can be markedly changed, however, by land treatment. Drainage of wet lands is an outstanding example; areas of low or negligible productivity can be transformed to good tree-growing sites by installation of a system of drainage ditches lowering the water table and changing physical and chemical soil properties. Subsoiling treatments to break up an impenetrable hardpan formation is another. Under intensive practice, irrigation and use of fertilizers can markedly change site quality as reflected by tree growth.

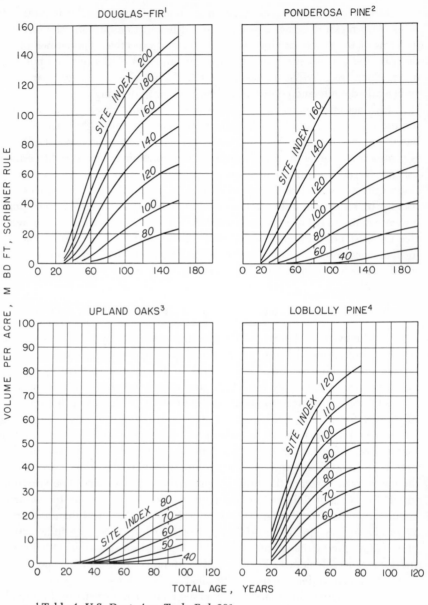

[1] Table 4, *U.S. Dept. Agr. Tech. Bul.* 201.
[2] Table 16, *U.S. Dept. Agr. Tech. Bul.* 630.
[3] Table 15, *U.S. Dept. Agr. Tech. Bul.* 560.
[4] Table 55, *U.S. Dept. Agr. Misc. Pub.* 50.

FIG. 2.2. VOLUME PER ACRE OF FULLY STOCKED STANDS OF REPRESENTATIVE TIMBER SPECIES.

TABLE 2.1. COMPARATIVE YIELDS PER ACRE FROM
FULLY STOCKED STANDS OF REPRESENTATIVE
EASTERN AND WESTERN UNITED STATES SPECIES
(VOLUMES IN M BOARD FEET PER ACRE)

Site index, ft	Eastern species, age 70 years, 50-year site-index base			
	Upland oaks[a]	Red gum[b]	Loblolly pine[c]	Longleaf[c] pine
40	4.2	.....	....	3.5
50	8.1	.....	....	9.0
60	12.8	.....	22.0	18.0
70	17.7	.....	29.5	29.0
80	23.1	23.1	38.0	40.0
90	.....	31.9	47.0	51.0
100	.....	41.9	57.0	61.0
110	.....	53.0	68.0	69.0
120	.....	64.0	79.5	

Site index, ft	Western species, age 120 years, 100-year site-index base			
	Douglas-fir[d]	Sitka spruce–[e] western hemlock	Western white[f] pine	Ponderosa[g] pine
40	.....	.....	....	1.5
50	.....	.....	....	7.0
60	.....	15.0	7.6	12.5
70	.....	.....	....	19.0
80	14.7	29.5	16.0	26.2
90	21.8	.....	....	34.7
100	30.4	53.5	32.2	44.6
110	40.7	.....	....	55.4
120	52.4	86.5	59.0	68.2
130	63.9	.....	....	82.8
140	75.0	124.5	81.0	
150	85.5			
160	95.5	157.5	96.0	
170	105.1			
180	114.1	186.0		
190	122.5			
200	131.1	211.5		
210	139.0			

[a] *U.S. Dept. Agr. Tech. Bul.* 560. International ⅛-in. rule, to a 5-in. top inside

Control of tree species, subordinate vegetation, and general vegetative density can also affect site quality over a period of time. There is evidence that site quality does change, even in natural stands during a period encompassed by average tree life spans. Only by rather drastic treatment can management make a good site out of a poor one; natural processes are slow. In general, one can not only grow more timber on a good site than on a poor site but do it at less cost.

Following are some important points to bear in mind about interpreting and using site-index data:

1. When making site-index comparisons, be careful to identify what age the index is based upon. For example, site index 80 on a 50-year base is excellent for upland oaks, whereas site index 80 for Sitka spruce and western hemlock in the West, which are rated on a 100-year age base, indicates a poor site.

2. A site index based on one age cannot be converted to another base according to any simple numerical relationship. Site index 60 on a 50-year base does not mean the same thing as site index 120 on a 100-year base unless the trees of the species involved are exactly twice as tall at 100 as at 50 years. Site indexes can be converted from one base age to another only by reference to the site curves themselves, which show actual tree heights at different ages. For example, dominant Douglas-fir trees on site index 140 on a 100-year base are shown in Fig. 2.1 to be about 95 ft tall at age 50. Site index 140 at 100 years would consequently correspond to about site index 95 on a 50-year base.

3. Similar site indexes for different species or species groups do not necessarily mean similar sites even when the same age base is used. Site measurement is relative to a particular species or species group. For example, site index 140 is very good for ponderosa pine but the same index is only fair for Douglas-fir in the Pacific Northwest. This may be partly because pine in general does not occupy as good sites as does West Coast Douglas-fir, but it is also due to the fact that the two species are very different as to tolerance and general habits of growth. The pine does not grow as tall as the fir even on the best sites. Consequently, pine and fir sites cannot be compared directly on the basis of site index alone.

Measured by site index, therefore, what is a "good" site for one species in relation to the areas on which it grows is not necessarily "good" for another species. If some universal measure of site could be developed, then "good" would always mean the same thing, even though individual species would naturally react differently on the same site. Various attempts have been made to develop a universal site measurement system but they have not been successful; tree height remains as a useful and consistent index. It must be remembered that site indexes compare dominant tree heights at a certain age; no more and no less.

4. Site-index measurements may indicate different site qualities for the

same species and area. These situations can be puzzling. One is the case in which height-age measurements indicate different site quality for the same age group, as an even-aged stand, at different time periods in its development. As pointed out previously, site quality can change. Although such changes are usually slow, aside from major changes like installation of a drainage system, they can be fairly quick and leave their growth imprint. For example, a series of wet years may impede soil drainage and aeration significantly, affect height growth, and induce tree damage, as reported for red pine (Stone, Morrow, and Welch, 1954). Another explanation is that trees of the same or different species do not react the same to site over time. For example, trees on porous soils may grow slowly at first but, because of opportunity for root expansion and the effect of certain zonal structure, later grow much more rapidly. Height growth is also affected by genetic differences within a species.

A more general explanation lies in the way conventional height-over-age site curves are constructed. The sampling basis may not be well balanced, more data being taken for certain ages and sites than for others. Further, curves are usually harmonized on the assumption that the curves are of the same shape for all sites, which is often not true. In reality, one is dealing with a whole family of curves represented only by broad averages, as in Fig. 2.1. Stands on certain sites may not follow these trends. In Douglas-fir, Carmean (1956) shows that serious error can result from using conventional curves for stands growing on gravelly or sandy soils or on those with imperfect internal drainage.

5. The unit of volume measure employed has a large influence on the productivity differences between sites. The comparisons in Table 2.1 are based on board feet. The differences are relatively much less when measured in cubic feet, including the total woody stem volume for trees of all diameters. Similarly, board foot volumes measured by the Doyle rule will show much greater differences between sites, and particularly in young

---

bark, including all trees having at least one 16-ft log.

[b] *Southern Forest Expt. Sta. Occas. Paper* 54. International ⅛-in. rule; trees 6.6 in. in diameter, breast high and larger; minimum top diameter 5 in. inside bark, including all trees with at least one log 12 ft long.

[c] *U.S. Dept. Agr. Misc. Pub.* 50. International ⅛-in. rule; trees 7 in. in diameter breast high and larger; minimum top diameter 5 in. inside bark; scaling by 16-ft logs.

[d] *U.S. Dept. Agr. Tech. Bul.* 201. Scribner rule; trees 12 in. and larger in diameter at breast height; minimum top diameter 8 in.; scaling by 16-ft logs.

[e] *U.S. Dept. Agr. Tech. Bul.* 544. Scribner rule; trees 11.6 in. and larger in diameter at breast height; minimum top diameter 8 in.; scaling by 16-ft logs.

[f] *U.S. Dept. Agr. Tech. Bul.* 323. Scribner rule; trees 12.6 in. and larger in diameter at breast height; minimum top diameter 6 in.; scaling by 16-ft logs. In the bulletin, site index is based on height at 50 years. It was converted to a 100-year base for use in this table by doubling the site-index values, since the curves show that trees are very nearly twice as tall at 100 years as at 50 years.

[g] *U.S. Dept. Agr. Tech. Bul.* 630. Scribner rule; trees 11.6 in. and larger in diameter at breast height; minimum top diameter 8 in.; scaling by 16-ft logs.

stands on the threshold of merchantability, than will be the case when the International rule is employed, because the former gives much lower board foot volumes for small trees.

6. The higher the value premium for production of quality timber, the more important site quality becomes, and vice versa. In growing hardwoods for furniture stock and veneer, site is tremendously important because large-size and high-quality timber can be grown more quickly on good sites than on poor ones. Conversely, in growing pulpwood on short rotations where any tree larger than 6 in. can be cut, site quality is relatively less important although substantial differences remain. In general, value production is more sensitive to site quality than is volume production.

7. In using site curves, it is important to know how the age and height of dominant and codominant trees were measured and averaged and how these dominants were defined. For one thing, it must be remembered that the average height of dominant trees can be arbitrarily changed by selection of trees in partial cuttings. Inconsistency and lack of uniformity in forest sampling and in measurement techniques are frequent reasons for difficulties in site quality comparisons.

The forest manager must be site-conscious and make full use of tree, soil, and vegetative measures where applicable. Site quality has a profound effect on the volume, value, and species of timber that can be best grown on an area. It affects regeneration and cultural practices such as cleanings, thinnings, pruning, and improvement cuttings. Management practice must be related to site. Under given economic conditions, good sites respond to and justify more intensive management for timber production than do poor sites. The concept of site, as described here, is applied to timber growing. The quality of land for other uses, such as watershed protection, recreation, or wildlife, must be rated on an entirely different basis.

forest stocking

Site quality determines how much timber can be grown on an area. Forest stocking measures the extent to which the realizable productive capacity of a forest site is being utilized by tree growth at a given time.[1] Most cutover and natural stands are only partially stocked. Improving stocking and maintaining it at a desirable level is a major objective of the forest manager. Understocking, both in total density and in trees of desirable species and form, is a widespread forest problem.

A particular forest site has a finite timber production potential for

[1] Stocking is defined by the Society of American Foresters (1958) as "an indication of the number of trees in a stand as compared to the desirable number for best growth and management; such as well-stocked, over-stocked, partially stocked."

a given species or species association. That is, full use of the existing soil, moisture conditions, temperature, and other ingredients of site can produce only so much woody growth per unit of time. Much research has shown that maximum or near-maximum growth can occur over a fairly wide range of stocking as it is commonly measured. Site quality is regarded as relatively constant, though it can change as pointed out in the preceding section.

A high proportion of the costs of forest land management are relatively constant by area. It costs as much, and often more, to protect a partially stocked area from fire, insects, and disease as to protect a well-stocked area. The same mileage of utilization roads is required. Taxes and administrative costs are determined primarily by area rather than by stocking. If an area is to be managed for timber production at all, there are consequently strong financial reasons why a forest manager wants to get and maintain a level of stocking that will lead to maximum value growth.

A knowledge of stocking and its measurement gives the forester a means of checking on the amount of growing stock present at a given time. If he knows the total amount of tree growth an area should support under his conditions of management, he can then effectively exercise judgment as to just what *kind* of trees should compose this total to suit his purposes best. To the extent he can thin and make other cuttings, he can exercise much control over the density of the stand and more particularly over the species composition, quality, and size of trees composing it. To a considerable degree, the forester can take his choice whether to grow few large trees or many small trees, good trees or poor trees for certain purposes, but the total amount of growth he can get is fairly definitely fixed by the site.

MEASUREMENT OF STOCKING

Forest stocking, as well as site, is essentially a relative matter as evidenced by the fact that stocking is almost always expressed as a percentage or index number in relation to some standard. For example, if the volume per acre in a particular stand is 3,000 cu ft and that in a stand used as a basis for comparison is 3,800 cu ft, the stocking is 3,000/3,800 × 100 or 79 percent. The same procedure holds for any other measurement units employed. It has been customary to measure stocking in relation to what is judged to be the maximum stocking physically possible for the age, site, and species involved. However, stocking must be considered for a stand not only as it is at a given time but also as it probably will be developed and used in the future. A given area may be only partially stocked in relation to what it could support at that time. But looking ahead to future utilization, one may find that the trees present are of a size, character, distribution, and number sufficient to produce the full harvest of which the site is capable. From this standpoint the stand is fully stocked, and greater stocking might even reduce future yields. If this were not so, there would be little purpose in making thinnings, aside from the value of the products obtained, as they certainly reduce current stocking. There is no infallible way to decide upon the proper base for determination of a stocking percentage. Judgment is essential; stocking is a relative rather than an absolute figure and this should never be forgotten.

For practical field use, a good measure of stocking should be easily measurable, consistent, definite, economical, and useful. A number of methods have been developed, and stocking has been the subject of considerable research. Important measures of stocking are described below with emphasis on their utility in management.

Volume. Volume can be and often is used as a measure of stocking. In the same way as it is used with site, volume directly measures the desired product and consequently is a logical measure. Ultimately, stocking must be expressed in terms of merchantable volume. The volume of a stand compared with a norm based on fully stocked stands for the species and site or with some other empirical standard gives a useful expression of stocking.

Stand data from an upland oak forest in the Lake States (Table 2.2) illustrate the point. As shown, the stand is apparently only about half-stocked in board feet measure. In cubic feet and basal area, the stand is about 80 percent stocked. What these figures mean depends on the validity of the comparison, that is, whether the standards and units of measurement are directly comparable (as they are not in this case), and on just what stocking this particular stand should have for best future growth. The latter depends on the precise kind, size distribution, and condition of trees making up the stand and on the purposes of management. Stocking figures based on volume are controlled by the method of their determination; strict comparability of measurement is essential for valid comparisons.

Basal Area. Basal area is defined as the total cross-sectional area of the trees in the stand measured in square feet (in the United States, outside bark at $4\frac{1}{2}$ ft above the average ground level). It has been found to be a con-

TABLE 2.2. STAND DATA FOR AN UPLAND OAK FOREST

Item	Fully stocked stand per acre (Schnur, 1937)	Actual stand per acre	Stocking percentage of actual stand
Volume, bd ft (International).....	17,000	8,980	53
Volume, cu ft.................	3,490	2,810	81
Basal area, sq ft...............	127	100.2	79
Average age main stand.........	85	85	
Site index....................	60	60	

sistent, easily determined, and useful measure of stocking directly measuring density, and is widely used. Basal area is often computed from a basal area table as included in the Appendix. A simple method of direct computation is to square the individual diameters in inches, weighting by number of trees if working from a stand table, and either to divide their sum by 183.35 or to multiply it by 0.005454. The result is in square feet.

Yield studies covering a wide range of species and localities have shown that stands tend to have characteristic and relatively stable basal area patterns in relation to age and site. Basal area in fully stocked stands increases rapidly during the youth of the stand and then levels off, increasing more slowly and sometimes not at all in later years. With some species, the basal area curve becomes fairly flat early in the life of the stand. Loblolly pine is an example. The basal area per acre in ponderosa pine levels off at about 60 years. For some other species, such as western white pine and Douglas-fir, basal area increases throughout the life of the stand, although it slows down considerably after about 100 years. Basal area per acre increases with site index, and the better the site, the more basal area increases with age.

While showing what stands can carry at different ages and on different sites is indicative of some general forest trends, basal areas as given by yield tables do not necessarily define what stands should carry under management to make best growth. The basic question is not what stocking an area can support but how much it should support in terms of specific kinds and species of trees.

Number and Distribution of Trees. Although the total number of trees per acre is a simple and logical measure of stocking, its use often offers difficulty in practice, basically because the total number of trees is unweighted by size, which affects stand density. Fluctuations in number of trees in natural stands are often wide and erratic, particularly in the smaller diameters. The total number is consequently strongly influenced by the lower diameter limit included, and the presence or absence of large numbers of little trees may or may not be of practical significance. For example, including trees 1 in. in diameter and larger in a pole-sized stand might indicate several times the number of trees obtained by measuring only trees 3 in. and larger without the difference meaning much. Disproportionate numbers of large trees also contribute to variable results. For these reasons, percentage comparisons of actual stands with desirably stocked stands in number of trees only usually give inconsistent results. Number of trees in the dominant stand is a more consistent and useful basis.

In very young natural stands, the number of trees measured in terms of their distribution rather than total number gives a useful measure of effective stocking that is widely used. It is termed the "stocked-quadrat method" (Cowlin, 1932; Haig, 1931; Lowdermilk, 1921; and others) and consists of determining, by field sampling methods, the percentage of square units of designated size that are occupied by one or more established seedlings or saplings of desirable species. The size of the quadrat used is essentially a matter of choice and depends on what is considered a good tree distribution unit under particular circumstances. Four milacres, a square 13.2 by 13.2 ft, is frequently used. An area 100 percent stocked on this basis would have a minimum of 250 well-distributed trees per acre, while an area 80 percent stocked in terms of 4-milacre quadrats means that there are at least 0.80×250, or 200 well-distributed trees per acre. The total number of trees on an area determined as 100 percent stocked on a 4-milacre basis would be considerably more than 250 per acre and is not determined by this method. However, it can be estimated in a general way from stocked-quadrat percentages, as has been done by Wellner (1940) and others.

Bole Area.   The actual surface or growing area of the main stem of the tree, termed "bole area," has been proposed as an expression of growing stock (Lexen, 1943). The approach offers interesting possibilities since it directly measures the total area of bole cambium, which, of course, is where all bole growth takes place. Using this measure, one can express growing stock in number of square feet of bole area per acre, which can be related to some standard. The measure is definite, quantitative, not particularly difficult to compute, and directly related to tree growth. As with tree height, it is most applicable in young conifers where the bole is mostly in a single and readily measured stem. In a spreading elm tree, for example, it is rather difficult to define what is the main stem and what are the branches.

Crown Closure.   The proportion of the total land area covered by the vertical projection of the tree crowns gives an expression of relative density of particular utility in connection with the use of aerial photographs. The relative density of a stand is readily apparent from the air, and various devices have been developed for measuring crown closure from aerial photographs (Spurr, 1960). It is usually expressed as a percentage of full canopy cover and is often grouped into broad classes such as dense, medium, or open, each expressing a specified range in percentage of crown closure. Crown diameter, number of crowns, and tree height (to a fair degree of accuracy in some stands) can also be determined from aerial photographs. Through integration of these measures, it is possible to estimate basal area and cubic foot and board foot volume from photographs, and stocking consequently can be estimated in at least general terms. Ground sampling is usually needed to give useful accuracy.

Stand Density Indexes and Ratios.   Certain mathematical relationships have been observed between number of trees, average diameter, basal area, and volume that can be utilized in constructing indexes and ratios as a measure of stand density or stocking. A stand density index developed by Reineke (1933) is well known and has been used to some extent. It is based on the fact that in even-aged natural stands, the number of trees in different diameter classes is distributed in a fairly definite frequency pattern often approaching that of the normal curve of error or symmetrical bell-shaped distribution. The form of the frequency curve varies somewhat by species but for a given species is fairly consistent and characteristic regardless of age or site. Since the distribution pattern is reasonably constant for a given species, and to a considerable degree between species, it may be approximately described by the average diameter alone. For a stand of given average diameter, consequently, the greater the number of trees, the higher the stand density.

The stand density index is built on this principle. In application, the number of trees and the average diameter for a particular stand are obtained by field sampling. By means of a reference curve giving corresponding values for fully stocked stands, the relative density of the stand can be determined, usually expressed in percentage form. The method does not require the determination of either age or site for its application. It has the disadvantages of limited applicability in uneven-aged and abnormally stocked stands and the fact that it places much weight on the total number of trees.

This principle has been applied to measuring density in relation to yield tables for fully stocked stands by Bruce (McArdle, Meyer, and Bruce, 1949), who revised the Douglas-fir yield tables to base them on average stand diameter. He prepared a table giving the number of trees and other stand values in relation to the average diameter without reference to either age or site. For example, for an average dbh of 12 in., the table gives 280 trees as normal for fully stocked stands. If an actual stand of the same average diameter had 210 trees, it could be considered as 210/280, or 75 percent stocked.

As shown, there are a number of methods of widely varying types for measuring and expressing forest stocking. The forest manager needs a general knowledge of them so that he can use the one best suited to his purpose. Ultimately, all measures must be related to the volume units in which the forester is interested. It should always be kept in mind that the management purpose of measuring stocking is to find how much stocking there is in relation to what there should be as a guide to cutting practice.

spacing figures and guides

While the space actually occupied or required by the roots and crowns of individual trees is difficult to determine, average space-size relationships can be estimated. In general, trees occupy and need space in proportion to their size. Hence, all spacing figures must be based on some measure of tree size whether it be diameter, height, crown spread, or crown volume. Advantage can be taken of arithmetical relationships existing between tree spacing, tree size (diameter), tree height, number of trees, basal area, cubic and board foot volume, and stocking to develop several useful rule-of-thumb guides to stocking and spacing. It is important to understand clearly their nature and application.

GUIDES BASED ON DIAMETER

Stocking as measured in basal area can readily be expressed in terms of tree diameter and number of trees per acre in a very useful way. Suppose, for example, that a young stand is to be thinned to leave 90 sq ft of basal area per acre in well-distributed trees of desirable form and species. What number of trees and average between-tree spacing is necessary to obtain this stocking? For 6-in. trees, as an illustration, the solution is as follows: The basal area of a 6-in. tree is 0.196 sq ft. There consequently would have to be 90/0.196, or 459 trees per acre, if they averaged 6 in. in diameter. The average land area per tree is the number of square feet per acre, 43,560, divided by 495, or 95 sq ft. Assuming that trees tend to be arranged at the corners of squares of equal size, the average between-tree spacing is $\sqrt{95}$, or 9.7 ft.

For 10-in. trees and the same basal area, a similar calculation gives

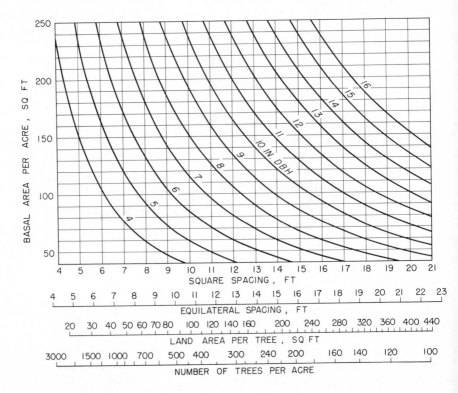

FIG. **2.3.** SPACING DIAGRAM.

165 trees per acre and 16.2 ft as the average spacing between them. These calculations can be made for any other tree size and basal area assumed. Figure 2.3 is a spacing chart useful in graphic solution of such problems. Arithmetical solutions for most spacing problems are given in Table 2.3.

It should be noted that two kinds of spacing, square and equilateral, are shown in the horizontal scales of Fig. 2.3. The easiest arithmetical as-

TABLE 2.3. SOLUTION OF SPACING PROBLEMS, SQUARE SPACING, ACRE BASIS

Given	Desired	Formula for solution	Numerical example
No. of trees BA	1. Between-tree spacing 2. Av diam (diam of tree of average basal area) 3. "Diameter times" spacing figure 4. "Diameter plus" spacing figure	1. $\sqrt{\dfrac{\text{sq ft per acre}}{\text{no. of trees}}}$ 2. $\sqrt{\dfrac{183.3\ \text{basal area}^a}{\text{no. of trees}}}$ 3. $\dfrac{\text{spacing per tree}}{\text{av diam}}$ 4. Spacing per tree minus av diam	Assume 200 trees and 90 sq ft of BA: 1. $\sqrt{\dfrac{43,560}{200}} = 14.8$ ft 2. $\sqrt{\dfrac{183.3 \times 90}{200}} = 9.1$ in. 3. $\dfrac{14.8}{9.1} = 1.6$ 4. $14.8 - 9.1 = 5.7$
BA Av diam	Number of trees	$\dfrac{\text{BA per acre}}{\text{BA per tree}}$	Assume 100 sq ft BA and av stand diam of 12 in. (0.785 sq ft): $\dfrac{100}{0.785} = 127$ trees per acre
Between-tree spacing Av diam	1. Number of trees 2. BA	1. $\dfrac{\text{sq ft per acre}}{\text{spacing}^2}$ 2. No. of trees $\times$ BA per tree	Assume average spacing of 10.5 ft and av diam of 8 in. (0.349 sq ft): 1. $\dfrac{43,560}{10.5^2} = 395$ trees per acre 2. $395 \times 0.349 = 138$
BA	"Diameter times" spacing figure	$\dfrac{15.4^b}{\sqrt{\text{BA}}}$	Assume 125 sq ft BA: $\dfrac{15.4}{\sqrt{125}} = 1.38$
"Diameter times" spacing figure	BA	$\left(\dfrac{15.4}{\text{spacing figure}}\right)^2$	Assume spacing figure of 1.4: $\left(\dfrac{15.4}{1.4}\right)^2 = 121$ sq ft BA

[a] The basal area in square feet of the tree of average diameter $= \dfrac{\pi d^2}{4 \times 144}$.

Also the basal area of tree of average diameter $= \dfrac{\text{basal area per acre}}{\text{no. of trees per acre}}$.

Equating the two expressions, $\dfrac{\pi d^2}{4 \times 144} = \dfrac{\text{basal area}}{\text{no. of trees}}$.

Solving, $d = \sqrt{\dfrac{183.3\ \text{basal area}}{\text{no. of trees}}}$.

[b] See derivation of this formula given on p. 45.

sumption is that trees tend to be distributed at the corners of squares, in which case the between-tree spacing is the square root of the average number of square feet available per tree. It is equally logical, however, to suppose that trees are spaced equidistant in all directions and hence tend to occupy the corners of equilateral triangles. The space occupied per tree is then hexagonal in form. The between-tree spacing is accordingly twice the distance from the center of the hexagon to the midpoint of a side. An equilateral arrangement is the most efficient spacing possible, and between-tree spacing can be determined on this basis. Letting A equal the area of the hexagon and S the between-tree spacing, or twice the radius of the hexagon,

$$A = 6 \left[\left(\frac{S}{2} \right)^2 \tan 30° \right]$$
$$A = 0.866S^2$$

Also

$$S = \sqrt{\frac{A}{0.866}}$$

To illustrate the use of these formulas, assume that the average between-tree spacing is 18 ft and that the trees are equilaterally distributed. The average area per tree is consequently $18^2 \times 0.866$, or 281 sq ft, and there are $43,560/281$, or 155 trees per acre. The process can be readily reversed to solve for the spacing if the number per acre is known. For example, suppose there are 250 trees per acre. What is the average equilateral spacing? The average area per tree is $43,560/250$, or 174 sq ft. The between-tree spacing is accordingly $\sqrt{174/0.866}$, or 14.1 ft.

Except in plantations, trees in the forest are not distributed in any fixed geometric pattern. In well-stocked young natural stands, with uniform soil conditions, it is reasonable to suppose that trees tend to assume a more or less equilateral distribution as a result of competition. This distribution is upset, of course, by inequalities in the soil and various agencies causing damage to the stand. The effect of these agencies is likely to become increasingly evident as the stand becomes older. Even-aged mature natural stands usually exhibit a rather irregular and patchy tree distribution pattern. Matters of spacing are most important in pole-sized stands in which there is considerable competition. Here, an assumption of equilateral or the somewhat less efficient square spacing becomes a reasonably good approximation of average distribution. Square spacing is the simplest assumption and is commonly employed. In Table 2.3 and elsewhere in this book all spacing figures given are based on the assumption of square spacing. It is well to bear in mind, however that square spacing is not the only kind, and equilateral spacing is possibly a more logical assumption where trees are in direct competition.

For use as a field marking guide it is convenient to express spacing directly as a ratio of diameter. As determined previously, the average square spacing of 6-in. trees, when there are 90 sq ft of basal area per acre, is 9.7 ft. The ratio is accordingly 9.7/6, or 1.62. This means that for every inch of diameter there should be 1.62 times as much spacing in feet $(6 \times 1.62 = 9.7 \text{ ft})$. For convenience, this ratio is here termed a "diameter times" spacing figure as an abbreviation of "diameter times a constant." For 10-in. trees and the same basal area the relation is 16.2/10, or also 1.62. For any specified basal area per acre, the ratio between diameter in inches and spacing in feet is a constant; mathematically it has to be.

A formula useful in computing the "diameter times" spacing figure or constant for any given basal area per acre is

$$C = \frac{15.4}{\sqrt{\text{basal area}}} \quad *$$

* This formula is derived as follows:

Let S = spacing between trees, ft (square spacing)

$\quad d$ = tree diameter, in.

$\quad C$ = spacing figure or S/d

BA = basal area per acre

Then

$$S = \sqrt{\frac{\text{number of square feet per acre}}{\text{number of trees per acre}}}$$

The basal area in square feet per tree is determined as follows:

$$\text{BA} = \frac{\pi d^2}{4 \times 144}$$

Note: The area of a circle is $\pi d^2/4$ sq in. To get square feet, this result is divided by 12×12, or 144.

The number of trees per acre then equals

$$\frac{\text{Basal area per acre}}{\text{Basal area per tree}} = \frac{\text{BA}}{\pi d^2/4 \times 144} = \frac{183.3 \text{ BA}}{d^2}$$

Substituting this expression for the number of trees,

$$S = \sqrt{\frac{43,560}{183.3 \text{ BA}/d^2}} = \sqrt{\frac{43,560 d^2}{183.3 \text{ BA}}}$$

Dividing and bringing d out from under the radical,

$$S = d \sqrt{\frac{237.6}{\text{BA}}}$$

Extracting the square root,

$$S = d \frac{15.4}{\sqrt{\text{BA}}}$$

Therefore

$$\frac{S}{d} \text{ or } C = \frac{15.4}{\sqrt{\text{BA}}}$$

Applying this formula, spacing figures for a range of average-acre basal areas found in forest stands are as follows:

Basal area per acre	"Diameter times" spacing figure	Basal area per acre	"Diameter times" spacing figure
30	2.81	110	1.47
40	2.43	120	1.41
50	2.18	130	1.35
60	1.99	140	1.30
70	1.84	150	1.26
80	1.72	160	1.22
90	1.62	170	1.18
100	1.54	180	1.15

These spacing figures can be used in two main ways. First, as a field guide in determining the average spacing between trees when it is desired to leave some specified total basal area per acre. For example, to get 80 sq ft of basal area per acre, the "diameter times" spacing figure is 1.7, which holds regardless of tree diameter. For 6-in. trees, the indicated spacing is 6 × 1.7, or 10.2 ft; for 10-in. trees, 10 × 1.7, or 17 ft; for 14-in. trees, 14 × 1.7 or 23.8 ft; etc. Where trees of different diameter are adjacent, as is usually the case, an average spacing figure should be used, e.g., for a 6- and a 10-in. tree allow 10.2 + 17.0/2, or 13.6 ft. These spacings cannot, of course, be applied precisely in the woods as trees do not grow neatly spaced except in plantations, and the crown and the general situation of the tree as a whole must be considered. Also, as pointed out, square spacing is an assumption only. It is impossible to determine precisely the space actually occupied or needed by a particular tree. Considerable judgment is necessary. With a little practice, however, it is possible to mark a stand so as to leave a certain basal area with surprising consistency. What a given basal area figure means must be interpreted in terms of the average diameter and board foot or cubic foot volume desired for stands of various ages and conditions. It must be remembered that as stands grow older there is a strong tendency for total basal area to level off and remain relatively constant. This enhances the value of basal area as a stable guide to stocking, but it also necessitates that the size and kind of trees that compose it be defined.

Second, spacing figures are useful to estimate basal area in the field. The procedure can readily be reversed and used to estimate basal area. For example, if trees average about 10 in. in diameter and are spaced approximately 4 ft apart on the average, reference to Fig. 2.3 shows that there is a little over 120 sq ft of basal area per acre. This can be calculated directly by a rearrangement of the spacing-figure formula just given. The spacing figure C in this case is 14/10, or 1.4. Since $C = 15.4/\sqrt{BA}$,

$$BA = \left(\frac{15.4}{C}\right)^2$$

Applying the latter formula, the basal area per acre is $(15.4/1.4)^2$, or 121 sq ft.

Another kind of spacing figure based on diameter and used considerably is the "diameter plus" type as contrasted to the "diameter times" figure just discussed. This type is popular as a rule of thumb in part because of its simplicity—it is easier to add than to multiply—and works satisfactorily if the range of tree diameters to which it is applied is not great and an appropriate constant is used. For example, a common rule of thumb for hardwoods is "diameter + 6." This means that the spacing in feet should be the diameter plus 6. For example, the spacing for a 10-in. tree would be 16 ft. This spacing figure does not bear any constant relation to basal area; i.e., it cannot be used as effectively as the "diameter times" type in marking a stand to leave a specified amount of stocking as measured in basal area, or volume. The relationship between the two types of diameter spacing guides is brought out in Table 2.4. As shown, if the basal area is held constant, the "diameter times" figure is also constant but the "diameter plus" ratio is variable and increases with diameter. If this latter ratio is held constant, then both the basal area and "diameter times" spacing figure change for each diameter. Used with intelligence and discretion, either kind of figure will give satisfactory results, though the "diameter times" type seems the sounder because of its direct mathematical relationship to basal area.

One caution should be observed concerning the application of both kinds of spacing figures. They mean little in either very young or in mature stands. In reproduction and sapling stands, distribution is more important than spacing in relation to diameter, and basal area means little. Applied in a stand of $\frac{1}{2}$-in. trees, a spacing figure based on diameter gives meaning-

TABLE 2.4. SPACING FIGURES FOR TREES OF VARIOUS DIAMETERS FOR 100 SQUARE FEET OF BASAL AREA PER ACRE

Diameter breast high	Number of trees per acre	Spacing between trees, ft	"Diameter times" spacing constant	"Diameter plus" spacing constant
4	1,149	6.2	1.5	2.2
5	735	7.7	1.5	2.7
6	510	9.2	1.5	3.2
7	375	10.8	1.5	3.8
8	287	12.3	1.5	4.3
9	226	13.9	1.5	4.9
10	183	15.4	1.5	5.4
11	152	16.9	1.5	5.9
12	127	18.5	1.5	6.5
13	108	20.1	1.5	7.1
14	94	21.5	1.5	7.5

less, even ridiculous, results. In a mature stand, the character and form of the individual tree is much more important than its spacing. Spacing figures are most useful in intermediate stands of pole size (with average diameters of about 3 to 10 in.), where basal area and volume mean something and yet individual tree differences are not large.

GUIDE BASED ON TREE HEIGHT

Tree height has been suggested as a guide to spacing, and there are some sound reasons why this is a good measure in young stands (Wilson, 1946; Gevorkiantz, 1947). It is well known that in general the taller the tree, the more growing space it needs. The essential feature of the approach is to express spacing as a proportion of tree height, the exact proportion depending on silvicultural experience. For example, if 20 percent of the total height is assumed as a desirable spacing for dominant and codominant trees of a particular species and age, then if these trees average 70 ft tall, they should be spaced 70×0.20, or about 14 ft apart. It is not difficult to learn to estimate spacing in relation to height instead of diameter. The number of trees per acre is determined by the formula

$$N = \frac{43,560}{(hf)^2}$$

where N = number of trees per acre
  43,560 = number of square feet per acre
  h = height of tree or stand, ft
  f = proportion spacing is of height (expressed as a decimal)

Thus for 70-ft trees and a 20 percent spacing factor, the number of trees per acre is

$$N = \frac{43,560}{(70 \times 0.20)^2} = \frac{43,560}{(14)^2} = 222$$

The basal area per acre is determined by the product of the number of trees and the basal area of the tree of average diameter.

The spacing factor f can be used as a comparative measure of stand density. For a given average tree height, the lower the factor, the higher the stocking. An actual stand consequently can be compared to some norm, as a fully stocked stand of desirable form and distribution, on the basis of height-spacing factors.

The main limitation of height as a measure of desirable spacing is the fact that height growth is comparatively insensitive to stocking. It is for this very reason that tree height is used as a measure of site quality. The significance of total height must also be considered in relation to depth and density of the crown which vary widely by species and circumstances. Spacing in relation to height is most significant with conifers and particularly young trees in plantation stands where tree form and distribution is fairly uniform. Height-spacing relationships have less utility when applied to hardwoods, which tend to be more variable in form. The total height of hardwoods is also more difficult to measure and frequently is not a particularly meaningful figure. Effective merchantable height often becomes comparatively fixed fairly early in life by major forks in the stem, and diameter growth thereafter is more significant in measuring spacing needs and volume than is growth in total height.

A spacing guide based on height cannot be directly related to either basal area or volume measure. While of the same general type as the "diameter times" figure, spacing based on tree height cannot be directly related either to it or to the "diameter plus" ratio, since the relationship between tree height and diameter is not constant. An illustration of the interrelation between tree height and diameter spacing guides is given in Table 2.5. The tree-height data in this case are taken from Table 25 of the *U.S. Department of Agriculture Technical Bulletin* 201 (revised October, 1949) and represent the heights of trees in fully stocked Douglas-fir stands of various average diameters. These relationships would be somewhat different for another species having a different height-diameter relationship. In this

TABLE 2.5 RELATION BETWEEN TREE HEIGHT AND DIAMETER
SPACING FIGURES FOR FULLY STOCKED EVEN-AGED
DOUGLAS-FIR IN THE PACIFIC NORTHWEST[a]

Average dbh of stand, in.	Number of trees per acre	Average height of tree of average diameter, ft	Spacing as 20 percent of tree height, ft	Corresponding "diameter times" spacing figure	Corresponding "diameter plus" spacing figure
2	4,466	22	4.4	2.2	2.4
4	1,530	39	7.8	2.0	3.8
6	818	55	11.0	1.8	5.0
8	524	69	13.8	1.7	5.8
10	371	83	16.6	1.7	6.6
12	280	97	19.4	1.6	7.4
14	221	110	22.0	1.6	8.0
16	180	123	24.6	1.5	8.6
18	150	135	27.0	1.5	9.0
20	127	147	29.4	1.5	9.4
22	110	157	31.4	1.4	9.4
24	96	167	33.4	1.4	9.4
26	85	176	35.2	1.4	9.2
28	76	185	37.0	1.3	9.0

[a] *U.S. Dept. Agr. Tech. Bul.* 201, Table 25.

instance, neither the "diameter times" nor the "diameter plus" figures are constant when a fixed percentage of tree height is used as a base.

determination of desirable stocking

The measurement of stocking and the development of various spacing guides still leaves unanswered the fundamental question: What *is* desirable stocking for specific species, sites, stand conditions, and purposes of management? Roth gave a succinct answer many years ago, "room to grow but none to waste," that pointed in the right direction. But what is enough room and what is wasted space? Determination of what constitutes desirable growing stock under stated conditions is a central problem of forest management and should be so regarded (Davis, 1956). The problem has already been encountered in this book and will come up repeatedly in ensuing chapters. Some decision regarding desirable stocking must be made every time trees are cut in thinnings and other partial cuttings and when a stand is regenerated; the practicing forester is constantly faced with this problem.

Its answer is a much more complex matter than measurement of stocking and development of spacing figures and one that cannot be solved by mathematical deduction. If desirable stocking is known, measurement of stocking and its expression in some readily applicable form to help in selecting trees to cut or leave is comparatively easy. There is a tendency for mensurational zeal over the latter, which can be treated with apparent mathematical precision, to obscure the more basic character of the first question.

Determination of desirable stocking is difficult because it is multi-dimensional, requiring integration of much biological, technological, and economic information. There is no simple and final answer to the question either; knowledge is increasing, and changing technological and economic conditions constantly demand new answers and applications. Once sawlog forestry was dominant; now it is fiber and other derived products plus sawlogs. Discussion here is limited to the biology of growth; technological and economic considerations are dealt with in Chaps. 7, 8, and 9 particularly.

As has been pointed out, a given site can produce a finite amount of woody growth. It is the job of the forester to capture as much of this growth as possible in usable products. Much research has shown that approximately full utilization of a particular site can occur over a considerable range of stocking. If stocking is very low—a few trees per acre—additional trees will add to total growth in full amount. With more trees, competition occurs and growth per acre increases but at a declining rate in relation to the additional stocking. As stocking is increased, there comes a point beyond which growth does not increase with stocking. As stocking is further increased, growth may decline because of stagnation. Though much is known, information is decidedly incomplete on stocking levels for full site utilization for different sites, species, tree ages, and growing conditions. But these general relationships between site, stocking, and growth are known to exist and can be approximately identified on the ground. Knowledge that there is a zone of tolerance in stocking within which reasonably full site utilization can occur is of much practical significance to the practicing forester, for it gives him latitude in controlling growing stock to serve the purposes of management.

There can be many practical expressions of desirable stocking levels based on experience. A common one is to specify the amount of basal area per acre, and, in general, the character and distribution of trees that should be left on the ground following a periodic cut to give best growth of desired species and quality. In old-field loblolly pine stands, for example, a rough rule of thumb suggested is to carry a basal area per acre equivalent to the site index for stands of intermediate age. That is, for site 60 carry 60 sq ft of basal area, etc. This works only within limits. Another approach is to establish a "diameter times" spacing figure as a general guide. For example, in mixed loblolly–shortleaf pine stands in southern Arkansas a fig-ure of 1.7 (a spacing in feet to equal 1.7 times the tree diameter in inches) has been found to work well for most sizes of trees. This figure indicates about 80 sq ft of basal area per acre. In practice, and because of holes and other breaks in the canopy, the result is between 70 and 75 sq ft on the average. Since a spacing figure of the "diameter times" type defines the basal area, it can be used as a general guide for given species and growth conditions. Spacing based on height can be used in the same way.

3
forest yield and yield tables

The forest manager engaged in timber production is continually and vitally concerned with the yield of products obtainable from the forest. His bread and butter depends on it; timber harvest, including merchantable intermediate cuts, is the purpose and the reason for the whole production process. It is consequently necessary that the nature of forest yield and its expression through various kinds of yield tables or related means be well understood. Also, such understanding clears the way for analysis of growth, from which yield derives, as presented in Chap. 4.

Foresters use the term "yield" in two ways. First, it is used to express the flow of forest products, whether measured in volume or value units, harvested from a forest at a particular time or during a given period. This is the common agricultural usage of the term; a farm or a particular field can or may yield a certain number of dollars or bushels a year or for a period of years. While there is usually some implication of capacity to continue the yield for an extended period without significantly reducing the base from which it is obtained, this is not a necessary connotation. Just as a farm field may be overworked, forest yields may be currently obtained that bear little relation to the sustained capacity of the site. The term "sustained-yield management," as brought out in Chap. 1, means maintenance of a continued capacity for yield.

Second, the term is used to express the volume or amount of forest products, however measured, that may be present in a specified stand at a given time, or attainable from it over a period of time, without reference to whether it is actually harvested or not. A forest yield table is an illustration. A yield table, as it is commonly presented, gives the volume of forest products that can be expected per unit of area for a given age, site, stocking, and method of management. This can include volumes taken in partial cuttings. Such a table merely gives volumes that occur or may be predicted under stated conditions in a given stand. It does not necessarily define yield that can be or should be harvested on a continuing basis from an actual forest area including many stands under management. A yield table, since it indicates accumulated forest growth, does, however, give a useful basis for estimating harvested yields that might be obtained from a given property. This is the major reason why foresters are so interested in yield tables.

On a farm, when one says the yield is 60 bu of corn per acre, this necessarily means annual growth and that this growth is harvested; it cannot be kept in the field an extra year. In forestry it can, as crops take many years to grow and there is a wide range of alternatives as to when and how the harvest is taken. One of the peculiarities of forestry is that there is a very high proportion of marketable inventory on the ground at any one time in relation to products that could be currently cut. There is no clear demarcation between the "factory" (the forest growing stock) and the yield or product. No yield is actually realized until the timber is cut regardless of what might be cut or when.

kinds of yield information

The need of the practicing forester for systematic information related to site on yields obtainable from stands by species or species groups, age, stocking, and other stand characteristics is as old as forestry. What does or can the forest yield is a most natural question. Attempts to answer it in useful form have occasioned a tremendous amount of research and field study throughout the world. As might be expected, initial emphasis has been given to stands of natural origin and growth as they are the most numerous. Much attention has been given to yields obtainable from fully stocked well-distributed stands that give a sort of "par value" basis for judging attainable yield. Such information is valuable in appraising possible yield from a wide range of natural stands encountered in practice that are not fully stocked in one or more respects. Harvest from partial or intermediate cuts of stands under some schedule of management must also be considered. With greater application of artificial regeneration, primarily through planting by which species composition and distribution is much more strictly controllable, increasing attention has been given to plantation yields under management.

Primarily because they are more abundant, more easily managed, and in general the more valuable, by far the greater amount of study has been given to even-aged stands. Yields in uneven-aged stands, stands that cannot be classified by age and which are more complex structurally, are less susceptible to systematic determination. Substantial yield information applicable to such stands has accumulated, but so far it has not been susceptible to systematic tabular presentation.

Over the years, a great amount of yield information, primarily for even-aged stands, has been accumulated and is commonly expressed in what are known as yield tables. It is well to understand their nature and uses from a management standpoint. It should be noted, however, that a tabular form itself is not the basic criterion. Yield information can be and commonly is given through statistically derived equations or related techniques based on measurable stand variables. Tabular presentation is essentially an end result and is so regarded here.

Yield information for even-aged stands can be classified usefully as applied to:

Fully stocked unmanaged stands of natural origin

Partially stocked stands of natural origin including a wide range of stocking and based on stands either cut or uncut under management

Plantation stands including stands that may or may not be partially cut under management

All yield information for uneven-aged stands necessarily relates to those of natural origin. Except for limited underplanting, such stands are never plantations. Information may be derived from:

Unmanaged stands—stands as they are found

Managed stands—based on cumulative cutting experience obtained from stands under management

yield of fully stocked unmanaged even-aged natural stands

Numerous studies of yield of fully stocked unmanaged even-aged stands of natural origin have been made in many forest areas of the world. A prime objective of mensurational research in the earlier days of forestry in the United States was preparation of yield tables for the principal commercial forest species or species associations. The same has been true in general in Canada. In the United States, most such yield studies were published between 1920 and 1940. The reasons why rather few general studies have been made since are (1) most of the principal areas have been covered, (2) availability of suitable uncut natural stands has greatly diminished since about 1940, and (3) limitations of such studies in meeting managment needs became more fully recognized, somewhat dimming their earlier popularity.

Because of their importance in many parts of the world, these studies are discussed in some detail. Also, many of the considerations involved apply to yield studies in partially stocked stands.

Key considerations in making yield studies in fully stocked natural stands are:

1. Definition of geographic areas to be included. This may be the commercial occurrence of a certain species or a species association in a more restricted area. This is a major initial consideration and affects applicability of results. For example, even-aged stands of ponderosa pine occur over an area of about 1,000 by 1,400 miles in mountainous parts of the western United States. Growing conditions are extremely diverse and, as pointed out in Chap. 2, a species may react differently to soil and site conditions during the normal lifetime of a stand. Besides being a very large undertaking, a yield study for such a diversely located species inevitably means that the results are likely to be less specifically applicable to a particular part of its range; more total variation is included.

2. Species or species groups to be included. Some species naturally occur in pure or nearly pure stands; ponderosa pine, the southern pines, jack pine, red gum, and aspen are American examples. Other important species, such as western white pine, white spruce, balsam fir, and the Douglas-fir, characteristically occur in mixed stands, and a yield table for the single species in natural stands is impossible. A yield study must include all trees of all species occurring on the sample areas; yield data necessarily are expressed per unit of area.

3. Definition of site and stocking. Site is most commonly determined in terms of site index (Chap. 2) or broad site classes, although ecological bases such as key vegetative plant indicators are also used, particularly in Scandinavia. Consistency and accuracy in site determination are extremely important since this gives the basis for quality classification. Stocking is an extremely critical consideration. As has been brought out (Chap. 2), stocking is a relative matter and what constitutes a "fully stocked" or "well stocked" stand cannot be precisely defined. Some concept has to be developed and consistently followed; just what criteria were employed is a key point in appraising any yield study. Usually some "average best" concept is used which is adjudged to represent full utilization of the site. Both site and stocking must be as uniform as possible for each study plot area, which should represent essentially undisturbed past growth conditions.

4. Sampling problems. Data are not obtained from a random sampling of an area. Rather, stands, each representing a single age and site, are individually selected. The aim is to sample adequately all site conditions, to obtain a full range of significant ages, and to get enough data to give a desired degree of accuracy.

5. Availability of stands for study. It is rare indeed that natural stands well distributed by site and age classes are available to meet sampling data needs. Age classes are chronically unequally distributed by age and site because of major forest disturbances of the past such as major cuttings, fires,

blow-downs, or insect epidemics. This limits both the accuracy and applicability of the yield data.

6. Mensurational-statistical techniques employed in collecting and analyzing data. These cannot be dealt with here but may have a considerable bearing on the field interpretation of the end result.

All these considerations are important in appraising the applicability of yield information. They apply in general to any kind of yield study. There is a natural tendency to accept published data in tabular or equation form without inquiring closely into their basis. Serious error in field application may result as a consequence; the forest manager needs a thorough working grasp of yield-study methodology.

A number of such studies are cited in the Bibliography, and a good illustration of the principal information given is illustrated in Table 5.1. They are commonly called normal yield tables. The following data are commonly given as a part of a yield study of fully stocked even-aged stands, usually in tabular or graphic form as an end result.

Site-index curves, in 10- or 20-ft class intervals based on a key age, usually 50 or 100 years, showing height in relation to age and covering the range of sites and ages studied as illustrated in Fig. 2.1. Site may also be shown in broad qualitative classes as I, II, and III. Site curves can be and often are determined independently of yield studies, but such studies necessarily include them, and yield studies are one of the best sources of information on relative site quality.

The yield tables proper giving by age and site the number of trees, basal area, average diameter, and volume in cords, cubic feet, board feet, or other units either singly or in combination. Values are always given per unit of area.

Increment tables and ratios showing mean annual increment, periodic annual increment, and sometimes some other relationships and ratios computed from the yield data.

Stand tables showing, usually in cumulative percentage form, the number of trees and volume in each diameter class by average stand diameter and sometimes site. These data are valuable in studying the structure of fully stocked stands and of other stands in relation to them.

Volume tables may be included with yield studies but are not a necessary part of them.

These yield tables give a composite picture of a large number of fully stocked stands of varying age and site, each measured only once. They do not portray the actual or historical development of individual stands except by inference. This fundamental fact is often overlooked and is a common source of misunderstanding about such yield tables. They do not, except in a general deductive way, show how a stand came to be what it is; they merely show stands that may be found at varying ages on different sites.

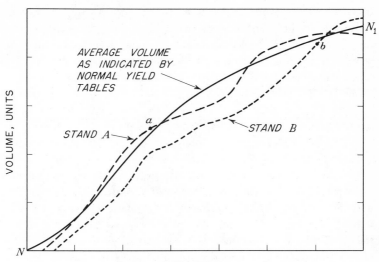

FIG. 3.1. THE DEVELOPMENT OF ACTUAL STANDS COMPARED WITH
THE GROWTH TREND INDICATED BY A NORMAL YIELD TABLE.

Figure 3.1 will help to make the point clear. The solid line NN_1 shows
the average relation existing between stand age and volume for a particular
site class as given by a yield table. The actual volume development of two
individual stands, A and B, is shown by the broken lines, as labeled. These
curves are based on repeated measurements of these particular stands
made throughout their life. In making the yield study, it happened that
Stand A was measured at age a and Stand B at age b. Their effect on
the average yield-table curve is consequently limited to these two points
only. But observe the actual development history of these stands. Stand A
has more or less followed the "normal" curve. It started out somewhat below
normal as regards volume, was above normal for a while, and at about
the time it was measured was headed for a considerable period below normal. It gradually picked up again, built up stocking above that indicated
by the normal curve, and then suffered another reverse. Stand B was below
the normal curve nearly all of its life. It started out with a relatively small
number of trees that tended to depress total volume. It more or less paral-
leled, but was below, the normal curve for most of its life; but at age
b, when it was measured for the yield study, the relatively few trees had
developed a volume bringing it approximately up to the normal curve. If
either of these stands had been visited at a time when they were considerably
below full stocking, they would probably not have been included in the
yield study at all.

Data from stands periodically remeasured show, as would be expected, that individual stands have their ups and downs as they go through the vicissitudes of life even if never cut by man. Climatic cycles, insects, disease, storms, and the like collectively affect a stand in a haphazard manner. Like people, they have good and bad periods, and observing them only at a particular time does not cast much light on the dynamics of their development. It is for this reason that normal yield data should be used with much caution in predicting what a particular stand will do. Individual stands may depart widely from the so-called normal pattern of development.

It has been consistently observed that stands understocked or overstocked in terms of normal yield tables tend to approach normality, the particular rate depending on age, site, species, degree of understocking or overstocking, unit of measure employed (basal area, cubic or board feet), number of trees, and other circumstances. Stand *B* in Fig. 3.1 is an illustration of the approach of an understocked stand to full stocking. This fact should be taken into account in using normal yield tables to predict growth of particular stands as brought out in Chap. 4 on growth. There is considerable indication that stands considered to be fully stocked at the time they happen to be measured for normal yield study purposes tended to be understocked previously.

It is unfortunate that the word "normal" has become attached as a standard of comparison to the concept of stands fully stocked at a given age; for there is nothing normal about them in the sense that the word is generally used, as meaning "usual" or "regular." Except in a few forest areas, they are exceptional and occur in small patches only. Over any extensive area an average of 80 percent or more of full stocking in yield-table terms is very good; the average is usually much less. Furthermore, experience in management has shown that, from the standpoint of best future growth, normal yield tables picture considerably overstocked stands and that stands with considerably less than full stocking as measured by yield tables may be fully stocked from the standpoint of what they should have for best future growth. A great deal depends on the precise distribution and character of trees that make up the stand. Consequently, the word "normal" as applied to yield tables should be thought of as a norm, a base, and without any implication of normal in the sense of being usual or necessarily desirable.

USES AND LIMITATIONS

With the nature of these yield tables kept in mind, the following summarizes their principal values and uses:

1. They show the maximum volume, number of trees, and basal area that a given site can support at a given age. If the definition of stocking upon which they are based is consistently followed and represents a biologi-

cal potential, yield tables set a practicable upper limit of fundamental significance that furnishes a valuable basing point in estimating stocking and yield under management.

2. They give a useful measure of comparative site productivity. Frequently, they are the only unified and consistent data available and are very useful for such purposes as measuring relative differences between sites at various ages, as was done in Chap. 2.

3. They give a unified and useful composite picture, even though synthesized, of average development of well-stocked stands. With study and experience, the statistical data given in a yield table for a given species can be translated into a narrative account of how natural stands develop on the average over the years.

4. The stand tables usually included as a part of a yield study give a useful picture of stand structure in natural stands that is also very helpful in making comparisons with the structure of other stands of various sorts.

5. They are useful in estimating growth if certain precautions are observed. For young stands they may furnish the easiest and quickest means of making approximate growth estimates.

Some cautions and limitations that should be observed in using these yield tables follow:

1. They do not represent the range of stands, either natural or cutover, encountered in practice, where the stand structure may be profoundly different from that found in fully stocked stands. Such empirical stands cannot be expected to grow as do those rather arbitrarily pictured by these yield tables, and the various corrections and adjustments necessary to relate them to such tables may be more trouble than the results justify.

2. The high per-acre values shown by the tables do not necessarily indicate either attainable or economically desirable growing stock volumes to aim for in practice, even though they have a certain basing point value. From a management standpoint of best stocking for future growth, normal yield tables picture overstocked stands and consequently give little aid in answering the fundamental question of what *is* desirable or optimum stocking under management. Stands are purposefully altered all through their life, and there is little point in trying to relate them to fully stocked natural stands that scarcely even exist in cutover forest regions.

3. Mortality is "built-in" and shown only by inference. The difference between the number of trees per acre at two different ages on the same site is due to average mortality, but it cannot be specifically identified by diameter classes and nothing is determined about its cause. Furthermore, the nature, kind, and causes of mortality in cutover and other stands may bear no relation to average and more or less endemic mortality in fully stocked stands. For these reasons, conclusions about mortality drawn from yield tables should be made with extreme care.

4. They do not measure the total growth potentiality of a stand. They picture *net* volumes that may develop at specified ages only and do not measure the total woody growth produced by the site during a given period of time. In densely stocked stands such as they represent, many trees that grow for years must drop out through mortality as the stand grows older. As a stand approaches maturity, an increasing proportion of total or gross current growth is lost through mortality, and periodic net growth sharply decreases. The stand as a whole and individual trees within it may be making good growth but this is in part offset by mortality in potentially harvestable trees. Through application of intermediate cuttings, much of this growth could be captured. Normal yield tables consequently seriously underestimate the total growth made in a stand that is potentially harvestable under management.

yield of partially stocked even-aged natural stands

There is a great diversity of natural stands that do not fit into the category of fully stocked stands as discussed above. The forester is keenly interested in their yield; they are primarily what he deals with; they occur in endless variety; and they may be managed in many different ways. He needs consistent yield information, but getting it is inherently a difficult and elusive problem. There are no good or single answers such as may be obtained from the relatively narrow range of fully stocked undisturbed natural stands. Consequently, answers that have been obtained are varied in pattern. They may be considered in two general groups, yield of unmanaged stands and yield of managed stands.

UNMANAGED STANDS

The simplest expression of yield of unmanaged natural stands is given by forest survey data. Volume and related data classified by site, forest type and age class, and perhaps by level of stocking, constitute a yield table and portray what actually has grown on an area under more or less natural conditions. A good example is the British Columbia empirical yield tables (Fligg, 1960). These tables, based on over 13,000 sample plots, show volume per acre in cubic feet, and related periodic and mean annual increment, for several lower diameter limits classified by age and site for major forest types and regional zones. There is a mass of data of this general type available, and it is useful in managment since it represents average conditions as they are found. They can be applied, however, only by making the assumption that what naturally occurred in the past will continue into the future; i.e., continuation of static conditions. Information of this type is chronically conservative, for under management things are not static; better protection and application of cutting and other management measures should increase natural yields substantially.

MANAGED STANDS

A forester's primary interest, especially as he looks ahead, is in yield from stands in which cutting, regeneration, protection, and other management measures have been applied. Getting yield information from such stands is a problem basically very different from dealing with unmanaged stands. Yields obtained are obviously influenced by the management measures employed and data can be obtained only over time through repeated measurements of selected stands. A number of yield tables have been prepared from growth plots representing well-stocked stands in which some consistent partial cutting regime has been applied. Such tables are found mostly in Europe. In addition to volumes and other data for the main stand, they include intermediate yields. Mortality consequently largely drops out of the picture; it is mostly anticipated and harvested in the partial cuts. An inherent limitation of such yield tables is that they directly apply only to the specific kind and periodicity of partial cutting used. Fundamentally, they also tend to assume certain economics of management that may or may not apply generally. They do, however, give a much more complete measure of the total growth and potential yields than do the so-called normal yield tables.

Following the same general pattern, much attention has been given to yields obtained in actual practice. A manager of a forest property has a natural need for yield information specifically applicable to his particular forest conditions and management practices. Application of permanent sampling systems in which plots are periodically remeasured (Chap. 12) is increasingly supplying a basis for development of such yield information.

The basic limitation of this sort of approach, logical as it may seem, is that it is inefficient and the job is endless. No two properties are quite alike or managed quite the same. Further, the purposes of management on a property change and large volumes of empirical data obtained under past practice consequently may not apply well to future practice. More importantly, trees live and grow for basic biological reasons quite irrespective of property lines or immediate economic objectives.

A more basic and fruitful approach is to seek, identify, and evaluate basic measurable factors that affect tree and stand growth and yield under a wide range of site and forest conditions. Such information can be presented in useful equation, graphic, or tabular form. Not being restricted to any particular stand concept (as it is in the case of yield from fully stocked stands), to any arbitrary thinning or other partial cutting practice, or to a particular property, this kind of information is susceptible to flexible and wide application. Many studies of this kind have been and are being made. This matter is specifically considered in Chap. 4.

yield of plantations

The high return obtainable from plantations and their increasingly widespread development have focused much attention on plantation yields. Plantations differ from natural stands in several respects:

1. Species composition is controlled, usually to one or two species. Most stands are strictly even-aged.

2. Initial tree distribution is closely controllable, hence the initial stand density and the need for early thinning. The better spacing obtained in plantations is the reason why foresters accustomed to natural stands tend to underestimate plantation yields.

3. Genetical variation can be controlled through selection of planting stock; the major application of tree improvement is through planting.

4. Values per unit of area are usually high in both costs and returns, normally justifying fairly intensive culture in site preparation, partial cutting, pruning, and perhaps in use of fertilizer. Planting for commercial production is concentrated on good sites.

Aside from these differences, plus whatever may result from planting versus seedling origin, plantations grow like other stands, and the general problem of yield determination is much the same. In the southern United States and elsewhere, there is interest in yield of uncut plantation stands for short rotations at various ages. A large mass of yield information exists but it tends to be piecemeal and few systematic studies resulting in yield tables have been developed. Much study has been given to plantation management, and yield tables including the results of a thinning regime have been prepared, though very few in North America. The technical problems are, in general, parallel to those encountered in preparing yield tables for managed natural stands. Any "management" yield table, whether for natural or planted stands, necessarily represents a particular schedule of management which may or may not have general application. As with natural stands, the tendency is to focus attention directly on measurable characteristics affecting growth and to seek flexibility in expression of yield so that the basic data can be widely applied.

yield of uneven-aged stands

Since by their nature uneven-aged stands are continuous and have no point of termination when the mature stand is removed and a new one is started, yield information for them cannot be presented in the same form as that for even-aged stands. Data cannot be presented in terms of stand age, which is indeterminate, since all age classes are more or less intermixed and simultaneously present on an area. Yields in terms of total stand volumes only are meaningless, because, if the entire stand is cut, there is no longer an uneven-aged stand to give further yields. Yield must be determined in terms of harvest cuts. Useful information can be obtained only from managed stands, since unmanaged stands yield no data on annual or periodic harvests. Finally, stands must be managed under some form of the selection system which alone can produce and maintain uneven-aged stands.

Formal yield tables for uneven-aged stands do not exist for two principal reasons: One is that uneven-aged management has been much less systematically and widely applied than even-aged management. In very few areas has it been applied long enough to give information that could be expressed in systematic form. The other and more basic reason, that applies with even more force than in the case of yield tables for managed even-aged stands, is that the job is endless. Uneven-aged stands are almost without exception composed of several species usually including hardwoods, and a desirable volume and diameter species distribution usually has to be determined area by area.

Much information on yields obtainable in uneven-aged management is being accumulated, although it has not been assembled into yield tables for general use. It is possible to do so, however. In whatever form presented, yield information for uneven-aged stands must include the following basic elements:

1. The volume, diameter classes, and probably species distribution of the reserved growing stock left on the ground immediately following a cyclic cut. This is the basic forest capital.

2. The site quality determined in the same general way as for even-aged stands.

3. The cutting cycle or interval at which cuttings take place in the stand. The interval may be as short as 1 year but usually is 5 years or more.

4. Yields obtainable per acre per cutting cycle from the reserve growing stock. Such yields would be expressed in kind, size, and volume of product removed.

The application of such information in specific terms can best be expressed in narrative form, although it could also be tabulated. For example, assume that management experience has indicated, in a specific forest type and stand, and for a particular distribution of the number of trees by diameter classes, that on Site II land with a reserve growing stock of 7,000 bd ft per acre, 1,200 bd ft can be cut every 5 years. The annual yield is consequently 240 bd ft per acre for this growing stock and cutting cycle. This is basic yield information. Management of uneven-aged stands is given in Chaps. 8 and 9.

4
forest growth

Growth[1] is the lifeblood of forest management for continuing timber production. The major aim of management is to capture the largest possible proportion of the productive capacity of the site in yield of economically harvestable products. Without consideration of growth, a plan of management becomes merely a guide to the installment liquidation of an existing forest crop. Although the timber industry of most countries initially developed on an accumulation of forest capital in existing mature stands, it must be based on growth of young stands to continue. It is consequently necessary to take a broad and searching look at forest growth as the physical foundation for any continuing plan of operation. The forest manager must know what methods are available to measure growth and how to use them effectively.

importance of growth in timber management

There is increasing need for accuracy in growth determination; it is not an academic matter. In the initial stages of forestry, rather rough estimates are all that can be made and in general suffice for the immediate need. Indeed, a primary problem has often been to convince people that trees and forests actually do grow. The concept of a forest as a static entity rather than as a growing thing has been strong; traces still linger on. An error of 20 or 30 percent

[1] "Growth" is well established as a general term in forestry and is used here when speaking of growth in general. "Increment" is more specific and preferred usage when applied to the increase in volume or value of particular trees or stands over time and is used in this context.

in the estimation of growth does not matter so much when the pressing problem is how to cut and utilize large volumes of old-growth timber which makes little net growth anyway. With timber management increasingly accepted as a business and based on young and growing stands, accurate determination of growth becomes necessary, because crucial decisions rest directly upon it.

Estimates of growth are of vital importance in timber production planning in a number of respects. They are here focused on a particular operating unit supporting a continuing forest business but the same considerations readily can be applied to planning problems in a large area or region.

1. *Timberland needs.* Is more land needed to support a present or desired level of production? If so, how much and of what kind?

2. *Timber procurement policy and program.* To keep a plant running, how much timber must an industrial concern purchase in addition to what can be cut from owned lands? Can the processing unit be enlarged on the basis of increased timber yields anticipated from available sources, or must it be reduced?

3. *Processing procedures.* What species and kinds of products are or will become available? A plant that does not give close attention to the *kind* of timber that is growing on forest lands supporting it is headed for business trouble.

4. *Depreciation and depletion policy.* Must equipment be depreciated over a limited period or can it be used for its full working life? Is forest capital being liquidated or is it being maintained or increased through growth? What depletion schedule for income taxation should be adopted?

5. *General competitive status of the business.* What is its status now and what will it likely be in the future as regards control of and access to raw materials? The results of planting and stand improvement practices are measured by harvestable growth.

As indicated, accuracy in determination of growth can be exceedingly important to the operator of a forest business dependent on a continuing supply of raw material. An error of 10 percent in available cut based on growth estimates may be of crucial importance and spell the difference between profit and loss. Profit margins are often narrow in the business world. Determination of forest growth is consequently far more than an exercise in techniques; it is a central business problem.

Growth is most commonly thought of in terms of volume units. They are the easiest to measure and certainly the most obvious. But in the final analysis, growth in value is a more important consideration and is too often overlooked. Management aimed at mere volume production is not enough. Timber needs to be grown to the most profitable size and specification. Quality differences in sawtimber, i.e., whether it will make veneer, furniture stock, millwork, or common lumber, are well recognized, but quality control has been incorporated in timber-growing practices to only a limited extent. Fiber yield for paper production and other products is also variable in quality and total amount per unit of wood volume. Growth conditions can profoundly affect the physical and chemical properties of wood and its suitability for many uses. While measurement of growth in volume units is a first and most immediate problem, translation into value units is a necessary final step.[1] In this chapter, attention is directed primarily toward techniques for measuring growth in volume. Value considerations are introduced in later chapters.

nature and components of forest growth

Tree and forest growth is inherently complex and its determination elusive. By their nature trees accumulate growth over many years, a layer per growing period. Growth occurs over the total tree, branches, bole, and roots, although only the bole and sometimes major branches are commonly utilized. The total accumulated growth of a stand of given age is the present volume plus whatever volume may have been taken in intermediate cuts. There is no easy or direct way, as there is with agricultural crops, of measuring current annual growth. Except in research work using precise instruments, bole growth cannot be measured annually or for shorter intervals but is determined over a period of years. Trees do not grow according to a standard form any more than do people. They grow short and thick, tall and slim, and with all intergradations. Measurement of bole form is a major mensurational problem. Similarly, growth of a stand is a variable and dynamic process including not only the performance of individual trees but mortality and other results of complex tree interactions.

The most helpful approach to forest growth is to look at it in total potential per unit of area. Figure 4.1 shows in schematic form aboveground growth (measured in weight of dry wood produced) of a well-stocked stand fully utilizing any site that may be assumed. Level *A* represents total woody growth either in total or currently produced (annual or periodic) including all branches to their tips. If the whole tree could be utilized, this would represent the total growth potential. This total growth exists, but it is difficult to measure and little known. Research has shown that on many sites and species associations this potential is relatively fixed over a substantial range of stocking for a particular species association growing on a given site. As brought out in Chap. 3, site quality is not fixed either; it may increase or decrease over time by natural causes or be changed artificially by soil treatment, watering, or by use of fertilizer.

---

[1] Weight is a valid and useful measurement unit increasingly being applied. It is more closely related than volume to fiber and other products derived from wood.

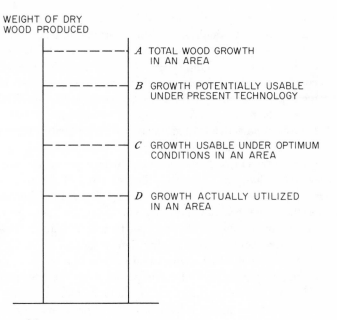

WEIGHT OF DRY
WOOD PRODUCED

A TOTAL WOOD GROWTH
IN AN AREA

B GROWTH POTENTIALLY USABLE
UNDER PRESENT TECHNOLOGY

C GROWTH USABLE UNDER OPTIMUM
CONDITIONS IN AN AREA

D GROWTH ACTUALLY UTILIZED
IN AN AREA

FIG. 4.1. FOREST GROWTH POTENTIALS.

Level *B* indicates a somewhat lesser woody growth potential that is usable under present technology if it could be fully applied. This level is not fixed either; it can be increased by technological breakthroughs in wood chemistry, adhesives, fiber utilization, etc. Level *C* portrays woody growth potentially utilizable under optimum operating conditions in an area. Level *D*, and usually a considerably lower level, shows what is actually utilized under average woods conditions in that area.

None of these levels is fixed but changing and interrelated—and consequently shown by broken lines only. Definitions of significant levels other than the ones rather arbitrarily given here could be used. Better accessibility and markets can permit raising average utilization (level *D*) to more nearly the potential possible in the area (level *C*). Technological developments (level *B*) can raise levels *C* and *D* to the extent they can economically be applied. Similarly, an increase in site quality, as application of watering or fertilizer in a plantation, can directly raise levels *D* and *C*. It should be emphasized that the levels shown in Fig. 4.1 are intended to indicate general relationships only. Defining them quantitatively is the crux of the problem discussed here.

The virtue of considering forest growth in terms of potentials in this way is that it orients the height of the growth ceiling, which is higher than commonly realized, in relation to what is being utilized. It also defines the job of the timber manager, which is to capture economically the greatest possible woody growth potential from the site in terms of harvested products. This is done through silvicultural cutting practices and logging methods with due consideration to maintaining the productive capacity of the site. Such analysis also emphasizes the need and significance of thorough and complete study of forest growth to give a factual basis for timber management planning aiming for more complete utilization. Thinking of this kind also leads to the useful concept of establishing a sort of "par value" as a working objective for harvested growth attainable in an area.

With a total-growth concept in mind, the next logical step is to consider increment of trees and stands over a period of time focusing attention on the volume of currently utilizable parts of the tree, primarily the main stem or bole. Increment is made by living trees but its sum is not that of the stand because mortality and trees that may be cut must be taken into account. Also, while new growth is by its nature always of sound wood, it is often laid on trees having defects caused by decay or other agencies. The result is that net sound wood volume of a tree may or may not increase during a growth measurement period even though external diameter and height measurements taken indicate an increase.

For these and related reasons, it is necessary to divide increment into component parts to arrive at consistent definitions of growth. Commonly used components, adapted from Meyer, 1953, Beers, 1962, and Society of American Foresters, 1958, are:

V_1 = Volume of living trees[1] measured at the beginning of a growth measurement period.

V_2 = Volume of living trees measured at the end of a measurement period of n years by the same standards as at V_1.

M = Volume of trees dying during the measurement period.[2]

C = Volume of living trees cut during the measurement period.[2]

I = Volume of ingrowth, i.e., of trees measured at V_2 but which were below the minimum diameter recognized at V_1. If all trees are measured, there is no ingrowth.

D = Deterioration. This is decrease in merchantable wood volume, V_1 to V_2, resulting from breakage, increased decay, cracks, etc. It could include trees measured at V_1 but which were classed as cull trees at V_2. Deterioration volume is very difficult to deter-

---

[1] Basically, this volume includes bark since standing trees are commonly measured outside bark which also grows. Increment is, however, normally expressed in wood without bark, and this is assumed here.

[2] Strictly, the volume of mortality and of trees cut should be determined at the time they died. Their increase in volume between V_1 and the time they died is increment and may be substantial. In practice, the date of mortality and volume at that time is frequently not determined. The date trees are cut is usually known but it is often not practicable to measure volumes at that time. Consequently, volume of both mortality and of trees cut is commonly determined as of V_1.

mine but may be extremely important. An estimate may or may not be included in the measured volumes.

It is evident from these components that increment during a measurement period can be expressed in several ways, choice depending on purpose. Given below are a number of them that apply to a stand if the latter is measured in totals for a unit of area.[1]

Gross increment
including ingrowth
(common practice) $= (V_2 + M + C) - V_1$
Gross increment
of initial volume $= (V_2 + M + C - I) - V_1$
Net increment
including ingrowth $= (V_2 + C) - V_1$
Net increment of
initial volume $= V_2 + C - I - V_1$
Net increment of
surviving trees in
initial volume $= V_2 - C - I - V_1$
Net increase in
growth stock $= V_2 - V_1$

Deterioration is left out of the above because it is not consistently measurable and is usually not estimated as a separate component. If determinable, it is a subtraction from net increment. It would be included in gross increment.

As indicated above, it is extremely important to be precise in definition of increment. A forest manager may be badly misled by undefined "growth" information. It should also be recognized that unless deterioration is taken into account both gross and net increment definitions given are gross in that they include sound as well as cull tree volumes.

basic considerations in growth determination

The timber manager is concerned with measurement of growth in two major ways: The first is as a measure of performance—what happened on an area over past time. This is essentially a matter of evaluating successive forest inventories (Chap. 12). The second is as an indispensable basis for management planning and design, looking to the future as the forester must. This is growth prediction, which is the major focus of this chapter. The two

---

[1] As pointed out by Beers, 1962, and others, a somewhat different analytical procedure is required if growth of survivor trees are individually matched at successive measurement periods.

are different in objective although both employ similar techniques of growth measurement. What happened in the past is valuable. It is based on performance and gives a general planning base that progressively gets better as experience accumulates. But the future is not the past, especially in the initial stages of management application. Growth that occurred under past conditions, often in unmanaged, partially protected, and poorly controlled stands, may be a poor measure of growth that can be captured in harvestable products from managed stands in the future.

Foresters, as well as others, rather traditionally tend to forecast on the basis of what happened in the past. This is natural enough but, under developing management practice, estimates based on the past tend to lag behind present or future performance. A forester must plan ahead and important business commitments have to be based on growth predictions. These predictions are, consequently, future-oriented and necessarily include a certain act of faith that estimates will be supported by application of requisite management measures on the ground.

Foresters in different parts of the world perforce deal with a great diversity of forest conditions. There are unmanaged and uncut natural stands of widely assorted ages, species, stocking, and condition. The same range of natural stands have been subjected to some form of cutting further changing their character. The greatly increasing area of artificially established stands offers a further and most important dimension in management opportunities and needs for useful growth information.

The many forest conditions encountered offer widely differing problems in growth determination and estimation. There are no single and simple answers and this is a first point to keep clearly in mind. Foresters have struggled with growth problems for years and will continue to do so. The timber manager can expect to spend a substantial share of his time and energy getting and applying growth information.

SOURCES OF DATA

The importance of source of data in growth estimation is greater than commonly recognized. On first thought, the best source of information would seem to be the stand or forest to which it is to be applied, and this is often true. Such information may be obtained from repeated measurements of sample areas over a period of years or from increment borings of sample trees (in temperate regions where there are consistent growth rings). In areas under continuous and stable management it is possible to accumulate good local growth information undoubtedly superior to any other source. Foresters tend to work in this direction. But it should not be overlooked that such an approach requires much time and money. There are also many technical problems and pitfalls involved in sampling procedure, in establishment and consistent remeasurement of growth plots, in taking increment borings, and in the analysis and interpretation of data that are often not fully appreciated.

A deeper question is whether past growth in a stand is the best and most efficient basis for estimates of its future growth. A particular area may not offer the range and completeness of conditions necessary to furnish well-balanced growth data applicable to changing conditions and needs. Future treatment of the stand and resultant growth conditions may be substantially different, rendering growth data obtained from past performance at least partially inapplicable no matter how carefully they were obtained. Climatic cycles often have substantial effect on growth—which is too often ignored.

For these reasons of cost and applicability, and also because growth is basically independent of individual owner property lines, there is sound reason to favor broader, more regional forest growth studies and development of methods to apply them to local conditions. This permits a more fundamental approach, the gathering of a much larger and more complete fund of data, and greater flexibility in meeting changing forest conditions. Such an approach tends to shift emphasis, from the standpoint of the individual owner, from the costly and laborious process of accumulating growth data to its application.

The source of data and the cost of obtaining it consequently may have a large bearing on the choice of methods employed in estimating growth. The essential point is not where the data came from but whether they are truly applicable and adequate to the purpose.

TREE MORTALITY

From a management standpoint, tree mortality must be considered separately from any method of growth estimation. A prime objective of management is to maintain healthy and well-distributed stands in which so-called endemic mortality is held to a minimum. The aim is to forestall mortality through cutting practice and to utilize that which does occur. When a tree dies and is not utilized, all the growth it has accumulated is lost. Loss of a large tree, and it may be very valuable as well as likely to die, may offset the current growth of many trees.

Estimates of mortality are always uncertain no matter how much experience information may be available. Trees die for all sorts of reasons, some largely unpredictable except in a general actuarial sort of way. Death may occur suddenly and in restricted areas from fire, storm, insect, or disease epidemics, or it may occur more generally and usually in a periodic wavelike pattern as a result of natural suppression or cyclic climatic-disease-insect interactions.

What mortality really means is determined by management and utilization practice, which is apart from any specific method of estimation. If vigorous stands are maintained and there is good opportunity to forestall or utilize mortality at least in merchantable trees, the volume lost is relatively small and it may be largely ignored in estimates. If not, then a direct estimate must be made with all its attendant difficulties and uncertainties. For these reasons, mortality should be estimated in consonance with the actual management situation.

METHODS IN GENERAL

In broad terms, the job of developing useful methods of growth estimation is (1) to identify the fewest number of tree and stand variables of greatest predictive value that are practically and objectively measurable, (2) to obtain adequate information on these variables, and (3) to apply this information to specific stands or forest areas. Methods differ primarily in the variables considered and how they are applied to stand data.

There are two general methods of making growth estimates, indirect and direct. Indirect methods make use of yield or growth tables, which may also be presented in graphic or equation form. These data are often derived from sources other than the stand itself and the estimation process is basically comparative. It is assumed that the growth of a particular stand will follow some definable and predictable pattern in relation to the trend established by the yield table. Appropriate adjustments are made, based on measurements taken for the stand for which a growth estimate is to be used. As brought out in Chap. 3 there are several different kinds of yield tables. In Canada and the United States the best known are the so-called normal yield tables based on a not precisely definable concept of fully stocked stands. In Europe and elsewhere there are yield tables for managed stands including yields from intermediate cuttings. There are also a number of variable density tables representing stocking levels of something less than what is considered attainable full stocking and different kinds of stand structures. These range from studies based on selected "well-stocked" stands (Schumacher and Coile, 1960) to the highly empirical type of table derived directly from sampling inventories.

Direct methods are based on analysis of a particular stand in terms of measured variables. It is not a comparative approach as is use of yield tables although data taken from outside the stand are often employed as part of the procedure. There are a number of such approaches. Some deal with various measures of a stand as a unit. Others, as in stand-table projection, break the stand down into component parts, such as diameter and tree classes.

Indirect and direct methods will be presented through selected illustrations.

indirect methods—yield tables

USE OF NORMAL YIELD TABLES FOR
FULLY STOCKED EVEN-AGED STANDS

Estimation of growth from normal yield tables representing fully stocked and even-aged natural stands is considered in some detail because these tables have been and are widely used. Collectively, they furnish the largest volume of available data; frequently they are the only source. Also, problems and techniques in their use apply generally to the use of all yield tables. It is assumed that the source and nature of these tables as given in Chap. 3 are understood.

The comparative nature of yield-table use is illustrated in Fig. 4.2.

Curve NN_1 represents the trend of net volume growth as given by a normal yield table for a given site. Curves SS_1 and SS_2 represent two possible growth trends of an actual stand growing on the same site that is 60 percent stocked in relation to the yield table at age A. This stand, with volume S, was measured at age A and its volume is to be estimated

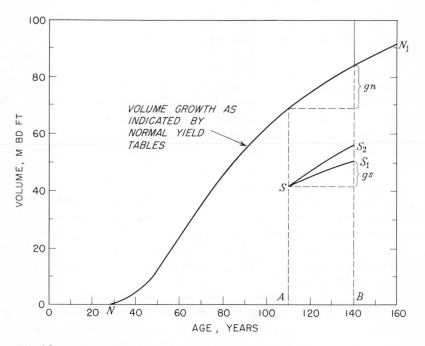

FIG. 4.2. GROWTH OF A SAMPLE STAND IN RELATION TO THE TREND INDICATED BY NORMAL YIELD TABLES.

at age B. One possibility is that growth may maintain a constant percentage relation to the normal yield curve as is shown by SS_1. The net volume at age B is consequently 60 percent of the normal volume at that age. The net volume growth made by the fully stocked stand is measured by gn and that for the actual stand by gs, and gs is therefore 60 percent of gn.

It is known, however, that so-called understocked stands grow at a faster rate than fully stocked stands and tend to approach a volume approximately as indicated by normal yield tables. This is termed "approach toward normality" and is illustrated by curve SS_2. In general, and within limits, the younger and more understocked the stand, the greater the rate of approach; that is, the faster it grows in relation to its growing stock. Similarly, overstocked stands grow more slowly than fully stocked stands and tend to decrease in density. The precise character of the stands, i.e., the species composition, size, condition, and distribution of the trees making up the stand and whether the understocking means uniform sparsity or includes actual holes in the stand, has much to do with the rate of growth.

Various measures have been devised and proposed for measuring and estimating this approach to normality in applying yield tables. Two general methods are possible: (1) to estimate the probable change in stocking or (2) to apply a correction factor to the growth indicated by a normal yield table.

Estimate of Change in Stocking. A direct estimate can be made of the probable change in the stocking of a given stand over a specified period. Studies in a particular type may show that understocked stands approach full stocking at certain average rates. Assume, for example, that in board foot volume the rate is about 7 percent in 10 years for stands approximately two-thirds stocked. Consequently, if a stand is now 60 years of age and 70 percent stocked in board feet, it will be about 77 percent stocked 10 years hence and its estimated volume at age 70 is 77 percent of the normal yield-table value for that age. Such percentage adjustments can be shaded up or down depending on age, degree of stocking and its character (patchy or uniform), site, anticipated mortality trend, and the like.

In Douglas-fir, for example, Briegleb (1942) has developed useful regression equations to estimate the percentage change in stocking in 5-year periods based on present age and percent of stocking in terms of number of trees, basal area, cubic feet, and board feet in the Scribner and International scales, respectively. Similar information has been obtained for other species and forest types.

Judgment and experience are needed to apply percentage stocking corrections, as each stand offers an individual problem. Average change over a large area may be estimated with considerable confidence, but it must constantly be borne in mind that individual stands have their ups and downs, making predictions applied to small areas more uncertain. Mortality is always more or less unpredictable in a particular area and may upset all calculations.

Use of a Correction Factor Applied to Growth—Gehrhardt's Formula. Instead of attempting to estimate the change in stocking percentage, another approach is to apply a correction factor in some systematic way to the estimate of growth itself as obtained from a normal yield table before applying it to an actual stand.

A useful method of this type has been developed by Gehrhardt (1930). It is used in Europe and has been tested and applied to some extent in the United States. The method consists of an empirical formula for estimation of approach toward normality by 10-year periods. It has been stated in general terms by Duerr (1938) as follows:

$$g = dG(1 + K - Kd)$$

where g = 10-year growth of understocked stand
  d = density, or percentage of stocking in relation to fully stocked stands expressed as a decimal
  G = 10-year growth of fully stocked stand of same age and site
  K = constant for the species or species group for a 10-year period

The $g = dG$ part of the formula estimates the growth of the actual stand g from the normal yield-table growth G as directly proportionate to density d. The multiplication factor, the $(1 + K - Kd)$ part of the formula, applies the correction. The formula was originally developed for estimation of cubic foot volume with close utilization. When it was tested with both hardwood and softwood species in the Lake States (Duerr, 1938; Gevorkiantz, 1937), consistent results were obtained and it was found that the value of the constant K is apparently not significantly affected by using board foot instead of cubic foot measure.

Measuring density or stocking in the same unit as growth and using normal yield tables applicable to the species, the following values of K were determined by Duerr:

For intolerant species................ 0.6 to 0.7
For intermediate species............. 0.8 to 0.9
For tolerant species................. 1.0 to 1.1

It was also found that the formula, with appropriate adjustment of the constant used, could also be used with empirical yield tables not representing fully stocked stands. The principle of the formula is not necessarily limited to normal yield tables. Correction factors for Gehrhardt's formula are given in Table 4.1.

A significant point about the nature of Gehrhardt's formula is that stands half stocked make the fastest approach per year toward normality measured in percentage. This follows arithmetically from the fact that a constantly increasing correction factor is applied to a constantly decreasing

TABLE 4.1. CORRECTION FACTORS FOR GEHRHARDT'S FORMULA

Stand density, d	Value of correction factor $(1 + K - Kd)$ when K is:					
	0.6	0.7	0.8	0.9	1.0	1.1
0.9	1.06	1.07	1.08	1.09	1.10	1.11
0.8	1.12	1.14	1.16	1.18	1.20	1.22
0.7	1.18	1.21	1.24	1.27	1.30	1.33
0.6	1.24	1.28	1.32	1.36	1.40	1.44
0.5	1.30	1.35	1.40	1.45	1.50	1.55
0.4	1.36	1.42	1.48	1.54	1.60	1.66
0.3	1.42	1.49	1.56	1.63	1.70	1.77
0.2	1.48	1.56	1.64	1.72	1.80	1.88
0.1	1.54	1.63	1.72	1.81	1.90	1.99

density base. At the halfway point, the total net effect is the greatest.

Gehrhardt's formula does not take stand age into account and assumes that mortality bears a constant percentage relation to growth. Briegleb (1942) and Briegleb and Girard (1943), working with second-growth Douglas-fir, have shown that age is an important factor in this type, principally because mortality is not necessarily a constant percentage of growth but tends to increase with age. Briegleb also found that constants for K in Douglas-fir covered a considerably wider range of values than those determined by Duerr in the Lake States.

It is doubtful whether any correction formula of this type can be generally applicable. Gehrhardt's formula gives a useful approach and is helpful in casting light on the nature of the problem.

Estimation of growth—an example.   The application of normal yield tables in estimating growth in a stand can best be shown by an itemized example.

INFORMATION NEEDED   Most of the necessary information is obtained from the stand by an inventory. The items are as follows:

1. *Area.* Since total volume and growth estimates are directly affected by area, reasonable accuracy is necessary. The stand should be reasonably homogenous as to age, site, and stocking. It is also important that the stand include only areas actually stocked, with all surveyable holes and openings eliminated. An opening in the stand large enough so that trees on its periphery derive but little benefit from the space is obviously growing no timber and inclusion of such areas upsets the relationship between fully and partially stocked stands upon which yield-table predictions are based. To push the point to extremes, if one acre is fully stocked and its neighbor

is not stocked at all, one cannot assume the average stocking to be 50 percent in making yield-table predictions. The nonstocked area should be eliminated entirely from the calculation to the degree this is practicable.

2. *Site.* The average site index should be determined in the same way as done for the yield table. In American practice, site index is usually determined from the average total height and age of sample dominant and codominant trees. For this average height and age the corresponding site index is read from height-over-age site curves (as illustrated in Fig. 2.1).

Another method is to average the basal areas of sample dominant and codominant trees and determine the diameter of the tree of average basal area. A height-over-diameter curve for the stand is then constructed, and the height of this average tree used in determining site through use of site-index curves. Various procedures are possible; the main thing to bear in mind is to determine site index to a degree of accuracy believed sufficient for the purpose and comparable in derivation with the yield tables used.

3. *Volume Data.* The precise volume data obtained will, of course, depend on the nature of the survey, and usually more than growth-prediction purposes are involved. Volumes may be in whatever units are pertinent: board feet, cubic feet, cords, etc. It is important that the diameter limits included, the merchantability standards followed in estimation, and the volume tables used in computing volumes either correspond to those employed in the yield tables to be used or be capable of adjustment so that they will correspond.

One of the greatest practical difficulties in the application of yield tables to field data is lack of agreement on one or more items of volume-determination technique. For example, if a yield table is based on the gross volume of all trees 8 in. dbh and up, merchantability to a fixed top diameter of 5 in., and the International ⅛-in. rule is used for board foot volumes, there will be all sorts of difficulties in applying it to field data where only trees 10 in. dbh and larger were included in the cruise, net volume was estimated to a variable top diameter, and the Doyle log rule is used in figuring volumes. This will be true no matter how accurate are the data on area, age, and site. Since the method requires comparison of yield-table data to actual stands, the basis of comparison obviously must be consistent if good results are to be expected.

4. *Stocking.* Since normal yield tables are based on full stocking and average stands seldom are so stocked, relative stocking must be estimated. This is often a vexing problem.

In general, stocking should be measured in terms of the same unit that is employed in the growth prediction. If growth is to be estimated in cubic feet, then stocking ordinarily also should be measured in cubic feet. If board feet, Scribner rule, are the unit, then stocking should be figured on the same basis. If, however, stocking percentages based on board foot volume seem out of line because of lack of uniformity in measurement standards or some such reason, deviation from this general procedure may be advisable. No set rule is possible. Stocking percentages for a particular stand when measured in different units often differ considerably and for a variety of reasons. One reason is that yield tables themselves are empirically constructed; there is no set mathematical way to determine what is "full stocking" in all units of measure. Basal area is the best single criterion when other measures are uncertain or suspect for one reason or another. It is consistent and easily computed. Any stocking comparison based on volume may be upset if merchantability and other standards used in the actual stand are not in accordance with those used in the yield tables.

5. *Approach toward Normality.* While often ignored, stands understocked in relation to a yield table do grow at a faster rate than indicated by a yield table. Unless a correction is made, growth estimates will be conservative. There is more than one method of making a correction as previously explained; a choice must be made.

ESTIMATION PROCEDURE   With the necessary area, site, volume, stocking, and approach-toward-normality information assembled, the final step is estimation of growth using an applicable yield table. The specific process is illustrated in Table 4.2 as applied to an actual stand.

A check on the accuracy of the estimate is possible in this instance since the stand was remeasured at the end of the same 10-year growth period. No correction for approach to normality is made in Table 4.2, and growth in basal area, cubic feet, and board feet is estimated, using stocking percentages each based on the unit of measure employed; i.e., growth in cubic feet is estimated on the basis of stocking in cubic feet, etc.

As shown in columns 9 and 10, the estimates are not good in relation to what the stand actually did. Growth in basal area, cubic feet, and International board foot volume are grossly underestimated in relation to actual growth. The estimate in board foot growth, Scribner rule, agrees closely with actual growth but this is probably a happenstance. There are several possible reasons for these discrepancies. The standards of measurement employed are not the same in the yield tables and actual stand. This is particularly true in International measure. The yield tables are in terms of the $\frac{1}{8}$-in. rule and give gross volumes to a 5-in. top. The actual stand is measured by the $\frac{1}{4}$-in. rule and gives net merchantable volumes to a variable top diameter. There are also some differences in the exact diameter limits included. Stocking percentages (column 6) are fairly consistent except for International rule, which further suggests that this measure is not comparable. Also to be considered is the possibility of inconsistencies in the yield tables themselves; they cannot be assumed to be perfect. Finally, mortality in the actual stand may differ from the average in the yield table.

The estimates can be improved considerably by adjusting for known discrepancies and making an allowance for approach toward normality,

TABLE 4.2. APPLICATION OF NORMAL YIELD TABLES IN ESTIMATING GROWTH (ACRE BASIS)

Item	Fully stocked stand[a]			Beginning of growth period		Actual stand — End of 10-year growth period			
	Beginning of growth period	End of growth period	Growth during 10-year period	Stand data	Percent of stocking	Total stand est.[b]	Total stand, actual	Growth only, est.	Growth only, actual
(1)	(2)	(3)	(4)	(5)	(6)	(7)	(8)	(9)	(10)
Age, years................	75	85		75					
Site index................	60	60		60					
Basal area, sq ft.........	119[c]	127[c]	8	86.1[d]	72.4	91.9	99.2[d]	5.8	13.1
Volume, cu ft.............	3,150[c]	3,490[c]	340	2,131[d]	67.7	2,363	2,566[d]	232	435
Bd ft, International rule..	14,200[e]	17,000[e]	2,800	5,313[f]	37.4	6,358	7,358[f]	1,045	2,045
Bd ft, Scribner rule......	7,000[g]	9,700[g]	2,700	4,660[h]	66.6	6,460	6,507[h]	1,800	1,847

[a] *U.S. Dept. Agr. Tech. Bul.* 560, yield, stand, and volume tables for even-aged upland oak forests.
[b] Estimated directly on basis of respective stocking percentages.
[c] Trees 0.6 in. dbh and larger.
[d] Trees 1.6 in. dbh and larger.
[e] Gross volume (International ⅛-in. rule) to a 5-in. top inside bark of all trees having at least one 16-ft log.
[f] Net volume (International ¼-in. rule) to a merchantable top diameter, Girard Form Class 79.
[g] Gross volume to an 8-in. top inside bark of all trees having at least one 16-ft log.
[h] Net volume to a merchantable top diameter, Girard Form Class 79.

TABLE 4.3. ADJUSTED GROWTH ESTIMATES APPLYING GEHRHARDT'S FORMULA

Unit of measure	Fully stocked stand		Actual stand		
	Total growth	Growth reduced to 70% stocking	Gehr-hardt's cor-rection factor	Estimated growth, corrected, gross volume	Actual growth, net
Cubic feet............	340	238	1.21	288	435
Bd ft, International ¼-in. rule.............	2,534	1,774	1.21	2,146	2,045
Bd ft, Scribner rule.....	2,700	1,890	1.21	2,287	1,847

which should be expected. Since basal area and cubic volume are the most consistent measures of stocking, they might be roughly averaged and about 70 percent assumed as a good stocking figure. International ⅛-in. measure can also be converted to ¼-in. measure by applying a converting factor of 0.905.

Making these adjustments and applying Gehrhardt's formula, assuming a K factor of 0.7 applicable for semi-intolerant oaks, results in growth estimates as shown in Table 4.3. As shown, the board foot estimates are more in line with actual growth when these adjustments are made. If actual growth had been measured in gross volume, as is used in the yield table, instead of net volume, the estimates would probably be very close. For some reason not apparent from the stand data, the cubic foot volume estimate is still out of line. This case gives a good illustration of the sort of things that must be considered in applying yield tables to actual data.

It should be evident from the foregoing that no infallible procedure can be specified for the use of yield tables in estimation of growth. To attempt to do so would almost surely be an oversimplification of the problem and might lead to serious error. Good growth estimates can be made with yield tables, particularly for large areas, and for young stands more or less uniform in general structure and density. They must, however, be applied with judgment and with full understanding both of the yield tables and the stand data to which they are applied to ensure the comparability upon which the method is based.

YIELD TABLES FOR WELL-STOCKED MANAGED STANDS

In Europe particularly, a number of yield tables have been prepared for well-stocked stands to which a consistent schedule of thinnings have been periodically applied (Chap. 3). They are based on remeasurement of sample areas. Yield tables used in Germany and in Britain are examples (Wiedemann and Schober, 1957; Hummel and Christie, 1955; Waters and Christie, 1958). Generally, such tables represent well-stocked stands. The thinnings, especially the heavier grades, reduce densities and consequent volumes in the older ages somewhat.

From a growth-estimation standpoint, these tables are essentially similar to normal yield tables in that they represent a norm, a basing point, with which actual stands can be compared. Similar problems of comparability as regards density and structure must be met in using them to predict growth for a period of time in any actual stand.

In practice, such tables are used more as a guide to silvicultural treatment than as a basis for growth prediction. It should be recognized that, when management has become established to the degree that such tables can be prepared and have direct meaning in practice, problems of growth estimation are correspondingly less important. For this reason, they are little used for growth estimation except in rather young stands where yield tables, in general, can be most effectively employed.

VARIABLE-DENSITY YIELD TABLES

Limitations to the use of normal yield tables in estimating growth in stands with less than "full stocking" have long been recognized. Such stands are often of a distinctly different character in structure and do not grow like uniformly understocked even-aged natural stands. This is particularly true with residual stands left after a partial cutting in which certain sizes and kinds of trees are cut and others are left; the natural structure is basically altered. For these reasons, the general concept of yield tables has been directly applied in a number of ways to stands of variable density without any assumption of "normality" or full stocking.

One modification is represented by the "Weyerhaeuser Empirical Yield Tables for Douglas Fir" (McKeever, 1947). These are directly based on the Douglas-fir normal yield tables of McArdle and Meyer, 1930, but with a correction for approach toward mortality built in to them on the basis of studies by Briegleb and Girard, 1943. The tables give only board foot volumes, Scribner rule, for trees 12 in. in diameter and larger. For convenience in field use, the tables are presented in three stocking levels: good, 70 to 100 percent; medium, 40 to 69 percent; poor, 10 to 39 percent. Stocking is relative to the original yield tables. To apply the empirical yield tables to a particular stand it is necessary only to determine site, age, and stocking and read estimated future volumes by 5-year periods.

Schumacher and Coile (1960) have prepared yield tables for well-stocked stands. It is not possible to define just what "well-stocked" is; it is a function of the field data taken, the average of which was assumed to be 100 percent stocking. These tables can be used directly to estimate growth of stands of similar stocking; for others an adjustment for present and estimated future stocking is necessary following the same general procedures outlined for normal yield tables. To deal with growth estimation in other than well-stocked stands as given in the tables, the authors derived a series of equations and graphs from their basic plot data that, in effect, dispense with the yield tables as such and substitute a direct stand-structure approach such as is considered on p. 85.

Another simple but useful approach is to prepare a yield table directly from inventory data (Chap. 3). To use in growth estimation, it is assumed that the volume of a given stand in the future will be the same as that of another stand that has already attained that future age. For example, if natural stands at 100 years average 70 M bd ft per acre, it is assumed that a younger stand, for example 60 years of age, will attain this volume in 40 years or at age 100. If the 60-year stand has a current volume of 40 M, the indicated growth in 40 years is 70 minus 40 or 30 M, or an average of 750 bd ft per year. The basic assumption is that history will repeat itself. Data from such tables often can be presented usefully in growth percent or average annual increment for application.

Such tables can be prepared from inventory data in a number of ways, usually employing statistical or graphic means to establish consistent trends. All stands in an inventory unit may be averaged or they may be segregated by forest types, by broad site classes, and possibly by a few major stocking groups. The method is usually applied to stands that can be classified by age but it can also be applied to stands that cannot be. The British Columbia Empirical Yield Tables (Fligg, 1960) are a good large-scale example of even-aged tables derived from inventory plots.

This approach is applied in management planning in the United States on the western national forests which support large areas of natural stands of a wide range in ages. Inventory data give a basis for establishment of an age-volume trend line. Growth estimates so obtained are based on present realities and will become progressively better with successive inventories as the results of better management become evident on the ground. Such tables are easy to apply to large areas and no adjustments are needed. The approach is, however, inherently conservative in that results, as measured in harvest-age cuts, underestimate the cumulative effect of continued management on volume per unit of area. The simplicity of the method, its conservatism, and the lack of better data are the main reasons why it is employed.

Yield tables for cutover stands.   One kind of variable-density yield table, that for cutover stands, is of interest, since considerable study has been given to this problem and it is an intermediate step and a transition from the indirect yield-table approach to the direct stand-structure type of analysis described later in this chapter.

It was early recognized that there were distinct limitations to the application of normal yield tables in estimating the growth of residual stands left following cutting. Through cutting, the natural structure of even-aged stands is basically altered. Certain kinds and sizes of trees are heavily cut and others are left. This frequently creates a stand of distinctly different character, not merely a uniformly understocked even-aged natural stand. A frequent question is: What growth could be expected of the residual stand following a first or second cut? Since interest centers on the growth of the residual stand, it was logical to prepare yield tables specifically for such cutover stands with the volume of the reserved stand, the elapsed time since cutting, and site as the key variables rather than total stand age and site as in the case of normal yield tables. A number of tables for cutover stands have been prepared.

A thorough study of growth in selectively cut ponderosa pine forests in the Pacific Northwest by Meyer (1934) gives an excellent example of this kind of approach. A regionwide study was made of selectively cut stands, typically of a many-aged character, from which a set of tables were prepared giving average growth per acre for various reserved stand volumes. "Then an analysis was made, one by one, of the factors that cause a departure of growth from the average, and methods were developed of correcting growth and yield estimates for these factors." To put it briefly, a particular kind of yield table was constructed and a special study made to apply it.

Gross yields for average sites were presented in a series of tables with accompanying alignment charts giving the growth at 10-year intervals 10 to 60 years following cutting in terms of varying amounts of basal area and cubic foot and board foot volume left in the reserve stand. A portion of a table for board foot growth reproduced from Meyer's study will make the arrangement clear (Table 4.4).

In addition to initial reserved volume and time since cutting, an analy-

TABLE 4.4. BOARD FOOT VOLUME GROWTH, SCRIBNER RULE,
IN SELECTIVELY CUT STANDS OF PONDEROSA PINE OF
AVERAGE STRUCTURE, SITE QUALITY IV[a]

Volume of reserve stand at time of cutting, bd ft	Volume of reserve stand per acre after an interval of:					
	10 years	20 years	30 years	40 years	50 years	60 years
1,000	1,400	1,800	2,300	2,800	3,200	3,600
2,000	2,700	3,300	4,000	4,600	5,200	5,600
3,000	3,900	4,500	5,400	6,100	6,700	7,300
4,000	4,900	5,700	6,700	7,400	8,100	8,700

[a] After Meyer (1934).

sis was made of other factors influencing the growth of these partially cut stands. The following were selected as particularly important and measurable:

1. Site quality and stand structure. Site quality in broad classes measured in terms of site index was determined the usual way. Stand structure was expressed in terms of the percentage of the stand made up of certain tree classes (Dunning, 1928).

2. Mortality.

3. Number of poles. In ponderosa pine, as in other forest types, an important factor affecting board foot growth is the number of small trees that grow into merchantable size during the growth period (termed "ingrowth").

Methods of adjusting average gross growth as read from the tables were worked out for each of these factors giving a final net estimate of growth. The particular factors and the best procedure for handling them will naturally change with different forest types, but the approach of identifying which they are and of making appropriate allowance for them remains of fundamental significance.

A normal yield table revised for general application.   To complete this survey of variable-density yield tables used in growth estimation, it will be instructive to review a revision of normal yield data to make them more easily usable and of wider application.

Bruce revised the Douglas-fir yield tables (McArdle, Meyer, and Bruce, 1949) proposing a single and simplified yield table based on average stand dbh as the independent variable, and with number of trees per acre (those over 1.5 in. dbh), height of trees of average dbh, cubic foot, and board foot volumes as independent variables. For use in growth estimation three additional tables were prepared, the first two from the same basic data:

1. Individual tree height by diameter for stands of given average diameter.

2. Estimated average diameter growth per decade by stand age.

3. Estimated 10-year approach toward normality for different stocking levels (based on data of Briegleb and Girard, 1943).

Site was eliminated as a variable and stand age assumed a minor role; mensurational research has shown that neither have a high predictive value in estimating stand increment.

The following shows in outline form the use of these tables in estimating growth. The following data are obtained for an actual stand.

Average number of trees per acre
Average diameter (diameter of tree of average basal area, in inches)

Heights in feet of sample trees of approximately average diameter
Average age in years

To make the estimate, present volume (in cubic feet or board feet)
is interpolated directly from the single yield table on the basis of present
stand diameter, with a height-growth correction obtained from the sample
trees and the first additional table. Predicted average stand diameter, degree
of normality, number of trees at the end of the growth period, and finally
a volume per acre increment estimate for the growth period are obtained
from these four tables.

Although this method is based on normal yield-table data, the procedure departs widely from the yield-table estimation procedure described in
the preceding section. It further illustrates some of the problems of growth
estimation and shows the way toward direct approaches which dispense with
yield tables entirely, such as are given in the following section.

direct estimation of growth—stand structure methods

Despite their wide appeal and many uses, yield tables have distinct limitations in estimation of growth as have been brought out. The comparative
nature of the approach is a particular limitation; yield tables cannot be
applied directly to stands which are different in one or more respects from
those on which the yield tables are based, making various adjustments necessary. Mortality is "built in" (except in tables for managed stands in which
thinnings have been consistently applied) and, as has been pointed out (p.
71), its effect on growth estimates depends on what can be done to forestall
or utilize it through cutting. Mortality should be considered separately. Further, mensurational research has clearly shown that age and site, the two
usual independent variables in yield tables are not of high predictive value.
Age is particularly unsatisfactory and is also difficult to measure consistently.
Site is tremendously important but not good as a predictive variable primarily because it cannot be precisely defined or measured. It is better to
incorporate the effect of site into measurable items directly related to volume
production such as diameter and height growth.

These considerations have led to much investigation of variables
affecting growth in relation to measurable stand attributes and have led
also to development of growth estimation procedures applicable to the wide
range of stand conditions found in practice. They are grouped here as
stand-structure methods, having in common the technique of measuring important variables affecting growth and applying them directly to a stand.

As adapted from Spurr (1952), a good general growth prediction
method should:

1. Give growth directly per acre (or in other surface-area units)

2. Include the fewest possible variables of highest possible predictive value that are capable of precise definition and simple and objective measurement.

3. Require a minimum of field-stand data, of sampling classes, etc.

4. Be applicable to all kinds of stands, even- and uneven-aged, and of different structures and densities.

5. Give estimates in cubic measure, a valid unit of growth which board feet and cords are not. Conversions can subsequently be made to any merchantable unit desired.

6. Treat height growth separately from diameter or basal area growth. These are two major measures of growth and are not closely correlated.

7. Not have stand age as a primary variable.

The basic procedure in growth prediction, also applicable to yield tables, is:

1. Obtain from the stand whose growth is to be estimated the specific measurement data needed to apply whatever growth prediction method is to be used—diameters, number of trees, heights, volume, age, etc.

2. Project these stand data into the future by the growth method applied.

3. Make adjustments for factors not directly measured—mortality, ingrowth, change in stocking.

A considerable number of growth prediction methods of the stand-structure type have been devised for different purposes and employing different variables and techniques for handling them. The usual data basis is a growth study designed to determine and evaluate the predictive value of selected variables in estimating growth. The results are usually expressed in equation or graphic form and procedures are devised for their specific application to stand conditions. A few major approaches are presented here to illustrate general techniques.

TWO-WAY AND RELATED METHODS

Following detailed study of existing growth estimation methods and analysis of variables associated with growth in permanent sample plots, Spurr (1952, 1954) proposed a basic approach he called, for want of a better term, the two-way method. It is an attempt to meet the requirements for a good general approach.

This method rests upon the fact that growth in volume is a function of growth both in basal area and in height. These two primarily control volume growth and are directly measurable and objective variables. It follows that if they can be estimated closely good growth estimates can be readily made with a minimum of stand data. Growth in basal area is largely a function of stand density. Growth in height is primarily a function of site plus stand age. Change in stand form during a growth period can also be taken into account in volume computation but its effect is usually small for a limited period of about 10 years for which most estimates are made. Mortality, as usual, must be separately estimated.

To use the method, the following data are needed:

From the stand

Average age of dominant stand.

Basal area per acre. This can be computed from a stand table or by other means—such as an angle gauge.

Cubic foot volume per acre (or any cubic measurement unit).

A representative sample of increment borings to give a basis for estimate of diameter and basal area growth. If growth conditions are expected to change during the estimation period as a result of cutting, for example, and past growth is considered inapplicable, an outside source of increment data may be substituted.

A representative sample of total tree heights.

From other applicable sources

A cubic foot volume table.

Factors for converting cubic feet to board feet, cords, or other merchantable units.

Site-index curves (giving height of dominant stand over age).

To apply the method, separate estimates of basal area and of height growth must be made. Growth in basal area can be directly estimated from increment cores taken in the stand if this is deemed an applicable source. If not, they should be obtained elsewhere; their applicability to expected conditions during the growth estimation period is the point and not the specific source of data. Various computational techniques can be applied that are mensurational matters not dealt with here. Spurr (1954) gives an illustration. Ingrowth is not a problem provided the estimate base includes the total stand down to a diameter limit well below utilized diameter.

The procedure for estimation of stand height growth also depends on the particular situation and data available. Use of applicable site-index curves is one good method. From the present average height and age of the stand, these curves can be used to estimate height at some time in the future. If the height-age relationship is expected to change significantly, adjusted curves should be used. Again, the specific method is not so important; what is important is to get the best estimate possible of change in height from whatever sources of data are available. Knowledge, judgment, and skill are inescapable requisites.

Once growth in basal area and height are estimated and present cubic foot value determined, the next job is to estimate growth in cubic foot volume. If the stand form factor is assumed to remain unchanged, then the relationship between (1) the product of basal area and height and

(2) present cubic foot volume will hold for the future period. Expressed mathematically:

$$\frac{\text{Present BA} \times \text{present height}}{\text{Present cu ft volume}} = \frac{\text{future BA} \times \text{future height}}{\text{future cu ft volume}}$$

By substituting values, future cubic foot volume is calculated and the difference between this and present volume is the increment for the growth period.

The final step is to convert cubic foot to board foot, cord, or other mechantable units if desired. This is not difficult for appropriate conversion factors can be obtained that are well within the range of accuracy of the growth-estimation process as a whole. The importance of making growth estimates in a valid measure of volume, such as cubic feet, is stressed. Conversion to as imprecise measurement units as board feet or cords should be a final and separate step and not be allowed to contaminate primary measurement units.

Estimation of mortality is not a part of the method as is true with any other stand-structure approach. This must be dealt with separately and there is no single or simple solution (p. 71). One way is to estimate increment for the main stand (dominants and codominants), or some other arbitrary segregation such as including only the largest of 80 percent of the total number of trees in the estimate and assuming that the volume of the smaller trees will be equivalent to the mortality. In general, however, it is best to estimate gross growth without regard to mortality and then directly appraise anticipated mortality and what can be done about utilizing it as pointed out previously. If stand tallies made in the field are available indicating particular trees expected to die during a growth estimation period, these trees should be taken out of the data base and treated separately.

The method is flexible; it focuses attention on major measurable variables affecting growth and requires a reasonable minimum of stand data of a kind that is commonly obtained. Full use of growth data taken from outside the stand is possible. Indeed, it illustrates the fact that application of any such method can and usually does utilize outside data. The method can be applied to either all or to a part of a stand but in the latter case techniques are more complicated. Accurate estimates of growth in basal area and stand height are not easy to make; adequate data are necessary as always. Mensurational competence is needed to develop techniques and good judgment must be exercised in applying them. In one way or another, factors of site, density, age, and stand structure must be considered; there is no escape. The significance of the method lies in the selection and direct use of the fewest possible number of measurable variables affecting growth.

A related approach dealing specifically with southern pines is given by Schumacher and Coile (1960). In addition to preparing yield tables for well-stocked stands, a method of growth estimation applicable to southern pine conditions was derived from structural analysis of the same sampling data. The basic stand measurements required are age, site index, number of trees per acre, and basal area per acre. Through a series of statistically derived growth and conversion factor graphs, the authors present a procedure for estimating growth of six southern pine species in stands of widely varying structure and including the effect of hardwood components.

Duerr and Gevorkiantz (1938), working in the Lake States, made a structural analysis of uneven-aged stands, mainly northern hardwoods. It was found that most of these stands are really not all-aged but consist of an essentially even-aged main stand with one or more subsidiary age groups and can be treated like even-aged stands. Strong mathematical correlations were found to exist between (1) basal area and average stand diameter, (2) volume-basal area ratio and average stand diameter, and (3) age with average stand diameter that were utilized in making growth estimates. Volume growth in these stands was found to be mainly controlled by site, age, density, and the proportion of small trees of near mechantable size (the ingrowth). Utilizing these relationships, a series of charts and tables were prepared from which growth could be estimated from the following items determined for a particular stand:

Board foot volume per acre
Basal area per acre
Average main-stand diameter
Average main-stand age

Working in uneven-aged Appalachian hardwoods, Buell (1945) has presented a method of growth estimation based on the diameter distribution of the stand. By means of multiple regression equations, the net growth in board feet per tree per year for any diameter class was determined as a compound of (1) growth of surviving trees, (2) mortality of trees dying during the growth estimation period, and (3) growth of trees entering the diameter class during the period—the ingrowth.

All these methods, and there are others, have in common the stand-structure analysis approach. They differ mainly in the primary variables used and the mensurational handling in meeting particular stand conditions. Some methods have been applied in practice and some have not. They are all significant in the continuing search for objective and measurable variables affecting growth and in the addition to knowledge of stand structure.

STAND- AND STOCK-TABLE PROJECTION METHODS

Stand projection methods have in common estimation of growth from an average-acre stand or stock table representing the stand whose growth is to be estimated. The approach is direct, logical, and widely used. The stand or stock table is obtained from inventory data and is prepared by diameter classes, usually by species or species groups, and sometimes by tree classes as well. Any breakdown desired can be used; the purpose is to segregate stand components significant in growth so that they can be treated separately.

The problem then to be solved is how much will these trees grow during some growth projection period of 5, 10, or perhaps more years. There are two general procedures. The first, and most commonly used, is to project a stand table ahead for a growth period. Volume can then be computed for the present and for the estimated future stand table with the difference between them consequently being the stand increment for the period. The second, is to apply appropriate growth rates to a stock table.

Stand-table projection. The essence of stand-table projection is to estimate a future stand table on the basis of a present one. Mortality, as always, is a problem and one which must be handled separately as previously discussed in this chapter. Stand-table projection itself is apart from mortality; it assumes live trees only.

To estimate a future stand table, diameter growth information must be applied to each diameter class. There are two problems here. One is to use truly applicable data. Past increment in the stand as obtained from sample plot measurements or increment borings is most commonly used.[1] As pointed out, however, past stand growth is not a good prediction basis if growth conditions, stand structure, etc. are expected to change in the future. There is no substitute for experience-based judgment in determining the most appropriate diameter increment to use. No textbook can answer this question; it can only point out the considerations involved.

The second problem is how to apply diameter increment data to the stand table; differences in projection methods largely revolve around what method to use. Three general approaches are possible:

1. *Application of Average Diameter Increment to the Midpoint of the Diameter Class.* The simplest assumption is that all trees fall at the diameter class midpoint and grow at the average rate for the class as illustrated in Table 4.5.

Estimating future diameter classes by regrouping trees on the basis of average diameter increment applied at the class midpoint is a rather crude procedure. As shown in column 3, when 1-in. classes are used, trees growing up to 0.5 in. are not credited with any growth at all but stay

---

[1] A technical question about using increment core borings is the diameter base to use. One assumption is that a tree will maintain the radial growth it made in the past. That is, if a tree now 12 in. dbh grew 2 in. in the past 10 years, it will also grow 2 in. in the next 10 years. Another, is that a 12-in. tree now will grow as did a 12-in. tree 10 years ago when it was a 10-in. tree. While both are tenable assumptions, neither may hold if growth conditions change, as is often the case. A 12-in. tree now may be in a better or poorer condition to grow than it was 10 years ago. Choice depends on what seems the most reasonable assumption under the circumstances. Growth in bark thickness also may be appreciable and necessitate some adjustment of diameter increment which is commonly measured outside bark.

TABLE 4.5. APPLICATION OF AVERAGE DIAMETER INCREMENT
TO THE MIDPOINT OF THE DIAMETER CLASS

Present diameter class (class midpoint)	Estimated diameter growth during 10-year period, in.	Diameter class 10 years hence	Diameter 10 years hence based on class midpoint, in.
(1)	(2)	(3)	(4)
1-in. classes			
10	0.4	10	10.4
11	0.6	12	11.6
12	0.8	13	12.8
13	1.0	14	14.0
14	1.3	15	15.3
15	1.6	17	16.6
2-in. classes			
10	0.5	10	10.5
12	0.9	12	12.9
14	1.4	16	15.4
16	1.8	18	17.8
18	2.0	20	20.0
20	1.9	22	21.9

in the same class. Trees growing over 0.5 but less than 1.5 in. all move up one full diameter class, regardless of the wide spread in actual increment. This difficulty is even more pronounced with 2-in. classes where trees can grow up to an inch without changing diameter class at all. Trees growing from 1 to 2 in. all move up one class. Depending on just how average increment happens to be distributed in relation to the diameter structure of the stand, a considerable overestimate or underestimate of volume can result.

A refinement in procedure is to compute volumes on the diameter of trees in fractional inches at the end of the growth period, as shown in column 4 of Table 4.5. This eliminates the jerky effect of estimating growth by full classes only but also necessitates interpolating volume. It is possible, however, to prepare tables that show by diameter classes the change in board foot volume for different rates of growth. This will greatly speed up and simplify the process. Kemp and Metcalf (1948), for example, have prepared such tables for several northern Rocky Mountain species in terms of radial increment and number of rings in the outer radial inch.

This method of stand projection is often used and gives fairly good results if used with discretion and for short periods. However, it ignores two important facts about tree growth and distribution: (1) trees within a given diameter class grow at variable rates for a number of reasons and

(2) actual tree diameters do not fall at the midpoint but are distributed through the class.

2. *Application of Average Diameter Increment Recognizing Dispersion within Classes.* Even though the actual distribution of tree diameters within classes is not known, it can be approximated by assuming even distribution through the class.[1] The proportion of trees advancing into higher dbh classes can be defined as a movement ratio

$$m = \frac{g}{i} \times 100$$

where m = movement ratio expressed as a percentage
   g = periodic diameter increment, in.
   i = diameter class interval, in.

Assume, for example, that $g = 1.6$ and $i = 1.0$ in. Then,

$$m = \frac{1.6}{1.0} \times 100, \text{ or } 160 \text{ percent}$$

In interpreting this movement percentage ratio, the first two digits from the right indicate the percentage of the trees advancing one diameter class beyond the number of classes indicated by the third digit from the right. In the above example, 60 percent of the trees move up two classes and the rest one class. None remain in the initial diameter class. If the movement percentage ratio was 75, then 75 percent of the trees would move up one class and the remaining 25 percent would stay in the same class (the third figure from the right being zero). A percentage of 240 means that 40 percent move up three classes and the rest two classes. Table 4.6 illustrates how this works with several increment rates and 1- and 2-in. diameter classes.

In application, the movement percentages are calculated and applied to each diameter class of the stand table. The change in the number of trees in each diameter class is estimated accordingly. The results are summed by diameter classes to obtain the number of trees in each diameter class at the end of the growth period. It is important to include diameter classes in the stand table sufficiently below the lower merchantability limit so that ingrowth, the growth contributed by smaller trees growing into merchantable diameter classes during the growth period, is fully taken into account.

3. *Application of Variable Diameter Increment to Actual Diameters.* A third approach is based not only on the fact that the actual diameters of trees within a given diameter class are distributed throughout the class, but also on the fact that trees grow at variable rates. For example, with 2-in. classes, the 14-in. class extends from just over 13 in. to just under 15 in. If a particular tree, say 14.4 in. in diameter, grew 0.5 in. in 10 years it would stay in the 14-in. class even though it was toward the upper limit of the class to begin with. Another tree, say 13.2 in., might grow

---

[1] The assumption is subject to some statistical errors of grouping, as Meyer (1942) has pointed out.

TABLE 4.6. TREE DIAMETER MOVEMENT RATIOS APPLIED TO VARIOUS
INCREMENT RATES AND DIAMETER CLASSES

Periodic increment in dbh, in.	1-in. diameter classes						2-in. diameter classes			
	Tree movement ratio	Percent of trees advancing					Tree movement ratio	Percent of trees advancing		
		Zero classes	One class	Two classes	Three classes	Four classes		Zero class	One class	Two classes
0.5	50	50	50	...	..	..	25	75	25	
0.8	80	20	80	...	..	..	40	60	40	
1.0	100	0	100	...	..	..	50	50	50	
1.5	150	0	50	50	..	..	75	25	75	
1.8	180	0	20	80	..	..	90	10	90	
2.0	200	0	0	100	..	..	100	0	100	
2.4	240	0	0	60	40	..	120	0	80	20
2.8	280	0	0	20	80	..	140	0	60	40
3.3	330	0	0	0	70	30	165	0	35	65

2 in. during 10 years and consequently get into the 16-in. class. Almost any such combination may occur in nature. Variation in increment is commonly much greater within than between diameter classes. That is, the average growth rate may and often does change but little from class to class although there are wide variations between trees within the same class. These differences, which are of large management significance, are obscured by averaging growth rates by diameter classes. It is only by recognizing actual rates within diameter classes that one can account for the observed fact that in an actual stand some trees attain diameters far in excess of those that can be predicted by any average growth-rate method. Dominant trees, for example, grow faster than codominant trees of the same diameter and have grown faster all their lives or they would not be dominants. Trees of good vigor grow substantially faster than trees or poor vigor of the same diameter.

A large amount of increment data from trees growing under conditions comparable to those whose growth is to be estimated is necessary to apply this method. Instead of estimating the proportion of trees that move up one or more diameter classes on the basis of assumed dispersion and an average increment for each diameter class, the movement is determined from the performance of individual trees. A graphic procedure for obtaining these actual movement percentages is illustrated in Fig. 4.3 for two sample diameter classes. The actual diameter and increment of each tree in the initial diameter class is plotted on a graph. The movement into larger diameter classes can be seen by inspection and readily reduced to a movement percentage. Tree *A* for example was initially 14.7 in. dbh and grew 2.4 in. during a 10-year growth period. It consequently moved up two dbh

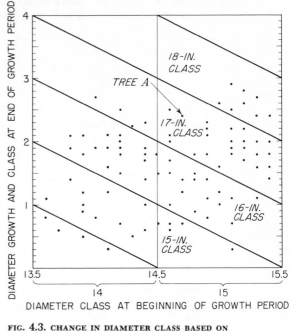

FIG. 4.3. CHANGE IN DIAMETER CLASS BASED ON
ACTUAL DIAMETER AND 10-YEAR INCREMENT.

classes, which can be determined by inspection, since it is in the second full diagonal band above the initial class. For any initial diameter class, the movement of trees into diameter classes at the end of the growth period can be determined by counting the number of dots in each diagonal diameter class band. These numbers can readily be converted to movement percentages. In the initial 15-in. class, for example, there are 55 trees represented by dots on the diagram. The movement percentages are determined as shown in Table 4.7:

TABLE 4.7. GROWTH-MOVEMENT PERCENTAGES

Diameter class 10 years hence	Movement in number of diameter classes	Number of trees in each diameter class 10 years hence	Movement percentage
15	0	5	9
16	1	17	31
17	2	25	45
18	3	8	15
Total.......	..	55	100

These percentages are then applied by diameter classes in the same way as are movement percentages based on an assumed dispersion.

This method is in accord with the facts of tree growth and can give more precise results than any other method, provided the growth data used are applicable to the situation. There is always the possibility, however, that data collected from past growth in a stand, no matter how carefully and voluminously, may not apply to future growth. Another difficulty in using the actual dispersion method is the problem of getting a sufficiently large volume of applicable growth data from which to determine reasonably stable movement percentages. These percentages obviously change with the age, site, condition, and treatment of the stand. For these reasons the method is good where sufficient data can be obtained but not so good where consistent percentages are hard to get. It is particularly illuminating as a concept of growth.

4. *Determination of Volume Increment.*   With a present and a future stand table prepared by whatever method is most appropriate, the final step is determination of volume. This involves increment in height as well as in diameter. The relationship to the two-way method is apparent; it projects the stand ahead as a unit using basal area growth, whereas stand-table projection does it by diameter increment applied to individual diameter classes. A common practice is to assume that the height-diameter relationship does not change. This relationship can change, however, and the effect on volume determination may be substantial necessitating adjustment of height-diameter data for the future stand table.

With increment in diameter and height estimated, present and future volumes are computed from the two stand tables by use of applicable volume tables. The difference between them is increment during the period. Initial computation in cubic feet is preferable; conversions to other desired units can then be made. Mortality must be dealt with separately as previously pointed out.

Stock-table projection.   In stock-table projection, as distinguished from stand-table projection, the process starts with a stock table giving volumes by diameter classes (and tree classes if the latter are also used). Increment is directly estimated for each diameter class (or tree class within diameter class). This means that average volume per tree for each class is determined and its estimated increment for the growth period. This can be conveniently applied to the stock table by converting the growth to an annual or periodic percent of tree volume and multiplying each class by the appropriate percentage. The sum of all classes is the estimated growth for the period. The process is well illustrated by Briegleb (1945) working with ponderosa pine.

Increment in diameter and height are incorporated in these growth data and their determination involves all the problems of applicability of data encountered in stand-table projection. Growth data may be obtained from the stand but it is also possible to utilize general growth data gathered on a broad basis that, by suitable adjustment for variables such as site, density, and age, can be applied to a particular stand. Ingrowth must be estimated separately in volume projections of this sort as the numbers of submerchantable trees that may grow into merchantability during the growth period are not included in the stock table. Mortality must also be separately treated.

The general nature of the process is illustrated in Table 4.8. For simplicity a single tree and an average volume per tree is used for each diameter class. Increment in value as well as volume is shown. As indicated, a 20-in. tree is estimated to grow 189 bd ft in 10 years. Since the present volume is 410 bd ft, the average annual growth is 18.9/410 × 100, or 4.6 percent. To estimate growth for some desired period, multiply the present volume in the diameter class by the growth percent in decimals and the number of years.

The process also indicates the rather tricky nature of growth percentage in general as applied to either trees or stands. A percentage expressed in annual terms could be used to estimate increment for any period but it must be kept firmly in mind that the percentage was determined for a particular period of time from increment cores of sample plot data and can be applied to some other period only with extreme caution. The main difficulty with growth percent is that it is not a quantity but a relationship. It is useful as a means of expressing growth but not as a means of determining it.

As a tree grows, the percentage growth rate tends to decline, since growth is measured against a constantly increasing total volume base. Few trees can grow fast enough to maintain a constant rate. As shown in Table 4.8, the annual growth per tree measured in board feet and dollars (columns 5 and 6) increases with diameter, but the growth percentages in both volume and value decrease with increasing diameter.

Applied to the growth of a stand instead of to trees individually, the same difficulties in the use of growth percent remain. Stand growth percentages must be applied with care although they can be useful. A poorly stocked stand will have a much higher growth percent than a well-stocked stand, despite the fact that the latter is making much greater volume and value growth per acre, the real basis for evaluation. This happens both because understocked stands tend to grow relatively faster than well-stocked stands and because the base on which growth percent is measured is smaller in understocked stands. Growth percent has meaning when it is applied to a managed forest of approximately constant growing stock. In this case, growth equals yield, and it means something to say that the forest returns a certain percent annually on its growing stock. Even here, however, comparisons may be misleading and a quantitative measure of volume or value growth per acre per year is more meaningful.

TABLE 4.8. VOLUME AND VALUE GROWTH IN A MANAGED
SHORTLEAF–LOBLOLLY PINE STAND[a]

Diameter breast high	Utilized volume per tree, bd ft	Value per M	Value per tree	Estimated 10-year growth		Average annual growth, percent	
				Volume	Value	Volume	Value
(1)	(2)	(3)	(4)	(5)	(6)	(7)	(8)
14	127	$15.00	$ 1.90	122	$ 4.84	9.6	25.5
16	201	22.80	4.58	153	7.37	7.6	16.1
18	298	29.89	8.91	174	9.99	5.8	11.2
20	410	36.56	14.99	189	12.29	4.6	8.2
22	533	42.81	22.82	202	13.53	3.8	5.9
24	665	47.75	31.75	213	13.75	3.2	4.3
26	805	50.88	40.96	223	14.04	2.8	3.4

[a] Data courtesy of R. R. Reynolds, U.S. Forest Service. Columns 5 and 6 are based on an estimated diameter growth of 3 in. in 10 years. A tree now 14 in. in diameter will be 17 in. in diameter 10 years hence and will have the volume and value of a tree of that size as interpolated from columns 2 and 4.

Discussion of stand- and stock-table projection methods. Stand- and stock-table projection methods have certain advantages and limitations in common. On the positive side they have the following advantages:

1. They are good for irregular stands that do not fit any normal pattern and where most of the growth is made by relatively good-sized and well-established trees whose performance is reasonably predictable. They are particularly useful with uneven-aged stands.

2. The methods are useful for estimating the growth of a certain part of the stand which may be of particular interest. Any species or species group desired can be singled out for separate analysis.

3. They are good in focusing attention on the specific structure and nature of the stand. Growth is specifically identified by diameter classes. The methods are excellent in bringing out the relationship between stand and individual tree growth.

Some problems and limitations to keep in mind are:

1. They offer no advantage in young, well-stocked, and rapidly growing stands which may be better and more simply handled by yield-table or other stand-structure methods.

2. They can be fairly laborious to apply in contrast to other stand-structure methods which may be complex in development but are usually relatively simple to use. Close attention to detail is necessary, and if the stand table is broken down by species and perhaps tree classes the process becomes complicated.

3. There is always some uncertainty about the applicability of the increment data used but this problem is common to all methods of estimating growth.

4. The methods are subject to the same errors of sampling of any other growth method. The growth estimate can be no better than the representativeness of the stand and stand table to the total area it represents, and the applicability and accuracy of the growth data used.

5. Prediction for long periods is uncertain, which is true of any stand-structure method. No average growth rate will represent the dynamics of actual tree and stand growth over an extended period. Yield table methods are, in general, better for long-range predictions.

forest growth in summary

Problems of forest growth determination have been considered at some length because they are so vital in timber management. There are no single or simple solutions nor is there any such thing as a standard growth-estimation method. No one method possibly can meet all situations and needs.

Growth gives a measure of forest performance as determined by successive inventories, and the final check on the efficacy of silvicultural methods applied. Growth predictions are necessary in planning ahead, as a forester continually must, but such estimates are always more or less uncertain. In addition to the difficulties of getting good tree diameter and height increment data, mortality and the effect of cyclic climatic changes are only partly predictable. Because of these uncertainties, refinements in prediction techniques can pass the point of diminishing returns as a practical matter.

Thinking beyond evaluation of performance and prediction as such, the most basic use of growth information is in the *design* of the timber management system, in determination of the number, character, and timing of intermediate cuts, of the length of the rotation or cutting cycle, of desirable species composition, and in other key decisions. Growth is a predictable consequence of these decisions. If the best ones possible are made, then a maximum amount of harvestable products will be grown.

The forest manager should have no prejudice about methods of estimating growth; there are a number of them of widely differing type. Each is useful under certain conditions and has certain advantages and disadvantages. A practitioner should have a good general knowledge of methodology and use or adapt, if necessary, the method best suited to his particular need. Finally, there is no substitute for close observation and knowledge of tree and stand behavior, application of good judgment, and mensurational skill.

5
the regulated forest

The organization of a forest property to provide a sustained flow of harvested products is the heart of forest management for timber production. Some principal working tools of management, those of site, stocking, growth, and yield, have been presented in Chaps. 2 to 4. The purpose here is to use them in obtaining a continued yield from a managed forest.

What are the reasons why the idea of sustained yield is so firmly embedded in forestry thinking and literature? First and foremost, it is important to recognize that the reasons are essentially external to the forest itself; they are derived from the purposes of management and are economic and administrative in nature. If the forest is well protected and cared for, it makes little difference biologically whether the harvest is even in flow or not.

As stated by Roth (1925) but somewhat revised, the following indicate the results from and desirability of obtaining a regular harvest from the forest.

1. A yearly cut of an approximately equal volume, size, quality, and value of timber provides a stable business planning base. It also defines the need for additional timber if needed to supply dependent processing plants which must operate on a regular basis, often within rather narrow limits.

2. A current harvested growth and income is obtained from a forest growing stock no larger than necessary. Growing stock represents invested capital upon which a maximum rate of return is desired.

3. To a private owner particularly, there are strong reasons why an approximate balance between yearly expenditures and receipts is important. Land and income taxes are levied annually as are many other costs; financial man-

agement is facilitated by a reasonably current equation between income and outgo.

4. A maximum degree of safety from fire, insects, diseases, and other dangers is maintained because the forest is kept growing, vigorous, and usually well distributed in size, age, and condition over the forest area. This is a forest reason but of large economic import.

5. There is maximum opportunity for correlation with other forest land uses—recreation, wildlife, watershed protection, and forage—on a stable planned basis.

6. A regular harvest ensures continuity of work load. An efficient forest organization cannot be maintained with a widely fluctuating annual job. Regular employment must be provided; a cutting program cannot be turned off and on at will nor can a scheduled timber procurement schedule in a competitive situation. Administrative reasons for reasonable application of sustained-yield management are powerful.

Despite these reasons, which collectively add up to very strong forces pressing toward forest harvest continuity, it is perfectly true, as pointed out in Chap. 1, that there are many individual owners who for a variety of reasons and at different times do not seek an even flow of forest business. In a competitive and fluctuating market situation there may be good financial reasons for cutting more heavily at some times than at others. The forest manager usually works with unbalanced properties and must consider the costs of working toward a balanced situation; it is a question of rate of progress desired.

For these reasons, organization of a forest for a sustained and approximately even harvest flow should be regarded as a generally desirable objective that is seldom fully achieved. It is so approached. If there were no need for such an objective there would be no subject of forest regulation to consider.

structure of a fully regulated forest

How is a forest organized for continued production? The fundamentals can be most clearly presented and grasped by analyzing the nature of a fully regulated forest through which continued production is most completely achieved. A fully regulated forest is consequently a valuable concept in forest management, and knowledge of its structure is necessary to the understanding of the problems and needs of actual forests, which usually fall far short of regularity.

The essential requirements of a fully regulated forest are that age and size classes be represented in such proportion and be consistently growing at such rates that an approximately equal annual or periodic yield of products of desired size and quality may be obtained. There must be a progression of size and age classes so that harvestable trees in approximately equal volume are regularly available for cutting.[1]

It should be recognized that while there is a general relationship between age and size, i.e., small trees are normally younger than large trees, the relationship is not direct and often not even close. The size and condition of a tree and its capacity to grow is much more significant than its actual age. What is essential in a regulated forest is that all sizes of trees be represented in balanced proportion and that these trees be capable of growing as trees of their size should. This means, for example, that 10-in. trees should not be long-suppressed trees that in relation to their age should be 20-in. trees but are now weakened and incapable of normal future growth. Ten-inch trees should be able to grow as normal 10-in. trees. If they can do this, then actual age does not matter. A good distribution of ages usually ensures that vigorous trees of all sizes are present. Age group is used here more or less synonymously with size group, and the general relation between age and size should be kept in mind.

From a regulatory standpoint, there are only two basic kinds of forest units: those composed of even-aged stands and those composed of uneven-aged stands. There are, of course, stands that are not clearly even- or uneven-aged and all kinds of combinations occur. But for forest organization purposes, stands need to be grouped into one category or the other.

An even-aged stand is one whose individual trees originated at about the same time, either naturally or artificially. It grows, is cared for, may undergo various intermediate cuttings during its development, and is ultimately removed in one or more major harvest cuts, after which a new stand is established. Such a stand consequently has a beginning and an end in time. A representative life pattern of an even-aged stand is shown in Fig. 5.1.

An uneven-aged stand is one whose trees originated at different times so that the stand tends to include trees of all ages and sizes. The age-size distribution is seldom perfect. There may be two, three, or more age groups intermixed in various ways. The distinguishing feature of an uneven-aged stand, large enough to be of practical importance as a management unit, is that it has no identifiable beginning in point of time, nor has it an end because if it did the next stand necessarily would be even-aged.

[1] The terms "normal increment" and "normal growing stock" have been applied in describing stocking and growth requirements. However, these terms usually include also the implication that the increment and stocking is the best obtainable for the site and species. While the aim naturally is to get the greatest possible increment and stocking and consequently yield consistent with management purposes, establishment of a fully regulated forest does not require that any particular level of management be practiced. This follows the concept of sustained yield which, as was pointed out in Chap. 1, does not depend on any particular level of management. A fully regulated forest certainly gives a sustained yield. The amount of the yield depends on the intensity of management applied.

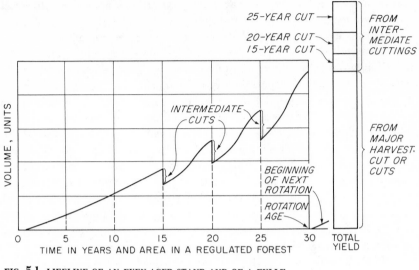

FIG. 5.1. LIFELINE OF AN EVEN-AGED STAND AND OF A FULLY
REGULATED FOREST OF EVEN-AGED STANDS.

The general growth pattern of an uneven-aged stand is shown by the heavy line in Fig. 5.2. As indicated, one starts with a stand having a certain volume of growing stock, the stand grows for a period of time (a cutting cycle), a cut is taken, and the sequence is repeated.

The application of management to even- and uneven-aged stands is given in Chaps. 7 to 9. The purpose here is to introduce them but consider only their general structure and nature as a necessary part of developing the concept of a regulated forest. Attention will be focused on the management of even-aged stands because they are the more common and more easily understood.

The best way to visualize the structure of a regulated forest is to consider it as composed of a series of even-aged stands each occupying approximately equal area with one stand of each age.

This is graphically portrayed in Fig. 5.1, showing a model forest all of the same site quality managed on a rather short harvest age rotation (R) of 30 years. This means that timber is grown to an average age of 30 years when it is assumed to be ready for final harvest cutting. Consider the diagram as showing the volume profile of 30 such stands, one for each year from 1 to 30, instead of indicating the life growth line of a single stand. Perhaps it will help to think of the diagram as representing a series of stands arranged along a road in order of age from the youngest to the oldest. The total area (A), whatever it may be, is consequently divided into 30 stands of equal area; if there were only 30 acres in the forest, there would consequently be 1 acre in each. If there were 6,000 acres, again

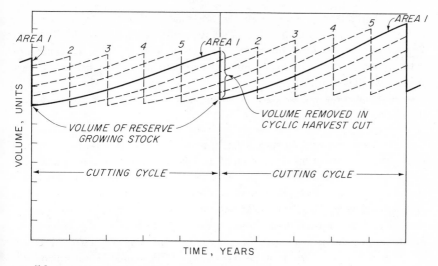

FIG. 5.2. LIFELINE OF AN UNEVEN-AGED STAND AND OF A
FULLY REGULATED FOREST OF UNEVEN-AGED STANDS.

all of the same site quality, there would be A/R or 200 acres in each stand or group of stands of the same age. The stocking of each should be consistent and in proportion to its age. If the areas in the various age-size groups are unequally stocked in relation to the stocking that stands of each age class should carry for the level of management being practiced, then the cut will also tend to be irregular and the forest will not be fully regulated. The annual cut is obtained by cutting the stands most ripe for final harvest, normally comprising the oldest age class which has just reached rotation age, plus intermediate cuts that can be taken from other parts of the forest. The annual cut is the sum of these two parts and consequently represents the total harvested growth of the forest.

In a forest composed of uneven-aged stands, it would be necessary to have as many stands or groups of stands as there are years in the cutting cycle. These areas are shown by broken lines in Fig. 5.2 assuming a 5-year cutting cycle. Approximately ⅕ of the total area is cut each year, removing from each of the stands cut a volume equivalent to 5 years of net growth in addition to whatever adjustments may be made (plus or minus) in the level of reserved growing stock. A slight increase in reserve growing stock is assumed in Fig. 5.2.

A generalized annual schedule of work in a forest managed on an even-aged basis would be as follows:

1. Timber which has reached rotation age on A/R acres is harvested.

2. A similar area recently cutover is regenerated naturally or by planting as may be most desirable.

3. A number of other cuttings are made. These might include, for example, a cleaning in 5-year-old stands and thinnings in 15-, 20-, and 25-year-old stands. Each operation is done on A/R acres. A substantial or even major part of the total annual net growth of the forest may be harvested through thinnings.

4. Protection is given, roads are maintained, and taxes are paid over the entire forest.

An area operated on such a basis, with all age classes represented and with uniform conditions of increment and stocking, is a fully regulated forest. It is not at all necessary that each age class be in any neat geometric pattern or in one place. They may be fairly well distributed over the forest area as a whole. It is the balanced presence of all age and size groups that is essential rather than their physical distribution on the ground. In intensive plantation management where ages are known, stands differing as little as 1 year in age may be recognized. With stands of natural origin, stands are usually grouped into 5, 10, or larger age classes. In Fig. 5.1, a 5-year grouping is shown by the broken lines. Since there is usually a range in ages and sizes within each age group, it is normally best diagrammatically to show them by a sloping line as shown rather than horizontally, for there would be some gradient in volume if not in age. In making thinnings or harvest cuttings, those stands most ready for cutting would be selected each year. Calendar age is not strictly observed in practice.

It is not necessary that each age group occupy equal areas. In fact, it would be most unusual if they did, as this could only occur when all parts of the forest were of the same site quality. To illustrate, assume that the sample forest is loblolly pine and includes lands of different site quality with an average site index of 90 ft. The relative productivity of the different sites included in the forest consequently can be measured in relation to site 90. As has been brought out, normal yield-table data give a useful measure of the comparative productivity of different sites. Using applicable yield-table data for loblolly pine, the following tabulation shows the number of acres of lands of various site quality necessary to equal the productivity of 1 acre of site index 90 land which is used as the basis of comparison:

Site index	Relative productivity in percent as measured by normal yield tables; site 90 assumed as 100%	Number of acres required to equal in productivity 1 acre of site 90 land
70	65	1.54
80	82	1.22
90	100	1.00
100	118	0.85
110	135	0.74
120	153	0.65

As shown, it would take about an acre and a half of site index 70 land to equal one of site 90, but only two-thirds of an acre of site 120 land. Where age groups differ in average site quality, different areas would be necessary to give equal productivity. This means that the horizontal axis of Fig. 5.1 is not necessarily graduated in equal area units; the purpose is to have areas of equal productivity by age classes.

To reemphasize, it is the existence of age (or size) class and increment consistency that makes a regulated forest, not the particular way sites and ages are distributed on the ground, nor the level of stocking. A fully regulated forest may be only partially stocked. If a forest can yield an annual or periodic crop of approximately equal volume, size, and quality of product, it is a regulated forest regardless of how it may be arranged on the ground.

measurement of the growing stock and yield

The forest manager is concerned with regularity as measured in acres and age-class distribution and also with the amount of growing stock necessary to support a regulated forest and the volume of annual cut obtainable. Obviously, he wants to get and maintain the right amount and proportion of growing stock appropriate to his purposes and conditions of management. What is the right amount? The only way he can tell whether the stocking of the various age classes is what it should be is to measure the volume of growing stock they contain and compare these volumes to some standard. Ideally, this standard should be a well-managed forest similar to his own, upon which experience and study over a number of years have indicated what is a desirable distribution and volume of growing stock. Such forests are few in number in the United States although research and experience are steadily augmenting the volume of information available. Normal yield tables, despite their limitations, give a basis for comparison and are useful in showing the nature of a fully regulated forest. They are so employed here.

Meyer (1942) has prepared normal yield tables for even-aged fully stocked stands of loblolly pine in northern Louisiana in compact and useful form. Data from his study (Table 5.1) are used in developing the analysis of a fully regulated forest. The following situation is assumed:

1. A fully regulated even-aged forest operated on a 60-year rotation.

2. A total area of 60 acres with all age classes present, 1 to 60 inclusive, each represented on 1 acre.

3. All land of site index 90 quality.

4. All stands fully stocked, as measured by the normal yield tables. The fact that stocking would in all probability be something less under practical management does not lessen the significance of the illustration.

5. A single harvest cut at rotation age; for simplicity, intermediate cuts are not included.

TABLE 5.1. YIELD OF EVEN-AGED LOBLOLLY PINE[a]

Age, years	Site index, ft					
	70	80	90	100	110	120
Number of trees per acre 3.6 in. and larger in diameter						
20	810	710	630	560	500	445
30	528	437	373	333	303	279
40	289	240	205	183	166	153
50	219	181	155	138	126	116
60	198	164	140	125	114	105
70	186	154	131	117	106	98
80	176	146	124	111	100	93
Basal area per acre of trees 3.6 in. and larger in diameter						
20	104	107	110	112	113	114
30	127	131	134	136	138	139
40 and over	129	133	136	138	140	141
Average diameter of trees 3.6 in. and larger in diameter						
20	4.9	5.3	5.7	6.1	6.5	6.9
30	6.6	7.4	8.1	8.6	9.1	9.6
40	9.0	10.1	11.1	11.8	12.4	13.0
50	10.4	11.6	12.7	13.5	14.3	14.9
60	10.9	12.2	13.3	14.2	15.0	15.7
70	11.3	12.6	13.8	14.7	15.6	16.2
80	11.6	12.9	14.2	15.1	16.0	16.7
Cubic measure per acre, including stump and tip but not bark, trees 3.6 in. and larger						
20	1,250	1,500	1,750	2,000	2,300	2,650
30	2,500	2,970	3,440	3,930	4,400	4,870
40	3,120	3,710	4,290	4,910	5,490	6,080
50	3,450	4,090	4,740	5,420	6,070	6,720
60	3,680	4,370	5,070	5,790	6,480	7,170
70	3,870	4,600	5,330	6,090	6,820	7,550
80	4,030	4,800	5,560	6,350	7,110	7,870
Board measure (International ¼-in. rule) per acre; trees 6.6 in. and larger to a 5-in. top ib						
20	900	2,200	3,400	4,700	6,100	7,400
30	6,200	9,500	12,800	16,000	19,100	22,400
40	13,400	17,900	22,300	26,700	30,800	35,100
50	17,200	22,100	27,000	31,900	36,700	41,500
60	19,100	24,300	29,600	34,900	40,100	45,300
70	20,600	26,100	31,700	37,300	42,900	48,400
80	21,800	27,600	33,500	39,400	45,200	51,100

[a] Meyer (1942), Tables 4, 5, 6, 7, and 8.

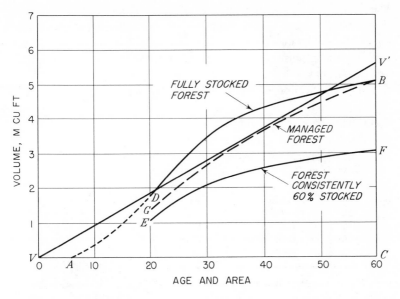

FIG. 5.3. GROWING STOCK FOR A FULLY REGULATED
FOREST OF LOBLOLLY PINE.

The growing stock per acre at different ages for such a forest, measured in cubic feet, is as shown by the curve DB in Fig. 5.3. Volumes
for stands below 20 years of age were not measured. The broken continuation of line DB to A indicates probable cubic volumes for these young
age classes. The growing stock for a forest consistently 60 percent stocked
is shown by curve EF and for an actual forest assumed to be under intensive
management by the broken-line curve GB.

The total measured volume of growing stock for the fully stocked and
partially stocked forests of 60 acres each is the total area under the respective curves (curves DB and EF). It cannot be determined merely by adding
the yield-table values of Table 5.1 because they show volumes at 10-year
intervals only. It could be obtained by the laborious process of reading off
from the curve the volume of each of the 60 separate even-aged stands
represented and adding. The total volume could also be obtained graphically
by measuring the total area under the curve by a planimeter. A simpler
method is to apply a summation formula giving the total volume on the
basis of the values given by the yield table. The formula is as follows:

$$G_r = n\left(V_n + V_{2n} + V_{3n} + \cdots + V_{r-n} + \frac{V_r}{2}\right)$$

where r = total period in years and total number of acres
$\quad G_r$ = total volume of growing stock on r acres
$\quad n$ = number of years between entries in yield table
V_n, etc. = yield-table volumes per acre for ages n, $2n$, $3n$, $\ldots$, $r - n$, and r
$\quad\quad\quad$ years

The formula[1] assumes that the volume between any two ages given by the yield table increases as a straight line, i.e., an arithmetical series, and sums up all the intervening values. The formula will slightly overestimate areas under concave portions of the curve and will underestimate areas under convex portions.

The application of the formula to the sample 60-acre forest, having 1 acre of each age class from 1 to 60 years, can best be shown by an illustration (data from Table 5.1):

Age, years	Volume per acre, cu ft (site 90)	Term in formula
20	1,750	V_n
30	3,440	V_{2n}
40	4,290	V_{3n}
50	4,740	V_{r-n}
60	5,070	$V_r/2$

Since volumes are not given below 20 years, the volume at that age becomes the first term V_n of the formula. The total growing stock volume for the 60-acre forest is then

$$G_{60} = 10 \left(1{,}750 + 3{,}440 + 4{,}290 + 4{,}740 + \frac{5{,}070}{2} \right)$$
$$= 167{,}550 \text{ cu ft}$$

[1] The formula is derived as follows:

$$\text{Volume 0 to } V_n \text{ years} = n \left(\frac{V_0 + V_n}{2} \right)$$

$$\text{Volume } V_n \text{ to } V_{2n} \text{ years} = n \left(\frac{V_n + V_{2n}}{2} \right)$$

$$\text{Volume } V_{2n} \text{ to } V_{3n} \text{ years} = n \left(\frac{V_{2n} + V_{3n}}{2} \right)$$

$$\text{Volume } V_{r-n} \text{ to } V_r \text{ years} = n \left(\frac{V_{r-n} + V_r}{2} \right)$$

Adding all volumes, V_0 to V_r, and combining terms (note that each volume term except the first and last occurs twice),

$$G_r = n \left(\frac{V_0}{2} + \frac{2V_n}{2} + \frac{2V_{2n}}{2} + \frac{2V_{3n}}{2} + \cdots + \frac{2V_{r-n}}{2} + \frac{V_r}{2} \right)$$

Since the volume at V_0 is zero, the first term drops out and the formula becomes

$$G_r = n \left(V_n + V_{2n} + V_{3n} + \cdots + V_{r-n} + \frac{V_r}{2} \right)$$

If it is desired to apply this formula to determine the total volume under a curve not beginning at 0 but at n years, then the first term is V_n rather than V_0 and does not drop out but becomes $V_n/2$. The formula then reads

$$G = n \left(\frac{V_n}{2} + V_{2n} + V_{3n} + \cdots + V_{r-n} + \frac{V_r}{2} \right)$$

The average volume per acre is 167,550/60 or 2792.5 cu ft. According to the nature of the formula and the problem it is designed to solve, a zero volume is assumed for the age class the next interval below the lowest age shown in the yield table. In the above illustration, the youngest age class measured is 20 years and the interval of measurement is 10 years. The volume at age 10 is consequently assumed to be zero and a volume for the 10–20-year age group is included on the basis of straightline interpolation from zero at age 10 to the volume indicated (1,750 cu ft in this instance) at age 20.

It should also be noted that the formula gives the total growing stock for the same number of area units as there are years in the period involved. Thus for 60 years, the answer is for 60 acres, since the yield table gives volumes per acre.

For a forest consistently partially stocked, the total volume of the growing stock may be obtained in the same way by taking 60 percent of the yield-table values, or more simply by merely taking 60 percent of 167,550, the total growing stock volume of the fully stocked forest. The summation formula can be used with any kind of a yield table and for any volume unit, provided values are given at regular intervals. If given at irregular intervals, the total growing stock would have to be determined by direct summation of inventory data.

RELATIONSHIP BETWEEN TOTAL GROWING STOCK AND YIELD—HUNDESHAGEN'S FORMULA

There is obviously a relationship between the total growing stock volume required in a regulated forest and the annual yield of mature timber. In this example of a fully stocked and fully regulated forest, a total growing stock of 167,550 cu ft produces an annual cut of 5,070 cu ft (leaving intermediate cuttings out of account). This is the volume of the oldest age class which reaches rotation age and is cut each year. This volume necessarily also equals the total annual harvested growth made by the entire forest (excluding any intermediate cuttings that may also be obtained). For the forest as a whole, growth consequently averages 5,070/60, or 84.5 cu ft per acre per year. Expressed as a percentage of total growing stock, the cut is 5,070/167,550 or 3.026 percent. If the forest is partially stocked but approximately regular in distribution and its total growing stock is known, the annual timber harvest could be estimated by applying this percentage to the total growing stock volume. If the forest averages 60 percent stocked, the annual growth would be 100,530 × 3.026 percent, or 3,042 cu ft which, it should be observed, is also 60 percent of the volume of the oldest age class in the yield table.

This is the assumption made in a well-known formula bearing the name of the German forester Hundeshagen. The formula is essentially a means of estimating growth from a yield table. Hundeshagen's formula assumes that growth or yield in an actual forest approximately regular in distribution bears the same relation to its total growing stock as growth in a desirably stocked regulated forest (as here represented by normal yield tables) bears to its growing stock. Expressed as a proportion:

$$\frac{Ya}{Ga} = \frac{Yr}{Gr}$$

where Ya = growth or yield in an actual forest
Ga = growing stock in an actual forest
Yr = growth or yield in a fully stocked forest
Gr = growing stock in a fully stocked forest

Therefore

$$Ya = \frac{Yr}{Gr} Ga$$

If the ratio Yr/Gr is expressed as a percentage, as was done in the illustration above, a quick approximation of the harvestable growth in the actual forest can be made by merely multiplying this percentage, as obtained from normal yield tables, by the actual growing stock Ga. The same procedure could be used if the yield table includes a schedule of thinning, reflected in Ya, that is substantially to be followed in the actual forest. This method has, however, all the limitations regarding comparability of data, standards of utilization, effect of understocking, and the like inherent to the direct application of yield-table data to actual stands, as has been discussed in Chap. 4.

While direct use of ratios based on yield tables has limitations, the principle of estimating the yield for an actual forest from a norm or base of some sort is useful and has practical application. If the stocking and yield data used as a standard of comparison are based on practical management experience, and the actual stand to which they are compared is approximately regular, good estimates of yield can be simply and quickly made. This explains why an experienced forester, with a good eye for growing-stock levels, can estimate a sustainable yield with considerable accuracy through application of an experience-based growth percent of the kind described here.

VON MANTEL'S FORMULA AND ITS APPLICATION

As an approximation method, Hundeshagen's formula can be simplified and the necessity for a yield table eliminated. It has been observed that in an approximately fully regulated forest, there is a fairly regular and often more or less linear increase in volume by age classes. This suggests the possibility that the growing stock can be represented by a right triangle, ıch as the triangle $VV'C$ in Fig. 5.3. If this is assumed, then the total rowing stock Gr corresponds to the area of the triangle. The base is repre-ınted by a sample of R acres, so that the number of acres equals the ımber of years in the rotation. The altitude is the yield at rotation age r, indicating the annual cut exclusive of thinnings. Applying the usual ırmula for the area of a right triangle,

$$Gr = \frac{R(Yr)}{2}$$

This value for Gr can be substituted in Hundeshagen's formula making read

$$Ya = \frac{Yr(Ga)}{R(Yr)/2}$$

ʰhich simplifies to

$$Ya = \frac{2(Ga)}{R} \quad \text{or} \quad Ya = \frac{Ga}{R/2} \quad \text{and} \quad Ga = Ya\frac{R}{2}$$

This substitution was made by von Mantel and the formula commonly ears his name. It has been termed the method of "glorious simplicity." ʌll that is needed to make an estimate of the annual yield is knowledge f the total growing stock and the rotation. The formula has done much ɔ further understanding of the fundamentals of regulating the cut. The ɔncept of a regulated forest as a right triangle is the simplest and most asic way of describing the nature of a managed and growing forest in ɔntrast to a stand composed entirely of mature timber, which would be ɛpresented by a rectangle. Von Mantel's formula has been widely applied ɪ making quick estimates of the allowable annual cut from extensive forest ɪroperties having some approximation of regularity in age-class distribution. ʰhe formula is obviously inapplicable unless there is some semblance of ɛgularity.

The accuracy of the formula (when assuming an approximately regu-ʌr age-class distribution) depends on two fundamental points: (1) the pre-ɪse nature of the actual stand to which it is applied and (2) how closely ɪe right triangle concept represents a desirable distribution of volume by ɡe classes in a regulated and well-managed forest. Both of these points ʰould receive careful scrutiny.

Referring back to the fully stocked, 60-year, 60-acre forest shown in ʰig. 5.3, application of von Mantel's formula to the total growing stock ɪves the following result:

$$\text{Annual cut} = \frac{2(167,550)}{60}$$
$$= 5,585 \text{ cu ft}$$

ʰhis yield is shown on the chart as V', and $VV'C$ represents as a triangle ıe same volume of growing stock as determined by the summation formula

for the curve *DB*. As indicated, the calculated yield of 5,585 cu ft exceed
the yield of 5,070 cu ft for age 60 as given by the yield table (Table 5.1
It would exceed it still more if all the growing stock existing for stan
under 20 years of age was included. This brings out the first point abo
the accuracy of von Mantel's formula, namely, the precise nature of th
forest to which it is applied. In this case, normal yield tables show tha
growth in cubic feet increases very rapidly between about 20 and 40 yea
but thereafter levels off. Applied to cubic foot growth in such a stan
there is a tendency for the straight-line relationship assumed in von Mantel
formula to overestimate the allowable cut (and realizable growth), esp
cially if the growing stock is entirely measured.

In other forest types, and for board foot measure particularly, th
growing stock curves assume somewhat different forms, as is brought o
in Fig. 5.4. These curves show board foot volumes in Scribner rule on ave

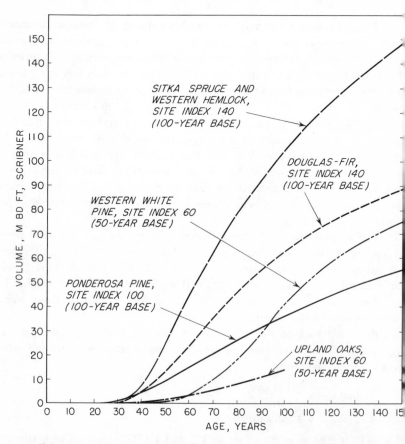

FIG. **5.4.** BOARD FOOT VOLUME PER ACRE OF
FULLY STOCKED STANDS ON AVERAGE SITES.

TABLE 5.2. ESTIMATION OF ANNUAL CUT BY
VON MANTEL'S FORMULA, YIELD-TABLE DATA

Species	Assumed rotation and forest area	Total growing stock by summation, M bd ft	Annual cut as indicated by yield table, M bd ft	Annual cut by von Mantel's formula using full rotation, M bd ft	Annual cut by von Mantel's formula based on $R - a$ years, M bd ft
(1)	(2)	(3)	(4)	(5)	(6)
Sitka spruce–hemlock[a]..	120	5,900	124.0	98.3	131.1
Douglas-fir[b]............	120	3,466	75.0	57.8	77.0
Western white pine[c].....	120	1,814	59.0	30.2	51.8
Ponderosa pine[d]........	120	2,060	44.6	34.3	45.8
Upland oaks[e]..........	80	149	8.3	3.7	6.0

[a] *U.S. Dept. Agr. Tech. Bul.* 544, site index 140.
[b] *U.S. Dept. Agr. Tech. Bul.* 201, site index 140.
[c] *U.S. Dept. Agr. Tech. Bul.* 323, site index 60.
[d] *U.S. Dept. Agr. Tech. Bul.* 630, site index 100.
[e] *U.S. Dept. Agr. Tech. Bul.* 560, site index 60.

age sites for a number of species as given by normal yield tables. These curves can be assumed to represent fully regulated "model" forests with as many age classes as there are years in the rotation and with each age class occupying 1 acre. Annual rotation-age cuts as estimated by von Mantel's formula for these model forests are given in Table 5.2.

As indicated in column 5, the formula, when applied to the full rotation and with board foot measure, considerably underestimates the annual cut as indicated by the yield table, which shows a volume realizable at rotation age. A major reason for the discrepancy is that Scribner volumes are figured for the larger trees only—ordinarily trees 12 in. dbh and larger—and consequently the growing stock in smaller trees is entirely left out of account. The triangle approach, using R or the full rotation as a base, assumes that board foot volumes begin to develop in even proportion from the zero age on. This is obviously not the case. Trying to fit such data into such a triangle arbitrarily reduces volumes in the older age classes to fill the gap of unmeasured growing stock under the triangle in the younger age classes. In the case of board foot measure, this growing stock is nonexistent. Applying a straight edge between the year zero and the volume at rotation age for any of the species shown in Fig. 5.4 will bring this out graphically; the properties of a right triangle need only to be remembered. The area is the total growing stock as determined by summation

from yield-table data. The base is the rotation. Since the base and are
are fixed, the only way to make the area of the triangle equal the tota
growing stock is to adjust the altitude which indicates the annual cut.

A simple and realistic method of allowing for the fact that appreciabl
volumes do not appear until some time after origin of a stand is to bas
the calculation on the period when volumes actually are present. This mean
changing the formula to read

$$Ya = \frac{R - a}{2(Ga)}$$

where a is the period before volumes develop. By reference to Fig. 5.4 i
can be seen that measured board foot volumes of all species shown excep
western white pine begin at about 30 years of age. For western white pine
they begin at about 50 years. The annual cut, making these adjustments
is given in column 6 of Table 5.2. As shown, these annual cut figures ar
much more nearly in line with the yield-table data.

The second point concerning the accuracy of the formula is more basi
and relates to its normal yield-table lineage. This is the question of whethe
either a straight line or the trend curve shown by normal yield-table dat
represents a desirable distribution of growing stock in a managed forest
This goes back to the basic question raised in Chap. 2 about what is desir
able growing stock.

There is considerable reason seriously to question whether a curve indi
cated by a yield table for fully stocked stands or a straight line is desirabl
in practice. It is well known that stands understocked in normal yield-tabl
terms tend to improve their stocking in relation to normal yield tables, whicl
are very conservative in showing *rates* of growth attainable unde
management.

An indication of what desirable stocking in a fully regulated and well
managed forest might be is shown by broken line *GB* in Fig. 5.3. In thi
forest, stocking in the younger age classes is held below that indicated by
yield tables, but the stand includes an ample number of trees of desirable
species, form, and spacing to form a full stand at time of final harves
cutting. This could be true with intermediate cuts even if thinnings wer
made. It is assumed that the final yield at age *B* will equal that show)
for normal yield tables, which are used here as a guide to how much volum
a given site can reasonably support at a given age. There is absolutely n
reason to assume that a stand say 65 percent stocked in yield-table term
at age 20 will thereafter stay just 65 percent stocked. It will approach nor
mal yield-table values at a rate that depends on the species and site bu
more importantly on just what is done under management to improve the
spacing and character of the stand.

Von Mantel's formula might fit a managed stand fairly well. In thi
assumed case, the total growing stock of the managed forest is, by summa

ion, about 143,000 cu ft. Then $143,000 \times \frac{2}{60}$ gives an indicated final harvest cut of 4,767 cu ft, which is not far from the 5,070 which is indicated by a yield table as a possible volume to attain at 60 years.

In general, Hundeshagen's and von Mantel's formulas are chiefly helpful in gaining an understanding of a regulated forest and in focusing attention on the importance of growing-stock and cut relationships. Von Mantel's formula is useful as a quick and easy method of estimating the allowable cut from limited information. It may give a good estimate in some instances and a poor one in others—usually on the conservative side when applied to board foot measure. This explains why the formula is alternately praised and condemned. As a method to use in practice, it is crude and should be used only for lack of better data and with full knowledge of the assumptions upon which it is based, its limitations, and the structure of the forest to which it is applied.

effects of over- and undercutting

With the nature and structure of a fully regulated forest in mind, consideration of the effects of over- and undercutting will help to understand some of the dynamics of forest regulation. The total annual cut or yield from a managed forest composed of even-aged stands is made up of two parts: (1) the harvest of mature timber at rotation age and (2) the harvest from intermediate cuts taken from younger stands by thinnings. Over- and undercutting can take place in either part.

As a point of beginning, assume a regulated forest managed on a stable basis. Now assume that substantial over- or undercutting in either intermediate or harvest cuts is applied to the forest over a considerable period. What will be the result? Let H stand for harvest cut and I for intermediate cut. There are three levels of each which can be denoted by subscripts:

    1 = Substantial and continued overcutting
    2 = Present level of cutting
    3 = Substantial and continued undercutting

For example, H_2I_2 would represent the present plan of management or no change. Since there are two factors with three levels of each, there are 3×3, or 9 possible combinations to consider. The results are shown in Table 5.3. It is cheerfully admitted that these assumptions are arbitrary but they are instructive and the result of many of these cutting combinations can be seen in the field. The reader is encouraged to set up any particular forest situation desired and speculate on possible effects.

As an illustration of how specific assumptions may be put into this generalized framework, consider a forest of even-aged pines now managed on a 60-year rotation that is to be overcut in major harvest-size timber

TABLE 5.3. EFFECTS OF OVERCUTTING AND UNDERCUTTING
IN A REGULATED FOREST

Level of cutting	General result of cutting	Effect on rotation length	Effect on total yield
H_1I_1	Will reduce forest growing stock	Shorten	Very high for a while then decrease
H_1I_2	Same as above except more young timber will be left	Shorten	High initial yield will gradually decrease as average is reduced
H_1I_3	Same as above except still more young timber will develop. If overcutting is severe with no concern to get reproduction, is a typical "cut out and get out" situation.	Shorten	High but limited to mature timber only
H_2I_1	Unlikely situation; would open up subdominant stand	No change	Will eventually reduce harvest yield
H_2I_2	Continuation of present practice	No change	No change
H_2I_3	Loss of growth that might be captured through intermediate cuts. Typical of management in areas of limited markets for intermediate cuts.	No change	Harvest yield may reduce slightly
H_3I_1	A charcoal, fuel, or a pine pulpwood cutting situation with low-value overstory developing	Lengthen	Substantial decrease in quantity and quality of yield
H_3I_2	Unlikely combination but would produce large timber of high quality	Lengthen	Decrease quantity but increase quality
H_3I_3	General undercutting approaching natural forest conditions. Much growth lost in mortality.	Lengthen	Decrease both quantity and quality

about 50 percent in relation to the present plan. Intermediate cuttings are not changed (combination H_1I_2). The consequence is a harvest cut made each year on 1.5/60 of the total area instead of $\frac{1}{60}$ on a 60-year rotation. The immediate result is that the annual cut of rotation-age timber will be increased about $1\frac{1}{2}$ times, since that much more area is cut over. This cut, however, represents a partial liquidation of the forest capital in growing stock. Instead of cutting only timber 60 years of age, half of the 59-year age class is also cut. The next year the cut takes the other half of the present 59-year age class, which is then 60 years old, plus all the timber then 59 years old (the present 58-year age class). If continued, such cutting will, in 40 years, shorten the rotation to 60/1.5, or 40 years, so that the harvest cut each year comes from 1.5/60 of the total area and from timber not over 40 years of age. The forest will become regulated on this rotation but the timber cut will be smaller in average size. The annual volume cut of rotation-age timber may be as great or even greater in cubic feet than with the 60-year rotation but sawtimber quality will be lower.

The volume and quality of wood obtained from thinnings will be progressively reduced since there is less time for thinnings to be applied, and the size of timber removed will average smaller. The exact effect of overcutting in the mature stand on the total annual cut will depend on the species, site, and utilization. In general, the result will be to trade some quality for quantity.

As brought out, the effects of overcutting and undercutting are many, and the results often not immediately apparent. A regulated forest can be overcut for several years without much change being evident. But the results will become evident sooner or later. Reversing the process and undercutting is an equally deliberate matter. Quantity and quality of both rotation age (or size) of timber and of intermediate cuttings must be considered in relation to each other. One can cut too little as well as too much.

6
determination of the cut

A final and inescapable responsibility of the timber manager is to recommend, and usually to determine, what, when, where, and how much timber to cut from the forest. All of his skill and knowledge are needed and come to focus here. The timber harvest is the objective and culmination of the whole timber-growing sequence. It is through cutting that the forester exerts his most decisive influence over the forest. Determination of the cut is consequently of fundamental importance both in currently supporting a forest business and in shaping its future. The purpose of this chapter is to present the nature of the problem and principal approaches to its solution, building on the concept and nature of a regulated forest developed in Chap. 5. The application of regulatory methods to even-aged and to uneven-aged forests is considered in Chaps. 7 to 9.

purposes and objectives

The questions that must be answered in determining the cut can be stated briefly. It is necessary to know for a period of usually from 5 to 20 years, and approximately annually:

1. The total volume of timber that should be cut.
2. The kind, quality, and size of timber that should be cut to compose this volume.
3. Where this timber should be harvested and under what cutting specifications in taking it from the forest.

Answering these questions is not a simple matter, for many things must be considered and brought into working balance. The principal items to take into account are:

1. *The purposes of management.* This includes such things as operating policies and aims, income needs, dependency of processing plants or communities for raw material, and continuity of operation desired. Public agencies often have large responsibility to place a relatively constant amount of standing timber on the market.

2. *Markets for different kinds of timber.* This involves both current or prospective market conditions related to timber availability. An example of the former would be a currently depressed pulpwood or sawtimber market. An example of the latter would be prospects for a greatly improved pulpwood market.

3. *Silvicultural needs and exigencies.* These may include: the kind or kinds of regeneration methods most applicable; the condition of particular stands with respect to stocking, age, disease, and insect situations; and forest exigencies such as those caused by fire, storm, or epidemics. Such items will affect determination of the proper harvest to take from the forest during a particular period.

4. *Logging problems.* In many forest areas, cutting cannot be carried on at will anywhere but must be planned and scheduled in relation to an economic volume cut per acre, transportation facilities, availability of labor, housing facilities, and the like. These matters frequently place definite limits on what can or cannot be cut.

5. *Forest regulation or degree of harvest continuity desired.* This means establishing a cut, within the sustained productive capacity of the forest, which will make satisfactory progress toward, or maintain, as the case may be, desirable forest regularity regarding distribution of timber age, size, and quality.

It can be seen from the above that determination of the amount, character, and location of timber to be cut requires reconcilation of many and often more or less conflicting considerations. Capital costs of ownership may call for a large cut, but market conditions may be unfavorable. Silviculturally, a heavy salvage or improvement cut should be made in an area without adequate roads or markets. High costs of road construction may necessitate a volume of cut in conflict with both silvicultural and regulatory aims.

The saving feature to what might otherwise sometimes seem to be an impasse is the nature of a managed forest. Contrast a forest crop with an annual agricultural crop. The latter must be harvested annually and usually sold currently too. Many crops are perishable and cannot be stored; others can be stored on the farm or elsewhere for only limited periods and at considerable cost. In any event, the nature of the crop forces its prompt removal from the land. In a forest, the nature of the crop seldom forces immediate removal except in cases of salvage following sudden mortality. The forest crop can be stored on the stump, frequently for very long periods, as a part of the producing forest "factory" giving the forest manager much flexibility in the selection and scheduling of the stands in which cutting is to be done. A particular stand seldom *has* to be cut in a certain year or period. It is this flexibility, inherent in the nature of a managed forest, that makes it possible to reconcile the diverse elements involved in deciding what, when, where, and how much to cut and to carry on a successful forest business in the face of many uncertainties both within and without the forest.

There is a tendency to think of determination of the cut as being primarily a technical matter of applying certain regulatory techniques more or less independently, regardless of other forest considerations. As brought out above, this is not so. Regulatory problems are but one of several to be taken into account, and the end result is frankly a compromise, an integrative managerial decision basically. Nevertheless, if a forest business is to be maintained, some degree of forest regulation is necessary to establish a cut that is within the capacity of the forest to sustain and that will promote or maintain a reasonable degree of forest regularity. Regulation alone, of the five considerations listed above, is specifically aimed to ensure a continued flow of harvestable products. Its function is to bring this about in an orderly and systematic manner. Without it as a basic framework for forest continuity, other objectives of a sustained forest business cannot be achieved.

The forest will demand its due. It is senseless to seek markets or build plants that the forest cannot support. Logging and silvicultural plans cannot be applied effectively without some overall forest control. The effects of overcutting or undercutting or of poor distribution of age and size groups may not be readily apparent or immediately felt (Chap. 5). But their results, though often delayed, are none the less sure and the remedy correspondingly slow if the forest is allowed to get seriously out of balance.

For these reasons, the regulatory part of the total problem of determining the actual cut remains of fundamental importance if continuity of forest harvest is desired. The emphasis in this chapter is primarily upon these regulatory aspects, but there should be full understanding that, in practice, other things, frequently of dominating importance, also must be considered. In Chaps. 7 to 9 more consideration will be given to these other factors and to the compromise nature of the problem as a whole.

conditioning factors

It is necessary to have a clear perspective regarding methods of cut determination. They cannot meaningfully be considered except in relation to the purposes of management and the forest situation. A number of important conditioning factors are given below.

Choice of method is definitely related to the intensity of management practiced. Under extensive management and especially in its initial stages, forest information, particularly regarding growth, is limited (Chap. 4). It is necessary to estimate a sustainable cut utilizing the kind of forest information available. As will be seen, a number of methods have been developed primarily to meet such situations.

With more intensive management, better forest information, more stabilized operating conditions, and accumulated production experience, the character of the problem changes. Greater sophistication and accuracy are possible. At the same time, the need for large-scale overall cut estimates becomes less, for better cut information normally can be obtained by smaller forest units. Consider, for example, an intensively managed plantation forest with a well-developed intermediate and final harvest cutting schedule. The area, age, site, and condition of the individual plantations, and also the yield attainable from them, are known within fairly narrow limits. Each plantation consequently has its timetable of cutting and cultural operations. Some adjustment in cutting rates may be made to bring about a better overall age-class distribution (Chap. 5). This would be a matter for administrative decision.

Under such conditions, there is really no need or place for application of any overall determination of cut formula. The cut for a given desired period can be simply and most accurately determined from a direct scheduling of plantation harvests in accordance with the cutting regime established, plus whatever adjustment for improvement in age-class distribution may be considered necessary. This is an illustration of the point made at the close of Chap. 4 that, in a managed forest, growth and basically the cut are direct consequences of the management design adopted. This has to be so in the long run; the harvest is the final measure of net growth. Accordingly, as management becomes more intensive and stabilized, determination of the cut tends to merge with the management system adopted and becomes less of a separate calculation.

The importance of cut determination and needed accuracy varies with the timber supply-and-demand situation. In areas where the demand for timber is less than the available supply, an allowable cut determination is an objective, a goal to work towards in forest development. As long as the demand is substantially less than supply, close accuracy in cut determination is not of critical importance, and general estimates obtained by overall methods may suffice. Such situations prevail in some areas in the United States and in many parts of the world. However, where demand presses available supply, the allowable cut becomes a limit of critical importance, and accuracy counts. For example, in Finland, a country in which three quarters of its vital export trade is based on wood, determination of a sustainable cut becomes very serious national business indeed. The same is true on many national forests of the United States, particularly in the

West, where there is a strong demand for a continuing supply of timber from a large segment of the industry dependent on Federal stumpage (U.S. Forest Service, 1962).

An important characteristic of cut determination is its periodic and provisional nature. A specific cut is almost invariably applied to a limited period, usually of not more than about 10 years. Long-range planning, usually of a rotation or more, is often involved in the calculation, and the aim is to derive a sustainable cut consonant with long-range forest objectives. But the fact remains that the actual cut is set for a relatively short time only. Considerable latitude is allowed within a cutting budget period, and yearly fluctuations are often large for a number of reasons. A limit of 5 to 10 percent may be set in total cut for 5-year periods but with the aim of balancing out fairly close for 10 years. At the end of the planning period, whatever it may be, the entire situation is reassessed and another cut established. Forest catastrophes of various kinds may enter the picture and necessitate current changes in cutting; better forest information becomes available; and purposes of management may change. These things are all taken into account in setting a new cut figure, which can be done at any time significant changes occur. There is, consequently, a periodic corrective process that keeps the forest from getting very far out of line from a regulatory standpoint and which also makes the forest enterprise responsive to changing purposes of management.

Another significant point is that the allowable cut[1] comes in at least two parts. The cut obtained from harvest of mature age classes at or approaching rotation age is of major importance from a regulatory standpoint, because such cutting controls the rate of new stand formation through regeneration. Usually, the major volume and value of timber also comes from such cuts. Substantial volume often comes, however, from intermediate cuts, essentially thinnings, that may or may not be a regularly scheduled part of the cutting plan followed. In addition, there may be salvage of dead, dying, or undesirable trees not a part of any regularly scheduled cut. Forest catastrophes like insect epidemics or fire may result in involuntary major harvest cuts or thinnings. Where economic harvest from thinning or salvage operations is uncertain or limited, the allowable cut is often defined in terms of major regeneration harvests only.

An estimate may be made of additional material that may be taken from thinning or other partial cutting operations, but it may or may not

---

[1] "Allowable cut" is introduced here as a term in general usage denoting the amount of timber considered as available for cutting during a specified planned period of operation. It may or may not represent a strictly sustainable cut as special circumstances (such as desire to remove an excess of mature timber or need to restrict cutting to bring about a better age-size class distribution) may affect cut determination. The allowable cut may also be limited to timber for which there is assumed to be a reasonably active or stable market. The term is so applied on the western national forests of the U.S. Forest Service (1962).

be included in the cutting limitation imposed by the allowable cut. The basic reason is that such cuts may not be certain and do not, in general, affect the regulatory situation in that they do not create new age classes—although they certainly can affect the volume and quality of timber taken in final harvest cuts. If taken, they constitute a more complete capture of the potential growth from the forest (Chap. 4). If not, they are an opportunity foregone, since the timber is mostly lost through mortality.

The practice of segregating the allowable cut into parts is sometimes extended to forest species or types for which there is currently limited market. For example, there are extensive lodgepole pine types on some western national forests in the United States for which there is currently limited market. To avoid calculating a rather meaningless cut figure for such timber, it is left unregulated or unbudgeted with no restriction on the volume cut until such time as markets make establishment of a cutting figure worthwhile.

For these reasons, it is well to define just what is included (or not included) in an allowable cut figure. It is desirable to specify the sizes and classes of timber involved in addition to volume by species or species groups. This is not always done, and omission can result in serious misunderstanding and confusion as to what the allowable cut actually includes.

A final general point about determination of the cut is that the size of forest area to which it is applied can have some affect on the allowable cut. The major reason is related to the analysis of sustained yield given in Chap. 1. When dealing with more or less natural conditions, the smaller the forest area, the poorer the age-class distribution is likely to be, and vice versa. Consequently, if a fairly uniform sustained yield is desired, a larger area usually offers a better total age-class distribution, and a larger cut is often indicated as a result.

The above considerations apply to determination of the cut in general. As indicated, they may strongly condition both the methodology and the importance of the process. They should be kept in mind in the following sections dealing primarily with methodology.

methodology in general

Over the years of forest history, a great many methods of determining the cut have been developed in various parts of the world, principally in Europe. Recknagel, in "Theory and Practice of Working Plans," first published in 1913, describes 18 of them and more have been devised before and since. The larger number of them have not been applied to any large extent in the woods, being designed to meet more or less special situations. Even so, they are frequently helpful and useful in understanding the nature of regulatory problems and in suggesting possible approaches to their solution. Only a few methods have been widely applied in practice.

While there are many specific methods, they can be classified into a few groups and their essentials readily grasped. There are only two general approaches to determination of the cut: (1) through area control and (2) through volume control. With both, the answer is always in terms of the amount of timber to be cut, and neither can be applied exclusively in giving a complete answer. Area and volume are inherently complementary, like two sides of a coin. The relationship is fundamental and inescapable. Timber volume is necessarily cut in whole trees that occupy land area. When trees are cut they release space—land—which is the fundamental production base of a forest enterprise and not the individual trees. The relationship is very simple with a clear-cutting. A certain volume is on a certain area. When the relationship (volume per acre) is known, it makes no real difference whether a given volume to be cut is defined in volume or in area to cut over. A timber volume to be cut has no real physical meaning until it is identified on the ground in terms of certain trees or stands that will equal it.

Consequently, although area and volume control can be thought of as alternative approaches and are so treated here, it must be kept firmly in mind that the end result sought is the volume to be cut from areas and that neither approach can give a complete answer.

area control

The principle of area control is very simple; it means that the volume to be harvested is defined by the timber to be removed on the area allocated for cutting. Cutting is scheduled on a forest under management, so that each year a certain area of timber is available for harvest.

APPLICATION TO EVEN-AGED STANDS

The simplest expression of area control is in a fully regulated forest composed of even-aged stands managed according to a clear-cutting plan. Assume, for example, such a forest operating on an 60-year regulatory rotation, all of about the same site quality. Each year $\frac{1}{60}$ of the area would reach rotation age, be clearcut, and regeneration for another crop would be started if the process had not already been begun, as under a shelterwood system. The volume cut would be the average volume per unit of area multiplied by the area cut. The same schedule would hold for thinnings or any other cuttings regularly applied. With a 30-year thinning, for example, again $\frac{1}{60}$ of the area would receive such a thinning each year, and the volume cut per acre would be that normally removed in such thinnings. The same pattern would apply to application of shelterwood or any other type of cutting applied on a regular basis.

For a regulated forest such as this, area control would be the simplest and most logical method of estimating the annual or periodic cut. In practice, considerable flexibility and adjustment would be possible and probably necessary. No one would expect to cut over exactly $\frac{1}{60}$ of the total area in timber of precisely the same age and volume per acre each year. Forest life is not that perfect; no forest can be perfectly regulated, and there are always weather fluctuations and various forest mishaps to deal with. Control of cutting by area will ensure continued regularity of the forest. Also, so long as *in general* the proper area-age proportions are maintained and consistent cutting practices applied, a predictable and substantially uniform annual cut will be obtained.

Applied to an irregular forest and strictly followed, area control would yield irregular cuts in volume, size, and quality of timber. Consider, for example, establishing regulation on a forest area of which about half supports mature timber and half newly established reproduction. Application of strict area control, taking the most mature timber first, would result, over a half-rotation period, in cutting progressively older timber, increasing to an age of about a rotation and a half. Considerable mortality losses might result from holding this timber so long. After half a rotation period, the supply of mature timber would be exhausted, and the cut would then have to come from timber of approximately one-half rotation age (the present reproduction). The cut would drop sharply in both amount and quality, although it would increase to rotation age by the end of the rotation. The only virtue to area control in such a situation is that after a full rotation period the forest would be completely regulated. Thereafter, a uniform annual cut from rotation-aged timber could be obtained—if the owner were still in business to obtain it!

There is absolutely no way an approximately uniform annual cut can be obtained from an irregular forest by strict area control. Any forest can be regulated by area control over a rotation period, but if the forest is seriously unbalanced in age-class distribution to begin with, the uniformity of annual cut will be sacrificed while the forest is being regulated. Conversely, if the volume of the cut is made approximately constant, much less progress toward regulating the forest can be made. The same difficulties apply, in general, to any regulatory method, which is but another way of saying that there is no painless or perfect way to regulate an irregular forest. A strictly uniform annual cut should not be expected. Compromises and adjustments have to be made as a practical matter.

APPLICATION TO UNEVEN-AGED STANDS

Area control can be applied to a forest composed of uneven-aged stands in much the same general way as to an even-aged situation. To illustrate, assume the following:

1. A regulated, uneven-aged, mixed hardwood forest of 5,000 acres.
2. An average annual increment of 200 bd ft per acre.
3. A 10-year cutting cycle. This means that each particular portion of the forest is cut over once in 10 years, removing a volume equal to approximately 10 years' growth from that portion.

Such a forest would be subdivided into a number of cutting areas, and a cutting budget would be made providing for cutting approximately $\frac{1}{10}$ of the total area or 500 acres each year. This annual cutting area would not have been cut for the past 10 years so that there would be an accumulation of 10×200, or 2,000 bd ft per acre available for harvesting in mature and other trees that should come out of the stand over and above the basic reserve growing stock which must be maintained for future growth. The total annual cut from the forest would be consequently $500 \times 2,000$, or 1,000,000 bd ft. Note that, while the amount to cut per acre is determined by growth calculations, there is a definite area pattern to the cutting.

In practice, of course, no forest could be so perfectly regulated that a uniform area could be cut over each year and precisely the same volume obtained. Considerable give and take would undoubtedly be necessary. But, just the same, the annual area allotment would have to be observed *on the average* if the cutting cycle and regularity of the forest are to be maintained. A common misunderstanding about area control is that it has to be slavishly followed every year. This is not true; it should be regarded as an overall guide susceptible to considerable yearly adjustment to meet current situations. It is not at all necessary, for example, that the oldest timber be cut each year. So far as establishment of future age classes is concerned, it does not matter what age of timber is currently cut. The fact that considerable flexibility is possible and desirable in its year-by-year application does not, however, lessen the importance of area control as a basic framework.

APPLICATION WHERE DIFFERENT SITE QUALITIES ARE PRESENT

It seldom happens in practice that a forest of any extent occurs on land of the same site quality. Considerable variation is common. This circumstance complicates but does not upset the application of area control. If variations in site quality are more or less randomly distributed over the forest, as in a gently rolling area where bottom, slope, and ridgetop sites are closely intermingled, an average site may be assumed and site differentials handled as a matter of on-the-ground adjustment. Where the forest includes lands of substantially different site quality, recognition of this fact is necessary in dividing the area up into cutting units, and this is true whether an even-aged or uneven-aged plan of management is applied.

The problem can best be illustrated by an example. Assume a managed forest, as shown in Fig. 6.1, occupying a typical drainage. The area has been mapped by site-index quality. As shown, the south-facing slopes along the north side of the drainage average fairly low in site quality. Site is better on the north slopes, and there is a cove of particularly good quality at the head of the drainage. The areas marked by Roman numerals are compartments comprising logical logging and management units as defined by topography and accessibility. These areas are not of equal size, and each area includes land of more than one site quality.

With even-aged management, it would be necessary to cut, on the average, total area/rotation acres of mature timber of approximately rotation age each year. The same would be true for the area of intermediate cuttings for each age group treated. These cutting areas would be of about the same size only if all lands were of equal site quality. They would not be of the same size in this forest because of large differences in site quality over various portions of the area. It is important to note that the basic aim is to get areas of *equal productivity* rather than of equal surface area. This does not upset the framework of area control; it merely makes it more realistic. It would obviously be necessary to cut over more acres of site index 70 land than of site index 100 land to get the same total yield. The problem is further complicated if lands of more than one site quality are logically included in the same cutting area, as is often the case in practice.

A solution to the problem can be indicated for the forest assumed

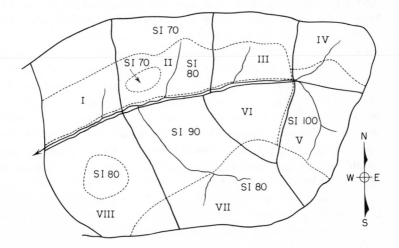

FIG. 6.1. A FOREST IN A SAMPLE DRAINAGE
MAPPED BY SITE QUALITY.

TABLE 6.1. TOTAL FOREST PRODUCTIVITY

Site index	Area, acres	Yield-table productivity index, M bd ft[a]	Total productivity, area × volume
70	550	19.1	10,505
80	885	24.3	21,505
90	815	29.6	24,124
100	250	34.9	8,725
Total......	2,500	....	64,859

[a] Volumes at 60 years used.

here that will be illustrative of a general approach. Assume further: (1) that the total area is 2,500 acres; (2) that the forest is being managed on a 60-year rotation; (3) that average site-quality differentials are indicated by differences in board foot yields as indicated in Table 5.1, Chap. 5. Any applicable source of information on comparative productivity by site could be used.

Using these yield-table values as index weights, the average productivity and site quality of the forest are determined as shown in Table 6.1. The average per acre is 64,859/2,500, or 25.9 M bd ft. By interpolation in Table 5.1, this average productivity of 25.9 M corresponds to a site index of 83 for the forest as a whole.

The average annual cutting area is 2,500/60, or 41.7 acres, but this would apply only for lands of average productivity and not to any particular area in the forest which almost surely would be better or poorer than the average. It would consequently be necessary to adjust the average cutting area upward or downward to compensate for differences in site quality. This can be done by expressing lands of different site quality as an index of the average site quality (Table 6.2). According to these ratios, if the site quality in a particular cutting area was 90, approximately 41.7 × 0.87, or 36 acres, should be included to maintain age-class–area regularity for the forest. Where lands of different site quality are necessarily included in the same cutting area, as would frequently be the case, the total area should be adjusted proportionately according to the proportions of land of different site quality included.

If this sample forest is handled on an uneven-aged basis, the problem is substantially the same. Instead of having to consider a large number of cutting areas and a full range of more or less separate age classes, it would be necessary to have only as many cutting areas as there are years in the cutting cycle adopted. For example, if an 8-year cutting cycle were employed, approximately ⅛ of the total area would be cut over each year.

TABLE 6.2. LAND PRODUCTIVITY AS AN INDEX OF AVERAGE SITE QUALITY

Site index	Yield-table pro-ductivity index, M bd ft	Number of acres productively equal to 1 acre of average site quality
83 (av)	25.9	1.00
70	19.1	1.36
80	24.3	1.07
90	29.6	0.87
100	34.9	0.74

There would be the same need to make these cutting areas of approximately equal productivity and the same general site-quality differentials could be applied.

In practice, site differences often cannot and need not be determined with precision, and the picture is also confused by differences in stocking and treatment. Judgment, experience, and common sense are essential in working out a practical solution in line with real needs. Nonetheless the general fact that it takes more acres of poor land than of good land to yield the same volume is important and demands some recognition if the differences are substantial.

APPLICATION OF AREA CONTROL SUMMARIZED

The principal applications, advantages, and limitations of area control are summarized as follows:

1. It is simple and direct. The principle of area control is easily grasped and requires little arithmetic and no formulas to apply.

2. It has the fundamental virtue of identifying the area to be cut with areas on the ground. It cannot be applied in practice without such identification. This must be done ultimately under any regulatory method. Area control forces the issue promptly.

3. Area control is especially helpful in situations where the main need is to bring about general silvicultural improvement of the forest. By dividing the area up into identifiable cutting units and deciding upon an overall rate of cutting in covering the forest, attention is focused on the needs of particular areas along with a schedule for meeting them. Area control ensures that areas needing attention are treated.

4. If consistently followed, it will bring about complete forest regularity in any forest after one rotation period.

5. It is particularly suited to a forest composed of even-aged stands. Such a forest cannot be successfully managed for any substantial period without area considerations being taken into account.

6. Applied in an uneven-aged forest, area control must be combined with volume control based on the actual growth of stands.

7. Applied to an irregular forest, strict area control will not give satisfactory results. It must be combined with volume control to work out some compromise solution giving the maximum and most uniform annual cut consistent with silvicultural and business needs and reasonable progress toward bringing about a more regular age- and size-class distribution.

8. Any regulated forest can be managed according to an area plan as a guiding framework. In fact, any forest continuously managed will almost inevitably drift into some area pattern of cutting, whether or not volume controls are also used. As Roth (1925) stated many years ago:

> If faithfully persisted in and carefully revised every ten or twenty years, and if Silviculture and Protection are attended to, either of the two plans [area or volume control] will regulate . . . [the] . . . forest. If he regulates by volume, he must begin somewhere and cut a sufficient area to get the volume estimated to be right, and he must do this year after year. After going over the property once or twice, he will almost certainly drift into a method, cutting over each year the area he cut during one year on his former round; in other words, a regulation by volume is practically certain to change into a regulation by area, which as Cotta correctly foresaw over a century ago, is the final in all Forest Regulation.

volume control

In volume control, the determination of the cut is approached through the volume and distribution of the growing stock and its increment. Since these items are susceptible to mathematical treatment, foresters have concocted numerous formulas and mathematical schemes for determining the cut by volume methods. A good working knowledge of volume methods is valuable both as a guide in actual practice and for the light they cast in understanding possible approaches to cut determination.

In the following, a number of methods, old and new, are grouped by type, their use is illustrated, and their application is reviewed.

METHODS BASED ON THE VOLUME OF GROWING STOCK ONLY

Von Mantel's formula is the classic example of a method based entirely on growing stock (Chap. 5). In this formula a uniform and linear increase in volume of the growing stock with increasing age is assumed, and the growing stock of the entire forest is represented by a right triangle. The annual growth or yield to be cut is expressed by the formula

$$Ya = \frac{2(Ga)}{R} \quad \text{or} \quad \frac{2(Ga)}{R-a}$$

where Ya = growth or yield in an actual forest
Ga = growing stock in an actual forest
R = rotation in years
a = age when volume first measured

As brought out in Chap. 5, the accuracy of the formula in application can often be increased by subtracting from the rotation the factor a, representing the average number of years before measurable volumes appear. To apply this formula it is necessary only to know the total volume of the growing stock and the rotation. If the forest is approximately regular in distribution and the volume of the growing stock is determined with reasonable accuracy and completeness, the formula may give entirely reasonable results. Its main advantages are simplicity, the usually conservative results, and the small amount of data necessary for its use. It is primarily useful in making a preliminary overall estimate of the cut as a rule of thumb. The derivation and limitations of this formula are discussed in Chap. 5.

No method based on the volume of growing stock only can serve as more than a rough approximation. Both the distribution of the growing stock by age or size groups and its increment are ignored, and these have much influence in determining how much should be cut.

METHODS BASED ON INCREMENT ONLY

Since in the fully regulated forest the yield necessarily equals net increment, nothing would seem more logical than to determine the cut on the basis of current increment. This is indeed the ultimate basis for the annual cut and a long-range objective. In a selection of all-aged forest which is properly balanced by size or age groups and which has the desired volume of reserved growing stock, all that is necessary to determine the annual cut, so far as total volume is concerned, is to estimate total current net increment.

In practice, however, the problem is not so simple, because it is necessary to deal with forests that are not well regulated and stands that are not desirably stocked. A number of methods primarily based on increment have been developed which are essentially growth percent approaches. Two of American origin are presented here.

Amortization formula—Meyer.   Meyer (1952) has presented a compound interest formula with special reference to its application in forest areas supporting immature and unmanaged natural stands. The formula states some assumed relationships between growing stock volume and increment expressed as compound interest rates. In its general form, it reads as follows:

$$V_n = V_0(1 + i_t)^n - a\frac{(1 + i_m)^n - 1}{i_m}$$

where V_n = desired future volume of growing stock

V_0 = present volume of growing stock

i_t = compound rate of growth of total stand including ingrowth

i_m = compound rate of growth of merchantable stand cut only, without ingrowth

a = annual cut

n = number of years included in estimate period

The formula can readily be restated to solve for the annual cut if V_n and V_o are known, as follows:

$$a = i_m\frac{V_0(1 + i_t)^n - V_n}{(1 + i_m)^n - 1}$$

The two growth rates, i_t and i_m, are used to take into account the fact that growth of the total stand necessarily includes ingrowth (trees that grow into merchantable size during the growth period), whereas merchantable trees that are cut seldom include ingrowth, and their growth rate is normally substantially lower. The growth rates can be obtained from any applicable source. Meyer assumed they came from an increment study made in the particular area concerned.

When applied to a forest situation, the formula, which is used in loan amortization (Chap. 16, p. 348), implies certain limiting assumptions that should be recognized. These are:

1. That any or all parts of the forest area will grow at the rates assumed.

2. That stands will grow at the rates assumed before and after cutting regardless of stocking—just as interest accrues on a dollar regardless of the number of them.

3. That cutting is equally distributed over all size classes; the relative situation is thus undisturbed by cutting.

Analysis of the formula as first given above shows that it is in two parts. The first gives the increase in present stand volume V_o if no cutting is done and uses the total growth rate i_t. The second part deducts the annual volume cut plus its accumulated growth at rate i_m without ingrowth. Any desired V_n may be obtained by varying the annual cut a. Conversely, in the second form given, a desired annual cut may be obtained by substituting an appropriate value for V_n. If one wished to cut growth only, then $V_n = V_o$. It should be noted that the formula expresses relationships only; an annual cut can be determined only in relation to an assumption about V_n. By its nature, the formula gives an annual cut which can be applied to any period, n, for which the growth rates used are assumed to be valid.

The formula does not and cannot include any provision for where or how cutting areas should be allocated on the ground and thus has no direct relation to area control. It is most applicable to areas handled on an uneven-aged plan of management. The principle of amortization used in the formula has been employed in other related methods.

Allowable cut formula—Grosenbaugh. Grosenbaugh (1958) has devised a growth percent formula somewhat similar to Meyer's, discussed in the preceding section, but employing simple rather than compound rates. The formula is as follows:

$$\frac{V_c}{V_0} = \left[\frac{1 + nG_2 - V_n/V_0}{nG_2} \right] [mG_1] \left[\frac{1 + (m/2)G_0}{1 + mG_0} \right]$$

$$\qquad\qquad (1) \qquad\qquad (2) \qquad\quad (3)$$

where n = number of years from start of the current period until time when the ultimately desired stand will be attained

m = number of years in the current and shorter period for which allowable cut will be calculated.

V_0 = stand volume at beginning of n- and m-year periods

V_n = stand volume desired n years hence

V_c = total volume of allowable cut for the m-year period

G_0 = simple periodic net annual growth rate of merchantable trees comprising the allowable cut

G_1 = simple periodic net annual growth rate of entire stand over m-year period (all survivor growth less mortality, plus expected m-year ingrowth)

G_2 = a speculative simple periodic net annual growth rate expected for entire stand over a n-year period as a result of improvement in growth through application of better management practices.

The formula is a series of ratios and not as complicated as it looks. The V_c/V_0 term gives the end result as a ratio of V_c to V_0, the beginning volume, which readily solves for V_c the cut for the period m. The right-hand side of the equation consists of the product of three bracketed ratios each supplying a part of the total estimate. The first term combines a long-range expected growth percent with a change in growing stock level for the same n period. As the author says, the first term is "decidedly speculative," and it would be difficult to determine in practice. Further, the growth rate and the change in growing-stock level V_n/V_0 are directly related, as evidenced by the fact that if this ratio is 1 so is the entire term in the bracket, regardless of growth rates expected. It should be possible to consider growth rates and desired growing-stock levels separately. Also, the first term, in effect, counts chickens before they are hatched. The second term gives total net stand growth for the m-year period. The third corrects this figure for the fact that the trees comprising the allowable cut will be cut on the average at the midpoint of the period and are growing at a different average rate, G_0, than for the total stand G_1.

In practice, this formula will give about the same result as Meyer's; both include provision for a difference between growth rates in the entire and cut portion of the stand. Also, there is little difference between simple and compound growth rates when applied to a limited time period. The formula expresses a useful concept of stand growth. Like Meyer's, it is best applied to stands managed on an uneven-aged basis.

Hundeshagen's formula.   Hundeshagen's formula has been described in Chap. 5 in connection with developing the concept of a regulated forest and will only be summarized here. The formula reads:

$$Ya = \frac{Yr}{Gr} Ga$$

where Ya = growth or yield obtainable in an actual forest
$\quad\quad Yr$ = growth or yield in a fully or desirably stocked forest (frequently, but not necessarily, expressed by yield tables)
$\quad\quad Gr$ = growing stock in a fully or desirably stocked forest
$\quad\quad Ga$ = growing stock in an actual forest

If Yr/Gr is expressed as a percentage, then the growth or yield in an actual forest is estimated by multiplying this percentage by the total actual growing stock. For example, if the average growing stock in an actual forest is 10,000 bd ft per acre, and what is considered to be an applicable Yr/Gr ratio is 3 percent, then the annual cut is 10,000 $\times$ 0.03, or 300 bd ft per acre per year. If the total area in the tract is 5,000 acres, the total annual cut is consequently 5,000 $\times$ 300, or 1,500 M bd ft.

Although the formula was initially designed to be used with yield tables as a base and to be applied to well-stocked stands, its principle is not so limited. It is obviously a growth percent approach and is subject to its limitations. The method is, however, simple and direct, and applied with discretion and understanding it is useful as a quick approximation of the amount that can be cut. Its main difficulty is that it provides no mechanism for taking into account whether the growing stock itself is too little or too much and in need of adjustment.

The above three methods illustrate both the application and the problems involved in using increment as the major basis for determination of allowable cut. The approach is direct and simple in well-regulated and uniformly stocked forest units where desirable cut does approximately equal growth. As emphasized, few such areas are in this condition, and management aims in working toward better regularity frequently dictate a cut in variance with increment. Current increment is often of limited significance, being overshadowed by pressing needs to bring about such things as improved stocking, a better distribution of size and age classes, needed reproduction, removal of unproductive trees, and solution of financial problems. In a forest dominantly of old-growth timber, increment is low and obviously a poor indicator of what should be cut. If the forest is composed of mostly young timber, the increment may be high but nonextractable from the forest in terms of timber of desired size and quality to cut. The volume of growing stock, by age or size classes, is never perfect but is constantly being adjusted upward or downward, which means that more or less than current growth should be cut.

A realistic figure for net current growth, necessarily periodic annual increment, is not easy to obtain, and its determination is usually expensive (Chap. 4). General growth (and mortality) conditions also change materially from period to period. Growth may be reduced during a period because of climatic, insect, or disease conditions, but the effect may be mostly on immature timber rather than on timber ready for cutting, which has already made most of its expected growth. With annual agricultural crops, if the season is bad, the current crop is also bad. In forestry, because of the long-term nature of the crop, the effects of changing growth conditions are cumulative and frequently delayed.

For these reasons, increment alone seldom can be used as a practical basis for determining the cut. Increment is more a quantitative measure of performance than a regulatory method. A cut equal to growth is the goal but is achieved only in a fully regulated forest. Even here, specification of the size and kind of trees to cut is as important as the total volume, for the reason that what trees are cut strongly affects growth.

METHODS BASED ON GROWING STOCK AND INCREMENT

Since neither growing stock nor increment alone is sufficient to establish an adequate volume control, it is necessary to combine them. This has been done in a number of ways, of which several are briefly described.

Austrian formula. The so-called Austrian formula, modified by Heyer and in its general form sometimes known as Heyer's formula, combines increment with a means of adjusting the volume of the growing stock either upward or downward. It employs a very useful principle. The formula in general terms reads:

$$\text{Annual cut} = I + \frac{Ga - Gr}{a}$$

where I = annual increment (usually determined on the basis of net periodic annual increment)
Ga = present growing stock
Gr = desired growing stock, whether indicated by yield tables or some other empirical standard
a = an arbitrary adjustment period, which may be a full rotation or any selected period considered reasonable.

In application, the increment term is often modified to average present and expected increment thus:

$$I = \frac{Ip + Ie}{2}$$

where Ip = average increment of the present growing stock
$\quad\quad Ie$ = average expected increment of future growing stock

The easiest way to visualize the application of the formula is in terms of an all-aged forest. Assume the following:

Increment or I equal to 275 bd ft per acre per year.
Present growing stock Ga averaging 8,500 bd ft per acre.
A desired average growing stock Gr of 10,000 bd ft per acre.
An adjustment period a of 20 years; i.e., it is estimated that the actual growing stock reasonably can be built up to the desired level in 20 years. Then

$$\text{Annual cut per acre} = 275 + \frac{8,500 - 10,000}{20}$$
$$= 275 + (-75)$$
$$= 200 \text{ bd ft}$$

Note that a part of the annual increment, 75 bd ft in this case, is retained on the ground to build up the reserve growing stock. If the situation is reversed, as in the case of an overdense natural stand, and it is desired to reduce the present average growing stock, the formula will also bring this about as the value of the $(Ga - Gr)/a$ portion of the formula may be either plus or minus. If, for example, $Ga = 10,000$ and $Gr = 8,500$, and other factors remain the same, then

$$\text{Annual cut per acre} = 275 + \frac{10,000 - 8,500}{20}$$
$$= 275 + 75$$
$$= 350 \text{ bd ft}$$

The principle of gradually building up or reducing the average growing stock by cutting less or more than the current growth over some adjustment period, whether an entire rotation or a part of it, is of general utility and widely applied. The Austrian formula gives the most direct expression of this principle and has been widely used whether recognized by name or not. It is particularly applicable in uneven-aged forests.

The approach illustrated by this formula has, however, some difficulties and limitations in application to be considered. These are:

1. An accurate figure for net annual increment is difficult and usually expensive to obtain—a major limitation of this or any other method employing increment as a major ingredient. This is particularly true in irregular and unmanaged forests where average annual increment for the area as a whole is a rather arbitrary and not particularly significant figure. With

such a forest composed of even-aged stands, usually the only thing known with any certainty is the approximate per-acre volume of timber at various ages. This can be converted into net average increment on the assumption that average annual increments equals yield divided by age.

2. Applied to even-aged stands, the formula does not necessarily work toward desirable age- and size-class distribution, which is one fundamental management objective. Assume, for example, a forest that is considerably understocked and with low increment. If a fairly high average growing-stock goal is set, the formula would permit a small or perhaps no annual cut at all, which certainly would not work toward desirable age-class distribution in the future. In such circumstances, it would be better to cut more heavily and regularly and rely on good silviculture and protection to increase the stocking of the younger stands. Approximately the same thing works in reverse when it is desired to reduce the rotation and surplus growing stock concurrently. The formula is not related to area or to any particular schedule of cutting and is not designed to bring about a desirable age-class distribution by area.

Hanzlik formula. The Hanzlik formula (Hanzlik, 1922; West Coast Forestry Procedures Committee, 1950; Gross, 1950) was developed to meet a common problem in the even-aged Douglas-fir stands of the Pacific Northwest, that of initiating management in unregulated forests including a large proportion of virgin timber. The formula reads

$$\text{Annual cut} = \frac{Vm}{R} + I$$

where Vm = volume of mature merchantable timber above rotation age
R = rotation adopted in years
I = increment

As stated, the cut is made up of two parts: (1) that from timber over rotation age distributed over the rotation period and (2) an estimate of increment. Attention is thus focussed on two key points: the rate at which old-growth timber should be cut and increment. The first is arbitrarily solved by prorating it over the full rotation, although, bearing in mind the provisional nature of an allowable cut (p. 122), this is not necessarily actually done for a rotation period. This part of the cut can easily be calculated, since age and volume of the timber stands is normally known and rotation has to be established as a planning base.

Determination of a meaningful increment figure is difficult. Knowledge of future net growth that reasonably could be expected in presently largely unmanaged natural stands is scanty. As originally proposed, increment was included only on stands under rotation age, which is a patently incomplete estimate. Older stands also grow and often make net increment too, certainly so if partial cuttings are made to salvage or anticipate mortality. In application, annual net increment is estimated for stands under rotation age, usually plus some estimate for older timber adjudged to be making net growth. Several procedures are used which will not be reviewed here. Essentially, yield tables are used and applied to individual age classes weighted by area and adjusted for stocking, for breakage and defect, and often for estimated approach toward normality (Chap. 4). The process is necessarily rather arbitrary and long-range in nature.

In practice, an allowable cut figure obtained by the formula is regarded as a preliminary figure only to be checked by a detailed stand-by-stand analysis as described on p. 141.

As a formula, the Hanzlik approach is indubitably arbitrary. It gives generally reasonable results only where a sizable but not too large a proportion of mature timber is present, and the formula gives no clue concerning what the proportion should be. If there is little mature timber over rotation age present, the Vm/R part of the cut becomes negligible and the formula reduces in effect to one based on increment only, with the weaknesses inherent in any such method. Conversely, if the proportion of mature timber is very large, the increment part of the formula becomes negligible and the Vm/R part merely distributes the cut of available mature timber over the rotation in the same way as strict area control. This would mean holding mature timber for very long periods, which would not be satisfactory from the standpoint of preventing or salvaging serious mortality losses in old-growth stands. In fact, there is no easy and fully satisfactory way to regulate a forest composed of mostly old-growth timber. The need for establishing reasonable age-class regularity for the future is in conflict with the silvicultural and financial desirability of fairly prompt removal of old-growth timber.

Provisional regulatory methods. As indicated in connection with the Hanzlik formula, a common problem in American forestry is to initiate management in heterogeneous, extensive, and irregular forests, for which forest information is often very limited. The prime need is to make a beginning, to accomplish a first step in putting a rather disordered forest house in order. No finely adjusted regulatory plan is either possible or needed, but some control is necessary. Many approaches are possible. Two of them, in formula form, developed in connection with management plans on the national forests, are given here as illustrations. Neither are what might be termed complete methods, but they have been considered useful in meeting specific situations. Both deal with the problem of handling considerable proportions of mature and overmature timber.

BLACK HILLS FORMULA This formula has been applied on the national forests of the Black Hills (Gross, 1950). Two broad condition classes of merchantable ponderosa pine timber are recognized: (1) mature stands in which it is presumed current mortality equals increment and (2) thrifty merchantable stands making net increment. The formula is as follows:

$$\text{Annual cut} = \frac{V_m(P_m) + [V_t + (G_t/2)]P_t}{n}$$

where V_m = volume of mature stands

$\quad P_m$ = percent cut in mature stands (an arbitrary figure, developed on the basis of silvicultural and related considerations external to the method itself)

$\quad V_t$ = volume of thrifty merchantable stands

$\quad G_t$ = increment of thrifty merchantable stands during the cutting period (area of these stands times the periodic growth per acre)

$\quad P_t$ = percent cut in thrifty merchantable stands (an arbitrary figure determined in the same way as P_m)

$\quad n$ = cutting period in years

The application of the formula is illustrated by the following data from a management plan for the Spearfish Working Circle (mostly ponderosa pine timber), Black Hills National Forest, South Dakota.

Total net productive area.............................. 238,459 acres
Area of thrifty merchantable stands..................... 90,517 acres
Volume of mature stands (V_m)......................... 147,474 M bd ft
Volume of thrifty merchantable timber (V_t)........... 373,468 M bd ft
Rotation.. 160 years
Cutting period (n).................................. 40 years
Annual net increment per acre for thrifty merchantable
 stands.. 50 bd ft
Periodic increment per acre for thrifty merchantable stands
 (40 years × 50 bd ft per year)....................... 2 M bd ft
Percent cut, mature stands (P_m)..................... 70
Percent cut, thrifty merchantable stands (P_t)....... 50

Applying the formula to these data, the annual cut becomes

$$\text{Annual cut} = \frac{147,474 \text{ M}(0.70) + \left(373,468 \text{ M} + \frac{2\text{M} \times 90,517}{2}\right)0.50}{40}$$

$$= \frac{103,232 + 231,992}{40}$$

$$= 8,381 \text{ M bd ft}$$

In application, the indicated cut was reduced 10 percent to allow for fire losses and other deductions. As applied in this instance, the formula provides: (1) For cutting during a 40-year period 70 percent of the total volume of all mature stands which are assumed to be making no net increment; this would permit establishment of reproduction on these areas. (2) For a partial cutting (50 percent by volume) of all thrifty merchantable stands. The total cut is a little more than the increment expected during the cutting period. The average cut per acre in thrifty merchantable stands is 231,992 M bd ft/90,517 acres, or 2,563 bd ft, which should be compared to the estimated growth per acre during the cutting period of 2,000 bd ft. At or before the end of the cutting period, the plan would be reviewed and the allowable cut revised if there were substantial changes in growing stock, increment, or silvicultural practices followed.

Since it specifies a cutting period and partial cuts, the formula implies an uneven-aged form of management at least in so far as the general regulatory framework is concerned. Considerable latitude is, however, possible on the ground in actual application. These Black Hills forests tend to be mosaics of small areas of even-aged stands rather than true uneven-aged stands. In marking practice, the 50 percent cut in thrifty merchantable stands could be met by cutting very heavily in some even-aged groups ripe for harvest and lightly in others.

The method is intended to serve as an overall guide only. Much depends on good judgment in its execution. In application, a specific cutting budget would be prepared by 5- or 10-year periods defining the cutting priority of specific areas.

K E M P   F O R M U L A   The Kemp formula[1] was developed in the Northern Rocky Mountains to utilize forest survey data largely limited to areas by timber size classes and the volume of sawtimber stands. Four size classes were recognized and for this number the formula reads

$$\text{Annual cut} = \left[\frac{A_1 + 3A_2 + 5A_3 + 7A_4}{4R} \right] \cdot Vm_a$$

where A_1 = area of unstocked and reproducing stands
A_2 = area of seedling and sapling stands
A_3 = area of pole timber stands
A_4 = area of sawtimber stands
Vm_a = average volume per acre of sawtimber stands
R = rotation in years

The structure of the formula is shown in Fig. 6.2. The assumptions behind it are that, in a regulated forest, these classes, four in this case, should occupy equal areas; that volume increase and consequently increment are linear; and that they divide whatever rotation is assumed into equal age groups. In these respects, it is a relative of the von Mantel approach and of the old European practice (French Method) of grouping stands into a few major size-age classes. The relative volume and hence weight of each size class is geometrically determined as shown in Fig. 6.2. Three, five, or some other number of them could also be used and their volume weights determined by redrawing the triangle. The first term of the formula, shown in brackets, gives the area that should be cut annually. This is then multiplied by Vm_a to get the annual cut. The sum of

[1] Developed by Paul D. Kemp (U.S. Forest Service, 1958).

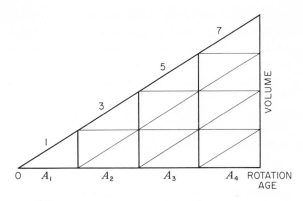

FIG. 6.2. STRUCTURE OF KEMP FORMULA.

A_1 to A_4 is obviously the total area weighted by volume. If the areas are equal, then the formula reduces to $16A/4R$ or $4A/R$ or simply total area/rotation, which is unmodified area control. In an unregulated forest, the areas are not equal; where the formula has been applied, sawtimber stands predominate. If, for example, the proportions of A_1 to A_4 are 10, 20, 10, and 60 percent, respectively, of the total area, substitution of these figures in the first term of the formula gives 1.35, which means that 1.35 times an unmodified area control cut would be indicated. Following the formula, this rate of cutting would be applied for a cutting budget period, say 10 years. At the end of this period, the cut would be recalculated and, since the area of sawtimber has been proportionally reduced by cutting it at a rate faster than unmodified area control, the 1.35 proportion would also be reduced. How much the reduction would be would depend on the length of the cutting period. The rotation assumed does not affect this ratio. The formula consequently works toward area control but in an arbitrary manner, which can be tested by substituting various assumed area proportions and cutting periods.

In practice, the assumptions behind the formula can only be approximately fulfilled at best, and the same limitations of the von Mantel approach are encountered. Volume increase is not linear, and the arbitrary survey-determined size classifications fit the four area-size groups assumed only in crude approximation. Using an average volume per acre of sawtimber stands tends to give a conservative cut, because it underestimates the volume of the older timber where initial cutting presumably would be concentrated. Nevertheless, the formula is easy to apply, utilizes the available information, and gives a reasonable provisional cut that is useful under the conditions where it is applied.

Stand-analysis methods. Application of any increment or combined increment and growing-stock formula method to an unregulated forest always leaves a question of how it will actually work out in practice. In forest areas dominantly composed of even-aged stands that can be classified by age classes, giving an answer to this question has led to various stand-analysis procedures projecting the indicated annual cut through a rotation period and utilizing the best growth information available to give a check on the total cut computation. Procedures of this kind, in one form or another, are fairly generally applied. Stand analysis seems the best general designation, although other names are also used. The general principle of the approach can be simply stated. Basically, it is the solution of a problem containing several conditions and assumptions as follows:

1. That the total operating area will be cut over during the planned rotation period (this is necessary by definition of a rotation).

2. That individual stands will be given final harvest cuts in some pre-established priority, normally by age and/or condition. These are the cuts that control establishment of new stands. Intermediate or salvage cuttings are considered separately.

3. That an approximately even flow of annual harvest volume is to be maintained at least for approximately a rotation period ahead. This is a common condition and is, for example, applied by the U.S. Forest Service, committed by law to the principle of a sustained cut.

4. That a certain existing distribution of age or size classes by area (which may also be classified by site and stocking) will grow at certain estimated rates.

5. That timber of not less than rotation age, or of some specified age less than rotation age, will not be cut during the rotation period. This condition may or may not be imposed.

Given these conditions, and others could be added, there is some volume of annual cut that will satisfy them. There could, theoretically, be more than one solution depending on the form of the growth curves used, but this possibility is not practically important. The volume is determined by a cut-and-try process starting with a trial cut figure (as determined from a formula calculation). The Hanzlik formula is commonly used as a starting point in national forest management in Douglas-fir in the Pacific Northwest. If the stand analysis does not show that the indicated cut can be sustained, another annual cut figure is used and the process repeated until one is found that can be maintained. This is a type of problem that could be solved by computer programming.

The process, as applied to a specific case, is illustrated in Table 6.3. Final harvest cuts only are considered, and, for simplicity, no delay in getting reproduction is assumed. In this case, growth is estimated by the simple expedient of deriving a curve from present age-volume relationships by age classes. After testing two trial annual cut estimates (von Mantel's formula was used as a first approximation), it was found that an annual cut of

TABLE 6.3. VOLUME CUTTING TIME CHECK ON ANNUAL ALLOWABLE
CUT ESTIMATE OF 32 M BD FT PER 100 UNITS OF AREA
ON A 100-YEAR ROTATION

Present age (class mid-point), years	Proportion of total area, percent	Average present volume per unit, M bd ft	Average cutting age, years	Average volume per unit when cut, M bd ft	Total volume cut, M bd ft	Cutting time, years	
						Per age class	Cumulative
(1)	(2)	(3)	(4)	(5)	(6)	(7)	(8)
over 120	25	35.5	146ᵃ	36.8	920.0	28.7	28.7
110	15	28.1	147.7	37.1	556.5	17.4	46.1
90	8	23.0	140.6	35.6	284.8	8.9	55.0
70	6	17.3	128.0	32.6	195.6	6.1	61.1
50	9	10.2	115.1	28.7	258.3	8.1	69.2
30	15		105.7	27.0	405.0	12.7	81.9
10	22		100.9	25.8	567.6	17.7	99.6
Total...	100	....	.....	....	3,187.8	99.6	

ᵃ Arbitrary estimate.

32 M bd ft could be sustained uniformly over the 100-year rotation (column 7).

The arithmetic of the process (Barnes, 1951) is as follows:

Over-120 Class. Ages and current volumes are variable in these stands. Average cutting age is arbitrarily estimated at 146 years, and the average volume per unit when cut is estimated at 36.8 M. The total volume to be cut is accordingly 36.8 × 25, or 920 M, which, at the rate of 32 M per year, will last 28.7 years (column 7).

110-year Class. Average age when reached is 110 + 28.7, or 138.7 years. It is estimated that the cut will last 18 years (one often has to try a couple of times to get a figure that checks fairly closely). Then the average cutting age is 138.7 + 18⁄2, or 147.7 (column 4), and the volume per unit is estimated at 37.1 M (from curve of yield data). The total volume to cut is consequently 37.1 × 15, or 556.5 M (column 6), which, cut at the rate of 32 M per year, will last 17.4 years (column 7).

The same process is repeated for each succeeding age class using the cumulative ages given in column 8.

There can be many variations in the estimation of growth. In the illustration given here, it was based on the simple assumption that past history will repeat itself, i.e. a yield table was made out of present age-volume data (p. 61). An applicable yield table for fully stocked even-aged stands could be used with correction for site, stocking, and perhaps estimated cull and breakage if considered important. Any applicable source of yield information could be used. If salvage or other partial cuttings could be made in advance of final harvest in the older stands, or thinnings applied in the younger stands, these volumes could be estimated by a similar stand-by-stand analysis and added to the final harvest cutting volume. These partial cutting volumes could not, however, be uniform over the rotation. The detail and specific form of the analysis can be varied to fit the circumstances but would follow the same general pattern of attempting to project a cutting plan for a rotation period.

The results of the procedure will vary depending on stand conditions, age-class distribution, kind of harvest cuttings applied, success in regeneration, and degree to which thinnings or other partial cuttings can be applied. As previously stated, there is no painless or perfect way to regulate an unregulated forest. If a substantially uniform volume of cut from an initially irregular distribution of age classes is desired, it will be obtained at the expense of improvement in age- or size-class distribution, certainly one objective in management. In the illustration given, a generally overage forest would be converted to one averaging significantly underage if the uniform cut of 32 M were applied over a full rotation. The reason, as can be seen from columns 2 and 7 of Table 6.3, is that the area of older timber is cut over more slowly than under straight area-control cutting because of its proportionately greater volume per unit of area, and whereas the younger timber is cut relatively faster because of its lesser volume per unit of area. The over-120 and the 110-year classes are cut over in 46.1 years instead of 40 years under area control. The 10- and 30-year classes are cut in 30.4 years instead of 37 years. The combined effect is to reduce the average age during the second rotation period to somewhat under rotation age, as can be verified by plotting the age-class distribution at the end of a rotation period by the method shown on p. 159. The present annual cut could not be then sustained unless there was a substantial increase in growth owing to application of effective silvicultural practice.

In practice, of course, a uniform cut would not be applied over a full rotation period. At the end of about 10 years, the entire situation would be reassessed and a new annual cut established which would periodically be revised thereafter. A virtue of the stand-analysis method is that it requires one to analyze the consequences of a proposed allowable cut figure. It does not, in actuality, insure a strictly uniform cut nor is needed improvement of age-class distribution specifically considered.

APPLICATION OF VOLUME
CONTROL SUMMARIZED

The uses and limitations of the various volume-control methods may be summarized as follows:

1. Volume control is most useful as an overall guide to proper cut and as an initial step in bringing an unmanaged forest under some degree of regulation.

2. Being mathematical in foundation, volume methods permit a quick approximation of the allowable cut, often from a limited amount of forest data. They are valuable in overall planning for this reason.

3. Volume control is most readily and realistically applied to uneven-aged stands where volume and increment estimates are necessary for management planning. In such stands, average cut per acre must be determined on the basis of growing stock volume and increment, although the distribution of the cut on the ground requires definition in terms of area as well.

4. Increment, which is required in most volume formulas, tends to be a weak figure. Its determination is difficult and frequently necessitates rather arbitrary and long-range estimation based on incomplete data. Good increment data applicable to specific stands are scarce and hard to get.

5. With any volume method, one is dependent on the accuracy of the volume and increment data used. If they are in error, there is no assurance that the forest area, which is normally known as a physical fact, actually will be treated in its entirety as planned.

6. Volume methods, by their nature not being related directly to area, have the serious weakness of not providing a measure of or a direct means for making progress toward a desired degree of age- and size-class regularity. This is, as has been stated, an important consideration in forest organization. These methods indicate the volume to cut but tell nothing about where and how it should be cut. As such they are necessarily incomplete from an overall management standpoint.

area and volume control combined

As was pointed out at the beginning of this chapter and subsequently, area- and volume-control approaches are necessarily complementary, and neither can provide a complete answer to determination of the cut. Because of this fact, it is logical to combine them in some way. A number of methods for so doing have been devised, and there are many possibilities for combinations designed to meet particular circumstances.

Such methods are characterized by flexibility and variability and do not have the neatness and apparent precision of volume formula methods. They are difficult to present in words and figures because considerable procedural detail is usually involved, requiring knowledge of specific forest situations. A combined approach is more a procedure, a framework for analysis, than a specific method definable as such. The Lake States Forest Survey procedure for the determination of the allowable cut (Guilkey and Gevorkiantz, 1949) is a good American example.

Combined approaches tend to dominate in practice. Two general pro
cedures are presented here to illustrate their possibilities.

DETERMINATION OF ALLOWABLE CUT
AS APPLIED IN FINLAND

A procedure for determination of allowable cut currently applied in
the forests of Finland as described by Kuusela and Nyyssönen, 1962, is illustrative of a well-designed combined volume and area approach. The genera.
pattern of the procedure is applied fairly widely elsewhere, although the
specific detail varies. It is based on good forest inventory and growth information backed by much research, experience, and judgment.

Information needed

1. *Present Growing Stock.* This information is obtained from a current forest inventory. The forest area, average site quality, tree species composition, and the distribution of forest area by age classes and/or stand-
development classes are determined. These classes are used as units of
calculation in determination of cut. The following stand-development classes
are recognized:

0 Open areas and seed tree stands
1 Seedling and sapling stands
2 Stands in the thinning stage
3 Stands in the preparatory stage for regeneration cutting
4 Mature stands to be regenerated
5 Shelterwood stands
6 Low-yielding stands

In the forest inventory, the volume, increment, and, in more accurate
work, site quality by stand-development or age classes are estimated. Proposed silvicultural treatment, its urgency, and resultant cut is estimated in
the field for a 10-year period. This is a field estimate and may or may
not be the final cut prescribed.

2. *Desirable Growing Stock.* A major feature of the procedure is establishment of desirable average growing stock volume objectives by forest
regions defined by stand age, major species groups, and site quality (vegeta-
tive-site types). This information is given in a series of tables which are
based on much growth and yield research. Thinning, and regeneration by
the shelterwood method are assumed. If stands are fully stocked, grown to
maturity, and artificially regenerated, the volume at the end of the rotation
is greater than the average and adjustment must be made. Decisions are
made as to what progress can be achieved toward a desired objective, usually
over a 20-year planning period.

Special attention is paid to the area to be regenerated during the planning period. In this context, guiding rotation is one important consideration, another is the age-class distribution and development-class situation by forest regions.

3. *Growth Information.* Increment by stand age, forest site, and species groups is determined from inventory and other growth-study information. It is commonly expressed in curves giving average annual compound rates by stand age. The rate used for a given time period is taken for each age class (or stand-development class) as the average of the rate at the beginning and end of the period. Experience under Finnish conditions has shown these stand increment percentages to be rather stable when applied to average stands.

Estimation procedure.   After the needed information described above is at hand, the calculation procedure is simple and straightforward. For each age or development class, the volume to be cut during a planned budget period is estimated by the following formula:

$$V_n = [V_0(1 + i)^{n/2} - C](1 + i)^{n/2}$$

and by rearrangement of terms,

$$C = V_0(1 + i)^{n/2} - \frac{V_n}{(1 + i)^{n/2}}$$

where C = total volume cut for budget period
V_0 = volume at beginning of budget period
V_n = desired volume at end of budget period
n = number of years in budget period
i = increment percent

In words, the formula says that the initial growing stock grows at a compound rate for $n/2$ years to the midpoint of the period. The cut C is then taken, and remaining growing stock grows at the same rate for the rest of the period to attain the desired growing stock volume at the end of the period. It is essentially similar to the Meyer amortization formula (p. 131) but gives a slightly higher cut owing to the midpoint assumption made. It also makes no differentiation between the average increment rate of trees cut and the total stand, as does Meyer's formula.

For old stands past normal maturity age, a low simple interest may be used rather than a compound rate in some cases.

Volume increment in seedling and sapling stands is estimated from yield tables.

The application of this formula to a sample stand unit of 100 hectares is illustrated in Table 6.4. The calculation is systematic and, for any size of forest unit, can be done on a single sheet of paper. Note that for a single development class a part of the total growing stock may be partially removed over the cutting period, and another part may be completely cut. The timing of the cut during the period may also be varied. This flexibility

TABLE 6.4. ILLUSTRATION OF ALLOWABLE CUT CALCULATION FOR A 20-YEAR CUTTING BUDGET PERIOD APPLIED TO A REPRESENTATIVE UNIT OF 100 HECTARES

Stand-development class	Age, years	Proportion of total area, percent	Initial growing stock (V_0)		Desired growing stock at end of cutting budget period (V_n)		Increment, percent, i	Interest factor $(1+i)^{n/2}$	Volume of initial growing stock plus growth to cutting period midpoint $V_0(1+i)^{n/2}$	Volume of growing stock after cut at cutting period midpoint $V_n/(1+i)^{n/2}$	Allowable cut, C cu m
			Volume per hectare, cu m	Total volume, cu m	Volume per hectare, cu m	Total volume, cu m					
(1)	(2)	(3)	(4)	(5)	(6)	(7)	(8)	(9)	(10)	(11)	(12)
Growing stock to be partially removed over 20 years											
1	23	5.3	28	148	75	398					80[a]
2	51	22.4	86	1,926	140	3,136	4.7	1.583	3,049	1,981	1,068
3	73	23.0	127	2,921	150	3,450	3.5	1.411	4,122	2,445	1,677
4	92	22.8	112	2,554	110	2,508	3.1	1.357	3,466	1,848	1,618
Total	...	73.5	...	7,549	...	9,492					4,443
Growing stock to be completely removed over 20 years[b]											
5	81	9.8	88	862	4	39	3.3	1.384	1,193	...	1,193
6	81	16.2	81	1,312	6	97	3.3	1.384	1,816	...	1,816
Total	...	26.0	...	2,174	...	136					3,009
Growing stock to be completely removed over 10 years[b]											
0[c]	...	0.5			20	10					
1[d]	90	(5.3)	22	117			3.1	1.165	136	...	136
Total	...	0.5	...	117	...	10					136
Grand total	...	100.0	...	9,840	...	9,638					7,588
Average	...	...	98.4	...	96.4	...					

Annual allowable cut = 7588/20 = 379.4 m³, or 3.8 m³ per hectare

$$\text{Annual increment} = \frac{V_n + C - V_0}{20} = \frac{9{,}638 + 7{,}588 - 9{,}840}{20}$$

= 369.3 m³, or 3.7 m³ per hectare

[a] Volume increment in seedling and sapling stands estimated from yield tables.
[b] Some volume in other stand-development classes could also be included in these categories, but were not in this illustration.
[c] The volume shown on this line is in reserved seed trees that, in this instance, are not to be cut.
[d] The volume here is also in seed trees but, because the area is regenerated, are cut at the midpoint of the period.

Derivation of columns: $10 = 5 \times 9$; ...

is needed to meet the fact that more than one kind of cutting often should be done in one of these rather broad development classes.

Although the calculation procedure is simple in principle, much forest information and good judgment is required in its application. The specific detail can be varied to suit circumstances and available information. Increment data are important in the procedure, but they are used in direct relation to desirable growing-stock objectives, and, as indicated, with regard to total age class and stand-development class improvement needs, as determined by area analysis and overall management objectives.

AREA AND VOLUME ALLOTMENT

The foregoing illustration combined volume and area considerations and emphasized increment and a particular technique for its calculation. What is here termed "area and volume allotment" is a more general procedure necessarily employing no particular formulas or techniques. As nearly as it can be defined, area and volume allotment means determining a periodic allowable cut based on joint considerations of area, volume, and silvicultural conditions of specific stands, all evaluated in relation to the policy and desires of the owner. It is not a specific procedure or method so much as a framework, a forum, in which the many considerations involved in managing a particular forest property can be appraised and a decision reached. Area and volume allotment is difficult to describe in a textbook, because the setting and peculiarities of a real-life situation are needed to give full perspective. To the extent it can be regarded as a more or less definite method or procedure, it dates back to Cotta and Judeich. According to Schlich (1925), "the system was developed by degrees in Saxony from Cotta's time [about 1820] onward, and put into a definite shape by Judeich."

A great many foresters have applied area and volume allotment in principle if not by name, and it has stood the test of time and experience. It is probable that more acres of forest land are handled according to this general approach than by any other method, although it is also probable that comparatively few recognize it by any particular name. To many, it seems only common sense applied in a systematic manner. The general procedure is presented here in outline with emphasis on major principles and elements involved rather than on any set form.

Application. Area and volume allotment can be applied in both even- and uneven-aged situations. With even-aged stands, it must be built around the structure of a forest unit composed of such stands with consideration given to maintaining or bringing about reasonable regularity by age classes. In uneven-aged stands, it is aimed at establishment of regularity in terms of achieving an optimum volume and distribution of reserve growing stock by cutting areas.

The general steps in application of the procedure are as follows:

1. Obtain forest inventory information including data on the area of stands by forest types and age or size classes as follows: (*a*) Merchantable volumes expressed in whatever volume units are applicable, such as cubic feet, board feet, or cords; (*b*) Stocking—at least of the older age classes; (*c*) Silvicultural condition and treatment needs by stands.

2. Pick out for analysis all stands that have any reason for being considered for cutting in the next cutting budget period or two. The period is arbitrary and a matter of judgment. If the aim is to develop a cutting budget for the next 5 years, probably all stands that might be cut in about the next 10 years should be included to make sure that all significant cutting alternatives are considered. If the stand is handled according to an uneven-aged plan of management, the budget period would probably be the cutting cycle.

In even-aged stands, any period considered desirable could be used. The individual stand units should be reasonably homogenous as regards species, age, and condition. They should also constitute practical cutting units. Legal land-survey subdivisions may serve identification purposes, although compartments and subcompartments defined by natural topographic and accessibility features are better.

The data for these stands should be tabulated in such a way that the essential items of information stand out clearly. Possible headings for such a tabulation follow: (*a*) Stand number or other identification; (*b*) location; (*c*) area; (*d*) average site—this is important if stands differ substantially as to site quality; (*e*) stocking—some information is very helpful even if only in "good, medium, and poor" categories; (*f*) growth—information on which to estimate volume to be taken from stands when cut is especially important; (*g*) accessibility, from a cutting and merchantability standpoint; (*h*) stand condition—items that determine the need and timing of treatment should be stressed; (*i*) volume, in whatever unit of measure and species grouping is desired. (If the stand should be partially cut, indicate what part should be cut and the total volume involved.)

3. Make an area control calculation estimating the annual major harvest cutting area and total annual cut from the forest as a whole. A similar calculation using a volume control approach might also be made. The purpose is to establish an overall guide for what should be done to bring about reasonable age-class regularity within the forest and to about how much in total can be cut. Whatever method or methods that seem appropriate to the need and the data available should be used.

4. Make an allocation of stands to be cut over in the next cutting period or two. This is the real heart of the matter and involves confidence, knowledge, and responsibility. As Roth (1925) aptly puts it, the process is a sort of "wrestling match." Many considerations enter in, and the net result is a compromise. Silvicultural and business needs may press for cutting

more or less than the amount that might be indicated from an overall regulatory standpoint. Whatever the final decision, it is made on the basis of full information and an understanding of the consequences of cutting on the short- and long-range development of the forest and of the forest business. Considerable give and take and adjustment are usually necessary.

On the basis of this "wrestling match," a specific cutting budget is drawn up for the next cutting period and, tentatively, for a second cutting period.

5. At the end of the cutting period, the process is repeated in whole or in part as circumstances may warrant.

Advantages of the Procedure.   Being both comprehensive and flexible, the general process of area and volume allotment can be applied to almost any kind of forest situation. Some items characterizing the procedure and its advantages follow:

1. Cutting is tied to the ground in terms of specific areas. This has to be done sooner or later under any kind of management. Area and volume allotment forces this from the start. The particular order and geographical distribution of the cut, which may be extremely important for logging and silvicultural reasons, is given specific consideration.

2. The annual cut is flexible within and between periods, and estimates progressively get better as more knowledge and experience accumulate. The cutting budget is built from the ground up, so to speak, and takes both forest and business needs into account. It is guided by an overall annual cut established for the forest as a whole, but immediate silvicultural and business needs also receive full consideration. The procedure emphasizes the integrative and compromise nature of practical forest management.

3. Major attention is given to stands in need of early cutting. This is logical. No matter what the future may bring, the cut for the immediate period ahead must come from stands containing merchantable timber susceptible to fairly definite measurement. The procedure largely gets away from placing much reliance on long-range estimates of increment in immature stands which may or may not be realized when they reach cutting size. As conditions change, the volume of the cut will be changed accordingly. As first developed by Cotta, the allotment was made for all stands in the forest and for a full rotation. A principal contribution by Judeich, and mostly followed subsequently, is to limit specific allotment consideration to stands in need of cutting in the next decade or two only. Other stands are important but their area, site, stocking, and cultural treatment needs are considered mostly as a basis for establishing an overall volume-cutting guide.

4. The procedure requires that the management plan be periodically reviewed and revised. This has to be done in any event; this procedure simply forces the issue.

5. Effective application requires much forest knowledge and entails considerable detail. This is particularly true in even-aged stands that are being handled under some cutting system involving several regeneration cuts as well as thinnings and other intermediate cuttings. A good knowledge of stands is necessary, since they may receive several different kinds of cuttings.

recurrent inventory systems

Mention should be made of recurrent inventory systems in relation to determination of the cut. These systems have had a long history and are popular. As a management approach, such a system was originated by the French forester Gurnaud and applied by the Swiss forester Biolley (1920) to intensively managed forest areas in Switzerland. Its application there is described by Knuchel (1953). Analyses of the approach with reference to American application have been made by Meyer (1942), Osborne (1947), Huber (1952), and others. It is variously termed the "control method" from the French *methode du controlle,* the "check" method, and in America rather loosely the "continuous forest inventory."

The basic idea is establishment of a permanent forest inventory system repeated at periodic intervals. As developed in Switzerland, 100 percent inventories were made. In the United States and Canada low intensity sampling systems are employed largely based on permanent and identically measured samples.

In one form or another, the thought is often expressed that these systems also constitute an allowable cut method—that the allowable cut can be directly determined from them by computational procedures. From what has been said in this chapter about the nature of periodic allowable cut determination, this cannot be true; the total problem is much more complex. It is true that good inventory information is absolutely essential to good management planning, and this point is emphasized repeatedly. But no inventory system as such can encompass the range of business, silvicultural, and regulatory considerations that must be managerially integrated in arriving at a cutting budget. Inventory information is an indispensable and major basis for cut determination but is not alone sufficient (Chap. 12).

determination of the cut in summary

The foregoing has brought out that determination of the amount and kind of timber to cut from a forest unit year by year and for a planned operation period requires integration of a good many considerations. The key forest-based elements involved in all the methods presented can be summed up as follows:

1. Forest inventory data giving indispensable information on areas, volumes, age- or size-class distribution, site, species, and stand conditions. As brought out, methods of cut determination employed depend in considerable degree on forest information available.

2. Some concept of desirable growing-stock levels and structure to work toward; an adjustment problem.

3. The regulatory need to maintain or work toward some desirable age- or size-class distribution by area for the forest unit as a whole. Again, an adjustment problem.

4. Forest growth information.

As has been illustrated, these elements are combined in various ways in different methods. These elements are always present and must be considered in one way or another. Basically, neither area nor volume approaches singly can give a complete answer. They are like two sides of a coin, and both must be considered.

All these forest elements are given direction by the purposes of management, whatever they may be and tempered as they are by business considerations. The essentially provisional nature of allowable cut determination has been stressed. However determined, the cut is budgeted for a particular and limited period at the end of which the entire situation is reassessed and the process repeated. Cut estimates get better and more realistic with experience. An alert forest manager needs to have a good working grasp of methodology and be able to use, and frequently adapt, the method best suited to his particular situation without prejudice or favor. Flexibility is essential to meet the dynamics of changing current conditions. Just the same, reasonable regulatory limits must be observed if the forest, which is the basis for continued production, is to be safeguarded. Determination of cut methods should be regarded as key working tools of the practicing forester to be used with understanding and discretion.

7

regulation of forests of even-aged stands

Chapters 5 and 6 presented the framework of forest regulation and methodology for the determination of the cut. The kind of forest was necessarily brought into the discussion, but the emphasis was on basic structure and concepts. The purpose of Chap. 7 is to apply this material to situations and problems encountered in the practical management of forests composed of even-aged stands. To do so, the chapter is built around three cases selected to exemplify a range of regulatory problems encountered in practice.

nature of even-aged management

Before going into case analyses, it is important to be clear on the nature of even-aged management. Silvicultural systems built around methods of reproducing the forest result in only two general forms of forests: those composed of even-aged and those of uneven-aged stands. Planting or seeding, shelterwood, seed-tree, clear-cutting, and coppice methods all produce even-aged stands. The selection method maintains uneven-aged conditions. As stated in Chap. 5, the essential feature of even-aged stands is that individual stands in the forest have a beginning and end in point of time (Fig. 5.1). Some reproduction may and often does occur at times other than when the main stand is started. Although it may be important in the management of the forest and offer problems, for example, an undesired hardwood understory developing under a more valuable pine stand, such reproduction does not ordinarily change the basic management structure of the forest or the rotation, which is determined in relation to the main crop.

A question that often causes considerable difficulty in practice is how small can a stand be and still be considered an even-aged stand. Many forests tend to develop as a mosaic of many small and more or less even-aged stands complexly intermingled. Should one consider such a forest as being composed of even-aged or uneven-aged stands from a management standpoint?

The basic definition of an even-aged stand must be silvicultural. An even-aged stand is one in which the dominant trees originated at about the same time and, following a period of establishment and, frequently, protection as under a shelterwood, develop under essentially full-light conditions without significant border competition. Such a stand is even-aged regardless of size. Its nature is frequently such that, silviculturally, it must be treated as an even-aged stand even though it occurs in a forest which as a whole is handled on an uneven-aged plan of management because of its generally mixed-aged character. Definition of a minimum size is largely a matter of appraising border effects. A tenth-acre group of even-aged reproduction in a mature forest is not an even-aged stand, because it is obviously dominated by the surrounding forest and cannot develop as a natural even-aged stand. This is true even though the opening may have been large enough to permit establishment of some of the less-tolerant species. Two acres of pole-sized timber might well be considered an even-aged stand, at least so far as the silvicultural condition and treatment is concerned. Where to draw the line is a matter of circumstance and opinion; there is no consistent agreement on this point.

For stands to be considered even-aged from a forest organization standpoint, they must be not only essentially even-aged silviculturally but also of sufficient size that they constitute significant management units. This means that individual age classes must be readily identifiable and surveyable on the ground and that inventory data must be obtainable and classifiable by age classes. In this chapter, analysis of even-aged management is confined to stands that can be considered even-aged not only because of their silvicultural condition, but also because they constitute practical operating units from a management standpoint. The minimum size of such units naturally varies with circumstances. It might not be more than an acre or two in an intensively managed forest, or it might be 20 acres or more in an extensively managed forest. The management of the more complex mosaic-like forest, supporting a mixture of even- and uneven-aged components, is treated in Chaps. 8 and 9.

In considering regulation of even-aged forests, there is a tendency, at least in textbooks, to assume that at some predetermined rotation age the entire mature stand is neatly removed in a single clear-cutting operation and a new stand is immediately established. Although convenient as a concept, it is not that simple in practice. A number of partial cuttings may be made in even-aged as well as in uneven-aged stands. With the shelterwood method, for example, there are several harvest cuts designed to bring in reproduction. A portion, often a substantial portion, of the parent stand remains for a period of time after reproduction is started, and some timber of more than rotation age is consequently produced. Even though the major harvest cuts are normally made at or near an average rotation age when a new stand is started, the volume obtained from major seed or reproduction cutting may be less than the total of other cuts.[1] In young well-stocked stands, the principal management objective is to capture the greatest possible net yield from the growing stock. This entails thinning and other cuttings to anticipate mortality and to improve the productivity of the stand.

It is only toward the end of the life of the stand that getting the reproduction needed to start a new crop must be faced and becomes an immediate consideration. It is of course desirable and sometimes essential that thought be given to the reproduction method to be employed earlier in the life of the stand. Provision for getting reproduction must be made when major harvest cuttings are initiated, but it often is not necessary to face this issue in immature stands. Many intermediate cuttings are made primarily to improve the stand and to get the most out of the existing growing stock without having any particular relation to regeneration methods at all.

One further general point about even-aged management should be made. Timber species and species associations that naturally grow or can be best handled on an even-aged basis are the most common and, worldwide, by far the most commercially valuable. In addition to this, practical and economical application of management measures is furthered by even-aged treatment. The basic reason is that cutting and other treatments can be more cheaply and effectively applied over fairly large areas. This is not possible under the selection system aimed toward maintenance of uneven-aged stand conditions wherein cuttings are necessarily made by trees or small groups of trees distributed throughout the stand.

For example, site preparation for regeneration usually can be done most efficiently over fairly large areas. Prescribed use of fire and use of mechanized equipment (such as disks, plows, or scarifiers) is not suited to small areas of an acre or two. The same is in general true of weedings, cleanings, and thinnings in immature stands; the work can be better systematized and economically done over areas of several acres. In making harvest cuts of timber of rotation age, substantial economies in logging costs

---

[1] As a matter of terminology here and elsewhere, a harvest cutting is defined as any cutting removing merchantable products, usually at a net financial return considering at least the direct costs of the operation. Removal of such material must be considered a harvest from the forest. Whether the cutting is silviculturally classed as a thinning or other intermediate cut or is concerned with removal of the stand to obtain regeneration will be made clear in the context.

can be made through use of mechanized equipment, especially in the case of clear-cuttings, applied fairly uniformly over substantial areas. In areas where labor costs are high and profit margins narrow, such economies must be made, and this inevitably leads to even-aged management. It is for these reasons, plus availability of suitable species, that even-aged management is so widely applied in the United States and in many other areas.

case I, initiation of management in a forest dominated by overmature timber

In many parts of the world it is necessary to initiate management in a forest area having a preponderance of overmature timber (in relation to a desirable management rotation) and with corresponding deficiencies in younger-age classes. Such a situation is given in Table 7.1 and graphically

TABLE 7.1. STAND DATA FOR A WEST COAST DOUGLAS-FIR
MANAGEMENT UNIT (AVERAGE SITE INDEX—140)

Age class, years[a]	Area acres	Proportion each age class is of total area, percent	Proportionate area and years occupied by age classes on a 105-year regulatory rotation	Volume, MM bd ft	Stocking in relation to yield tables for fully stocked stands, percent[c]
(1)	(2)	(3)	(4)	(5)	(6)
Overmature[b]	13,622	33.2	34.9	455.7	
120	1,180	2.9	3.0	42.6	50
110	0				
100	1,737	4.2	4.4	69.8	64
90	0				
80	6,314	15.3	16.0	202.0	70
70	860	2.1	2.2	17.5	58
60	0				
50	3,702	9.0	9.5	25.2	55
40	4,667	11.4	12.0	.....	60
30	0				
20	4,027	9.8	10.3	.....	52
10	3,689	9.0	9.5	.....	30
−5[d]	1,280	3.1	3.2		
Total or average	41,078	100.0	105.0	812.8	55 (av)

[a] Midpoint of 10-year classes.
[b] Ranging up to over 200 years.
[c] McArdle, Meyer, and Bruce, 1949.
[d] Areas recently cut over and not yet restocked.

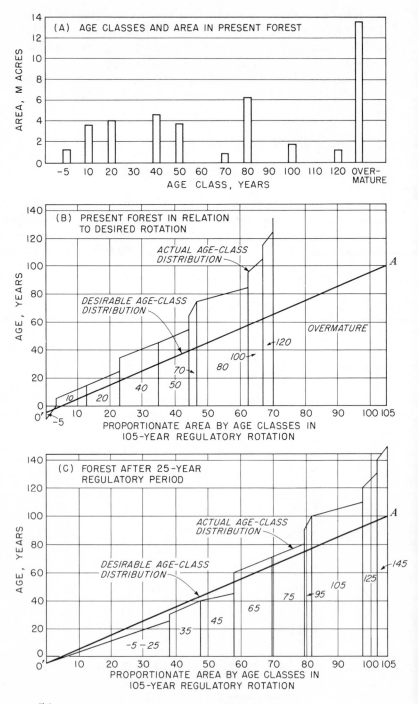

FIG. 7.1. REGULATION OF DOUGLAS-FIR MANAGEMENT UNIT.

shown in Fig. 7.1. This particular case is based on a large area of Douglas-fir in the Pacific Northwest region of the United States where this condition is common. Similar situations occur elsewhere, and the reader can substitute other species and areas without substantially changing the analysis. It is here assumed that the management objective is to work towards an average cutting age of 100 years for desirably mature timber and that sawtimber is the primary product. It is also assumed that it will take 5 years on the average to reestablish adequate regeneration after the final harvest cut.

As shown, the unit is far from being regulated. One-third of the total area supports overmature timber, much of it almost twice rotation age. Several age classes are not present at all, and the distribution of those present is irregular in area. Stocking is also uneven, offering a challenge to improve in the future. The general age-class distribution situation is shown in Fig. 7.1*A*. The preponderance of overmature timber and the comparative short-age of timber over 50 years (except for the 80-year class) is evident. If the forest were fully regulated, there would be an approximately equal area in each age class for the rotation. A simple bar chart of this kind does not bring out the real significance of the age-class distribution from a regulatory standpoint. This is given in Fig. 7.1*B* where the age classes are shown in relation to the regulatory rotation. It is important to be clear on the construction of this diagram and what it shows.

Since it is assumed that a 5-year delay in getting satisfactory regeneration will continue, the horizontal axis of the diagram is drawn for a regulatory rotation of 105 years. This means that it will take 105 years to grow timber to a desired cutting age of 100 years. There is no escape, except to shorten the cutting-age rotation. This also means that, to get the same production as would be obtained from immediate regeneration, 5 percent more forest land area is required. This is a direct production loss, the financial effect of which is greater than the proportionate years of lag in getting reproduction, as brought out by Davis (1965). The horizontal axis also shows the proportionate area occupied by each age class and consequently the number of years each would support the annual cut on a 105-year regulatory rotation under unmodified area control. For example, the overmature timber would last 34.9 years (column 4 of Table 7.1) and is so plotted on the diagram. Similarly, the 120-year age class occupies 3.0 years of the rotation, and so on.

The vertical scale is actual age in years.[1] For example, the 80-year

[1] Charts of this sort sometimes show volume per acre on the vertical scale instead of actual stand age (Matthews, 1935). However, this necessitates volume estimates for stands of all age classes. Such data are frequently not available, and their estimation, particularly in board feet, involves arbitrary and often meaningless assumptions, since the younger-age classes have little board foot volume except as these areas may also support remnants of older-age classes. Also, the actual volume in the younger-age classes is not so important as their area, site, and stocking. Volume becomes important only when these

age class groups stands from 75 to 85 years and is plotted to show the average gradient in age. Similarly, the present -5 age class is plotted from -10 to 0 actual cutting age to show an average lag of 5 years in getting regeneration. The existence of this negative age class of reproducing stands is a very real thing. It exists and cannot be ignored, for it occupies forest land area. The diagonal line $0'A$ shows the desirable age-class distribution for a fully regulated forest operated on a 105-year regulatory rotation. In essence, the actual situation is superimposed upon it.

The timing of regeneration in relation to regulation of the forest merits particular emphasis. There are three basic situations: (1) where reproduction is immediate or the delay is inconsequential, (2) where there is a significant delay, and (3) where advance reproduction comes in under the parent stand towards the end of the rotation. These situations are diagrammatically shown in Fig. 7.2 for a forest unit managed on a 50-year cutting-age rotation. To exaggerate a bit perhaps, a delay of 10 years and advance reproduction about 10 years old are shown in contrast to essentially immediate reproduction following major harvest cutting (Fig. 7.2A). As illustrated in B, a 10-year delay requires a 60-year regulatory rotation. Ten percent more land is required to get the same yield. This is expensive. Not only are regeneration costs likely to be high, but also the capital and administrative costs of the additional and essentially idle land must be reckoned (p. 463).

Natural reproduction frequently develops under the parent stand prior to major harvest cutting (residual shelterwoods after the main stand is removed are not included here). Many spruce-fir forests of the northern United States and Canada are examples. Such a situation is portrayed in Fig. 7.2C. As shown, the rotations overlap, and the regulatory rotation to produce timber of an average cutting age of 50 years is reduced to 40 years—compared to 60 years where there is a 10-year delay in reproduction. Some time gain is also possible through planting. Suppose, for example, that 3- or 4-year-old stock is planted immediately after cutting. This constitutes advance reproduction and, with short rotations, the time gain can be financially important.

The point of emphasis here is that the regulatory and the major harvest cutting-age rotations are different things. They are the same only when reproduction is immediate, which is often not the case. The timing of reproduction in relation to major harvest cutting is an extremely important financial consideration affecting the management of a forest unit.

To return to the Douglas-fir case, Fig. 7.1B gives a quick yet comprehensive grasp of the overall management situation. It shows not only the

---

stands approach cutting size. Diagrammatic presentation as a basis for regulatory analysis is much simpler and more accurate if volumes are left out of account, as has been done here.

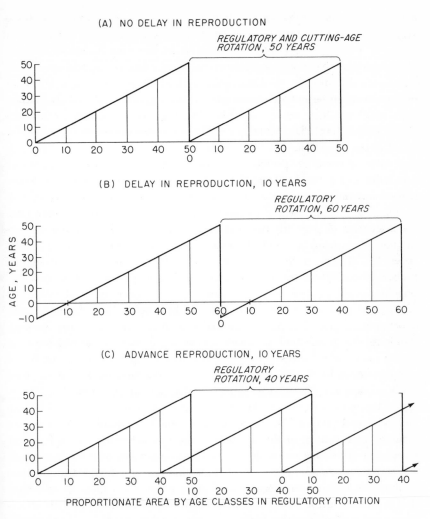

FIG. 7.2. EFFECT OF TIMING OF REPRODUCTION ON REGULATORY ROTATION.

area of the age classes present, but also their relationship to a desired regulatory situation. It is a good point of beginning for regulatory analysis.

As indicated, the major difficulty with this forest unit is that it is considerably overage for a 100-year rotation, being dominated by the ⅓ of the total area supporting timber considerably over desired rotation age. Although the area of individual younger-age classes is irregular and some are absent, this is not so important as the interrelationships of the entire age-class structure.

If unmodified area control were followed, no timber of less than rotation age would be cut, as the diagram shows at a glance; there is nothing below the desirable age-class distribution line. The age at which any stand would be reached for cutting can be scaled directly from the diagram. For example, the upper end of the 45–55 or 50-year class is about 15 years above the desirable age-class distribution line at that point, and hence cutting would be initiated in this age class when the oldest of it is 115 years of age. This can be readily checked from column 4 of Table 7.1 as follows: the sum of the years required to cut the older-age classes is $2.2 + 16.0 + 4.4 + 3.0 + 34.9$, or 60.5 years. This added to 55 years, the oldest of the 50-year class, is 115.5 years.

Since there is no problem of age-class deficiency, area control is one possibility as a general cutting and regulatory guide, and it certainly would make maximum progress toward regularizing the age-class distribution. Following such a plan, the cut for about the next 35 years would come from the large area of presently overmature timber. The annual harvest cut, assuming clear-cutting as would be followed in old-growth Douglas-fir, would cover $41,078/105$, or 391 acres per year. The average volume of mature timber is 455,700 M bd ft/13,622, or 33.45 M ft per acre. The indicated present annual cut considering major harvests cuts only, is consequently 33.45×391, or 13,079 M bd ft. It could be considerably higher initially, depending on just what part of the old-growth timber is cut first, for some stands in this group average much higher in volume. A natural tendency would be to select areas supporting the heavier and more mortality-susceptible stands for early cutting. The cut for the next decade or so could easily average 3 or 4 million ft higher from harvest cuttings alone.

The above calculation shows what straight area control would mean and is a good point of beginning in analyzing the situation. Whether unmodified area control in this instance would give desirable results from the standpoint of volume currently cut, or in the treatment of the present overage stands, is something else. Both silviculturally and financially it would be desirable to cut over the present mature stand much more rapidly than straight area control would indicate. These stands are making little if any net growth and represent a high and somewhat perishable investment value as well. The need to supply existing processing facilities may also press heavily for early liquidation. Aside from possible market or logging limitations, the objection to cutting the stands over rather quickly is regulatory, namely, the fact that a rapid rate of cutting cannot be long sustained and will require cutting timber much less than 100 years of age when the available mature-age classes are exhausted. Also, rapid liquidation of the mature timber will not make progress toward improvement of the age-class distribution, certainly one important objective of management.

Some compromise between regulatory, silvicultural, and financial objectives is needed, as is usually the case in such situations. Suppose the owner of the forest felt that it would be financially and silviculturally desirable substantially to accelerate the cutting of mature timber. This means that, considering the generally overage character of the forest for a 105-year rotation, he would prefer to harvest more timber now and expect to cut some timber under rotation age and attain something less than perfect age-class distribution in the future. In all probability, he would not be greatly disturbed over the prospect of cutting some timber perhaps 90 years of age 50 or so years hence. Many things can happen in 50 years. After all, the present carries by far the heaviest financial weight. There is no formula for compromise, but some speedup in cutting is clearly in order.

One reasonable solution, since there is no overall age-class deficiency, would be arbitrarily to decide to cut the overmature stuff in not more than 25 instead of 33 years, as would be the case under unmodified area control. At the end of this period, the development of the younger-age classes and the general situation would be reappraised. Cutting at this rate exceeds that indicated by area control but would not cause any serious difficulty in future age-class distribution, particularly if not continued for more than two or three decades when the whole picture may have changed considerably. As has been brought out, there is little point in trying to make specific plans more than a couple of decades ahead at the most; this is particularly true when management is first initiated in a forest.

If a 25-year liquidation period for the mature timber is decided upon, the annual cut of mature timber for the period would average 455,700 M/25, or 18.2 million bd ft a year, assuming no net growth. The age-class distribution of the forest at the end of this 25-year period is shown in Fig. 7.1C. It is assumed that the area cut over in the past 25 years will support reproduction up to about 25 years old, allowing for a continuing average 5-year lag in establishing it. This is added to the present nonrestocked area (the present—5-year age class) and all shown in the -5- to 25-year age class.

Following this 25-year initial regulatory period, unmodified area control could logically be applied as an overall control. This would involve cutting timber from 5 to 10 years under rotation age beginning when the 45-year age class is reached. However, this was foreseen when the initial 25-year regulatory period was adopted and was considered acceptable in view of the need to speed up the cutting of the old-growth timber. Whether or not unmodified area control is adopted at the end of the 25-year period would depend on a reappraisal of the situation at that time.

Approaching the problem from a volume control standpoint, Hanzlik's formula was applied by a West Coast study group. As described on p. 137, this method spreads the cut of overmature timber over the rotation and adds to it a rotation-length estimate of increment, in this case based on adjusted yield tables for fully stocked natural Douglas-fir stands. The result was 14,400 M bd ft per year (data for calculation not given here). A lag in getting reproduction was not taken into account. It was felt that this cut was too low and was increased to 17,000 M as a result of a detailed stand analysis applied as described on p. 141.

Von Mantel's formula can also be used as a guide. Using the formula,

$$\text{Annual cut} = \frac{\text{actual growing stock} \times 2}{\text{rotation}}$$

the indicated cut is 812,500 M/105 × 2, or 15,476 M. This is a rather rough—but quick—calculation, but in this instance, at any rate, the result falls within the general range of reasonability.

Whether the initial approach is through area or volume, both ultimately have to be taken into consideration. As shown, the end results are similar. This is about as far as the analysis can be carried on the basis of simple overall area and volume calculations based on the data given. From these data alone, it cannot be proved whether an annual cut of 13, 14, or 18 million bd ft or perhaps some other figure is the best, all things considered. These calculations do, however, give a basis for appraising the regulatory aspects of the problem.

It must be recognized that cutting for the next two decades or so will be dominantly in old-growth timber no matter what regulatory approach is followed. Regardless of what future markets may be and what volumes may develop in younger stands, the present problem is to decide how fast and in what sequence and way to cut the old timber. Once a guiding rotation has been set, final harvest cuts must be made in stands approximately arranged in order of their age and condition, guided by an overall area control, if much progress is to be made toward regularizing the forest. Adoption of a rotation in even-aged management inescapably introduces area control. The volume of the current annual cut must also be related to the per-acre volume produced by an age class at the time it attains harvest cutting age. With reasonable adjustment for differences in per-acre stand volumes because of variations due to rate of growth and other factors, an approximately uniform annual cut can be sustained by cutting on the average about the same area each year.

In practice, the whole situation of markets, available and needed roads, financial needs, and silviculture would have to be considered thoroughly and explicitly. In any event, a specific cutting budget should be developed for not more than one or two decades showing where the timber is to be cut and how. There may be special reasons, silvicultural or otherwise, for making harvest cuttings in young stands before they would ordinarily be cut on the basis of their age and size. The practicability of making improvement and thinning cuts would undoubtedly be explored. In the mature stands, the portions most in need of cutting to prevent loss would certainly be cut first, and partial salvage cuts in other areas might be made, transportation and logging methods permitting, to capture at least a part of the gross growth being made. If this can be done, the total allowable annual cut could be substantially increased. Various possibilities exist that can only be appraised on the ground. The only limitation is the desirability of keeping within an overall regulatory framework required to ensure the possibility of continuous production at a reasonably stable level.

As stated in Chap. 6, the whole situation would be reexamined at the end of this budget period, or whenever conditions changed enough to warrant such action. Another cutting budget would then be established including such adjustment and correction as was deemed desirable.

This case is general and is used to illustrate problems and possible solutions in initiating even-aged management in hitherto unmanaged forests, in this instance one with an excess of old timber. Many other situations could also be explored. For example, the case could be reversed to consider a situation, found in many areas, of an excess of young timber and a deficiency of mature timber. The key problem here would be to husband the stock of mature timber to provide time for a better age-class balance of young timber to develop and, at the same time, to get a reasonably adequate and stable cut of economically harvestable products. Much emphasis would have to be placed on intermediate cuts and good utilization to augment the yield obtained from the cutting of the mature timber. A rather extreme situation of this kind is given in Case III.

case II, regulation of a young forest with irregular age-class distribution

This case is developed to illustrate not only how to regulate a forest unit supporting a present irregular distribution of age classes but also how to deal with thinnings under fairly intensive management. It is developed in some detail to show the mechanics involved. The case is based on a 1200-acre forest unit of loblolly pine in the southern United States with yields gauged accordingly. However, it is general and illustrates a pattern of analysis that could be applied to almost any coniferous species handled on an even-aged basis.

The age-class distribution is given in Table 7.2. Site and stocking conditions are substantially uniform, and there is a good distribution of ages within the age class. Average site index is about 90. The following objectives and schedule of management are assumed:

1. Even-aged management for maximum volume of sawtimber and pulpwood on a 60-year rotation.[1] Prompt regeneration by planting is assumed; there is no significant regeneration lag.

[1] The rotation of 60 years is longer than average for loblolly pine, and more emphasis could be placed on pulpwood production. For application in

TABLE 7.2. AGE AND AREA DISTRIBUTION OF A
LOBLOLLY PINE MANAGEMENT UNIT

Present age class, years	Area, acres	Proportion each age class is of total area, percent	Proportionate area and years occupied by each age class in a 60-year regulatory rotation	Area after 32-year regulatory period, acres
(1)	(2)	(3)	(4)	(5)
1–10	250	20.8	12.5	180
11–20	375	31.3	18.8	180
21–30	70	5.8	3.5	180
31–40	0	0	0	235
41–50	355	29.6	17.7	350
51–60	0	0	0	75
60 and a little over	150	12.5	7.5	0
Total...............	1,200	100.0	60.0	1,200

2. Major harvest cut at rotation age yields per acre 25,000 bd ft in sawtimber and 5 cords of pulpwood partly from the tops.

3. A thinning schedule removing pulpwood yields per acre as follows:

Age 30, 6 cords
Age 40, 5 cords
Age 50, 5 cords

The proportionate age-class situation in relation to a 60-year rotation is shown in Fig. 7.3*A*, which is constructed following the same procedure employed in Case I. By inspection, it is evident that, in relation to a desired age-class distribution, there is a substantial age-class deficiency. The maximum deficiency of 11.3 years occurs at the upper limit of the 11–20-year age class. If unmodified area control were followed, the 11–20-year age class would be reached in 7.5 + 17.7 + 3.5, or 28.7 years, and the oldest of this timber would then be only 20 + 28.7, or 48.7 years old, which is 11.3 years below the desired rotation age. If harvest cuts of timber of less than rotation age are not to be made, it would be necessary to distribute the cutting of timber now older than 20 years over a 40-year period. The

the southern United States, the rotation might be reduced to 30 or 40 years with pulpwood as the major product employing a thinning interval of about 5 years. This would not, however, change the basic pattern of the analysis. The objective here is to give a general case, showing the interplay between sawtimber and pulpwood, with a rotation and thinning schedule more in line with northern species as well.

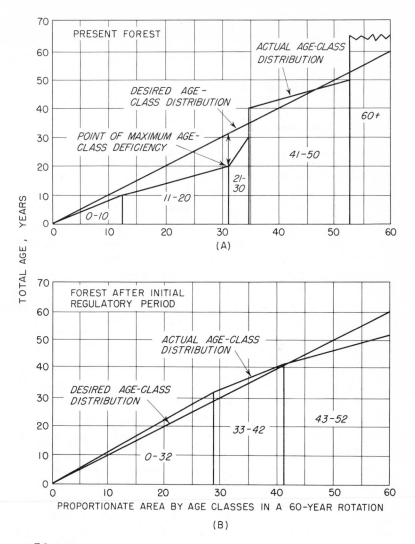

FIG. 7.3. REGULATION OF LOBLOLLY PINE FOREST.

period during which the timber older than the present 11–20-year age class should be cut is the key management consideration. A minimum period is 28.7 years, and a maximum 40 years. The first would give a larger current annual cut and bring about perfect future age-class regularity. But it would necessitate cutting timber considerably under rotation age near the end of the third decade. The second would give a smaller current annual cut and income. It would not bring about as good future age-class regularity but would ensure that no timber under rotation age is cut if this is regarded as important.

The question is what rate of cutting to adopt for an initial regulatory period. This is a key decision, as the whole management framework is affected by it. Here is where the necessity for compromise between the desirability of future age-class regularity and present yield and financial considerations becomes apparent.

The following considerations favor a short regulatory period:

1. It makes maximum progress toward regularizing age-class distribution.

2. It gives higher yields currently, since the annual average cutting area is larger. This is a potent financial advantage, as the present always weighs more heavily than the future.

3. It tends to promote greater total board foot growth per acre per year. A long regulatory period means temporary adoption of a longer rotation, and 60 years is past the culmination of mean annual board foot increment in loblolly pine, at least as indicated by yield tables. However, this may or may not prove to be true under future management.

4. While some timber substantially under rotation age will be cut during a period starting about 30 years hence, market shifts, technological changes, and better silviculture may make this less important then than it may seem now.

Some good arguments may also be made for a long regulatory period:

1. It promotes the growing of higher-quality products, since older timber will be cut. Quality timber is scarce in the South and commands a premium price; there is reason to expect continuance of this situation. Greater quality increment may outweigh decreased volume increment in terms of total value.

2. It is more conservative in several respects. There is more time available for establishment of new reproduction. With more timber on the ground, there is more margin to meet forest losses without seriously depleting forest growing stock or departing materially from the established rotation. Also, there is more timber in accumulated growing stock that can be cut in emergencies or to take advantage of good future markets.

There is no formula for compromise. Weighing the pros and cons, about a 32-year regulatory period would seem logical. This means giving the minimum period about two-thirds weight in making the decision. It should again be emphasized that such a decision is not immutable. By the nature of allowable-cut determination (Chap. 6), it represents only present best judgment. At the end of the next planning period, perhaps 10 years, the entire situation is reassessed, and the present decision may be either confirmed or changed. To gain full understanding of the consequences of adopting a regulatory adjustment period and of the effect of an irregular age-class distribution on harvest and thinning cuts, it is nevertheless worthwhile to estimate the cut for the full regulatory period. This is done in the following section.

YIELD DURING REGULATORY PERIOD

If 32 years is accepted as an initial regulatory period during which stands now older than 20 years are to be cut, then the annual cuts will be made as given in the following sections.

Major harvest yield. The average annual cutting area is

$$\frac{150 + 355 + 70}{32}$$

or 18 acres. The number of years it will take to cut over each of these three older-age classes is shown in Table 7.3. The oldest of the present 41–50-year class will be almost 60 years when reached $(50 + 8.3)$ and will average a little over 60 years of age during its cutting period. The oldest of the present 21–30-year class will be $30 + 19.7 + 8.3$, or 58 years when reached. The average cutting age during this 32-year period is therefore close to 60 years, and the harvest yield expected at that age can reasonably be used in estimating volumes to be cut.

The average annual major harvest yield during the regulatory period is consequently:

Sawtimber: 25 M per acre from 18 acres, 450 M
Pulpwood: 5 cords per acre from 18 acres, or 90 cords

Intermediate pulpwood yield. The yield from pulpwood thinnings must be calculated in relation to actual stand ages and estimated separately from the sawtimber. It is done here by 10-year periods.

1. First 10-year period:
    a. From 50-year stands. This comes from the present 41–50-year age class, one-tenth of which, on the average, reaches age 50

TABLE **7.3.** YEARS REQUIRED TO CUT OVER
DIFFERENT AGE GROUPS

Age group	Area	Area to cut annually	Years to cut
60+	150	18	8.3
41–50	355	18	19.7
21–30	70	18	4.0
Total.......	575	...	32.0

and is available for thinning each year. The annual thinning
harvest is therefore 355/10 × 5 cords per acre, or 177.5 cords
per year.

  b. From 40-year stands. No cut as this age class is not present.
  c. From 30-year stands. This must come from the present 21–30-
    year class. The annual cut is 70/10 × 6 cords per acre, or 42
    cords per year.

2. Second 10-year period:
  a. From 50-year stands. None available, since there is no present
    31–40-year age class to supply it 10 years hence.
  b. From 40-year stands. Taken from the present 21–30-year age
    class. The cut is 70/10 × 5, or 35 cords per year.
  c. From 30-year stands. Taken from the present 11–20-year class.
    The cut is 375/10 × 6, or 225 cords per year.

3. Third 10-year period:
  a. From 50-year stands. Taken from the present 21–30 age class.
    The cut is 70/10 × 5, or 35 cords per year.
  b. From 40-year stands. Taken from the present 11–20 age class.
    The cut is 375/10 × 5, or 187.5 cords per year.
  c. From 30-year stands. Taken from the present 0–10 age class.
    The cut is 250/10 × 6, or 150 cords per year.

4. Fourth 10-year period (first 2 years of it completing the 32-year
    initial period):
  a. From 50-year stands. Taken from the present 11–20 class. The
    cut is 375/10 × 5, or 187.5 cords per year.
  b. From 40-year stands. Taken from the present 1–10 age class.
    The cut is 250/10 × 5, or 125 cords per year.
  c. From 30-year stands. Taken from areas in the present 60+
    class that have been regenerated since cutting. Since these lands
    were cut over at an average rate of 18 acres a year, the average
    yield would be 18 × 6, or 108 cords per year.

It should be noted that the annual yield comes in two distinct and
separate parts: that from major harvest cuttings creating new age classes
and that from thinnings which are designed to capture net growth and
yield from stands of intermediate age before regeneration is a concern.
Yields from thinnings are determined in relation to the age, area, and condition of individual stands. Thinning tends to be a calendar affair; in general,
for a given site and thinning schedule, such cuts are made at certain ages,
although not precisely because stand condition and other factors are also
taken into account. As illustrated here, thinning yields are estimated independently of major harvest cuts and follow the actual age-class distribution.
They are related in area to the harvest cutting schedule only when stands
have grown up to thinning age following such cuts. This occurred after
30 years in this case when, for the last 2 years of the 32-year regulatory

TABLE 7.4. ANNUAL PULPWOOD AND SAWTIMBER YIELDS
DURING A 32-YEAR REGULATORY PERIOD

Cutting period, years hence	Pulpwood yield, cords					Sawtimber yield, M bd ft
	From 30-year thinnings	From 40-year thinnings	From 50-year thinnings	From final harvest cut	Total	
0–10	42	0	177.5	90	309.5	450
11–20	225	35	0	90	350	450
21–30	150	187.5	35	90	462.5	450
31–32	108	125	187.5	90	510.5	450

period, the 30-year thinning came from stands cut under the harvest cutting schedule, 18 acres per year in this instance.

Annual yields estimated for the regulatory period are summarized in Table 7.4. The age-class condition of the forest at the end of the 32-year regulatory period is shown in Fig. 7.3B and in column 5 of Table 7.2, where it is allocated proportionately to 10-year age classes to give a direct comparison to the initial age distribution.

DISCUSSION AND ANALYSIS

As shown in Fig. 7.3 and Table 7.2, much is accomplished during this regulatory period toward achieving a better age-class distribution. In a fully regulated forest of this area, there should be 1200/6 or 200 acres in each of the six 10-year age classes in the rotation. As column 5 of Table 7.2 shows, the result is not far from it. There is a shortage in the 51–60 class, but it is largely offset by the excess in the 41–50 class.

The yield for the balance of a rotation period, or for any other desired period, can be estimated following the same procedure as illustrated here. At the end of the regulatory period, the harvest cutting schedule presumably would change to unmodified area control, or from 18 acres per year to 1200/60 or 20 acres. The cut at that time would come from the present 11–20-year age class, the oldest of which is 20 + 32, or 52 years of age, which also can be scaled from Fig. 7.3B. The cut per acre would decrease as this younger timber is reached, but the total volume removed would be almost offset by the larger annual cutting area. As the diagram shows, the average cutting age would increase to 60 in about 17 years, be a little over 60 for a number of years, and finally level off at 60 at the end of 60 years. The total harvest cut would follow approximately the same pattern.

The yield from thinnings during the regulatory period is rather irregular, as Table 7.2 shows. This is because, as pointed out, they are controlled by the particular age-class distribution which is irregular. There would b difficulty in estimating thinning yield just after the end of the regulator period because the major harvest cut will come from timber about 53 year old. Obviously, the 50-year thinning and the major harvest cut will hav to be planned in relation to each other and some adjustments made. Th same will be true of pulpwood volume harvested in connection with th major harvest cut. This is a problem that must be worked out on th ground; it can seem more complex on paper than it really is. Much ca be done in practice to equalize annual pulpwood yields if this is desirable but basically they will be irregular as long as the age-class distribution b area upon which they are based is also irregular.

It should be recognized frankly that in no actual forest would thing work out as neatly and surely as they seem to do in this example. Age and sizes within the age groups recognized would not occur in even pro gression. Some stands will produce more timber per acre at a given ag than will others, even on approximately the same site. Thinnings probabl could be applied earlier and more frequently. There will be forest mishap and some good breaks as well. There is large scope and necessity for applica tion of the arts of silviculture and of financial management in growin trees. But regulatory planning, such as that carried through in considerabl detail here, primarily to show its mechanics, is invaluable in appraising th consequences of cutting plans and in establishing an overall framework an objective within and toward which the practicing forester can wor effectively.

This analysis has not explored the question of whether the 60-yea rotation assumed is in fact the best. It has been brought out that the whol cutting framework is related to the particular rotation adopted and woul of necessity have to be changed if the rotation is changed. Factors influ encing the choice of rotation are investigated in Chap. 10 and will no be dealt with here. The direct relation between the length of the rotatio and the cutting area can, however, be readily demonstrated. With even-age management, the average annual harvest cutting area (with site differential taken into account where necessary) is necessarily fixed by the rotation i future age-class regularity is sought. In this 1,200-acre forest, rotations ca be expressed in terms of average annual cutting areas as follows:

Rotation, years	Average annual cutting area, acres
40	30.0
50	24.0
60	20.0
70	17.1

In this analysis, an 18-acre annual cutting area was proposed for a regulatory period to give the young timber at the point of most critical age deficiency time to attain reasonably merchantable size by the time cutting reached it. As can be seen, this corresponds to a rotation closer to 70 than 60 years for the regulatory period, or 1,200/18, or 67 years to be precise.

It might be that 50 years is more desirable than 60. This would depend on what is the objective of management. The shorter the rotation, the less critical the age-class deficiency in the younger timber becomes. Re-analysis on the basis of a 50-year rotation will show that the forest is relatively older in relation to that rotation and that the maximum age deficiency occurring at the upper limit of the 11–20-year age class is 6 years instead of nearly 12 for a 60-year rotation. On a 40-year rotation, there would be a relative surplus of older timber, relative to the rotation, and the situation would somewhat resemble that in Case I. The case might be refigured on the basis of a 50-year or even shorter rotation, and in practice it probably would be desirable to do so and compare the results. The whole thinning schedule would have to be revised too. This brings out how deeply and intimately the choice of rotation affects the management structure of a forest composed of even-aged stands.

The analysis here is designed to explore regulatory problems on a physical production basis, as is necessary in organizing a continuously productive forest unit. But a very important consideration has been left out of account, that of financial costs and returns and their economic import in management. Using such data, the case could be refigured in financial terms. The length of the rotation, the number and weight of intermediate cuts, the best level of growing stocks to maintain, the most valuable product combinations, and reproduction and harvesting methods would receive careful scrutiny and undoubtedly adjustment for financial reasons. These matters are considered in Part III of this book. It is believed, however, that financial analyses can be most effectively undertaken only when founded on thorough knowledge of the physical-biological nature of the forest on which they are necessarily based.

The question can be asked: How useful are the various methods of cut determination applied in this situation? In terms of formula methods, the answer is largely negative. Considerable knowledge of yields under management and hence of net increment is assumed in this case. Some problems of irregular age-class distribution, such as are clearly exposed by the regulatory diagram used, have to be faced. The analysis falls rather naturally into the general pattern of area and volume allotment (Chap. 6). The major limitation of volume control is that it does not expose and provide a remedy for maldistribution of age classes. Only area analysis does this, and volumes, regardless of how determined, must be identified with specific areas before cutting can proceed. In the final analysis, the only way the volume yield of a forest can be increased is to increase the average net growth per acre. Both area and volume are necessarily involved.

case III, initial regulation of an understocked and immature forest

This case is drawn from a timber management plan for a pine-hardwood management unit in the southern United States. It is totally different in character from the preceding two cases and brings out another aspect of management planning. In this case, neither diagrams nor formulas are of any help, the rotation is not an immediate consideration, and no final harvest cuts are made during an initial 10-year period, which is all the plan covers. Yet it presents an exceedingly real timber management problem involving regulation.

Areas of the principal types included in the forest and total board foot volumes are given in Table 7.5. The area was purchased primarily for timber production purposes. All of it had been rather indiscriminantly cut over before acquisition and now supports generally understocked stands in poor condition. The job is to build up the forest. Most of the unit was originally a longleaf pine type, and it is estimated that it eventually will be converted to a forest dominantly composed of even-aged longleaf pine stands. Currently, loblolly and shortleaf pine are abundant and make up most of the conifer volume in the pine and pine-hardwood types. Shortleaf pine is heavily attacked by the littleleaf disease and stands are becoming depleted of this species. The pine-hardwood types are scattered in small areas and most of the trees are of low quality. The entire forest is young; practically no timber is over 45 years of age, and most of it is much younger.

TABLE **7.5.** FOREST AREAS AND VOLUMES OF AN IMMATURE
AND UNDERSTOCKED SOUTHERN FOREST UNIT

Forest condition class	Area in acres by forest types				
	Pine	Pine-hard-wood	Bottom-land hard-wood	Total all types	Volume, M bd ft, Scribner
5 M bd ft per acre and over..............	5,371	96	179	5,646	38,162
1–5 M bd ft...........	38,525	4,121	1,943	44,589	106,163
Total 1 M bd ft and over..............	43,896	4,217	2,122	50,235	144,325
Under 1 M bd ft.......	13,915	1,417	481	15,813	5,750
Total..............	57,811	5,634	2,603	66,048	150,075
Percent..............	87	9	4	100	

The objectives of management for the forest, as stated in the management plan, are as follows:

1. To salvage as much as possible of the shortleaf pine affected by the littleleaf disease in the first 5 years. This is a situation demanding immediate action. The disease is so bad and the outlook for the species in the area so poor in this forest unit that shortleaf is to be virtually clear-cut and not encouraged in the future. This is one of those forest exigencies which a forester must often face.

2. To build up the growing stock and improve conditions for future growth. Cut merchantable but low-quality hardwoods to improve species composition and increase the net growth rate.

3. To build up and maintain an adequate forest cover for better stream flow control.

4. To furnish a continuous supply of timber to the wood-using industries accessible to the unit. There is market for both sawtimber and pulpwood.

To accomplish these objectives, it was estimated that 10 years was the shortest practicable time in which the forest area could be cut over. The specific plan was accordingly framed for a 10-year period. All stands supporting at least 1 M bd ft per acre were considered operable by commercial cutting; i.e., a cutting that will at least pay its way. As shown in Table 7.5, there are 50,235 acres in all forest types supporting stands of 1 M bd ft per acre or more. The average volume is 144,325 M/50,235, or 2,873 bd ft per acre, at the beginning of the cutting period.

Regulation is effected by a simple area allotment of the operable stands. During the first 5 years of the period covered by the plan, an average of 5,296 acres are to be cut over annually. Emphasis in the selection of these stands for cutting is on salvaging shortleaf pine attacked by the little-leaf disease. During the second 5 years of the period, the balance of the operable area is to be cut over an average rate of 4,751 acres annually. Emphasis during this period is on improvement cuttings generally. Note that this is not area regulation, strictly speaking, for the area cut over is not tied to a rotation as is necessary in even-aged management. Also, it does not constitute a commitment to any particular cutting cycle as is involved in application of uneven-aged management. It is simply an average cutting area based on the minimum period practical to bring about needed silvicultural improvement over the entire area. The plan is, however, well suited to the purpose, which is what counts.

No harvest cuts are to be made during the entire cutting period—another unusual feature. The stands are all immature and support volumes far below what they should be. It is estimated that the average growing stock volume at harvest cutting time should be around 10 M ft per acre. The immediate problem is to build up the growing stock as much as is

consistent with salvage of shortleaf pine, to accomplish the needed improv
ment cutting, and to mark timber of sufficient quantity and quality p
acre to make a commercial cutting possible. The problem of making harv
cuttings and of getting necessary reproduction is passed to the future; tl
present purpose is to put the forest house in better order. In this sens
the plan cannot definitely be classed as either an even-aged or an uneve
aged plan. It is a stand improvement program, in this case with the inte
tion of eventually developing even-aged conditions. Almost exactly the san
procedure would be followed in building up a depleted forest for uneve:
aged management; there is often no real distinction. The immediate nee
is to bring about conditions promoting better stocking and growth; to c
first things first. At the outset, final decision as to the eventual form
management is neither necessary nor possible.

Taking all operable types together, it was decided to cut 1,338 l
ft per average acre. The overall result of the cuttings planned is estimate
in the plan as follows:

Board feet per acre

Present volume...............................	2,873
Net increment during 10-year period...........	2,812
Present volume plus 10-year increment.........	5,685
Average cut per acre........................	1,338
Estimated volume 10 years hence..............	4,347

Despite heavy cutting of shortleaf pine, stands will be built up to 4,34
bd ft per acre on the average, or an increase of 4,347 — 2,873, or 1,47
bd ft. The forest will also be in much better condition to make great
growth in the future. About one-half of the total increment

$$\left(\frac{1,474}{2,812} \times 100 = 52.4 \text{ percent} \right)$$

is to be retained on the ground to augment the growing stock. It should als
be observed that, poor stocking notwithstanding, the stands are estimated i
grow an average of 281.2 bd ft per acre per year in growth. This is indicativ
of the high timber-growing capacity of the area, and the figure would l
much larger were the stands more fully stocked. Increment was estimate
type by type, by stand projection using average growth by diameter class
and recognizing dispersion within classes as described in Chap. 4.

The increment and volume data fall naturally into the pattern of tl
Austrian formula for calculating the annual cut, as described in Chap.
and furnish an example of a situation in which the formula could be ar
plied. The formula is

$$\text{Cut} = \text{increment} + \frac{\text{actual growing stock} - \text{desired growing stock}}{\text{adjustment period}}$$

n this case the plan contemplates retaining 52.4 percent of the growth
aade during the 10-year period to build up the growing stock. The desired
rowing stock is consequently 2,873 + [2,812 (0.524)], or 4,347 bd ft. Filling
1 the formula on this basis,

$$\text{Cut} = 281.2 + \frac{2,873 - 4,347}{10}$$
$$= 281.2 - 147.4$$
$$= 133.8 \text{ bd ft per year}$$

'his indicates 1,338 as the average cut from an acre during the 10-year
eriod, which checks, of course, with the 1,338 figure given above.

A feature of the plan, both necessary and proper, is large dependence
n the forester on the ground to carry it out. The unit is divided into
2 compartments on the basis of logical topographic cutting units. In the
utting budget, 27 of the compartments are listed for cutting during the
0-year period in approximate order of cutting priority. The total volume
> be cut and left in each compartment was estimated in board feet and
ords. Beyond this, it is up to the man on the ground to carry out the
eneral policy of the plan by designating and marking the specific stands
> be cut. No plan can take the place of his skill and judgment in sizing
p the situation on the ground.

The plan in general furnishes an excellent example of an instance
here the overall regulatory problem can be very simply handled. The real
ob is a complex one of silvicultural application. The purpose of regulation
to furnish the necessary overall framework for forest continuity. So long
s this purpose is met, the simpler the regulatory mechanics, the better.

rea-volume relationships in even-aged management

n the preceding analyses, emphasis has been fairly heavy on an area ap-
roach as constituting the basic framework of regulatory control in even-
ged management. This was particularly true from the standpoint of one
aajor objective of management, that of working toward regularity of age-
lass distribution. The purpose here is to bring out more explicitly the rela-
onships between area and volume approaches toward determination of the
ut. It should be emphasized that with either approach the answer sought
the volume to be cut.

The relationships between increment, yield, and area in a regulated
orest managed on a rotation of R years are shown in Fig. 5-1. In this
lustration, it is assumed that three intermediate cuts in the form of thinnings
re made at 15, 20, and 25 years, with the main harvest cut made at 30 years.
n a regulated forest managed on this rotation, the volume of the oldest-age

class cut in the major harvest plus the yield from intermediate cuts *is* t net annual harvested increment from the forest. This is exactly the sa thing as saying that the net harvested yield of a single stand over its lifeti is the sum of all cuts made. If the net increment of the forest were painsta ingly measured, age class by age class, the total would have to be appro: mately the same figure. Obviously, the volume of the oldest-age class p the volume taken in from thinnings is more easily determined than t actual net increment of the entire forest obtained by direct measurement.

In this situation, increment can be translated directly into volun on cutting areas. It would make no difference on the average whether area, an increment, or a volume approach was employed in so far as det mining the annual volume to cut is concerned, except that the area a proach is much more simple to apply. To the extent intermediate cuts a made, a greater proportion of the total growth of the forest can be captur in net growth and the total yields increased as a consequence. The relati weight and emphasis between the amount of total yield that is desired intermediate products and the amount desired in timber of rotation a can, of course, be varied to suit the purposes of management, but this do not alter the basic nature of the area-increment-volume relationship.

In a forest with a disproportionately large amount of young timb and a deficiency of larger timber of around rotation age, annual increme would be high, probably higher than if the forest were fully regulated. B if this increment figure is used as a basis for determining the cut, a large than-normal area of timber would have to be cut annually to get this volun creating a maldistribution of future-age classes. The increment is bei made, but there is not the proper amount of growing stock in timber harvestable size to cut. To meet this situation and to work effectively towa better age-class distribution, it is necessary to cut something less than curre increment and to introduce area control to bring about reasonable futu age-class regularity. The same thing would be true, only in reverse, if tl forest had too much old timber and not enough young timber. Increme would tend to be low, and the actual volume that should be cut in applyir management to the forest would be underestimated.

As has been pointed out, volume approaches alone do not provic a complete answer to the management problem. Even if a proper estima is obtained of the volume of timber to be cut, the use of volume approach provides no information about where and how to cut it. It is somethir like buying wild horses in Montana in the open range days. The numbe could be estimated fairly well; the problem was to catch them! Introductic of area control is analogous to catching the horses; it necessitates definir the volume to cut in terms of area.

Trees occupy space and by their nature accumulate within themselv their growth at all ages. The larger the tree, the more space it needs. Whe a tree is cut, space is released that becomes available for the growth c other trees, whether new trees or existing trees. Similarly, a stand occupies space, and its volume at any age represents total accumulated net growth up to that age plus whatever may have been harvested through intermediate cuts.

The actual increment of a stand is never cut. All that one can do is to cut entire trees that in their total volume *represent* the increment of the stand. The trees cut release space. There is consequently a fundamental relationship between harvested increment and space which is utilized in area control.

The relationship can be illustrated numerically for a model regulated forest of 30 acres. Assume pulpwood cuts as follows: major harvest, 2,800 cu ft; 25-year cut, 600 cu ft; 20-year cut, 500 cu ft; 15-year cut, 400 cu ft. Each cut comes annually from 1 acre. A cubic foot of harvest cut is consequently equivalent to 43,560/2,800 or 15.6 sq ft of surface area. Similarly a cubic foot for the 25-, 20-, and 15-year cuts is equivalent to 73, 87, and 109 sq ft of area, respectively. This is no more than saying that if you want to cut a certain volume and know the volume per unit of area, you can readily convert the cut to area units. In a regulated forest, area and volume give exactly the same results, and both are expressions of increment.

8

regulation of forests of uneven-aged stands

In presenting the methods of timber management, there is a tendency to develop them in terms of even-aged stands as has been done in this book. In large part this is because the techniques of regulation have been mainly developed for forest species growing in even-aged stands, largely coniferous, which are the most abundant and most valuable commercially. Partly, it is because management techniques can more easily be explained and illustrated in terms of even-aged stands. Whatever the reason, the structure and practical management of uneven-aged stands have received much less attention. This is particularly true as applied to hardwoods, which often occur in uneven-aged stands and are profoundly different from conifers.

The man on the street tends to think of a forest as an entity from which trees are selected from time to time as they become "ripe" for cutting. This popular idea that forest management consists largely of cutting selected trees individually from the forest and leaving the rest to grow and new trees to start in an idyllic state of perpetual forest continuity frequently leads to confusion on the part of foresters and laymen alike. Widespread and often indiscriminate advocacy of "selective cutting" as a forest panacea which still persists is an excellent illustration of this basic confusion. As Dana (1951) stated: "The homage that even foresters often pay to so vague a generality as 'selective cutting' is an indication of biological illiteracy."

An uneven-age stand is defined by the Society of American Foresters (1958) as one "in which there are considerable differences in age of trees and in which 3 or more age classes are represented." A wide variety of forests may be classed as uneven-aged. In management thinking and planning there is a tendency to go from strictly even- to strictly all-aged stands, whereas most forests with which a forester must deal are composed of stands that are neither, but somewhere in between.

The range in conditions encountered can conveniently be broken up into three general classes. First, there is the true all-aged forest in which all ages and sizes are represented thoroughly and intimately mixed over the area. This is the prototype model upon which the selection system is built. However, forests composed of stands that either are all-aged or can economically be managed as such are much fewer than commonly appreciated. Second, and a much more common situation, is the forest composed of usually rather small and often irregular groups of more or less even-aged stands. The forest is uneven-aged in general, but trees tend to occur in groups of varying size, each containing one, perhaps two or three, but not all age classes. The groups are often not clearly separated and are usually complexly intermixed, but the fact remains, and this is of large silvicultural significance, that a majority of the trees are not actually growing under all-aged conditions. In the third situation, there is a mosaic-like pattern of readily distinguishable and essentially even-aged stands. Over any extensive area, all age or size classes may well be represented, but the trees themselves mainly originate and grow in even-aged stands. The difference between such a forest and one composed of definitely even-aged stands is one of degree. The ponderosa pine type of the western United States under natural conditions occurs extensively in both forms. This species tends to reproduce and grow best under full-light conditions, but over any fairly large area ponderosa pine forests tend to present an uneven-aged aspect and are often regarded as being uneven-aged.

From a timber management standpoint, forests in which even-aged stands cannot be distinguished as operating units must, for practical reasons, be handled on an uneven-aged plan so far as the overall regulatory framework is concerned. But this does not mean that, tree by tree or group by group, stands are treated as being all-aged. Some mature groups or patches may be clear-cut and the space replanted, or a shelterwood condition may be established. As organized management is developed, extensive areas now regarded as uneven-aged will certainly be subdivided and individual stands within it treated according to their particular needs.

It is perfectly possible and entirely logical that a forest be organized from an overall operating standpoint on an uneven-aged framework but silviculturally treated, at least in substantial part, as an aggregation of small even-aged stands. A clear distinction should be made between actual silvicultural treatment on the ground and the general management framework which practical circumstances may dictate. Much confusion will be avoided by keeping this distinction in mind. The importance of uneven-aged management as an operating framework is consequently not limited to the handling of literally uneven-aged stands. It offers a flexible means of dealing with situations that cannot be handled on an even-aged basis. It is particularly useful as an interim approach in initiating management on areas supporting irregular stands. Case III of Chap. 7 could have been handled according to an uneven-aged framework, except that here the 10-year objective was to build up stocking and improve growing-stock conditions working towards development of even-aged stands, which affects cutting practice on the ground to some degree.

structure of an uneven-aged stand

As was brought out in Chap. 7, the management framework of an even-aged forest is built around the rotation and the stand, which is classified by age or size class. In uneven-aged management, the cutting cycle[1] replaces the rotation as an operating control. Stands are not classified by age or tree size. Instead, they are described by volume, structure, and composition. Because stands are mixed in age, there is no beginning or end of a stand in point of time. In cutting operations, major attention is centered on individual trees or groups of trees. The general "lifeline" form of an uneven-aged stand and of an aggregation of stands composing a regulated forest is given in Fig. 5.2, p. 102.

There are three major aspects of the structure of an uneven-aged stand: volume, diameter distribution of trees of different sizes and ages, and species composition. Each is considered below, together with some of their interrelationships.

VOLUME

As shown in Fig. 5.2, p. 102 the management of an uneven-aged stand is directly related to and controlled by the length of the cutting cycle. The cycle starts with a certain volume of reserve growing stock. It grows for the number of years in the cycle at the end of which time a harvest cut is made removing selected trees equal in volume to the total growth made in the stand for the years in the cutting cycle, plus or minus whatever adjustments are made in the volume of desired growing stock. The level of growing stock may be increased or decreased. The general aim is to keep the stand growing and to cut before the rate of growth diminishes significantly.

---

[1] Defined by the Society of American Foresters (1958) as:

"1. The planned interval between major felling operations in the same stand.

"2. The planned period within which all portions of a working circle are logged in orderly sequence."

The volume of growing stock can be defined at three points or levels: the volume just after a cyclic cut, the volume just before a cyclic cut, or an average volume midway during the period. The first determines the amount of the forest capital reserved for future growth and must be defined whether the others are or not. The second is useful as an inventory point in determining growth and as a cutting guide. The difference between the volume before and after a cut is obviously the amount cut. The third defines the average volume of growing stock upon which growth is made. This figure is used in describing the average growing-stock level of a forest unit as a whole. Each measure has its usefulness but must be clearly differentiated from the others. Confusion will result if growing stock volume figures are stated without also defining at which point in the cycle they are being considered.

Growth in a particular stand is never uniform from period to period because of changing growth conditions and treatment needs. The level of desired reserve growing stock will vary with knowledge of what is the best amount to leave. There may be need to increase or to reduce the volume of growing stock to bring about a better size or species distribution. Fig. 5.2 is drawn for a 5-year cycle to show an increase in both reserve growing stock and in cyclic cut. The timber removed combines in one cutting all the elements of intermediate and major harvest that are handled in separate operations in even-aged management. In theory at least, the stand as a whole is given treatment in a single cutting.

The volume removed at the time of a cyclic cut from a particular stand is consequently the periodic harvest from the unit, and its amount depends on the length of the cutting cycle, growth, and whatever changes are made in the desired level of reserve growing stock. A numerical illustration will be helpful in bringing out these relationships. Referring again to Fig. 5.2, assume 6,500 bd ft per acre as the reserve growing stock at the beginning of the first 5-year cycle (left edge of diagram). On this base, growing-stock levels and cuts are proportionately scaled from the heavy line of Area 1 on the diagram and shown in Table 8.1. As indicated, the reserve growing stock increased over a 10-year period from 6,500 to 7,290, or 790 bd ft. The cut also increased from 2,270 to 3,300, or 1,030 ft in 10 years. Total net increment for the 10 years is 2,370 + 3,300 + 790, or 6,460 bd ft. The stand is on an excellent site, and growth during the second cycle was very good, as the annual rate increased from 8.3 to 11.1 percent. This is probably a combined result of a better growing stock and good growth conditions occurring during that particular cycle. Since increment is expressed in board feet and a vigorous growing stock is assumed, the increment percentages are rather high but entirely possible. They result from the nature of board foot measurement and the effect of ingrowth. The rates would not be so high for cubic measure.

Note that the cyclic cut is the full harvest cut from the stand but

TABLE 8.1. GROWING STOCK AND GROWTH RELATIONSHIPS IN AN UNEVEN-AGED
STAND, 5-YEAR CUTTING CYCLE, ACRE BASIS

Point in time	Volume before cut, bd ft	Volume reserved after cut, bd ft	Volume cut, bd ft	Increment percent[a]	
				For cycle	Per year
Beginning of first cycle...	8,770	6,500	2,270	....	....
End of first cycle.........	9,190	6,820	2,370	41.4	8.3
End of second cycle......	10,590	7,290	3,300	55.3	11.1

[a] Calculated as follows: Reserve volume at beginning of first cycle is 6,500 and at end 9,190, or a total 5-year growth of 2,690 bd ft. The percentage growth for the cycle is consequently 2,690/6,500, or 41.4 percent. The simple annual rate is then 41.4/5, or 8.3 percent.

that a part of the total cyclic increment is retained to augment reserve growing stock.

The simple rate for a cycle can readily be converted to a compound rate. For example, taking the first full cycle as an illustration, 6,500 bd ft of reserve growing stock grew to 9,190 bd ft in 5 years. The growth ratio $(1 + i)^5$, is consequently 9,190/6,500, or 1.414. By reference to compound interest tables, this corresponds to a compound rate of 7.2 percent for the period as compared to an 8.3 simple rate. Either kind of rate can be used applied to periodic increment; it makes little practical difference. It is often useful for a given rate of growth to estimate what percentage of a stand can be cut and restored by growth. Table 8.2 shows this for different lengths of cutting cycles and growth rates, simple and compound.

It is apparent from this table that the length of the cutting cycle has a controlling influence on the amount of timber removed at any one time and consequently the volume of reserve growing stock. As the cycle lengthens, the proportion of the total growing stock before a cut that is removed increases, in direct proportion to growth if only that is taken. This obviously can go to extremes. For example (Table 8.2), if the cutting cycle is 15 years and the compound growth rate is 10 percent (*very* unlikely for so long a period), 76 percent of the volume would be taken in a cyclic cut, which would leave only a shelterwood stand. This points out the fact that, as the cutting cycle is lengthened, a point is reached where uneven-aged conditions cannot be silviculturally maintained and even-aged conditions develop.

Some numerical examples will illustrate length of cutting cycle and volume cut relationships. Considering only data for the first full cycle given in Table 8.1, it is apparent that if a 1-year cycle were adopted, a reserve growing stock of 6,500 ft is too low. The growth of 2,370 bd ft for the

TABLE 8.2. PERCENTAGE OF A STAND THAT MAY BE CUT
AND RESTORED BY GROWTH FOR VARIOUS
CUTTING CYCLES AND RATES OF GROWTH

Cutting cycle, years	Growth percent															
	3		4		5		6		7		8		9		10	
	S^a	C^b	S	C	S	C	S	C	S	C	S	C	S	C	S	C
1	3	3	4	4	5	5	6	6	7	7	7	7	8	8	9	9
2	6	6	7	8	9	9	11	11	12	13	14	14	15	16	17	17
3	8	8	11	11	13	14	15	16	17	18	19	21	21	23	23	25
4	11	11	14	15	17	18	19	21	22	24	24	26	26	29	29	32
5	13	14	17	18	20	22	23	25	26	29	29	32	31	35	33	38
6	15	16	19	21	23	25	26	30	30	33	32	37	35	40	37	44
7	17	19	22	24	26	29	30	33	33	38	36	42	39	45	41	49
8	19	21	24	27	29	32	32	37	36	42	39	46	42	50	44	53
9	21	23	26	30	31	36	35	41	39	46	42	50	45	54	47	58
10	23	26	29	32	33	39	37	44	41	49	44	54	47	58	50	61
11	25	28	31	35	35	42	40	47	44	52	47	57	50	61	52	65
12	26	30	32	38	37	44	42	50	46	56	49	60	52	64	55	68
13	28	32	34	40	39	47	44	53	48	59	51	63	54	67	57	71
14	30	34	36	42	41	49	46	56	49	61	53	66	56	70	58	74
15	31	36	37	44	43	52	47	58	51	64	55	68	57	73	60	76

[a] S = simple rate.
[b] C = compound rate.

5-year cycle was made on an average growing stock of $(6,500 + 9,190)/2$, or 7,845 bd ft. For a 1-year cycle, the reserve should probably be around 7,700 ft. This cannot be determined mathematically, because, as pointed out in Chap. 2, growth is not a simple function of stocking, although there naturally is a strong relationship. If the cutting cycle were 10 years, then the 6,500 bd ft of reserve growing stock would be too high. If the stand grows at about the same rate and the present average growing stock of 7,845 bd ft is used as a midpoint base, the reserve growing stock would be $7,845 - 2,370$, or 5,475 bd ft. Following the same reasoning, the volume just before a 10-year cut would be $7,845 + 2,370$, or 10,215 bd ft.

Whether or not these volumes would constitute desirable limits cannot be deduced in any simple fashion like this, but they are reasonable approximations. A complex biological as well as financial balance is involved. Too low a reserve growing stock would fail to utilize fully the productivity of the site. Too high a growing stock would entail diminution of the rate of value and volume growth through overstocking. One cannot juggle growing stock volumes or make assumptions without careful scrutiny and evaluation of the facts of the particular situation involved. It must also be kept in mind that growth for a cycle, or any period, is subject to climatic and other variables. Growth data must always be appraised and interpreted with due regard to the conditions and circumstances under which they were actually obtained. Extrapolations are always somewhat uncertain.

The point should be clear, however, that the level or volume of reserve growing stock is closely related to the length of the cutting cycle. It is for this reason that it is not correct to speak of a given level of reserve growing stock without also specifying the length of the cutting cycle employed with it.

DIAMETER DISTRIBUTION OF GROWING STOCK

Maintenance of a desirable diameter distribution of the trees that constitute a given volume of growing stock is another major need in uneven-aged management. In fact, the whole concept of uneven-aged management presupposes that there is a good progression of growing trees by age and size to support the continuing cyclic cuts. The same basic idea underlies even-aged management; trees of all ages and sizes in proper proportion must be maintained to provide the basis for a continuing flow of timber harvest. The question here is: What is a desirable distribution for uneven-aged stands?

Some general diameter to number of tree relationships are shown in Fig. 8.1. From an economic standpoint an equal number of trees in all diameter classes, as shown by the horizontal line *A*, would be ideal. The minimum

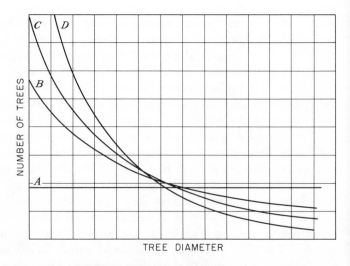

TREE DIAMETER

FIG. 8.1. DIAMETER DISTRIBUTION OF GROWING STOCK IN AN UNEVEN-AGED STAND.

possible number of trees for a succession of diameter classes would be provided and a maximum of the productive vigor of the site used to put increment on the larger trees of greater unit value. Biologically, however, this would not work out at all. All trees that start are not good trees nor do they survive. The general law of the forest is that many trees start but few live to attain desirable size and quality. Neither can the number of trees initially established be effectively controlled except by artificial means, which is not common under uneven-aged conditions. Nature often provides an overabundance of reproduction. Further, maintenance of a horizontal distribution means continuance of a rather full high-forest canopy which likely would make natural reproduction and development of new trees of desirable species difficult if not impossible.

For these reasons, a proportionately increasing number of trees are needed as diameter decreases to provide a base for mortality and selection of desirable stems. Curves *B, C,* and *D* show three such possibilities, and any number of similar curves could be drawn. Many studies in uneven-aged stands (Meyer 1943, 1952, and others) have shown that well-structured stands typically have an inversed J-shaped form and that a wide range of such curves naturally occurs. It should be noted that an average-acre stand table for almost any fairly large forest area supporting either even- or uneven-aged stands will exhibit a typically J-shaped diameter distribution by number of trees. Such a curve can be synthesized from even-aged yield data by combining the diameter distribution of all age classes proportionately. The fact of a J-shaped curve does not necessarily indicate uneven-aged management possibilities. It has been found that diameter distribution curves for uneven-aged stands tend to follow the pattern of a geometric series, which means that the curves are exponential and will plot as a straight line on a semilogarithmic graph. This was described many years ago by the French forester de Liocourt and is often referred to as the Law of de Liocourt (Meyer, 1952). Typical curves of this nature consequently can be mathematically described.

Basically, a good diameter distribution is determined by the biology of the forest and the purposes of management and not by mathematics, which are, however, useful in describing distributions found to be desirable. The key management question is how flat the curve can be. From an economic standpoint, the flatter the better. Answers must be based on the facts of species composition, site, and related biological factors, plus the objectives of management and the practical opportunity to achieve them.

A major problem in practice is how to get and maintain through cutting a satisfactory diameter distribution to constitute the level of growing stock volume desired. There are no simple answers; some of the problems and possible solutions are explored in Chap. 9. As the stand grows, surviving trees increase in diameter and tend to move the curve forward along its length toward the larger diameters. This indicates that some cutting should be made in most diameter classes to maintain the proper distribution. This is the general supposition that goes with selection management.

Such cutting is seldom practicable nor is it necessary. Naturally, it would be desirable to take only the largest trees following a diameter limit cutting; it would be nice if the curve would just slide ahead in its path so that it would only be necessary to cut at the large tree end. This is not possible either, although in practice cutting is mostly concentrated in the larger trees. It must be kept in mind that an uneven-aged framework of management is applied to a wide range of stand conditions, and actual cutting is usually in groups of the larger trees. Younger trees also often occur in groups of varying size and may be given little treatment. To a considerable degree, natural mortality will take care of excess numbers of small trees.

A factor that aids in maintaining a desired stem distribution without cutting in all diameter classes is that there tends to be a progressive increase in increment with diameter. Sometimes, this gradient is pronounced. In uneven-aged stands, it is usually the larger trees that have the best opportunity to grow. This moves the diameter distribution curve ahead faster in the larger than in the smaller classes and hence helps maintain the distribution.

In most situations, foresters must perforce work with diameter distributions that do not have a desirable form. Basically, it is the same problem as working with an irregular age-class distribution in even-aged management. A deficiency of number of trees in some diameter classes may not be particularly important if they are compensated by excess numbers in adjoining ones. Practical adjustments have to be made in working towards a desirable growing-stock goal.

SPECIES COMPOSITION

To complete the general analysis of uneven-aged management structure, the extremely important matter of species composition must be considered.

Aside from essentially interim situations in which an uneven-aged framework may be applied to a conglomerate of largely even-aged stands that are too small or irregular to be handled as even-aged units, a basic silvicultural requirement of uneven-aged management is that it be applied to species that will reproduce (naturally for the most part) and grow satisfactorily under uneven-aged conditions or in relatively small even-aged groups. A great many species, tropical and temperate, can meet this requirement, but not so many can also meet the economic test of commercial management under such a system. A number of species, mainly hardwoods, which almost always exhibit a considerable range in unit value related to tree size, are involved in most true even-aged situations. Quality is a major consideration. One of the most difficult problems of uneven-aged management is to maintain growing conditions that will favor reproduction and development of the more valuable species so that a desired species composition is maintained.

organization of a forest for sustained yield

Analysis of uneven-aged management has so far been in terms of its basic structure focusing attention primarily on the stand unit. Unless the cutting cycle were 1 year, a periodic rather than an annual cut would be obtained. To provide for a sustained annual yield from a forest as a whole, where the cutting cycle is longer than 1 year, the total area must be divided into area units equal in number to the years in the cutting cycle. Cutting is then scheduled so that one unit is cut over each year, removing the full cyclic cut from the stands in that unit.

This arrangement is diagrammatically shown by the broken lines in Fig. 5.2 for a 5-year cutting cycle. The forest is divided into 5 areas or parts of approximately equal total productivity and cut in sequence, one each year. It is not necessary that these areas be in one geographical unit; practical considerations of terrain and individual stand conditions will govern. In the field, cutting units are not likely to be arranged in any neat pattern such as can be shown in a textbook. Actual stand distribution of the ground may be and often is complex and confusing. This is particularly true in initiating management where no natural cutting sequence of stands exists. Adjustments of surface areas by site quality to get cutting areas of approximately equal productivity may be necessary.

What counts is that cutting areas be established and so scheduled that a cut of approximately equal size and quality of timber can be obtained annually. If they are unequally or irregularly stocked, then the forest is not regulated, and better conditions can be brought about only over time. This is the same basic test of regularity as applied in even-aged management. Exactly how cutting units should be arranged and cutting scheduled is something that can only be answered by the forester on the ground with full knowledge of the specific situation. Here is where the art of forestry in practice comes in and the textbook necessarily must stop.

determination of the length of the
cutting cycle

Since the length of the cutting cycle defines to so large a degree the framework of uneven-aged management, factors affecting or controlling its length should be carefully considered.

Silvicultural and related considerations mostly press toward comparatively short cycles of 10 years or less, which permit better biological control of the stand than do longer cycles. A cycle of 1 year, permitting some cutting every year fairly generally over the entire forest, is biologically ideal. Frequent cuttings are desirable to keep the stand growing steadily, to improve its species composition and size structure, and to cope effectively with or to avoid entomological and pathological difficulties. The shorter the cycle, the more nearly, in general, can the total productivity of the site be captured in net growth harvested; i.e., the less is lost through mortality. For some species, a long cutting cycle, which might entail cutting one-half the merchantable stand volume at the time of a cyclic cut (see Table 8.2), might result in excessive opening of the stand and induce mortality, sunscald, epicormic branching, and related difficulties. In other situations, this may not be a factor, and a relatively long cycle could be employed. As pointed out previously, the cycle can be lengthened to a point at which uneven-aged and even-aged management merge. Fairly heavy cutting may be needed in some forest types to bring in reproduction of desired species and to remove excess stocking of large trees, often of poor form or condition. This can often be accomplished by interim adoption of a short cycle, and a long cycle on a continuing basis is usually not necessary for this reason.

As a generality, the better the site, the more rapid the growth, and the more intensive the silviculture, the shorter the cutting cycle should be. The reverse is also true. For example, if the products to be grown are mainly sawtimber of large size, the management extensive, and the increment rate low, the cutting cycle can be fairly long—often up to 20 or even more years. Ponderosa pine in California east of the Sierras is a United States example of such a situation. Even here, however, frequent cuttings may be desirable for entomological reasons. A well-stocked pine-hardwood forest on a good site, producing both pulpwood and sawtimber, would be most productively managed on a rather short cycle of probably not more than 5 years. The same is true of the better hardwood sites.

There is a general relationship between the quality of products removed and the length of cycle. There is a tendency for the longer cycles to yield a smaller average size of product than shorter ones. This is because the average volume removed per acre is greater and includes a wider range of tree diameters and usually of tree value.

Because of this general trend and because the conversion value per unit of tree volume (product selling value less costs of logging and timber processing) usually increases substantially with diameter, there is financial incentive to apply a short cutting cycle to maximize the average unit value of the material harvested. In sawtimber production, for veneer especially, the positive effect of increasing tree size is normally pronounced; i.e., other things being equal, products produced from large trees are worth more per unit of volume than those cut from small trees, and the unit cost of producing them is less. There is consequently financial reason to produce trees of large average size for which a short cycle offers some advantage.

If there are large capital investments that must be currently made in forest development, there is pressure toward making a heavy cut per acre and consequently toward use of a long cutting cycle. This is particularly true when management is initiated in an area where extensive road and other improvements must be constructed that have to be paid off by the first cut. Such costs are often a controlling factor in setting the initial cutting cycle. If such capital costs can be financed on a long-term basis, they have little effect on the length of the cycle.

A prime requisite is that the cyclic cut remove enough timber per average unit of area cut over to make logging economically practicable. This necessity often puts a limit on the application of short cutting cycles, even when permanent forest development costs are not a factor. What constitutes an economic cut per acre naturally varies widely with circumstances. Timber marking and related technical costs are a factor too. It costs more per unit of volume to plan and mark a light cut per acre than a heavy cut. As permanent road systems are developed, lighter and more frequent cuts and consequently shorter cutting cycles become possible. Logging equipment and methods can be and increasingly are devised to make light cuts per acre efficiently and economically.

If transportation facilities are good so that almost any part of the forest can be readily reached and management is intensive, the entire forest may be looked over for cutting each year. In effect, this means a 1-year cycle on a flexible basis. A few trees or small areas are cut here and there. but no definite area schedule of cutting is established. With close control over the forest, such a system would be practicable and effective. There would, however, almost inevitably be a tendency to cut any particular area periodically according to some schedule. If so, a cutting cycle of more than 1 year is being applied, whether consciously or not.

Cutting cycles do not have to be as rigid in application as they may seem in theory. A 1-year cycle loosely applied amounts to about the same thing as a variable cycle so far as any particular part of the forest is concerned. A variable cycle, that is, one of no set length, would be extremely complex to work out in theory, but with skill and close knowledge of local conditions, it is not so difficult to apply. What may start out as a variable cycle is likely to settle down to some fairly definite average periodic cycle, even though it is not followed strictly. There must be adjustment to meet particular needs and circumstances such as market changes, blowdowns, insect attacks, and the like.

In practice, cutting cycles are usually set at an interval that will permit a practicable logging job and at the same time yield the highest volume and/or value of products possible. Basically, the problem is to obtain the integration of biological and economic considerations that will give the greatest possible net return for the particular situation and purposes of management. In general, the shorter cutting cycles yield more and higher-quality products, permit better control over the forest, and are financially more desirable than the longer cycles, say 15 or more years.

the cutting cycle and the rotation

The question may be asked: Where and how does the concept of a rotation fit into uneven-aged management and the cutting cycle? For a given site and intensity of management, the average size and character of the major forest products produced is a function of age. If products of a certain average size and quality are the desired aim, then time must be provided to produce them on the site in question. This general relation holds equally in even-aged and uneven-aged management. But this is where the similarity stops. In even-aged management a rotation also largely controls the management framework, since the cut is determined in relation to it.

This is not true in uneven-aged management. The cut is determined in relation to the cutting cycle, growing-stock level, and the rate of value and volume growth. The rotation does not directly enter in at all, except in the sense of an average age of major products harvested. Since age classes are more or less mixed up on the ground and cannot specifically be identified, the actual ages of trees are not known except in a general way. The forester judges more by size and condition of individual trees than by age as such. A tree is cut not because it has reached a certain age, or even because it has reached a certain size, but because it is adjudged to be less productive or needed than its fellows and should be cut. Some trees may be retained considerably past the average harvest age because individually they are good producers. Others may be cut at considerably less than this age because they are not good producers.

No relationship exists between the average age of major harvest and the length of the cutting cycle. Trees of large size, and consequently long rotation individually, can be produced as well under a short cycle as under a long one. Also, there is no reason, other than superficial arithmetical facility, why cutting cycles should be set at any round number like 5, 10, or 15 years or that they be any even multiple of the rotation, if a general harvest age cutting guide is applied. They can just as logically be set at 3, 7, 11, or 13 years. The length of the cutting cycle established should be based on careful analytical study of the particular situation and not be decided by any rule of thumb or arbitrary dictum. It is an important decision.

the cutting cycle in uneven-aged and even-aged management

Confusion sometimes arises from application of the term "cutting cycle" to both uneven- and even-aged management, without the distinction in meaning and implication being clear. Its essential role in the structure of uneven-aged management is clear, and the term is most meaningfully applied in this connection. What about its application to even-aged management? Strictly speaking, there is no such thing as a cutting cycle in even aged management, except the rotation, in the sense that there is any regular periodic schedule of major harvest operations in the same stand or that there is necessarily any planned period within which the entire forest or working circle involved is cut over. In even-aged management each stand has more or less its own timetable. That is, cultural measures and intermediate cuttings are applied at certain ages primarily because the stand has reached a certain condition and not because a certain period has elapsed since the last cutting. Harvest cuttings are scheduled in accordance with whatever regeneration system may be adopted. The same kind of cutting cannot be made at periodic intervals in an even-aged stand; it grows up and its character and treatment changes accordingly.

In making up a cutting budget for a forest handled on an even-aged basis, a definite schedule of cutting in different parts of the forest is naturally made. This is done in relation to logging conditions, markets, and silvicultural and other considerations. It may be considered desirable to visit most compartments regularly at periodic intervals and to do some cutting in them or at least to check their condition and treatment needs. It is also possible, and often desirable, to schedule operations so that cuttings of one sort or another are mostly confined to a particular part of the forest each year. But none of these circumstances constitute a cutting cycle in any fixed or regular sense. A change in the cutting schedule would not have the same management significance as a change in cutting cycle under uneven-aged management.

The meaning of a cutting cycle is consequently entirely different when applied to even-aged or to uneven-aged management. Much confusion can result from not being clear as to the differences. It is desirable that use of the term be restricted to uneven-aged management, where it has much more definite meaning. In even-aged management it is more helpful to talk about a schedule or periodicity of cutting rather than a cutting cycle.

changing the length of the cutting cycle

A problem closely related to that of determining the length of the cutting cycle is how to change it when it seems advisable to do so. Since the length of the cutting cycle affects so deeply the organization of the forest, a change will obviously necessitate a considerable rearrangement of the management framework. It will be helpful, briefly to show the nature of the problem and a general approach to its solution that is suitable for field application.

Assume that a 2,400-acre forest has been operated on a 12-year cutting cycle and that it is desirable to change to an 8-year cycle, a reduction of one-third. The principle involved is the same for whatever total area or length and change in cutting cycle might be assumed. With a 12-year cycle, the forest is completely cut over every 12 years, about 200 acres being cut each year. On an 8-year cycle, the forest would be covered in 8 years at the rate of about 300 acres a year. The problem is how to effect the change in schedule. The minimum period in which the shift can be made and the forest reregulated is 8 years, the length of the new cycle. It is assumed here that the change-over will be made in this period.

The general framework for changing the cycle to an 8-year period is indicated in Table 8.3. As shown in column 2, the average annual cutting area should be approximately 300 acres, instead of 200 acres as under a 12-year cycle. In the first year of the cutting cycle, 200 acres will have grown a full 12 years since the last time that particular area was cut, while the other 100 acres will have grown only 11 years, since under the old cycle it would not be cut for another year. Thereafter, the average number of years since the last cutting will gradually decrease, as shown in column

TABLE 8.3. CHANGING THE CUTTING CYCLE FROM 12 TO 8 YEARS
ON A 2,400-ACRE MANAGED FOREST

Year of cutting cycle	Approx. total area to cut, acres	Years of growth made since last cutover	Specific stands proposed for cutting; itemize individually	Actual stand acreage	Estimated volume when cut	Volume to be reserved	Volume to cut
(1)	(2)	(3)	(4)	(5)	(6)	(7)	(8)
1	200	12					
	100	11					
2	100	12					
	200	11					
3	200	11					
	100	10					
4	100	11					
	200	10					
5	200	10					
	100	9					
6	100	10					
	200	9					
7	200	9					
	100	8					
8	100	9					
	200	8					

3, until the eighth year of the new cycle, when about 100 acres will have grown for 9 years and 200 acres for 8 years.

The average volume to cut per acre cannot be so readily determined. It must be recognized that the cycle would not be changed without good reason. Presumably, the overall reason is that a greater total net return is expected from the shorter cycle. This would undoubtedly entail a change in both the level and the structure of the reserve growing stock. If the average level under the 12-year cycle is considered too high, then some liquidation of growing stock would be necessary in shortening the cycle. If too low, some reduction in the average cut would be in order to build up growing stock. In either case, the average volume removed per acre will tend to be the highest at the beginning of the new 8-year cycle and thereafter decrease. This is because the average number of years since cutting and consequently the total stand volume is the greatest the first year of the new cycle, and least during the last.

In working out the revised schedule of cutting on the ground, it would naturally be necessary to consider the individual stands and areas involved in detail. Columns 4 to 8 of Table 8.3 are shown by heading only to indicate the general procedure. In general, it follows the ancient and time-honored general approach of area and volume allotment. By using the acreage figures in column 2 and average reserved-stand volumes under an 8-year cycle as a guide and utilizing firsthand knowledge of the situation, a yearly cutting schedule could be worked out that would yield fairly regular cuts and at the same time effect the change to the shorter cycle. The job would not be as difficult in the field as it might seem on paper. The columns obviously cannot be completed except in reference to a particular forest with detailed information at hand. This would presumably be available if enough were known about the situation to recommend changing the cycle.

It must be recognized that a complex biological and financial balance is involved, susceptible to no nice theoretical solution. The present condition of the forest, the desired volume and distribution of the reserve growing stock, market conditions present and anticipated, changes in logging costs and methods, and the like, should all receive careful consideration. These things would have to be expressed in terms of revised timber-marking rules and cutting budget to put the new schedule into actual effect.

problems in applying uneven-aged management

This discussion of the nature and structure of uneven-aged management can helpfully be summarized by briefly stating the principal problems involved in its application.

Silvicultural Considerations. A heavy premium is placed on sound silvicultural knowledge and its field application. As brought out, the real operating unit in the forest is the individual tree or group of trees. There is no simple way to define which trees should be cut and which should be left to bring about and maintain good growing conditions and yield maximum financial return. A first essential in considering the application of an uneven-aged form of management is to be sure that the nature of the forest is such that it is amenable to the kind of treatment proposed. It is useless to go into elaborate management calculations and planning in setting up a pattern of cutting to which the forest simply will not respond. The essential need is that trees of the species desired can successfully be reproduced and grown in uneven-aged mixtures. This is not only a matter of tolerance. Under favorable conditions, many relatively intolerant species can be reproduced in small group cuttings and successfully handled under an uneven-aged general plan of management. On the other hand, there are conditions, sometimes involving the same species, which require that essentially even-aged conditions be maintained. A southern pine forest where there is strong competition from less desirable hardwoods necessitating general area treatment by prescribed burning or use of chemicals to keep them in check is an example. It is important that the forest manager get his silvicultural facts of life straight; expensive mistakes may result from failure to do so.

Length of Cutting Cycle. This is a key decision, since so much of the management framework is controlled by it.

Level and Structure of Reserve Growing Stock. This is another key decision. For a given cutting cycle, site quality, and purposes of management, there is an optimum level and structure of growing stock which will produce a maximum net return. Establishment and maintenance of a desirable growing stock at this level ensures that the productive capacity of the site is fully utilized. This is a complex and often difficult matter. In many situations, the principal management problem is to determine and to build up the growing stock to a desirable level. The forest cannot be fully productive until this is accomplished.

Economic Problems. Financial considerations, as always in management, are of pervading and controlling importance. They come to particular focus in determining the length of a cutting cycle and desirable growing stock and in guiding the individual selection of trees to cut and to leave in harvesting operations. These matters are considered more specifically in Part III.

Growth and Inventory Data. The character of uneven-aged management is such that its effective application places large emphasis on knowledge of growth and on good inventory control (Chap. 12). The allowable cut is necessarily based on periodic net growth, plus or minus whatever changes in the level of growing stock it may be desirable to make. This obviously cannot be determined unless growth, reserve growing stock, and volumes cut are known from repeated inventories.

Area Subdivision. The effectuation of a cutting cycle plan necessitates that actual cutting areas be defined on the ground. This entails much knowledge, skill, and judgment by the forester in charge. Literally, it is never done, as cutting plans are constantly being revised in the light of new conditions and increased knowledge concerning the forest.

Uneven-aged management can be summed up by saying that it is simple in general outline but complex to apply effectively.

9
application of uneven-aged management—case analyses

The application of uneven-aged management can best be presented in terms of specific situations, employing case data. As has been brought out in Chap. 8, an uneven-aged management framework can be and is applied to a wide range of forest conditions ranging from stands more or less all-aged to forests that are essentially a mosaic of small, largely even-aged stands. The following cases are selected to illustrate some of these situations and the application of an uneven-aged framework of management to meet them.

case I, all-aged selection management

An area of mixed hardwoods of good quality growing on a lowland site in central Michigan of the Lake States will serve as an example of a forest that can be managed on a selection basis although the stand is not truly all-aged. This particular area is mostly sugar maple and beech and has been selectively cut over a period of more than 20 years. The growing stock is of good condition, and the species distribution is desirable. A period of 9 years has elapsed since the last cutting, and the area is now considered ready for another cutting. The objective is to continue its management on a selection plan.

An average-acre stand and stock table for the stand just after the last cut and 9 years later is given in Table

TABLE 9.1. AVERAGE-ACRE STAND AND STOCK TABLE OF
UNEVEN-AGED HARDWOODS IN MICHIGAN

Dbh group, in.	Residual stand after last cut			Stand 9 years later		
	Number of trees	Basal area, sq ft	Volume, bd ft	Number of trees	Basal area, sq ft	Volume, bd ft
2	3	. . . . .	. . . . .	2		
3	12	0.6	. . . . .	9	0.4	
4	13	1.1	. . . . .	9	0.8	
5	24	3.3	. . . . .	18	2.4	
6	19	3.7	. . . . .	15	2.9	
7	36	9.6	. . . . .	26	6.9	
8	39	13.6	. . . . .	27	9.3	
9	33	14.6	. . . . .	28	12.4	
10	22	11.9	701	28	15.3	504
11	25	16.5	1,482	19	12.5	841
12	13	10.2	782	22	17.3	1,678
13	13	12.0	1,163	15	13.8	1,192
14	10	10.7	1,164	11	11.8	1,242
15	5	6.1	450	11	13.5	1,324
16	2	2.8	390	8	11.2	1,290
17	1	1.6	242	6	9.5	1,224
18	2	3.5	314	1	1.8	233
19	2	3.9	575	3	5.9	878
20	1	2.2	296	1	2.2	296
21	. . .	. . . . .	. . . . .	1	2.4	391
22	1	2.6	434	1	2.6	368
23	. . .	. . . . .	. . . . .	1	2.9	478
Total...	276	130.5	7,993	262	157.8	11,939

9.1. These data are shown graphically in Fig. 9.1, which is an important
aid in visualizing stand structure. As shown, the number of trees by diameter
class is irregular with a deficiency in number of trees about 7 in. or less in
diameter and some excess in 8- to 12-in. timber. Reasonable recruitment
of small trees must be provided or their deficiency will lead to difficulty in
the future. In this case, the deficiency is probably not yet serious for beech,
and especially maple, usually reproduce readily. The differences in number
of trees between the two measurements is due to natural mortality, further
indicating that reproduction conditions are not good perhaps because of
the somewhat heavy stocking of the area as a whole. It is assumed, at least
provisionally, that a 10-year cutting cycle is appropriate for this area and
that the volume 9 years after the last cutting is about right for the growing

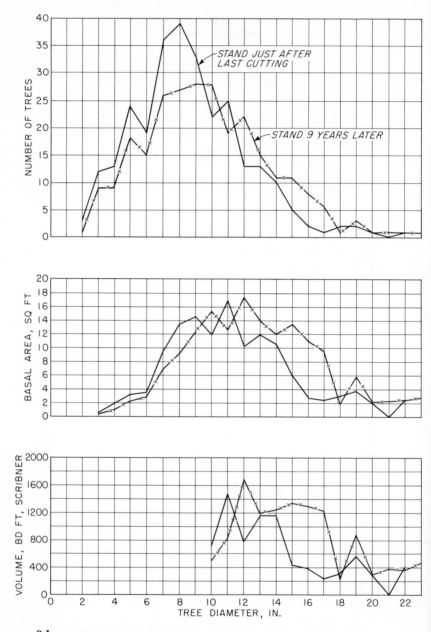

FIG. 9.1. NUMBER OF TREES, BASAL AREA, AND VOLUME OF AN UNEVEN-AGED
HARDWOOD STAND IN MICHIGAN, ACRE BASIS.

stock just before a cyclic cut. The problem is to determine a reasonable cyclic cut.

With a 10-year cutting cycle and no change in average level of growing stock, the cut will take 10 years of growth, which can be estimated on the basis of information available for a 9-year period. The increment for the last 9 years is 11,939 — 7,993, or 3,946 ft. On a percentage basis, this constitutes 3,946/7,993, or 49.4 percent for 9 years. The average annual rate is 49.4/9, or 5.5 percent. It is reasonable to assume that this 9-year rate could be sustained for 10 years. On this basis, the stand would increase 55 percent in volume in a 10-year period. The present volume of 11,939 ft is accordingly 155 percent of the volume to leave after a cyclic cut which consequently is 11,939 ÷ 1.55, or 7,703 bd ft. The average volume to cut per acre is consequently 11,939 — 7,703, or 4,236 ft, which is 35.5 percent of the present stand. This percentage cut can be readily identified by inter-polation in Table 8.2.

Another approach in estimating the increment and allowable cut is through the average growth made in board feet per acre per year. In this instance it is 3,946/9, or 438.4. If this increment is assumed for 10 years, the cyclic cut would be 4,384 bd ft per acre and the reserve volume conse-quently 7,555 ft instead of the 7,703 ft. While this is a possible assumption, and in this instance gives a reasonable answer, the basis for it is not sound, since it assumes that this volume of growth in board feet per acre per year can be maintained without regard to the volume of growing stock upon which it is based.

An illustration will make the point clear. Suppose that increment is to be estimated for a 20-year instead of a 10-year period on the basis of the 9 years of increment actually observed. If the annual increment of 438.4 bd ft were used, 20 years of increment would amount to 8,768 ft, and the reserve growing stock would be 11,939 — 8,768, or 3,171 ft. This 438.4 ft of annual increment would therefore have to be made on growing stock volume ranging from 3,171 to 11,939 ft, averaging 7,555 ft. The observed growth was made on an average growing stock volume of $\dfrac{7,993 + 11,939}{2}$, or 9,966 ft. Obviously, one could not expect the same physical volume of increment from these two widely different growing stock volumes. This illus-trates the fact that volume growth data apply directly only to the particular period and growing-stock and tree-diameter distribution upon which they are actually determined and cannot be extrapolated beyond without extreme care. The data available give direct information only for a 9-year growth period of a stand of certain age and size distribution with a reserve growing stock volume of about 8 M per acre. While reasonable estimates for other periods and for more or less growing stock may be made, it must be recog-nized that they are estimates only.

Similarly, it is not possible to deduce mathematically from the data at hand exactly which trees should be cut or which trees left to keep the stand producing at the best rate of value and volume growth. The simplest assumption would be to take the cut from the largest diameter classes only. If this is done, it can be estimated from Table 9.1 that a cut of 4,236 ft per acre would remove all trees 17 in. in diameter and larger plus about three trees per acre in the 16-in. class. It is well known, however, that strict diameter-limit cutting is not successful in selection management, even though most of the cut would naturally come from the larger trees. Some trees larger than any fixed diameter limit that might be set will undoubtedly be vigorous and fast growing and should be left. Some smaller trees should be cut to give better trees improved growing conditions and to remove individuals of less desirable form or growth potential. It is equally clear that most of the cut cannot be taken from the smaller trees. In this case, cutting heavily in the 12-, 13-, and 14-in. classes, even though these trees may be merchantable, will seriously deplete the reserve growing stock of trees that should constitute most of the next cyclic cut. For these reasons, only the man on the ground, with full knowledge of growth conditions and of market values of the various species involved, can specify the particular trees that should be cut to make up the average volume harvest indicated per acre and to leave the growing stock in the best possible condition. This is a situation that requires the art of forestry and the large amount of silvicultural and economic knowledge necessary to apply a selection system.

CHANGING THE LEVEL OF
RESERVED GROWING STOCK VOLUME

In the above illustration, it was assumed that the current volume less 10 years increment indicated a satisfactory level of reserve growing stock. Estimated volume is 7,703 bd ft. This volume is, however, fairly high for a selection forest in this general area, and a smaller volume of reserve growing stock might give a higher rate of increment and be more desirable, particularly if there is a regeneration problem. Assume, for example, that 7,000 bd ft is adjudged a better reserve growing stock volume and that the reduction should be made during one 10-year cutting cycle. The cyclic cut per acre is then 11,939 — 7,000, or 4,939 bd ft. Ten-year increment was estimated as 4,236 bd ft. Obviously, some growing stock, 4,939 — 4,236, or 703 ft, in this instance, is cut in addition to the growth.

The cut can also, if desired, be determined by use of the Austrian formula:

Annual cut = annual increment
$$+ \frac{\text{present growing stock} - \text{desired growing stock}}{\text{adjustment period}}$$

In this instance, the average annual increment for a 10-year period is estimated at 4,236/10, or 423.6 ft. The present average decadal growing stock is $\dfrac{7,703 + 11,939}{2}$, or 9,821 ft. The desired average growing stock will

be 703 ft less, or 9,118. Solving the formula,

$$\text{Annual cut} = 423.6 + \dfrac{9,821 - 9,118}{10}$$
$$= 423.6 + 70.3$$
$$= 493.9 \text{ bd ft per acre per year}$$

Since the cutting cycle is 10 years, the cyclic cut is 493.9×10, or 4,939 bd ft, as before. The formula, as such, offers no advantage; it is usually easier to work directly as was done here. It should be noted that the cut is based on increment made before the growing stock is reduced. After the reduction cut is made, increment figures would have to be revised to fit the new reserve growing-stock level of 7,000 ft. Increment might be as much or even more per acre than before because of acceleration of the growth rate due to increased growing space. This question can only be decided on the ground through a growth study.

CHANGING THE LENGTH OF THE CUTTING CYCLE

A 10-year cutting cycle is fairly long to maintain best volume and value growth in mixed hardwoods. Suppose it is decided that a 6-year cycle will permit better silvicultural control, yield a cut of economical volume to log, and give a higher total dollar net return. The data available are not sufficient to show what cutting cycle is the most desirable, nor exactly what cut could be taken. Nonetheless, a reasonable assumption can be made and a provisional answer obtained.

As was pointed out in Chap. 8, the length of the cutting cycle affects the volume of reserve growing stock; other things remaining the same, the longer the cycle, the smaller the reserve volume, and the shorter the cycle, the greater the reserve volume. Consequently, the reserve growing stock should be greater for a 6- than for a 10-year cycle. Exactly how much cannot be determined by mathematical means only, but a reasonable estimate can be made on the basis of available information. If the average growing stock of 9,821 bd ft for a 10-year cycle is about right as a midpoint, a comparable growing stock for a 6-year cycle can be estimated in relation to it. As calculated from Table 9.1, 438.4 bd ft per acre per year of increment was made during a 9-year period. While this level of increment cannot be safely extrapolated beyond the observed period, it is a conservative estimate for a shorter period, since there is a tendency for the rate of growth to decrease before the end of a 10-year growth period, particularly when the growing-stock level is fairly high as in this case. An estimate of 450 ft per acre per year for a 6-year cycle would appear entirely reasonable. If the estimate is made on this basis, the reserve growing stock should be

9,821 minus 3 years growth, or 8,471 bd ft, and the volume just before a cut would be $9{,}821 + (3 \times 450)$, or 11,171 ft. The 6-year cyclic cut would consequently be $11{,}939 - 8{,}471$, or 3,468 bd ft per acre. It should be noted that on the basis of these calculations somewhat more than estimated increment is to be cut ($11{,}939 - 11{,}171$, or 768 ft) since the stand will not again be built up to 11,939 ft before cutting.

The above assumptions are admittedly somewhat arbitrary, and the calculations are carried out to the last board foot in the interest of clear arithmetic only. Other approaches are also possible. But the illustration brings out the nature of the problem and some of the mechanics involved. Without actual field study, there is no way to tell just what change in growing-stock levels and rate of increment either in volume or value should accompany reduction of cutting cycle. The rate of net increment and average quality of the cut should be increased. This is due to better control over mortality and distribution of growing space resulting from more frequent cutting and to the fact that with a smaller cut per acre somewhat larger and presumably higher-value trees would be harvested. These advantages would have to be balanced against possible increased logging and other costs.

SUSTAINED YIELD FROM
SELECTION MANAGEMENT

Analysis of this case so far has been entirely in terms of defining the cyclic cut for a stand. To obtain a sustained annual yield from an area of this character, it would be necessary to divide it up into cutting units of approximately equal productivity, in number equal to the years in the cutting cycle. Ordinarily, there would be a range in individual stand volumes, even if the forest had not been under management. If the initial range were fairly even, from a little under 8 M to nearly 12 M per acre, cutting, logically, would be begun in the stands of highest volume. A sequence of cutting could be established, and average annual cuts could be obtained about as indicated in the foregoing calculations.

If there were little initial difference in volume and stand structure over the area, then equal annual cutting areas and volumes harvested could not both be achieved, and some compromise would have to be worked out in instituting a cyclic pattern of cutting. For example, if the average volume per acre were rather uniformly 10 M bd ft per acre over the entire area, and the stands were still growing well, equal areas cut annually would produce an increasing volume of annual cut. If the volume cut were held constant, then a decreasing area would be cut over annually, and obviously the forest would not be fully regulated for the next cutting cycle. This again brings out the point that there is no painless or easy way to regulate an unregulated forest. It is basically the same problem of adjustment en-

:ountered in even-aged management. A working balance and compromise must be struck between the need for a maximum and fairly uniform annual volume cut and future age- or size-class regularity, which basically is achieved by uniformity in area relations.

MANAGEMENT OF AN ALL-AGED STAND BY BASAL AREA CONTROL

Calculations of the allowable cut used in this analysis have all been based on some knowledge of increment, which in this instance is furnished by the measurement of 9 years of actual increment. In initiating management on an area, it may happen that no applicable growth information is available, nor is there any sound basis for specifying desirable reserve growing-stock levels. Some other basis is needed for establishing a reasonable cut pending acquisition of needed data. Matthews (1935) has suggested a provisional basis employing basal area as a guide. In brief, it is assumed that the structure of an all-aged forest is equivalent to a series of even-aged stands of all ages up to and including the major harvest age of the all-aged stand mixed in equal proportions. A yield table for an all-aged stand is synthesized from yield-table data for even-aged stands of generally similar character and is used as a basis in applying management to an unregulated forest of uneven-aged character. The key figure used is the percentage of total basal area in each age class or size group included in the all-aged forest yield table. The process of preparing a synthesized all-aged control table and of applying it to the data of this case follows.

A 10-year cutting cycle is assumed here for illustrative purposes, although the same general procedure could be applied to any cutting cycle.

1. *Select an Applicable Yield Table.* The average age of dominants in the sample stand is about 80 years, indicating 80 years as the approximate major harvest age of the timber. The average site index is 80. The most applicable hardwood yield table available in this instance is for upland oaks (Schnur, 1937). For site 80, basal areas for fully stocked even-aged stands including all trees 0.6 in. dbh and larger are given by the yield table as follows:

Stand age, years	Basal area per acre, sq ft	Stand age, years	Basal area per acre, sq ft
10	44	55	111
15	60	60	115
20	73	65	120
25	83	70	124
30	90	75	128
35	95	80	132
40	99	85	136
45	103	90	140
50	107		

2. *Prepare an All-aged Control Table.* Since it is assumed that a regulated all-aged stand would have all age or size groups present in equal proportions, an average acre for a stand managed on a 10-year cycle in this example would have eight 10-year age-size groups, each occupying approximately ⅛ of the area just before a cyclic cut is made. The average basal area in each group is consequently ⅛ of the total basal area per acre for that group as given in the yield table. The basal areas by age groups are determined as follows:

> For the 1–10-year age group:
> BA at age 1 = 0
> BA at age 5 = 0 (not measured; actually there would be some but
>   not much basal area)
> BA at age 10 = 44 sq ft
>   Total   = 44 sq ft
> Average BA for group = 44/3, or 14.7
> Average BA per acre for this group = 14.7/8, or 1.8 sq ft

> For the 11–20-year age group:
> BA at age 10 = 44 sq ft
> BA at age 15 = 60 sq ft
> BA at age 20 = 73 sq ft
>   Total   = 177 sq ft
> Average BA for group = 177/3, or 59
> Average BA per acre for this group = 59/8, or 7.4 sq ft

These average basal areas per acre for each group, as determined above, are entered in column 2, Table 9.2. The percentage each makes of the total basal area for an 80-year age range is shown in column 3. These percentages constitute the control table. It has been found that for a given harvest age rotation those percentages are surprisingly constant and stable for widely dissimilar forest types.

3. *Distribute the Basal Area of the Actual Stand According to the Basal Area Percentages in the Control Table.* This is done in column 4 by multiplying the percentages in column 3 by the total basal area of the actual stand at present as obtained from Table 9.1. The result shows the amount of this total basal area that should be in each age group.

4. *Allocate Tree Diameter Classes to Age Groups.* This is done in column 5 on the basis of the basal areas by diameter classes shown in Table 9.1. It is convenient to start with the oldest-age group first and work toward the younger-age classes. In this instance, trees in the 17-in. class and larger total 27.3 sq ft of basal area, whereas the control table indicates 28.4 sq ft (column 4 of Table 9.2) should be in this group. The difference is 28.4 − 27.3, or 1.1 sq ft, which is approximately the basal area of a 16-in. tree. One 16-in. tree is accordingly included in this group, with the other

TABLE 9.2. APPLICATION OF BASAL AREA CONTROL PROCEDURE
TO AN ACTUAL STAND

Age group	Control table			Actual forest data		
	Basal area, sq ft	Percentage distribution of basal area	Distribution of basal area by assumed age groups, sq ft	Diameters of trees included by age groups[a]	Number of trees	Volume, bd ft
(1)	(2)	(3)	(4)	(5)	(6)	(7)
1–10	1.8	2.0	3.2	0–5	38	
11–20	7.4	8.3	13.1	6–8[(9)]	50	
21–30	10.2	11.5	18.1	8[(18)]– 9[(27)]	45	
31–40	11.8	13.3	21.0	9[(1)] –11[(8)]	37	861
41–50	12.9	14.5	22.9	11[(11)]–12[(20)]	31	2,008
51–60	13.9	15.6	24.6	12[(2)] –14[(8)]	25	2,249
61–70	15.0	16.8	26.5	14[(3)] –16[(7)]	21	2,792
71–80	16.0	18.0	28.4	16[(1)] –23	15	4,029
Total....	89.0	100.0	157.8	....	262	11,939

[a] Where diameter classes are split between two age groups, the numbers in parentheses indicate the number of trees of the diameter indicated in each group.

trees of this diameter class included in the 61–70 group. This process
continued down through the different age groups, as shown in column
It is essentially a matter of classifying the 262 trees into assumed age
roups on the basis of their basal areas. When this is done, the number
trees and volume for each age group can be readily determined, as shown
columns 6 and 7.

It should be noted that those age groups are in reality size groups
nd do not represent actual ages. The same procedure could be applied
a stand table for an even-aged stand which also exhibits considerable
nge in tree diameters. What the control table does for the harvest age
eriod employed is allocate tree diameters to age groups on the basis of
desirable basal area distribution. If the stand were truly all-aged and
age is closely correlated with diameter—as it is in general—the actual
es of trees would match up fairly well with their indicated age group,
least closely enough for all practical purposes. As has been pointed out,
ctual age is not so important as size distribution and condition in uneven-
ed management. What is important is that trees of various diameters
re capable of growing as trees of their size and normal age should.

5. *Determine the Allowable Cut.* For a forest operated on a 10-year
ycle, the cyclic cut should remove the volume in the 71–80 age group,
10 years of increment. Ten years later this group would be replaced
y the 61–70 group, which would then be ready to cut. The indicated cyclic

cut per acre, as shown in column 7, is 4,029 bd ft per acre, the estimated volume of the 71–80 age group. This is close to the cut of 4,236 ft determined on the basis of actual increment data. In neither case would the forester on the ground necessarily mark just the largest trees to make up the indicated volume cut; silvicultural and economic considerations should also be taken into account.

Discussion. This method of arriving at an allowable cut is indubitably arbitrary, though it has uses. An all-aged stand is not simply a conglomeration of even-aged stands mixed in equal proportions, although, lacking better data, it is a reasonable working assumption. In practice, the method is likely to be tied to the use of yield tables for even-aged stands with all the limitations of application to managed stands inherent to them. Further, even-aged yield tables are naturally prepared for forest types or species that tend to occur in even-aged stands. Few such yield tables are prepared for species associations that can be handled on either an even-aged or an uneven-aged basis. Consequently, their validity in indicating desirable basal area distribution in a managed uneven-aged stand is open to question.

The method requires an estimate of the harvest age rotation in effect. In this case it seems to be about 80 years, since the dominant trees are about that age. If the rotation is estimated at 60 years, a calculation similar to that made to determine the percentage of basal area by age groups in column 3 of Table 10.2 indicates that 23.9 percent of the basal area should be in the oldest 10-year age group ready for cutting instead of 18.0 percent for an 80-year rotation. If the estimated rotation is 70 years, the corresponding percentage is 20.5 percent; if 90 years, it is 16 percent. As these figures show, the shorter the assumed rotation, the greater the indicated allowable cut, and vice versa. As brought out in Chap. 8, the rotation applied is not a structural part of uneven-aged management, nor can it be precisely determined. An attempt to define it specifically, as was done here, introduces uncertainty into the basal area control procedure, although 10 years more or less may make little practical difference. While, in natural stands, growth rates slow down as tree size increases, this is not necessarily true in managed stands. Through maintenance of good growing-space relations, it is possible under management to keep the larger trees growing rapidly and thus obtain a high proportion of the total increment in quality products. Within reasonable limits, there is no direct relationship between age as such and productivity. This illustrates the point made in Chap. 8 that in uneven-aged management a tree is cut because it falls behind in productivity and not because it reaches a certain age or size.

The only reason the concept of a rotation enters into uneven-aged management is that it takes a certain time to grow the size and quality of products desired from the major harvest. This time must be provided. If the average tree in the stand is too young to produce what is wanted,

en more of the larger trees must be left. This does not necessarily mean
ich, if any, reduction in the volume of the cyclic cut. If the stand is
ll stocked, a cut approximately equal to increment may be maintained,
t the cut must be so distributed that the age-size range is built up to
oduce the kind of products desired. This cannot be worked out according
any mathematical rule.

The usefulness of the basal control method is mostly in initiating man-
ement when directly applicable growth and growing-stock data are lack-
g. Used with discretion and understanding, it should produce reasonably
od results. The method does not, however, place emphasis on definition
desirable growing stock, nor does it provide any direct mechanics for
anging the cutting cycle or adjusting the level of growing stock. The
el of reserve growing stock can be adjusted only through the indirect
d rather uncertain expedient of changing the rotation. The method tends
continue the status quo. Trees that are overmature, susceptible to dam-
e, or in poor condition can be handled as a special group, but this is
t a part of the method itself.

se II, managing old-growth northern hardwood in the lake states

ie preceding case has dealt with the management of an all-aged selection
rest well stocked and in good condition to begin with. Emphasis was on
e mechanics of uneven-aged management. This case deals with the prob-
n of initiating managment in unmanaged hardwoods and emphasizes the
ecification and development of desirable growing stock, considering both
lume and structure. The material presented is based on much research
d experience in managing northern hardwoods in the Lake States. (Eyre
d Zillgitt, 1953; Arborgast, 1957). Converting irregular natural stands
managed stands of desirable structure is a job frequently confronting
e forest manager and one of large importance. The question to be ex-
ored here is: How should old-growth northern hardwoods be cut to create
inds adapted to continuous yield under uneven-aged management?

Natural stands in this forest type are overmature and irregularly com-
osed of trees of several age classes, including some trees 300 or more years
age. Stands are frequently heavily defective, ranging from 20 to 30 per-
nt of the gross volume and often higher. Growth of individual trees is
irly slow, and net growth of the stand is negligible.

An average-acre stand table for a large area is given in Table 9.3,
iich characterizes the general situation. Sugar maple is the dominant spe-
es and valuable. It reproduces readily, often excessively, under a forest
nopy. Yellow birch is the most valuable species but variable in its occur-
nce. It reproduces best under fairly open conditions but grows well under

TABLE 9.3. NUMBER OF TREES PER ACRE, OLD GROWTH NORTHERN
HARDWOODS, WEST HALF, OF UPPER PENINSULA,
MICHIGAN, (EYRE AND ZILLGITT, 1953)

Dbh class, in.	Merchantable trees by species						Cull trees	A) tre•
	Sugar maple	Hem- lock	Yellow birch	Misc. hard- wood	Misc. coni- fers	Total mer- chant- able		
2	68.39	12.93	7.76	22.31	28.63	140.02	1.37	141.
4	21.67	10.25	4.79	10.38	13.10	60.19	1.65	61.
6	8.92	7.20	3.08	4.90	7.10	31.20	1.79	32.
8	6.64	5.74	2.55	3.26	5.02	23.21	1.58	24.
10	5.55	4.63	2.27	2.10	3.03	17.58	1.45	19.
12	5.43	4.05	2.22	1.45	1.54	14.69	1.29	15.
14	4.82	3.12	1.90	1.20	.88	11.92	1.02	12.
16	4.38	2.69	1.92	1.05	.53	10.57	.85	11.
18	3.47	2.18	1.48	.66	.30	8.09	.84	8.
20	3.25	1.95	1.26	.48	.18	7.12	.60	7.
22	1.50	1.54	.87	.33	.06	4.30	.49	4.
24	.80	1.19	.66	.19	.04	2.88	.40	3.
26	.42	.80	.45	.11	.02	1.80	.22	2.
28	.19	.44	.27	.09	.01	1.00	.13	1.
30	.06	.36	.16	.05	.01	.64	.13	.
32 and larger	.03	.30	.14	.06	.02	.55	.13	.
Total number...	135.52	59.37	31.78	48.62	60.47	335.76	13.94	349.
Total basal area, sq ft....	48.52	41.74	23.94	13.63	10.97	138.80	13.34	152.

a range of overwood densities. The eastern hemlock is less valuable b
very abundant in some areas as a subtype and important in total. It
however, tending to go out of the forest and is not particularly encourage•
maple and birch are the key money species. There is also a variable a
mixture of other hardwood and coniferous species in the broad northe:
hardwoods type and several, such as basswood, red oak, American el
white spruce, and red maple, are good commercial species. Natural star
densities are high (Table 9.3) averaging around 150 sq ft of basal ar•
per acre, which is too high for desirable growth conditions.

Five different kinds of partial cuttings were applied in a homogeno
portion of the general area represented by Table 9.3, and detailed recor•
were kept for 20 years. The composition of this portion is about 80 perce•
sugar maple and 15 percent yellow birch. The cuttings were designed
test various alternatives considered significant at the time the studies we
initiated. Where the board foot growth occurred over a 20-year period
the stands studied is shown in Fig. 9.2. The particular names attached •

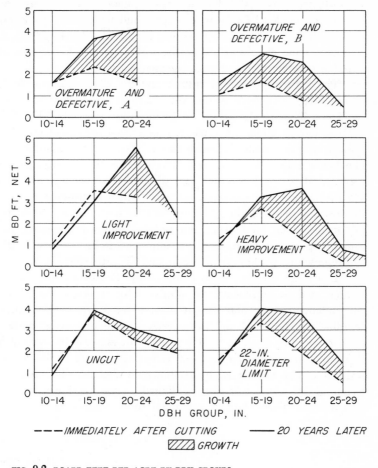

FIG. 9.2. BOARD FEET PER ACRE BY DBH GROUPS IMMEDIATELY AFTER CUTTING AND 20 YEARS LATER.

the cuttings are not significant. What the study essentially shows is the 20-year development of several different stand structures.

In appraising the results it must be kept in mind that, for a stand to be continuously productive on an uneven-aged basis, a distribution by diameter-age groups must be developed, so that trees of desirable size, form, and quality regularly become available for cutting for the cycle adopted. It is not a simple matter of cutting enough of the largest trees to total the allowable cut. All trees are not good trees; rot does not wait until a tree reaches best cutting size but may start in small trees 8 to 10 in. dbh and increase with age. To keep a selection forest growing in healthy condition, it is usually necessary at the time of a cyclic cut to remove some trees over a wide range of diameters.

What is a desirable volume, quality, and distribution of growing stock for northern hardwoods? This question cannot be simply answered, for it involves a complex balance of economic and biological considerations that must be defined in terms of particular situations. The data from these cuttings give some clues and are of the sort upon which decisions regarding desirable growing stock under management are based.

The light improvement cutting and the 22-in. diameter limit cutting do not give the answer. While they have resulted in good increment in the larger diameter classes, the 20–24-in. group especially (Fig. 9.2), heavy stocking left in larger trees has not permitted development of a suitable number of the middle diameter classes needed for continued production. The heavy improvement cutting which left a lighter growing stock gave a somewhat better distribution and stimulated a good rate of growth. The two overmature and defective cuttings "which distributed the cut among all sizes and reduced the growing stock to about 60 sq. ft. of basal area (10 inches d.b.h. and over) not only maintained the fairly good stand structure provided by nature, but improved it by bringing in classes not well represented in old growth" (Eyre and Zillgitt, 1953).

Using the size-class distribution of the two overmature and defective cuttings as a guide, plus a good admixture of experience in the forest type and judgment, Eyre and Zillgitt drew a basal area curve representing a desirable stocking level and size classes of reserve growing stock left after a cyclic cut. The stocking level is gauged for about a 10-year cutting cycle. This curve, in comparison to uncut old-growth stands in the general neighborhood of the cutting study, is shown in Fig. 9.3. The basal area and accompanying number of trees by diameter classes is shown in columns 1–3 of Table 9.4 These data in simplified form suitable as a marking guide

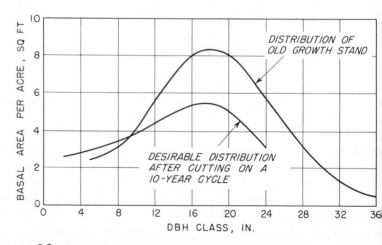

FIG. 9.3. BASAL AREA DISTRIBUTION IN NATURAL OLD-GROWTH NORTHERN HARDWOODS COMPARED WITH DESIRABLE DISTRIBUTION IN A MANAGED STAND.

TABLE 9.4. DESIRABLE RESERVE GROWING STOCK FOR FOUR MAJOR HARDWOOD AREAS IN THE EASTERN UNITED STATES UNDER UNEVEN-AGED MANAGEMENT

Tree diam class at breast height, in.	Northern hdw., Lake States[a]		Northern hdw. in Northeast[b]		Mountain hdw., in northern Applachians[c]		Southern hardwoods[d]		
	No. of trees	Basal area, sq ft	No. of trees	Basal area, sq ft	No. of trees[e]	Basal area sq ft[f]	No. of trees	Basal area sq ft	Volume[g]
(1)	(2)	(3)	(4)	(5)	(6)	(7)	(8)	(9)	
2	118	2.6	...	...	....	....	26.0	0.6	
3	53	2.6							
4	31	2.7	...	...	....	....	17.2	1.5	
5	21	2.9							
6	15	2.9	25	5	21.0	4.2	10.5	2.1	
7	12	3.2							
8	9	3.1	20	7	17.0	6.0	8.2	2.9	
9	8	3.5							
10	7	3.8	15	8	13.0	7.1	7.0	3.8	
11	6	4.0							
12	5	3.9	12	9	9.7	7.6	6.5	5.1	
13	5	4.6							
14	5	5.3	10	10	7.3	7.8	6.0	6.4	312
15	4	4.9							
16	4	5.6	8	9	5.7	7.9	5.3	7.4	503
17	3	4.7							
18	3	5.3	6	9	4.3	7.6	4.3	7.6	632
19	3	5.9							
20	2	4.4	4	8	3.4	8.4	3.2	7.0	688
21	2	4.8							
22	2	5.3	3	8	2.7	7.1	2.3	6.1	678
23	1	2.9							
24	1	3.1	2	7	2.0	6.3	1.6	5.0	524
26	...	...	...	...	1.6	5.9	1.10	4.0	561
28	...	...	...	...	1.3	5.6	.80	3.4	524
30	...	...	...	...	0.9	4.4	.45	2.2	369
32	...	...	...	...	0.7	3.9	.27	1.5	272
34	...	...	...	...	....	....	.11	.7	139
36	...	...	...	...	....	....	.04	.3	57
38	...	...	...	...	....	....	.02	.2	28
Total..	320	92	105	80	90.6	89.8	100.89	67.8	5,287

[a] Eyre and Zillgitt, 1953. Average sites, 10-year cutting cycle.
[b] Gilbert and Jensen, 1958. Average to better sites. Growing stock for high-valued products, 10-year cutting cycle.
[c] Trimble, 1961. Good sites. 5-year cutting cycle for "intensive selection."
[d] Putnam, Furnival, and McKnight, 1960. Average to better sites, quality production, 10-year cutting cycle.
[e] Read from logarithmic graph.
[f] Calculated from class midpoint.
[g] Volume of trees 2–12 in. is 264 cu ft. Doyle rule for bd ft.

TABLE 9.5. DESIRABLE RESERVE STAND IN NORTHERN
HARDWOODS, LAKE STATES

Crown class	Tree size class	Normal dbh range, in.	Recommended stocking per acre, basal area in sq ft.
Dominant........	Sawtimber	10+	65–75
Intermediate.....	Poles	5–9	10–20
Suppressed.......	Saplings	2–4	5–10
Total.........			80–105

for field use are given in Table 9.5 (Arborgast, 1957). As shown, there is a range in recommended stocking which depends on species composition, conditions of the stand, and site.

It is believed that stands distributed approximately as shown will remain thrifty and permit maintenance of a stand structure that will yield good growth and merchantable yields. This table represents a useful guide, based on solid experience, and its development illustrates the process of successive approximation characteristic of defining desirable growing stock under practical management. As more data and experience accumulate, the specification of growing stock can be improved and measures of quality added.

A recommended amount and distribution of growing stock for generally similar hardwood stands in the northeastern United States, as reported in two other studies, are given in columns 4–7 of Table 9.4. The growing stock recommendations are similar to those in the Lake States. Numbers of trees and basal area in small trees (less than about 6 in. dbh) are naturally variable, are not overly significant, and were not given in these two studies. What counts is to have enough of them in trees of desirable species and quality to provide needed continuing recruitment of new trees into the stand.

A SOUTHERN HARDWOOD COMPARISON

Desirable growing stock for northern hardwood types may be compared to a similar analysis made in southern hardwoods as reported by Putnam, Furnival, and McKnight (1960) shown in columns 8 and 9 of Table 9.4.

The stocking level is gauged for a good site and applies just after a cyclic cut for a stand operated on about a 10-year cutting cycle. The rate of growth obtainable in these stands is much greater than that of northern hardwoods. It is estimated that a thrifty stand stocked as shown can yield about 500 bd ft per acre per year, Doyle rule, of large-size quality sawtimber, plus some cordwood from small trees that should be removed for cultural reasons and from sawtimber top-wood. Ten years is probably too long a cycle for these growth conditions. With 500 bd ft per year increment, the stand volume at the end of a 10-year cycle would be over 10,000 bd ft per acre, and the cyclic cut would remove about half of it, which is a heavy cut in such a stand. A shorter cycle would be better. Because of the rapid rates of growth possible and the high-value premium for large timber of high quality, some trees up to around 40 in. dbh are to be grown. This accounts for the relatively small total number of trees and low basal area per acre. Growth is largely concentrated on tall, fast-growing stems of high quality, and no more than are necessary are kept on the ground.

The problem of developing a thrifty stand of desirable volume, form, species, and size-class distribution is both financial and silvicultural. Removal of the kinds of trees that should be cut to bring about desirable stand conditions and still make the cutting operation pay out satisfactorily is frequently a most stubborn and difficult problem in uneven-aged management. Also, the existing stand structure from area to area may not include desirable trees irrespective of financial limitations. The forest manager usually has to strike a working compromise and can only go part way in doing what should be done to bring about the best growth conditions. A period of adjustment, including two or more cutting cycles probably, is usually necessary in working with hitherto unmanaged stands. The rate of progress will depend on many factors, such as markets, species distribution, site, financial pressure for immediate returns, and purposes of management. Even though seldom entirely attainable in practice, there is a basic need for stocking goals such as those provisionally developed here. Having a concept of what constitutes a desirable stand gives the forest manager a large advantage in judging what can and should be done in a particular situation.

case III, building up a southern pine-hardwood forest

In Case II the problem was to apply management to old-growth northern hardwoods with excess as well as irregular and defective growing stock. An estimate of desirable growing-stock level and distribution was provisionally drawn on the basis of research and experience. In Case III, the situation is reversed, and the problem is to build up a desirable growing stock on an area initially severely understocked by cutting and fire. The data are based on a representative area in southern Arkansas in the shortleaf–loblolly pine hardwood type. The site quality is good, approximately site index 85. The area was given careful management for 10 years (Reynolds, 1950).

Many of the pines were either suppressed or defective, some of the area had no trees of any kind, and much of the acreage had been taken over by hardwoods. The stand was deficient in trees of sawtimber size, and the stand structure for any given acre was poor. The stand contained a reasonably good number of sapling and pole-size pine, but the possibility of selection management was far from ideal.

During the 10-year period, several light selection cuttings were commercially made on a combined harvest and improvement basis, removing

TABLE **9.6.** ACTUAL AND DESIRABLE STOCKING OF A SHORTLEAF–LOBLOLLY PINE AND HARDWOOD STAND (ACRE BASIS, VOLUME IN INTERNATIONAL ¼-IN. RULE)

Dbh class, in.	Stand when management began			Stand after 10 years			Desirable Stocking[a]		
	No. of trees	Basal area, sq ft	Volume, bd ft	No. of trees	Basal area, sq ft	Volume, bd ft	No. of trees	Basal area, sq ft	Volume, bd ft[b]
(1)	(2)	(3)	(4)	(5)	(6)	(7)	(8)	(9)	(10)
2	. . . . .	. . . . .	. . . . .	. . . . .	. . . . .	. . . . .	20	0.44	
3	. . . . .	. . . . .	. . . . .	. . . . .	. . . . .	. . . . .	18	0.88	
4	11.31	0.98	. . . . .	13.80	1.20	. . . . .	16	1.39	(12.8)
5	9.42	1.28	. . . . .	10.93	1.49	. . . . .	14	1.90	(23.8)
6	8.34	1.63	. . . . .	5.97	1.17	. . . . .	12	2.35	(37.2)
7	7.02	1.87	. . . . .	6.13	1.64	. . . . .	11	2.94	(57.2)
8	4.38	1.53	. . . . .	4.94	1.72	. . . . .	9	3.14	(70.2)
9	3.99	1.76	. . . . .	4.10	1.81	. . . . .	8	3.54	(85.6)
10	5.27	2.87	. . . . .	4.80	2.62	. . . . .	7	3.81	371
11	3.94	2.60	. . . . .	3.57	2.36	. . . . .	7	4.62	553
12	3.59	2.82	384	3.92	3.08	419	6	4.71	642
13	3.15	2.90	431	3.50	3.23	479	5	4.61	685
14	2.80	2.99	470	3.36	3.59	564	4	4.28	672
15	2.70	3.31	546	3.19	3.91	645	4	4.91	808
16	1.84	2.57	440	2.35	3.28	563	3	4.19	717
17	2.03	3.20	568	2.24	3.53	627	3	4.73	840
18	1.12	1.98	364	1.98	3.50	644	2	3.53	650
19	0.58	1.14	219	1.26	2.48	472	2	3.94	750
20	0.33	0.72	141	1.03	2.25	442	2	4.36	862
21	0.16	0.38	80	0.63	1.52	310	1	2.41	492
22	0.05	0.13	26	0.49	1.29	275	1	2.64	561
23	. . . . .	. . . . .	. . . . .	0.12	0.35	74	1	2.88	631
24	0.02	0.06	16	0.07	0.22	49	1	3.14	706
25	. . . . .	. . . . .	. . . . .	0.05	0.17	37			
Total . .	72.04	36.72	3,685	78.43	46.41	5,600	157	75.35	9,940

[a] Stand just before a 5-year cyclic cut.
[b] Volumes 4–9 in. given in cubic feet.

21 trees and 1,676 bd ft per acre. During the same period, total growing stock increased from 3,685 to 5,600 ft per acre, a difference of 1,915 ft (Table 9.6). This, plus the volume removed, totals 3,591 ft per acre or 359 ft per acre per year net growth. But the volume figures alone tell only part of the story. In addition to the better distribution by diameter classes, as evident in the table, timber quality and growing conditions were greatly improved during the 10-year period. The pines are of much better form and quality, and low-grade hardwoods present in the area have been largely eliminated by commercial cutting and by supplemental disposal treatment.

What should be the growing stock in this forest type for maximum production on an uneven-aged basis? No single answer can be given; much depends on the specific situation and purposes of management. On good sites, loblolly-shortleaf stands in this area can be managed on either an even- or an uneven-aged basis. Eighteen years of experience in southern Arkansas (Reynolds, 1959) indicates that well-stocked uneven-aged stands in this area should be stocked as shown in columns 8–10 of Table 9.6. It should be noted, however, that this growing stock is given just before a cyclic cut (assumed to be 5 years) rather than just after a cut, as is more usual. Assuming 500 bd ft per acre increment, which is a conservative growth rate for well-stocked stands on these sites, the reserve growing stock should be about 7,400 bd ft. If composed of trees of good form and vigor, this stocking promotes maximum quality growth in board feet.

As shown in Table 9.6, the stand has made good improvement in stocking in 10 years but has further to go, being only about 56 percent stocked in terms of being ready for a full cyclic cut on a desirable stocking standard. However, existing growing stock is well distributed over all diameter classes, and as it increases, so will the increment, which should be from 500 to 600 bd ft per acre per year in well-stocked stands in this area. In this example, a concept and specification of desirable growing stock is something worked toward from severely understocked stands, and it is entirely possible that ideas as to precisely what constitutes proper stand volume and structure and how best to attain it will change as management experience accumulates. The relative merits of an even-aged as compared to an uneven-aged form of management in this type are also a matter for further analysis and study.

case IV, management of mixed stands

The cases considered so far have been such that major management issues and problems could be isolated with considerable specificity. In practice, however, it is frequently necessary to deal with mixed and irregular stands not neatly fitting any category. Even- and uneven-aged forest elements are often confusingly intermingled, stand condition, stocking and treatment needs are frequently highly variable, and management objectives are diverse. While basic principles and approaches apply, it is often hard to see them in terms of a real-life situation. As a consequence, there is often considered to be a gap between "textbook" and actual management. There should be no gap, only a natural transition from underlying principles and common denominators to their application under field conditions.

Management problems of mixed stands cannot be dealt with effectively in any general book, since the detail of an actual situation is too specialized. To help see theory and practice relationships, it is possible, however, to sketch the nature of some actual situations and to indicate general management approaches that may be helpful. This is done for four situations involving mixed stands, both even- and uneven-aged. The cases selected are suggestive only, and there are many more that could be as logically considered.

LARGE PUBLIC OWNERSHIP IN THE LAKE STATES

Management Situation. The Ottawa National Forest in northern Michigan is covered by a recent timber management plan; inventory data on area, forest, types, stand conditions, growth, stocking, and volume are fairly good. Timber production is a major land use, but so are others, especially outdoor recreation. Timber cutting in some areas is restricted or modified to harmonize with recreational needs.

The area was purchased mostly about 30 years ago of timberlands that had been cut and burned over and were in generally poor condition. Through protection and planting over the succeeding years, forest conditions have been greatly improved, and the area is beginning to come into commercial production, although the timber is still mostly young. Stocking is now reasonably good, but a major need is to build and improve growing stock towards a better age-size distribution. Species of the northern hardwood type group occupy 50 percent of the area and aspen-paper birch 30 percent. The rest is in five conifer types. Accessibility is generally good, although more roads are needed. Markets are excellent for sawtimber and particularly for hardwood and veneer quality. The market for pulpwood, the product the Ottawa has in most abundance to sell, is only fair; markets are limited for the denser hardwoods particularly.

Management Approaches and Methods. At the time of the inventory, sample points were used to estimate cutting needs on the basis of silvicultural prescriptions established for each of the forest types. The areas to be cut and volumes indicated were modified to some extent by age-class distribution considerations in arriving at an average allowable cut, which is tabulated by area for each forest type. The northern hardwood group is handled on an uneven-aged basis and all other types on an even-aged basis with guiding rotations set for each. Only regeneration cuts are made in the aspen-birch type, much of which is approaching maturity and should be cut heavily. Very little regeneration or intermediate cutting can be done in the conifer types because of their immaturity. It will be difficult to sell the full allowable cut in pulpwood; the cut is a goal rather than a limit in this situation.

The amount of forest information available is sufficient to permit fairly specific planning. The methods applied both permit and require a large amount of judgment and knowledge by the man on the ground in the conduct of cutting operations.

SMALL PRIVATE OWNERSHIP IN THE LAKE STATES

Management Situation.   This is a situation of a private owner-operator who has acquired a forest property of about 15,000 acres. The area is small enough that he can know it intimately even though it is rather scattered geographically. He must also make a living from it. The forest lands are of all sorts and conditions, mostly cut over. Hardwood, softwood, and mixed types are represented in both swamp and upland situations. In many cases a cut of sufficient weight to pay most or all the investment cost was made shortly after acquisition. The owner must fit his schedule of cutting species and products to a changing market over which he has no control.

Management Approaches and Methods.   In all probability, the owner would not be interested in a particular regulatory scheme or formula or feel any necessity to set average annual total allowable cut figures, although he likely would make some general calculations to estimate the sustained yield capacity of the area. His approach would more likely be to make up a cutting budget for a few years at a time, following an area and volume allotment plan and utilizing directly his firsthand knowledge of the stands and their cutting needs. Actual cutting would be guided by current market, labor, seasonal, and other business considerations. The character of cutting practice applied would be determined by his knowledge of and ability to apply productive silviculture and by the necessity of getting a reasonable financial return from the property. With a good working knowledge of applicable silviculture, such a property could be operated productively with a minimum of paper work. In the long pull, management operations probably would settle down into a pattern that could be reduced to written plan form.

LARGE MANAGEMENT UNIT, CANADA

Management Situation.   A compact block of several hundred square miles of public forest land in Ontario is leased more or less permanently to a private timber company to be managed for sustained yield. Forest types are variable and about the same as in the Ottawa case discussed above, except that there is more merchantable timber. The company assumes much of the land management job as regards application of silviculture; protection against fire, insects, and diseases; access roads; and forest inventory. Pulpwood is the major product, but sawtimber is also cut. The company is pressed by high labor and other costs on the production side and by competitive and largely international market conditions on the selling end. The intensity of silviculture possible is low. Inventory data are from an extensive survey and mostly limited to areas by age classes and major types, and volumes by species within types. Growth information is scanty as is knowledge of growing stock conditions and desirable stocking levels.

Management Approach and Methods. The management situation permits only extensive planning. The immediate regulatory needs are to:

1. Develop a reasonable overall average annual cutting limitation for perhaps the first decade.

2. Establish an initial cutting budget in harmony with the allowable cut, putting first things first regarding selection of stands for cutting and cutting methods to be followed.

3. Initiate plans for collection of needed inventory and growth data, for study of silvicultural needs and problems, etc., so that a more solidly grounded operating plan can be prepared in perhaps 10 years.

A reasonable allowable cut from even-aged stands could be roughly estimated by breaking the area down into major types to the extent the available data permit and by making an adjusted area analysis along the lines illustrated in Chap. 7. Volume methods suitable to the inventory data available also could be used. In any event, volumes to be cut will have to be translated into cutting areas on the ground. For uneven-aged stands, some estimate of a desirable reserve growing stock volume and structure, cutting cycles, and growth would have to be made to obtain a provisional estimate of the volumes to be cut and where. With skill and imagination, a reasonable estimate of what could safely be cut from the area, and of where and how it should be taken, could be made with sufficient accuracy to guide an initial cutting program.

LARGE PULP AND PAPER COMPANY IN THE
SOUTHERN UNITED STATES

Management Situation. The company is definitely and permanently in the business of growing timber, pulpwood primarily but not exclusively. It is acquiring and leasing some additional lands, which of course continually affects overall regulatory calculations. The company is in a highly competitive business; costs and returns are closely scrutinized. It regards ownership of timberlands—enough to supply about half of mill needs—desirable both as an economical source of timber and as insurance of raw material supply. The forest types are mostly pine and pine-hardwood mixtures with also some bottomland hardwoods. Pine is preferred. Lands were in all sorts of conditions when acquired, most considerably understocked. Some require planting. Ownership is distributed over a large gross area but fairly well consolidated by working units. Inventory data are reasonably good. Accessibility is very good; almost any part of the area can be reached for cutting.

Even-aged management is the goal in pine and pine-hardwood types, but existing stands are often irregular in age and stocking and of undesirable species composition. There is, consequently, a large job to be done in getting better and more uniform stand conditions by compartments.

Management Approaches and Methods. Although company-owned lands are managed for sustained yield, the yearly cut may fluctuate in accordance with the pulpwood procurement situation and other factors. For this reason, it is more practical to set a periodic or annual quota to be cut from operating blocks or units, taking into account both the productivity of the area and the general supply situation, than it is to stress a uniform overall allowable annual cut figure for the property as a whole. Continued and increasing productivity of the land rather than strict uniformity of volume cut is the primary consideration.

A first need is to make some decisions concerning guiding rotation, desirable levels of stocking, and silvicultural cutting methods applicable to the products desired. From field inventory data, which should emphasize actual stand conditions, existing stands are each considered as to their respective condition and treatment need. One stand is ready for a pulpwood thinning; another is ready for a major harvest cut, others need planting or removal of low-value hardwoods, etc. A cutting budget and schedule is prepared for a fairly short period ahead, usually not more than 5 years, listing stands in priority of cutting. This illustrates the general utility of the area and volume-allotment approach. Plans and cutting procedures are constantly revised and changed as company needs dictate and as growth and other silvicultural knowledge accumulates. Regulatory techniques certainly have a place, but the actual management job is largely done compartment by compartment in administrative units.

10
determination of the rotation

A forest rotation is defined by the Society of American Foresters (1958) as "the period of years required to establish and grow timber crops to a specified condition of maturity." Determination of the length of the rotation, either for a forest operating unit as a whole or for individual species or groups of species, is one of the key decisions a forest manager must make. Its importance in even-aged management has been emphasized: the whole production structure is largely related to and determined by the length of the rotation adopted. Since trees take a long time to grow and time costs money, adoption of the most advantageous rotation has much to do with the financial success of the forest business. While the rotation does not enter directly into the framework of uneven-aged management, the concept of a rotation has meaning in indicating the time required to produce the general size and character of the principal products desired. In this sense, a rotation is but another expression of the rate of growth; the shorter the time necessary to produce a particular size and quality of tree, the more rapid the growth. The rotation also influences the volume and distribution of growing stock necessary to produce the desired products.

Factors affecting the length of the rotation consequently should receive careful and critical scrutiny. Although the concept of a rotation has been frequently used in previous chapters, the question of how it is determined has not been met. The problem is how to determine the time necessary to achieve the "specified condition of maturity" expressed in the definition above.

There are two basic groups of physical and financial factors that influence the length of the rotation: (1) what products are desired or can best be sold (largely a matter of markets or of demand in a general economic sense); (2) forest productivity, or what can be grown (supply). Obviously, costs and returns are involved in both groups. These factors must be integrated and a rotation determined according to the purposes of management, whatever they may be. Final decision is a matter of overall policy determination. To sum it up bluntly, the question is: What can you best grow and sell?

product values

Since the purpose of growing timber is to utilize it, the size and quality of timber that can be most advantageously sold as a raw material obviously exert a powerful influence on the length of the rotation. There is no point in growing timber that cannot be utilized effectively. Suppose pulpwood is desired as the major product and trees 12 to 14 in. dbh are found to be the best size to cut, transport, and mill for a particular operation. Yield tables applicable to the species and site involved will show the time required to grow trees to approximately this size. The answer will not be precise, but the average age can be estimated. So far as the most marketable size alone is concerned, this will define the average rotation necessary, if this product is to be grown as the main crop.

For sawlogs or for any other kind of product, a similar determination can be made. For example, if sawtimber is the objective and trees about 20 in. in diameter are considered the ideal size, then the rotation will be the time necessary to grow trees to about this size for the particular species, site, and kind of management involved. The production of Christmas trees in plantations is another illustration. The time necessary to grow trees to specified marketable size is relatively short and can be estimated within fairly narrow limits. Costs and returns of Christmas tree production are appraised accordingly.

In even-aged management, the rotation must be set for the major species and products involved, with other species and products fitted in around this ruling rotation as best they can be. Since several partial harvest and intermediate cuttings are usually made, a considerable range in the size and quality of products produced will result. While commonly expressed as a single number, the rotation in practice is an age range within which the major crop will be harvested and a new stand started.

A direct appraisal of desirable tree sizes and estimation of the time necessary to grow them is sometimes sufficient to set the rotation. The U.S. Forest Service, for example, feels that on the national forests there are sound reasons of public policy for growing quality sawtimber in an area as the major product, even though pulpwood is the most common, and possibly the most profitable, local product. The same can be true of private owners with particular interests. Management policy may dictate emphasis on pulp-wood production, for example, even though on a strictly financial basis, so far as the market value of stumpage is concerned, sawtimber may be more profitable.

Appraisal of the most desirable size of tree to grow may be facilitated and made more precise through the use of logging and milling data showing, for trees of different sizes, the margin per unit of volume between the cost of cutting, logging, and processing the timber and the value of the products sold. From a financial standpoint, it is not so much the fact that large trees produce more valuable products than small trees, as it is the increased margin that counts. Production cost as well as selling value must be considered. Figure 10.1 shows the margin available per M board feet for stumpage, profit, and risk when cutting sawtimber trees of different sizes on four

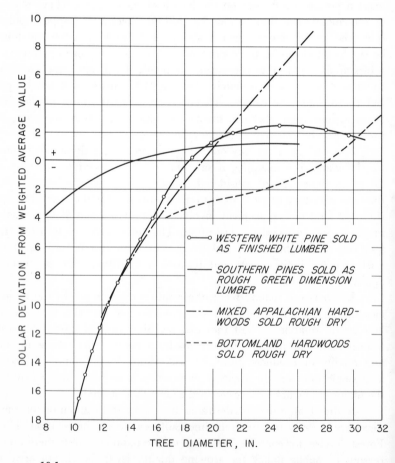

FIG. 10.1. MARGIN AVAILABLE PER M BOARD FEET FOR STUMPAGE, PROFIT, AND RISK WHEN CUTTING TREES OF SPECIFIED DIAMETER.

widely different study areas. The data are presented as deviations in dollars from the weighted average cost in each instance. This focuses attention on the shape of the curves, which is the point of emphasis here. The studies were made at different times with different price levels prevailing.

In the case of western white pine, which is cut in a region of high production costs, particularly where small-sized trees are involved, the curve shows that the margin increases very rapidly until trees of about 20 in. dbh are reached. The curve then starts to level off and reaches a peak at about 26 in. Larger trees do not show an increased margin per M; in fact it dropped somewhat after about 26 in. in this particular study. From a rotation standpoint, this means that between 20 and 26 in. is an optimum size. This puts a limit on the financial possibilities of short rotations that would produce a large percentage of the volume cut in trees less than about 18 in. dbh.

The curve for southern pine rough-green dimension lumber shows, as would be expected for this class of product, that the effect of diameter on value is not pronounced. The margin increases only about a dollar for trees between 14 and 26 in. dbh. Market value alone, as indicated by the margin, accordingly gives an indeterminate indication of rotation length although it does show that a fairly short rotation would appear to be financially possible. As a generality, the unit conversion margin of conifers tends to level off as tree diameters of around 25 in. are reached, largely because the unit value of the products they produce does not increase commensurately with logging and milling costs. As higher quality smaller trees are produced, as is possible with pruning, this tendency will be more pronounced. For example, a 25-in. log with a 6-in. knotty core produced from a properly pruned tree is a convenient size to handle and would produce a large amount of veneer. The unit value of larger logs might not be much more.

The situation with hardwoods is different. There is usually a higher value premium for large-size timber, as is illustrated by the two sample curves shown in Fig. 10.1. In neither case is there any tendency apparent for the value margin to level off with increasing tree size. This points up a key fact about market analysis as an indicator of the desirable rotation. So long as trees increase consistently in unit value until rather large diameters are attained, a market analysis indicates only the possibilities of a fairly long rotation, relative to the species, but does not of itself indicate any particular rotation as the most desirable.

It should be emphasized and recognized that the curves illustrated here are for particular case studies. Their specific form will vary with the product, the costs of production and selling prices applicable in a particular situation, and to some extent with the techniques employed in their determination. They are indicative of general trends and of a method useful in analyzing desirable tree size from a market standpoint.

In summary, product values exert a strong influence on the length of the rotation possible. For small-sized products, as pulpwood, where the range in desirable tree size is fairly narrow, or for large products, as saw timber, where general policy considerations may be controlling, direct market analysis may be sufficient to determine an approximate rotation. In general, however, product values only establish a range within which the rotation must be but do not alone determine the most advantageous financial rotation.

forest factors

The second group of basic forces affecting the rotation concerns the productivity of the forest itself—what can be grown. Included here are measures of physical wood volume productivity and pathological, entomological, and silvicultural considerations that operate essentially as biological constraints.

PHYSICAL PRODUCTIVITY

A major forest factor is the physical capacity of the forest to produce timber. At what age is maximum volume productivity achieved? An answer to this question can be illustrated by employing yield-table data for fully stocked even-aged natural stands. Figure 10.2 gives mean annual increment in cubic feet and board feet employing data for loblolly pine as presented in Table 5.1. The point of culmination of mean annual increment indicates the age at which average annual growth is the greatest and hence defines, for the fully stocked stands represented, the rotation of maximum volume-growth productivity. This point is also intersected by the curve of periodic annual increment as illustrated for site index 100. The values for this curve are obtained by dividing the increment made during each period, as given by the yield table, by the length of the period in years. The average value is plotted on the midpoint of the period. Periodic increment culminates earlier than mean annual increment and then decreases rapidly. The actual ages and increments are less important than the general form and nature of the curves, particularly in relation to site. Comparable data for managed stands, if available, would indicate somewhat different culmination ages and increments, although the relative picture would be about the same.

Several items of significance hold in general regardless of the source and kind of data. The first is that on any given site the indicated rotation for maximum board foot production is longer than that for cubic foot production. This is because of the nature of the board foot unit; large trees contain proportionately more board feet than do small trees in comparison to cubic foot measure. Also, board foot measure does not include all trees, only those above some specified minimum diameter limit. The second is that the rotation of maximum mean annual increment increases with decreasing site quality. As would be expected, this trend is much more strongly evident in board foot than in cubic foot growth. In addition to producing much less timber (see Fig. 2.1), the poorer sites take longer to reach their point of maximum mean annual increment. A third, and a very important point regarding determination of the rotation, is that mean annual increment curves tend to be flattish near their apex. This is a characteristic of most species and types, especially on the poorer sites. Consequently, culmination of mean annual increment is not particularly decisive as a rotation

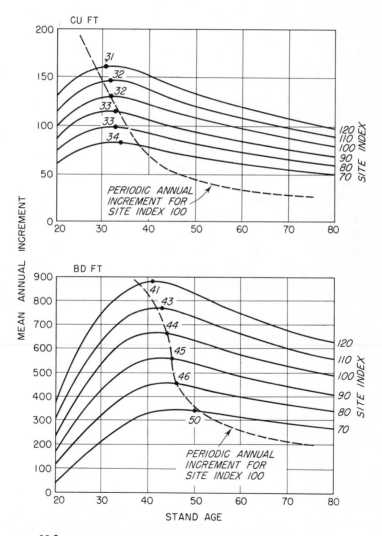

FIG. 10.2. MEAN ANNUAL INCREMENT OF LOBLOLLY PINE.

determinant; there is a considerable age range within which mean annual increment is about the same.

In summary, the age at which maximum mean annual increment is attained is an important factor influencing the rotation on a given site but is seldom alone decisive. It is only indirectly related to the age at which trees of highest product value are produced.

PATHOLOGICAL FACTORS

Mean annual increment as obtained from yield tables (Chap. 4) or from other net growth data is based upon the gross volume of trees found in selected stands that have survived to specified ages. These data consequently do not measure mortality that may have occurred in the past or the amount of defect that may be present in living trees. Pathological considerations are important in affecting the net growth of stands, both as regards mortality and the amount of defect in living trees. While the term "pathological rotation" is sometimes employed, it is more accurate to speak of limitations on the rotation imposed by pathological factors. In mixed stands and with even-aged management particularly, the shorter-lived key species in the stand tend to control the rotation applied to the stand as a whole.

It is well known that as a stand increases in age, it becomes increasingly subject to diseases, particularly those caused by the heart-rotting fungi. The incidence of disease with advancing age is highly variable by species, site, competition, and other factors. Aspen in the Lake States is notoriously short-lived and aspen stands commonly cease making net increment after 35 to 50 years of age and tend to break up rapidly thereafter. Balsam fir in the same region is also fairly short-lived. Butt rot and red rot in the upper bole cause both defect in the living tree and mortality through wind breakage. While conditions vary widely with site and other conditions, around 80 years is about the maximum rotation (Kaufert, 1935; Gevorkiantz and Olsen, 1950).

Similar analyses have been made for numerous forest types and species (Baxter, 1952; Boyce, 1961). For the most part, however, rotations under management are, for financial as well as forest productivity reasons, much shorter than those imposed by pathological limits. Pathological considerations are consequently more important as one of the many things influencing the rotation than as an actual determinant.

ENTOMOLOGICAL FACTORS

"Every operation in the forest influences the environment and thereby creates conditions that are either favorable or unfavorable for harmful insects" (Graham and Knight, 1965). Whether he is aware of it or not, the forest manager is an applied entomologist through his actions since almost everything he does affects insect food supply and modifies moisture, temperature, and other environmental factors in one way or another.

These are myriads of insects and the susceptibility of forests to their attack varies by forest composition, age, density, site, and vigor. Cutting operations can profoundly affect all these factors except site and even that to some degree. As a generality, extensive and pure even-aged stands are particularly susceptible to attack by destructive insects. Conversely, stands of mixed ages or species are less susceptible to damaging attacks; some such forests seem to be relatively safe from serious attack. Another generality is that as trees get older and particularly as they decline in general vigor, they become more susceptible to fatal insect attack. It is known, for example, that stands with a high percentage of balsam fir are increasingly susceptible to attacks by the spruce budworm as the stands become older (especially over about 60 years of age). Ponderosa pine becomes increasingly susceptible to bark beetle attack as it approaches overmaturity. There are many similar trends in forest types of all countries.

As affecting timber management practice, entomological considerations work in two general ways. First, they tend to put limits on the longer rotations. Second, and more importantly, they direct attention toward the composition, age structure, and vigor of the forest and place much premium on developing forest conditions not conducive to serious insect attack. In the long run, the most effective control of endemic pests is prevention, achieved through application of silvicultural practices creating a reasonably insect-resistant forest. Complete control can never be effected in this way, but insect losses and control costs can be greatly reduced.

SILVICULTURAL FACTORS

There are many and varied silvicultural considerations that condition or limit the rotation in one way or another. It should also be kept in mind that biological factors have definite financial repercussions.

The seed production characteristics of individual species are sometimes important. It is, for example, impractical to propose a plan of management depending on natural regeneration that entails making major harvest cuttings either before or after the effective seed-bearing age of the species involved.

The method and difficulty of obtaining regeneration often has a direct bearing on the regulatory rotation as emphasized in Chap. 7. While it is frequently assumed in even-aged management that a new stand is started immediately after the old one is harvested, such is frequently not the case. It may be 5, 10, or even more years following cutting before a new stand is fully established by natural regeneration. Planting or seeding is not always immediately possible or successful either.

There may be a tendency to lengthen the rotation where there is early and heavy competition from trees of undesirable species. It may take some time to eliminate these species and establish control of the site by trees of desirable species and form. If large-sized products are involved, a series to intermediate cuttings are often necessary to produce the form and quality of tree desired. This logically necessitates a fairly long rotation to give scope and time for such cuttings.

The reverse may also be true. Southern pines, for example, are amenable to rather short rotations for pulpwood. Where there is a strong hardwood competition factor, a short rotation, in conjunction with suitable site preparation and regeneration measures, may be indicated as a means of keeping hardwoods in check. The longer rotations, especially those involving several partial cuttings as a part of the silvicultural schedule, tend to intensify hardwood competition in situations where this is a factor.

Soil factors may also be important. Successive short rotations of pure stands, particularly of conifers, may not be conductive to long-term maintenance of desirable soil conditions, indicating the need for longer rotations and admixture of hardwoods.

The term "natural rotation" is sometimes employed to describe the average life of stands and species in wild forest. This involves a complex of silvicultural, pathological, and entomological factors operating in many and devious ways. By its nature, such a rotation is a rather vague concept and cannot be specifically defined. It is variable and overlong for stands under any kind of positive treatment, and the concept consequently has little management significance.

This discussion of silvicultural and related factors that may affect the rotation is by no means exhaustive but indicates some of the possibilities that should be considered. In general, silvicultural factors affect the rotation, sometimes profoundly, but do not determine it.

product values and forest factors combined—money yield tables

Market and forest factors in combination determine the value productivity of the forest. Their joint effect can best be illustrated and demonstrated through the device of preparing money yield tables. It is important that their construction be well understood because of the grasp this gives of product value and forest productivity relationships and because of the utility of money yield tables in furnishing a financial basis for determination of the rotation.

The first step is to obtain stumpage values for stands of different average diameters. Taking sawtimber production as a convenient illustration, it is common knowledge that small trees are worth less per unit of volume than larger ones; all logging and milling studies bring this out clearly. The reason is that logging and milling costs tend to decrease with increasing diameter, whereas the unit selling value of the products obtained tends to increase with the size of the tree. As a consequence of these trends, unit stumpage values are positively correlated with tree size.

If data on the volume by individual tree diameters occurring in stands of specified average diameter are available, it is possible to determine a weighted stumpage value for even-aged stands of different average diameter growing on specified sites. Stand and stock tables, often prepared in connection with yield tables, are a convenient source of such data and relate it to age. Such data are given in a study of the yield of even-aged stands of loblolly pine made by Meyer (1942) in part presented in Table 5.1. His data include a table showing, for various average stand diameters, the percentage of the total stand volume in the individual diameter classes comprising the stand. Combination of these data with the stumpage value of trees of different diameter, as obtained from applicable logging and milling data, gives a weighted average unit stumpage value for a stand of given average diameter. The process is illustrated in Table 10.1 for two sample average stand diameters. Using these weighted average stumpage values, a curve can be constructed, for the range of the data included, giving average stumpage value by average stand diameter.

The second step is to apply these average stumpage values to yield data, as given in Table 5.1, to obtain money yields. The detail of doing this is shown in Table 10.2 for a single site index. The completed money yield table for the range of sites and ages included in the yield study is shown in Table 10.3. This table is of exactly the same form as a yield table in board feet but is in terms of dollar instead of volume productivity. Note the rapid increase in value between 20 and 50 years of age particularly on the better sites. This brings out again the great importance of site quality as emphasized in Chap. 2. The value increase is brought about by the combined effect of two things: (1) the rapid growth that is characteristic of even-aged loblolly stands during this period and (2) the increase in the value of sawtimber per M as trees of larger average diameter are produced. The weighting of these two factors naturally varies widely from timber type to timber type.

If the value per unit of volume did not increase with tree diameter, a money yield table would give exactly the same relative picture as a yield table in timber volume alone and could be very simply constructed by merely multiplying all volume figures by a constant unit value. With pulpwood production, where unit values are not particularly sensitive to tree size except on the upper and lower limits of operable-sized timber, a money yield table gives about the same picture as a volume yield table. It is in situations where unit values are strongly influenced by tree size that money yield tables

TABLE 10.1. DETERMINATION OF AVERAGE STUMPAGE VALUE
PER M FOR STANDS OF SPECIFIED AVERAGE
DIAMETER, LOBLOLLY PINE

Dbh, in.	Stumpage value per M[a]	10 in.		14 in.	
		Percent of bd ft volume[b]	Weighted value[c]	Percent of bd ft volume[b]	Weighted value[c]
(1)	(2)	(3)	(4)	(5)	(6)
7	$ 1.20	3.0	3.6	0.4	0.5
8	3.40	4.7	16.0	0.7	2.4
9	5.20	7.5	39.0	1.2	6.2
10	7.60	9.8	74.5	2.2	16.7
11	9.70	11.0	106.7	3.3	32.0
12	12.00	11.5	138.0	4.9	58.8
13	14.60	11.5	167.9	6.5	94.9
14	17.40	10.5	182.7	8.3	144.4
15	19.90	9.0	179.1	9.5	189.0
16	22.80	6.8	155.0	10.0	228.0
17	25.60	5.2	133.1	9.8	250.9
18	27.70	3.5	96.9	9.2	254.8
19	29.40	2.4	70.6	8.5	249.9
20	30.80	1.6	49.3	7.5	231.0
21	31.80	0.9	28.6	6.0	190.8
22	33.00	1.1	36.3	4.5	148.5
23	33.90	. . . . .	. . . .	3.1	105.1
24	34.80	. . . . .	. . . .	1.9	66.1
25	35.60	. . . . .	. . . .	1.2	42.7
26	36.40	. . . . .	. . . .	0.7	25.5
27	37.10	. . . . .	. . . .	0.6	22.3
28	37.60				
29	38.20				
Total.		100.0	1,477.3	100.0	2,360.5
Weighted average stumpage value per M.		. . . . .	$ 14.77	. . . . .	$ 23.60

[a] As obtained from applicable logging and milling data, adjusted to current prices.
[b] Meyer (1942), Table 13.
[c] Stumpage value × percent of bd ft volume.

show quite a different picture than volume yield tables and are most
significant.

In appraising the construction and significance of money yield tables,
several things should be emphasized. A simplified illustration was given here
and developed in detail to show basic procedure. Values were for a single

TABLE 10.2. CONSTRUCTION OF MONEY YIELD TABLE FOR FULLY STOCKED
EVEN-AGED LOBLOLLY PINE, SITE INDEX 100

Stand age, years	Average Stand diameter, trees 3.6 in. and larger[a]	Average stumpage value per M[b]	Volume per acre, bd ft[a]	Stumpage value per acre
20	6.1	$ 4.70	4,700	$ 22
30	8.6	10.90	16,000	174
40	11.8	19.10	26,700	510
50	13.5	22.60	31,900	721
60	14.2	23.90	34,900	834
70	14.7	24.60	37,300	918
80	15.1	25.20	39,400	993

[a] As given in Table 5.1.
[b] Obtained by curving average stumpage values for even-inch average stand diameters as computed in Table 10.1.

product, sawtimber, and it was also assumed that only a single harvest cut was applied. The physical data came from yield tables for natural uncut stands, which are convenient for illustrative purposes and often the only integrated data available to show a range of sites and ages. The money yield tables so prepared do, however, give a significant overall picture of the combined effect of stand age, site, and stumpage values by tree diameter classes on total money yields.

Ideally, one should work with yields of managed stands from which different kinds of products with varying unit values are often cut, for example, sawtimber, pulpwood, and poles. If commercial intermediate cuts are made, they should be included and cumulatively added to obtain total

TABLE 10.3. MONEY YIELD TABLE FOR FULLY STOCKED
EVEN-AGED LOBLOLLY PINE

Stand age, years	Stumpage value per acre for site index:					
	70	80	90	100	110	120
20	$ 3	$ 8	$ 14	$ 22	$ 32	$ 46
30	34	70	119	174	237	309
40	162	268	384	510	628	758
50	272	411	567	721	881	1,033
60	325	484	657	834	1,003	1,173
70	369	543	735	918	1,107	1,283
80	405	591	801	993	1,189	1,380

values produced at different ages. For example, if intermediate thinnings are made at ages 15, 20, and 25, their stumpage value should be added to that at age 30 to get the total value produced up to and including age 30. The general effect would be increased total value production at all ages after intermediate cuts are begun, since a greater proportion of the total growth potential of the site is captured in merchantable products. The timing of these increases would depend on the site and the particular cutting schedule applied. Note, also, that this means directly adding values produced at different points in time. Financially, this makes a difference, since values occurring at different times are not worth the same at any one time. See Chap. 17 for financial treatment of this point.

Money yield tables for uneven-aged stands are difficult to prepare for the same reasons that volume tables are. See Chap. 3, p. 62. Information from managed stands is necessary, and consistent data of this kind are few.

It is evident that money yield tables are the end result of some rather complex integrations, and it is a good idea to keep this in mind. In practice, the problem can be considerably simplified. Only a fairly narrow range in stand ages, sites, and timber management methods may be significant in a particular situation. Also, average unit stumpage values for major harvest or other cuts may be estimated directly from experience data and the detail of working with tree diameter distribution, as in Table 10.1, eliminated. It is a reasonable end result that counts; the specific procedure can be varied to suit the purpose and data available.

Finally, it should be noted that timber-growing costs are not taken into account at all. In economic language, a money yield table is a total revenue schedule showing gross stumpage values of stands of different ages and on different sites. Both revenue and cost schedules, together with some financial objective, are necessary for direct economic analysis of rotation length, which is considered in the next section.

economic measures of the rotation

Economic considerations underlie most estimates of rotation length, whether expressly recognized or not. It should be recognized that physical measures may also have an economic basis. For example, the economic basis of an industrial pulpwood rotation set at maximum mean annual increment in cubic feet lies in the fact that the culmination of volume and value growth come at about the same time for this product. Similarly, maximum board foot rotations, such as are often used by public agencies in the United States, are based on knowledge that sawtimber trees of desirable quality and value will be produced. Further, a policy decision to grow quality sawtimber in a dominantly pulpwood-producing area is based on considerations of national welfare which are economic in foundation. Physical measures, which tend to be directly and fairly easily determinable, may consequently be indirect expressions of economic objectives.

The idea of maximizing net return is basic to most rational human activity, economic or otherwise. Applied to forested land in general, more than one measure of maximization is possible since the reasons for ownership are many, as was emphasized in Chap. 1. Applied to purposeful management for timber production, objectives, however, are dominantly economic and consequently directed to attainment of maximum net monetary gain.

There are two general viewpoints on maximizing returns from an operating forest, (1) those that center on maximizing profits or net returns per acre per year and (2) those based on maximizing the rate of return received from the investment. Applied to rotation determination, these are exemplified by two approaches, commonly termed "forest rent" and "land expectation value" methods.[1]

FOREST RENT

Forest rent is essentially the same thing as culmination of mean annual volume increment, except that the increment is measured in net dollars received instead of in volume units. Table 10.3 gives gross revenue based on board foot measure. By deducting estimated costs of producing the forest crop and dividing the net value remaining by the age of the stand, the mean annual net dollar increment is obtained; this is commonly called forest rent. The process of calculating this value for site index 100 is illustrated in Table 10.4. Figure 10.3A shows the results of this calculation carried out

[1] Other financial objectives of financial maturity are also possible. See Gaffney (1957) and Bentley and Teeguarden (1965). Also Duerr, Fedkiw, and Guttenberg (1956).

TABLE 10.4. CALCULATION OF ANNUAL FOREST RENT PER ACRE FOR FULLY STOCKED EVEN-AGED STANDS OF LOBLOLLY PINE ON SITE INDEX 100 LAND

Stand age, years	Gross value of stumpage	Timber-growing costs[a]	Net value per acre	Forest rent per acre
20	$ 22	$ 40	$ −18	$ −0.9
30	174	53	121	4.0
40	510	66	444	11.1
50	721	79	642	12.8
60	834	92	742	12.4
70	918	105	813	11.6
80	993	118	875	10.9

[a] Establishment and early development costs assumed to be $14 per acre and annual costs for taxes, administration, etc., $1.30 per acre per year.

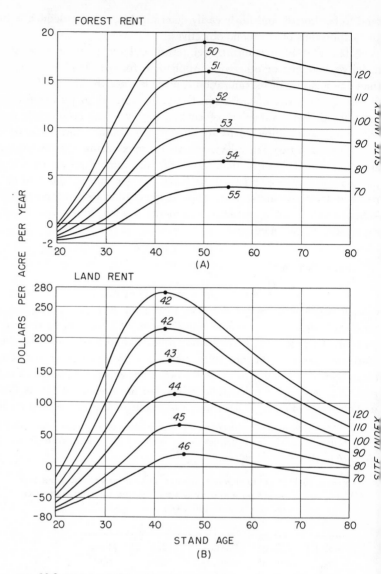

FIG. 10.3. FOREST RENT AND LAND EXPECTATION
VALUES FOR LOBLOLLY PINE.

for the full range of forest sites and ages. The rotations, as indicated by
the point of culmination of these curves for all sites except site 70, are
from 8 to 9 years longer than the rotations indicated by mean annual board
foot increment in Fig. 10.2. This is because stumpage unit values strongly
increase with size of timber, causing value productivity to maximize later

than volume productivity. If there were no increase in unit values, forest rent would indicate exactly the same rotation as would maximum mean annual increment.

Deduction of timber-growing costs has little effect on the final results so far as indicating the rotation of maximum forest rent is concerned. The height of the curves can be changed by increasing or decreasing costs and by adding revenue from intermediate cuts if applied. However, the form of the curve is strongly controlled by the rate of timber volume growth and the stumpage diameter value differentials applied to it. The culmination point is rather stable as can be checked by substituting other costs and an estimate for intermediate revenues in Table 10.4.

Forest rent, as a measure of the rotation, can be interpreted on two bases. First, it can be regarded as the performance of a single acre. The culmination point indicates the age at which the maximum dollar return per acre per year is obtained without reference to when costs are incurred or incomes received. That is, a dollar invested in establishment costs or in annual protection or administration is matched directly against harvest-cutting incomes. No cognizance is taken of the fact that, from the standpoint of a single acre, costs are incurred over a considerable period of time with income mostly delayed until the final harvest cut. Interest is not taken into account, and this interpretation consequently has no economic validity.

Second, and validly, forest rent can be interpreted as measuring net return from a "going concern." That is, it can be considered as the annual net return from a regulated forest for which certain costs are incurred and from which certain incomes are received each year. A regulated forest of even-aged stands operated on a 40-year rotation, for example, can be represented by 40 acres, one of each age class. A final harvest cut is made on 1 acre each year, another acre is regenerated, others may be given thinnings, and annual costs are paid on all 40 acres. A forest rent rotation consequently defines the maximum net income available each year from the property.

Maximum forest rent represents a logical rotation to work towards in managing a forest property of fixed area where no other business alternatives are considered. An entailed private estate, a public forest area—or an apartment house—could be examples. If the property is all one has to work with, and there are such situations, a rather natural objective is to get the most possible net income from it. Following such a course, one would increase costs as long as something more than cost is received in revenue as a result. As regards alternative choices within the forest, one should, of course, first do those things that give the greatest return per dollar spent. Priority choices between cultural operations, road development, etc. should be decided on this basis. Costs would be increased, however, as a general policy as long as they are exceeded by revenues and total net income is consequently increased. In economic terms, this means that additional expenditures would be made as long as marginal revenues exceeded marginal cost. To put it another way, expenditures would be made as long as the marginal rate of return is positive.

It is true that, applied to an operating forest property, attainment of maximum forest rent is a long-range objective and, like a fully regulated forest, seldom achieved. But with stable forest ownership and operating conditions, it is a goal to work towards. Probably, this accounts for the fact that the forest rent approach was historically developed and has received most support in northern Europe.

Since forest rent represents net annual revenue from an operating forest property, the capital value of such a property may be estimated by capitalizing at a significant rate of interest. For example, at 40 years the forest rent figure is $11.10 per acre (Table 10.4). At 5 percent this indicates a capital value of $11.10/0.05, or $222 per acre, in land and timber together.

This can be compared to existing market values. While not based on capital costs in its derivation, forest rent gives a basis for capital value estimation in the same way as does net revenue from an existing apartment dwelling or any income property considered for purchase or for sale. Whether or not the capital value (and rate of return that it indicates) is desirable depends on the viewpoint of the owner and market values for such properties.

LAND EXPECTATION VALUE[1]

In contrast to the net annual income maximization of forest rent, the land expectation value or land rent approach focuses attention on the rate of return from money invested in growing timber measured in terms of what could be paid for bare land as a forestry investment. For a given rate of return and a timber-growing schedule including all costs and returns over time, there is a rotation length that will yield a maximum present land value and hence the highest return for the interest rate assumed. The rate is determined by what is considered acceptable and possible.

The procedure is to estimate all these costs and returns, beginning with establishment of the stand, and to carry them all at compound interest to rotation age at an assumed rate of interest to get a net income at that time. It is assumed that this income will periodically and indefinitely be received at the end of succeeding rotations as the land will continue to have productive value. The land expectation value, or L_e, is the capitalized or present net worth of this series of future periodic net incomes beginning

---

[1] Usually called soil expectation value following Schlich, (1925) and as first presented by Faustmann (1849). However, land is a more accurate translation of the German *Boden* in a land management context, conforms to common English usage of land values, and is used here. It is also termed "maximum discounted economic rent," or "maximum land rent."

with that received at the end of the first rotation. The broader significance of land values is developed in Chap. 17. The purpose here is only to appraise their usefulness as a measure of the rotation.

The basic formula[1] is

$$L_e = \frac{a}{(1 + i)^r - 1}$$

where L_e = land expectation value or land rent
  a = net income at rotation age measured by all receipts received accumulated to rotation age at i percent less all expenditures also accumulated to rotation age at i percent
  i = rate of interest expressed as a decimal
  r = length of rotation in years

Employing the same cost and income assumptions as were used in the determination of forest rent, and using a conservative interest rate of 3 percent, the process of calculating L_e values is illustrated in Table 10.5 for site index 100. Values for the full range of sites included in the loblolly pine yield study are given in Fig. 10.3. They indicate, at a stated rate of interest and assuming certain costs and incomes, the investment value of an acre of bare land for forest production purposes.

Being largely controlled by accumulation of interest over long periods, L_e values are very sensitive to changes in the rate assumed and the timing of cost and return items. There is an L_e value not only for every production schedule assumed but also for every rate of interest used. Depending on the rate of interest, the L_e approach consequently can cover the possible

[1] The derivation of this formula is given in Chap. 16.

TABLE **10.5.** CALCULATION OF LAND EXPECTATION VALUES PER ACRE FOR
FULLY STOCKED EVEN-AGED STANDS OF LOBLOLLY PINE
ON SITE INDEX **100** LAND, INTEREST AT **3** PERCENT

Stand age, years	Establishment cost		Annual cost		Total cost at rotation age	Total income at rotation age (Table 10.3)	Net income at rotation age	Present land or L_e value
	Establishment cost in first year	Cost with interest at rotation age	Annual cost	Cost with interest at rotation age				
20	$14	$ 24.55	$1.30	$ 34.93	$ 59	$ 22	$ 37	$ 46
30	14	32.99	1.30	61.85	95	174	79	55
40	14	44.34	1.30	98.02	142	510	368	163
50	14	59.59	1.30	146.64	206	721	515	152
60	14	80.08	1.30	211.97	292	834	542	111
70	14	107.62	1.30	299.77	407	918	511	74
80	14	144.63	1.30	417.77	562	993	431	45

range of rotations, from short to long, in any production situation. With higher rates, more discount is placed on time, and the indicated rotation is consequently shortened, cost and return assumptions remaining constant. The rotation period may be shorter than the rotation indicated by maximum mean annual increment, although it cannot be much shorter, since in most forest types both physical and product-value productivity decline rapidly for rotations less than those indicated by the culmination of mean annual increment. In this instance, the indicated L_e rotation at 3 percent is 43 years on site 100 land, which is about the same as the rotation of mean annual increment in board feet (Fig. 10.2B). Note that these are all regulatory and not cutting-age rotations. Regeneration in the first year is assumed here. If there is delay in getting regeneration, it takes longer to get timber of a desired cutting age, and costs are increased, as was pointed out in Chap. 6.

As the rate of interest is reduced, the rotation indicated by the L_e value is lengthened up to a maximum defined by mean annual forest rent, which can be regarded as the end or limiting value of the land expectation series. It can be demonstrated mathematically that as the interest rate approaches zero as a limit, the L_e curve approaches culmination at the same value of r, or length of rotation as determined by a forest rent calculation. At 1 percent and for site index 100, the culmination of the L_e curve, also based on board foot measure, occurs at about 51 years as compared with 52 years for forest rent rotation (Fig. 10.3A). At $\frac{1}{4}$ percent it is 52 years, as nearly as can be determined graphically.

According to the nature of the L_e calculation, the capital value of the land upon which the rate of return is based necessarily increases as the interest rate is reduced. Since the bulk of the income (all of it in this example) is from the major harvest cut at rotation age, the income item remains relatively constant. The accumulated value of costs is reduced, however. This increases the net income at rotation age, which is the a numerator in the L_e formula. At the same time, the divisor in the formula, the $(1 + i)^r - 1$ part, is correspondingly reduced as the value of i becomes smaller. As a result, the ratio, or L_e value, approaches an infinitely large figure as the value of the interest rate i approaches zero. At 1 percent, for example, the indicated L_e value is about $950 per acre. At $\frac{1}{4}$ percent, it is approximately $4,800, a clearly ridiculous figure. This means that bare land bought *at these figures* theoretically would return 1 and $\frac{1}{4}$ percent, respectively, on the investment. The point, of course, is that bare land of this quality can be purchased for a fraction of these amounts, and the actual rate of return on such land would far exceed these percentages on a rotation of about 50 years.

Another and more general way to express this relationship of land value to the rate of interest is to point out the obvious fact that as less discount is placed on time, the contribution of future rotations increases.

At no discount, an infinitely long series of them with equal present value would be added up, naturally giving an infinitely large figure.

On the face of it, this would seem to indicate that a forest rent rotation or a regulated forest returns no interest at all. This is not true; it is not an interestless rotation. The reason is that both forest and land rent rotations, although determined for a single stand unit, are most meaningfully interpreted in terms of a regulated forest and in this context constitute marginal analyses. By its time-sequence nature, an individual even-aged stand necessarily progresses through its lifetime from infancy to maturity. A regulated forest is the same thing except that there exists at one time a sequence of stands of all ages in the rotation so that a regular annual harvest can be sustained.

Either rotation approach determines the length of time this production process is continued and defines a financial maturity age. Necessarily, all the other ages are represented too. In the case of forest rent, maturity is carried to a marginal rate approaching zero for this oldest stand, but it must be remembered that the rate is much higher for younger stands. The average rate of return from the forest as a whole is consequently higher than the marginal rate. As pointed out previously, the capitalization of the annual net income from a regulated forest unit managed on a forest rent rotation indicates an average timberland value which may compare favorably with existing market values. The capitalization process places the whole forest on an annual production basis.

With a land expectation value approach, the production process is continued until a marginal rate set by the rate of interest used is reached. In the illustration given here, the rate was 3 percent, but other marginal rates could have been used, depending on what is financially acceptable and also possible in the forest. Application of the financial maturity concept as developed by Duerr, Fedkiw, and Guttenberg (1956), which is a marginal analysis, gives essentially the same result except for the facts that only one rotation is considered, a land cost does not enter in, and timber-growing costs are not explicitly taken into account. The land expectation value approach gives a full framework for production analysis; any and all costs and returns may be included. See Chaps. 17 and 20 for more complete treatment.

The virtue of calculating L_e values as a measure of the rotation is that they focus attention on the effect of time on expenditure and receipt items and on the rate of return on the investment, the businessman's logical approach. For interest rates from about 3 to 6 percent, which cover the approximate range of business reality in long-term investments, rotations of maximum L_e value will fall somewhere between the range established by maximum mean annual increment on the short side and forest rent on the long side, which serve as practical limiting cases.

A weakness of the land expectation value approach is that the objective

of obtaining the highest possible rate of return (which means shorter rota
tions as the rate is increased) can lead to impractical extremes. The produc
value calculations upon which they are based may assume a market fo
large quantities of small-sized trees at the same price at which they ar
marketed in conjunction with larger trees. This is a questionable assumption
If everybody applied short rotations, the market structure might collaps
under a flood of small-sized products. These lower prices would upset th
calculation upon which the most profitable rotation was based and a longe
rotation would be more profitable (Matthews, 1935). Another limitatior
of the land expectation value approach is that values are arbitrarily anc
somewhat theoretically determined from long-range compound interest cal
culations that may bear no necessary relation to market values or to th
way businessmen or public agencies operate.

summary of rotation length determinants

A comparative presentation of rotation determinants is graphically giver
in Fig. 10.4. The question the forest manager must answer is how eacl
should be weighed in deciding on the ruling rotation or rotations to appl
in practice. It should also be clear that, although indicated rotations diffe
by species, site, and other factors, it is not feasible to have a lot of differen
rotations in practice; considerable lumping together and rounding off i
necessary. The answer depends basically on the purposes of management
This relates to the reasons for desiring a reasonably well-regulated fores
as given at the beginning of Chap. 5.

If the aim is maximum volume productivity, the rotation of maximum
mean annual increment is clearly the best guide. As indicated in Fig. 10.4,
there can be a considerable range in these rotation lengths. This is controlled
by the unit of measure and merchantability standard used. With cubic mea
sure including the entire stand, the rotation approaches a practicable limit
on the short side. With board foot or any similar quality-sensitive measure,
the indicated rotation is longer, especially if only the larger trees are included and merchantability standards are stringent.

If the long-range aim is to maximize net income per acre per yea
from a given forest property, a forest rent rotation is indicated. This rotatior
indicates a maximum financial rotation length. While it may indicate a
satisfactory rate of return on the investment, this would depend on what
the investment actually is, which must be determined by appraisal. To the
extent that better alternative opportunities for investment are available, the
rotation of maximum forest rent is overlong and results in building up forest
capital in increased growing stock volumes, some of which could be liquidated and invested elsewhere to yield a higher rate of return.

The rotations of maximum L_e value can cover the entire range of
possible rotation lengths, depending on the rate of interest used. Using rea-

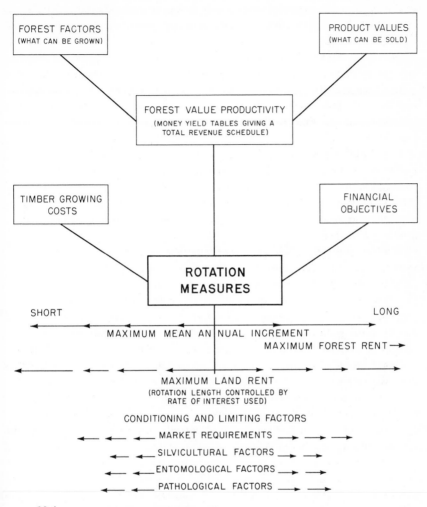

FIG. 10.4. FOREST ROTATION DETERMINANTS.

sonable interest rates for long-term investment, approximately 3 to 6 percent, L_e solutions will be usually somewhat longer than the rotation of maximum mean annual increment in cubic measure and be necessarily shorter than the rotation of maximum forest rent. This approach places emphasis on rate of return and is sound in principle. It presents, however, the problem of selecting a meaningful interest rate and necessitates long-range compounding of costs and returns that may be difficult to quantify—and sometimes to understand. It also may assume a market price structure that will not continue.

An appraisal of the size and quality of products most marketable underlies all other approaches but usually does not permit a direct numerical estimate of the rotation length. A range in the size and quality of products desired is usually involved, and it is a rather arbitrary matter to pick out just which is the key product or how many years are required to grow it. A rotation selected on the basis of product values gives no measure of the financial desirability of growing specified timber products, since it leaves the production side out of account. Direct estimation of the rotation from product value appraisal is, however, adequate in certain situations. As was pointed out, pulpwood rotations can be determined fairly well by direct estimation of the time required to grow trees to some desired marketable size.

In addition to these direct measures of the rotation and partly, but not entirely, measured by them, there are various pathological, entomological, and silvicultural factors to be considered. Sometimes they may be of critical importance, but more commonly, for rotations of practical management significance, they exert a conditioning or limiting rather than a deciding influence.

A general point about rotation length is that the costs of reestablishment should be given careful consideration. There are direct costs, uncertainties, and usually some loss of time in establishing a new stand of desirable spacing and species composition. The cost of delay in reestablishment has been stressed; every year lost extends the regulatory rotation just that much. With some species, having no serious pathological, entomological, or silvicultural limitations in their management, it is possible, through application of intermediate harvest cuts, to keep a stand growing at an acceptable financial rate of return for a relatively long time. In such a situation, rotation length can be variable. As long as a stand is producing well, there is no reason to cut it down and start over. As a general analogy, one does not demolish a factory that is serving satisfactorily just because it has been in use an arbitrary number of years.

It is impossible to generalize safely about the precise effect of thinnings on the length of a financial rotation. They certainly increase physical yield, and their usual effect is to lengthen the rotation. Net financial return from such cuts can, however, be low and not justify lengthening the rotation. Some species may be best managed financially on short rotations using a fairly wide spacing in initial establishment of the stand so that thinning is not needed before a single harvest cut.

To sum it up, a number of physical and financial factors influence the length of the rotation. They need to be combined and then integrated by some measure of economic policy in arriving at a definite answer to desirable rotation length. The forest manager needs a good working knowledge of these factors and measures, as have been presented. The choice of rotation is important and no single formula or procedure will suffice for all situations. The capabilities of the forest must be related to the purposes of management. In the final analysis, rotation length is a managerial decision.

2 organization of the forest

Building on Part 1, Part 2 treats the organization and management of a forest property as a whole. It begins with the administrative organization and subdivision of the forest necessary to carry out the purposes of management. Next are the means of getting the continued flow of forest inventory information needed to give technical control and to measure performance. This is brought together in timber management planning and plans, which integrate and order the entire operation.

11

forest organization
and subdivision

The application of management to a forest property necessitates establishment of an administrative organization
and subdivision of the area into workable units. Living,
transportation, and other facilities must be provided. Responsibilities for carrying out the purposes and policies
of management must be defined and executed through
an on-the-ground administrative organization. To apply
any regulatory system and to carry out an effective schedule of cutting and other forest management work, identification of particular stands and areas to be cut or otherwise treated is necessary. Records must also be kept in
terms of significant land units to measure performance
and to guide future operations.

The forest is a manufacturing mechanism like a factory. It works quietly, almost imperceptibly, and it is hard
to see what is going on. A forest is not subject to precise
controls; there is no roof over it. Man does not actually
grow trees; nature does that. He can only influence their
growth, mostly through cutting. The forest is a sprawling,
confusing thing, often scattered over many miles of rough
country. To an industrial factory manager, accustomed to
the precision and definiteness of the assembly line, it
might seem excessively dispersed from a managerial standpoint. But a producing factory it is, nonetheless, and the job
of the forest manager is to make this large field factory
efficiently productive in accordance with the purposes
of management whatever they may be—for timber, recreation, water, and the like, in varying proportion and combination. As with any factory, there must be an organiza-

tion to operate it, a physical plant must be maintained, inventory control established, and work performed according to certain standards. This necessitates organization and subdivision of the forest.

factors influencing forest organization and subdivision

The kind of organization and degree of subdivision needed naturally will vary widely with circumstances. The major influencing factors follow:

1. *Establishment and maintenance of land ownership.* How the land was acquired and is distributed in relation to other ownerships and land uses, the need for establishment and maintenance of exterior boundaries trespass and adverse land claims, access problems, and the attitudes of community and political units all have a bearing. For example, long exterior boundaries vulnerable to trespass may entail much expense in establishing marking, sometimes fencing, and in checking land lines. Access routes controlled by other owners may be blocked by locked gates and other restriction causing much difficulty. Local attitudes may aid or seriously hinder protection and management; they may require much time and attention.

2. *Future acquisition plans.* If additional areas are to be acquired where, when, and how much? The answer affects both administration and forest subdivisions.

3. *Scope and character of work to be done.* Is the work dominantly production of timber, or are other forest uses involved and in what degree This question is of major importance in public and of considerable importance in private ownership. Timber production may or may not be of major concern, and, in any event, there is increasing need to integrate and balance timber with other uses. In industrial ownerships, is the resident manager responsible for procurement of timber from noncompany lands in addition to the management of company lands? Is he responsible for the conduct of logging operations, for the building of roads and other forest developments, for fire control, etc.?

4. *Work load and supervision.* How large a work load and personnel unit can a professional man effectively direct on the ground? The size and structure of an efficient administrative field unit is primarily a function of the volume and complexity of the work to be done rather than of acreage The size and character of supervisory units above the direct field operating level are also strongly influenced by work load.

5. *Marketing areas.* A particular forest property or a part of it may logically be tributary to a particular mill, city, or community, and this will naturally influence its organization and division.

6. *Topography.* In many instances the character of the terrain may

ractically dictate and control forest subdivision. This is particularly true
n mountainous areas where the conduct of cutting operations is largely
etermined by drainage lines and other topographic features.

7. *Transportation facilities.* The availability of transportation facilities
xerts a powerful influence on the organization of a forest. In many forest
reas, transportation from stump to market is the limiting factor. Opening
p a forest area by good roads or waterways changes the whole administra-
ive situation. In such a situation, forest subdivision is largely controlled
y transportation. Although transportation means, such as railroads and
oads, are naturally related to topography, they are only partly controlled
y it.

8. *Character of the forest.* Whether the forest is dominantly of heavy
ld-growth timber or largely cut over, partially stocked, in need of artificial
egeneration, etc., has an important bearing on forest administration. Simi-
arly, the number and character of dissimilar and permanent forest types,
uch as hardwood, conifer, or swamp types requiring widely differing treat-
nent, affect the operation of the property.

9. *Inventory and record-keeping needs.* Some sort of inventory control
nd record of operations must be kept in convenient and meaningful sub-
nits of the forest (Chap. 12).

The above listing is not complete and could be greatly expanded. The
elative importance of these influencing factors varies widely from area to
rea and organization to organization. The enumeration does, however, in-
licate the range of considerations involved. The extent and character of
orest organization and subdivision needed in a given situation is controlled
y the interplay and comparative importance of these and related factors.

orest organization

The purpose of a forest organization is to get the job done. This should
lways be kept in mind and organization never carried beyond the point
where it serves a definite need commensurate with cost. Existing forest or-
anizations, while having many similarities, also have significant differences.
t is important to perceive the reason for these differences, to be chary
f custom for its own sake, and constantly to seek that organization pattern
est suited to the specific job at hand.

The beginning point in studying forest organization is the primary ad-
ninistrative unit responsible for on-the-ground administration. One charac-
eristic common to practically all successful forestry organizations is estab-
ishment of field units each in the charge of a professionally trained man
who is directly responsible for forest land administration. Such units are
usually evolutionary in development. Their size and the kind of work to

be done changes as the needs of management unfold. The geographic and land-management oriented nature of forestry strongly tends to require the existence of responsible field units.

In national forest administration by the U.S. Forest Service, the primary land operating unit is the district in the charge of a professionally trained man. The district ranger is the man on the ground directly responsible for the resource management of a specific forest area. As a part of a very large organization that is continental in scope with broad responsibilities, the ranger is guided by higher-level policies, procedures, and supervision. Nonetheless, the Forest Service is strongly decentralized, and the district ranger executes most of the resource protection and management work on his district, of which timber production is one though often not the dominant land use. To most forest users, national forest administration is what the district ranger says it is. He is a key man in a career position.

The size and character of the district staff depends on the job to be done. The ranger usually has one or more professionally trained assistants and several nontechnical men on a yearly basis. Because much work is of a seasonal nature, frequently strongly so, he often has a considerable number of seasonal employees for protection against fire, for forest development, timber sale, recreation, and other work. During peak work-load periods especially, the district ranger may direct an organization of substantial size. District size is highly variable. If timber and other work are intensive, the district may include not more than about 50,000 acres. If management is extensive and applied to lands of relatively low per-acre value with protection a dominant concern, the district may comprise several hundred thousand acres, 300,000 is not unusual.

With many variations, the same general organizational pattern is found in other public forestry agencies, Federal and state. Almost always, administrative organization is built on a district or similar field unit. Titles vary as do the character and intensity of the work. Organizational differences are greater in the supervisory organization, the form of which depends in considerable degree on the size and responsibilities of the agency.

Organization for timber production can be more clearly seen in large industrial ownerships in which utilization of the timber resource is the primary concern. Here again, a unit field organization is characteristic; there is a man on the ground, usually professionally trained and directly responsible for the administration of a particular forest area. Terminology is variable; such men are termed "district," "unit," "area," or "block" foresters. In the western United States, the term "tree farm" is sometimes used to designate a district operating unit employing a professional forester.

The size of field units is variable with the intensity of management practiced. In Canadian practice, they are often very large, approximating the size of large national forest districts in the United States. In United States industrial practice, operating units may also be rather large, but there is a strong trend toward smaller units that a single forester, normally with a small staff, can intimately know and directly administer. An area of 25,000 acres—or less—is increasingly coming to be considered as constituting a full work load under the direct charge of a forester. Forest units managed by individuals or small partnerships are usually much smaller. There is no such thing as a standard area and staff size; it all depends on the job to be done. In other countries in which practice is older and more intensive, small field units are common.

While the field unit is of major importance, it is necessary to consider the total organization of a forest property to understand its relation to the operation as a whole. The professional direction and supervision of a field forester comes from his superiors. Many jobs necessary in the operation of a large property cannot be done by the land manager. In United States industrial practice and elsewhere, the strong trend is to place full responsibility for all forestry activities in a single organizational unit, sometimes headed by a company vice president but, in any event, by a woodlands manager or director reporting to top management. In addition to management of company-owned lands, woodland organizations are usually responsible for purchase of timber from noncompany lands needed to meet mill requirements, for land acquisition and sale, for conduct of education and assistance work with small private owners, for the handling of public relations, and for other work incident to forestry interests.

Figures 11.1 and 11.2 give in condensed form the organization charts of two large woodland organizations that exemplify both significant similarities and differences in structure. In Fig. 11.1 management of company-owned lands is departmentally separated from procurement of timber from noncompany lands, although there is close field liaison. As shown, the woodlands division manager has a headquarters staff with the direct administrative line to the three levels of land managing units through the Land Department. There is a close relationship between the Technical Control Department, which is the general technical center of timber management work, and the field units. Forest inventory work is mainly done in the latter.

In the other organization (Fig. 11.2), the management of company-owned lands and procurement of timber from noncompany lands is combined and handled by the district foresters. The Chief Forester has a substantial staff and responsibility for the technical aspects of timber management, although line authority to field foresters is through the production superintendent. This use of the Chief Forester designation is fairly common, although this position may also carry direct line authority to the field. Most of the larger organizations are headed by a woodland manager, or person of similar title, illustrating the broad business responsibilities of woodland units that usually go considerably beyond management of company-owned lands.

Organizations vary considerably but have in common a manager in

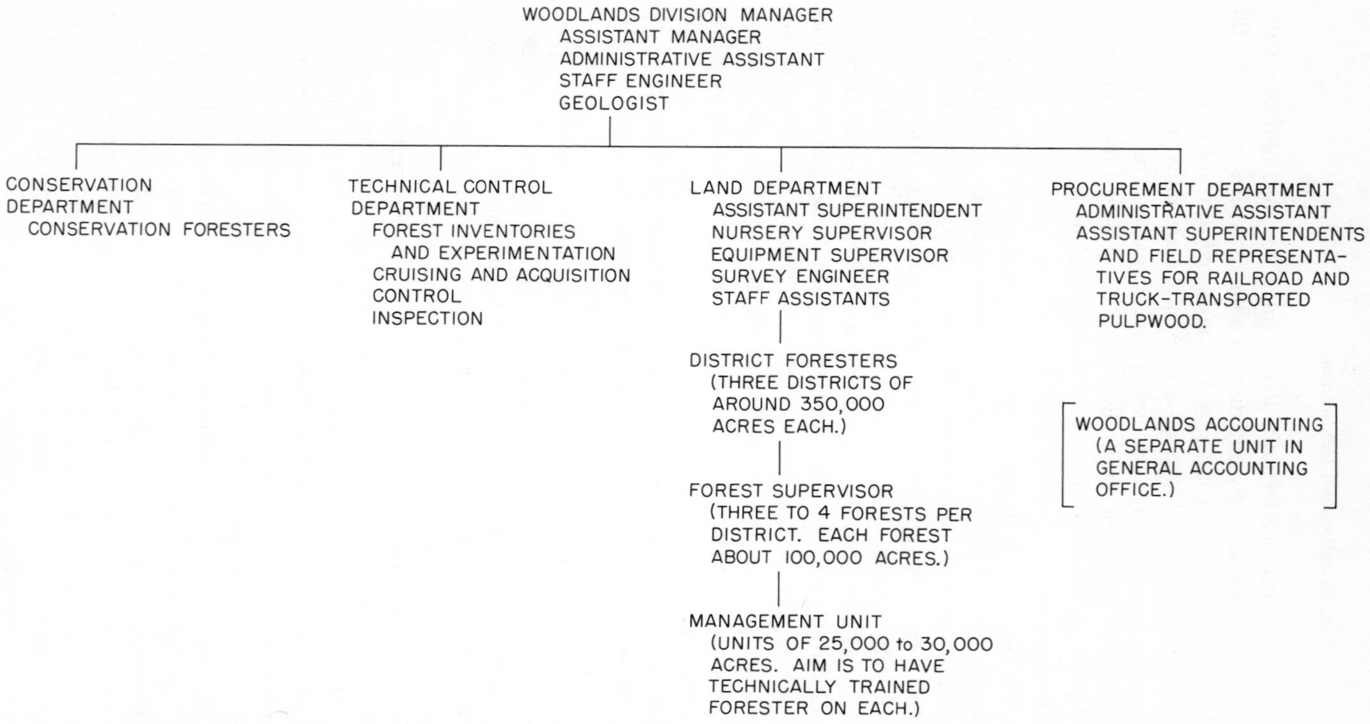

WOODLANDS DIVISION MANAGER
ASSISTANT MANAGER
ADMINISTRATIVE ASSISTANT
STAFF ENGINEER
GEOLOGIST

CONSERVATION
DEPARTMENT
CONSERVATION FORESTERS

TECHNICAL CONTROL
DEPARTMENT
FOREST INVENTORIES
AND EXPERIMENTATION
CRUISING AND ACQUISITION
CONTROL
INSPECTION

LAND DEPARTMENT
ASSISTANT SUPERINTENDENT
NURSERY SUPERVISOR
EQUIPMENT SUPERVISOR
SURVEY ENGINEER
STAFF ASSISTANTS

DISTRICT FORESTERS
(THREE DISTRICTS OF
AROUND 350,000
ACRES EACH.)

FOREST SUPERVISOR
(THREE TO 4 FORESTS PER
DISTRICT. EACH FOREST
ABOUT 100,000 ACRES.)

MANAGEMENT UNIT
(UNITS OF 25,000 to 30,000
ACRES. AIM IS TO HAVE
TECHNICALLY TRAINED
FORESTER ON EACH.)

PROCUREMENT DEPARTMENT
ADMINISTRATIVE ASSISTANT
ASSISTANT SUPERINTENDENTS
AND FIELD REPRESENTA-
TIVES FOR RAILROAD AND
TRUCK-TRANSPORTED
PULPWOOD.

WOODLANDS ACCOUNTING
(A SEPARATE UNIT IN
GENERAL ACCOUNTING
OFFICE.)

FIG. 11.1. ORGANIZATION CHART (CONDENSED) FOR WOODLAND OPERATIONS OF A LARGE PULP AND PAPER COMPANY IN THE SOUTHEASTERN UNITED STATES.

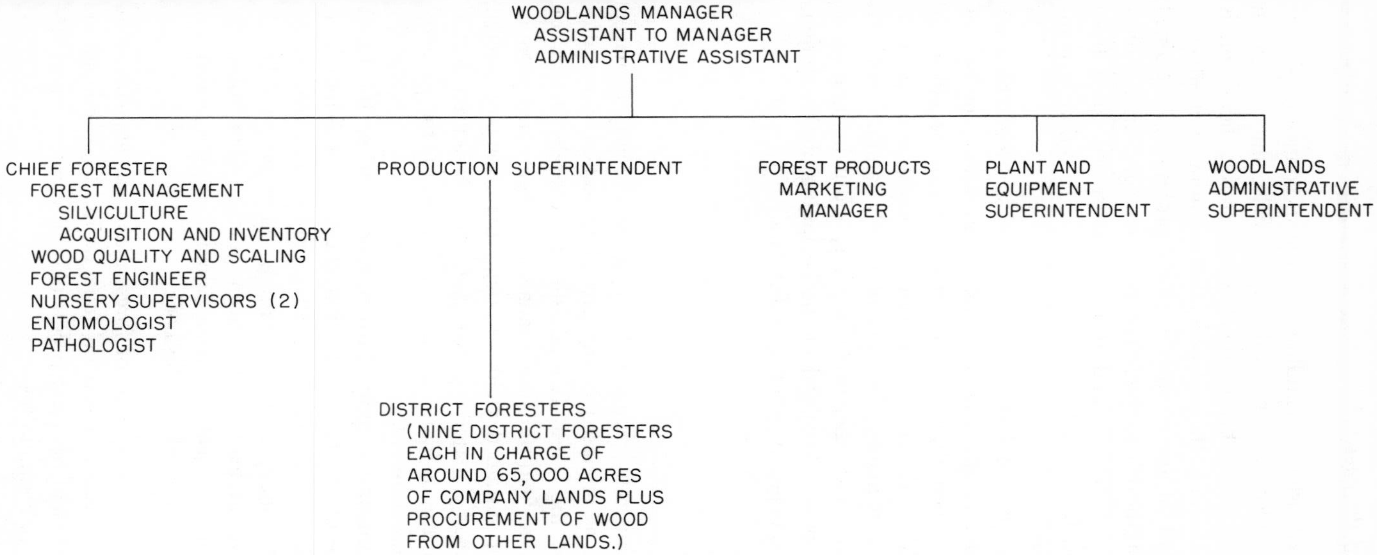

WOODLANDS MANAGER
ASSISTANT TO MANAGER
ADMINISTRATIVE ASSISTANT

CHIEF FORESTER
FOREST MANAGEMENT
SILVICULTURE
ACQUISITION AND INVENTORY
WOOD QUALITY AND SCALING
FOREST ENGINEER
NURSERY SUPERVISORS (2)
ENTOMOLOGIST
PATHOLOGIST

PRODUCTION SUPERINTENDENT

DISTRICT FORESTERS
(NINE DISTRICT FORESTERS
EACH IN CHARGE OF
AROUND 65,000 ACRES
OF COMPANY LANDS PLUS
PROCUREMENT OF WOOD
FROM OTHER LANDS.)

FOREST PRODUCTS
MARKETING
MANAGER

PLANT AND
EQUIPMENT
SUPERINTENDENT

WOODLANDS
ADMINISTRATIVE
SUPERINTENDENT

FIG. 11.2. ORGANIZATION CHART (CONDENSED) FOR THE WOODLANDS DEPARTMENT OF A LARGE PULP AND PAPER COMPANY IN THE LAKE STATES.

charge, a headquarters staff usually including a technical control or similar main office group, and a clear line of authority to field units of which there may be one or more levels before the basic operating field unit is reached. As with public agencies, there is general recognition that effective on-the-ground management of forest areas requires professionally trained foresters given sufficient authority to discharge land management responsibilities. Although policies, directives, and technical assistance come from the central office, the field forester is given considerable discretion in managing the area in his charge.

To summarize, a number of factors influence the size and character of field units. Work load and the kind of total organization are two of them. Also important are such things as an area that can be efficiently administered from a field headquarters without excessive time spent in travel, the need for the forest manager to become closely familiar with the forest, the location of schools and other urban services, and living and housing considerations for personnel. As stated at the beginning of this section, the primary consideration is to get the job done efficiently.

forest subdivision

The organization of administrative units within a forest property managed for continued production, as discussed in the preceding section, constitutes the primary subdivision of the forest. It establishes the overall pattern for management. Administrative field units are managed for continued production and in this sense for sustained yield, although uniformity of annual cut is usually not necessarily a major aim for each unit. A desired degree of continuity of harvest cutting is more commonly achieved for the property as a whole or for major subdivisions of it.

In addition to administrative units, further subdivision of the forest is usually necessary to execute timber production plans. Forest subdivision has had a long history, and over the years some terminology has been established that it is helpful to understand and employ consistently—although such is often not the case, at least in American practice. The following terminology applying to this subject has been adopted by the Society of American Foresters (1958) and is used in this book.

> *Working Circle.* The primary unit of forest management, with well-defined boundaries, usually based on topography, large enough to furnish a sustained yield of forest products sufficient to support dependent industries or communities.
>
> *Administrative Working Circle.* An area comprising one or more ownerships managed as a unit under a management plan.
>
> *Economic Working Circle.* A forest area tributary to a central market

or to manufacturing centers, but not necessarily under single ownership or management.

Working Group.   Comprises those parts of a forest that have the same silvicultural management and rotation.

Block.   A major administrative division of the forest usually based on topography and including several compartments and logging chances.

Compartment.   An organization unit or small subdivision of forest area for purposes of orientation, administration, and silvicultural operations, and defined by permanent boundaries, either of natural features or artificially marked, which are not necessarily coincident with stand boundaries.

Chance.   Strictly, any unit or operation in the woods; with many and varied applications, of which the most familiar is *logging* or *cutting* chance, a logging or pulpwood operating unit.

Subcompartment.   A subdivision of a compartment, requiring different treatment from that for other portions of the compartment, and based on the stand.

Stand.   An aggregation of trees or other growth occupying a specific area and sufficiently uniform in composition (species), age arrangement, and condition as to be distinguishable from the forest or other growth on adjoining areas.

Cutting Series.   An allotment of stands into a sequence of cutting areas for the purpose of securing reproduction and protection. Syn. *Felling series.*

Usage of these terms in American practice is given below.

WORKING CIRCLE

The term "working circle" is used to designate a primary and usually a rather sizable forest management unit in which sustained yield is a major consideration in forest organization (Chap. 1). It is a regulatory planning unit. The term is applied principally in the national forests wherein timber management is largely organized in terms of working circles of which there are about 425 recognized. Here, working circles normally coincide with an administrative unit. The trend is to organize working circles on a national forest basis, although a ranger district, or two or more districts constituting a natural group, is often regarded as a working circle unit. This brings out the fact that, although a working circle is a major forest operating and planning unit, it is not necessarily also a single administrative unit. In national forest practice, management plans are prepared by working circle units but may be subdivided, as by ranger districts where two or more are included.

Large industrial ownerships may be broken up into a number of operating units, each managed with a sustained-yield objective. Such units vary from a few hundred to 50,000 acres or more in area. Essentially, they are working circles, though often not designated as such. A factor in determining their size may be the need to establish stable local employment. If sparsely settled, an area large enough to make an economical camp operation on a stable yearly basis may be necessary. In other situations, smaller units, perhaps no more than enough to give regular woods employment to a family or two, may be desirable. (Several such units may be handled by one administrative officer.) The working circle concept of sustained-yield units is, consequently, very flexible in application. Support of dependent industry or community has largely dropped out of usage in the term.

BLOCK

Within a primary administrative unit (or a working circle if such a designation is used) there may be one or more levels of subdivision, depending on need and circumstances. The block is a land division, the general nature of which is well described by its definition, although in practice the term is often loosely and variously applied. Its use is one of administrative convenience in identifying a particular land area of considerable size, often several thousands of acres. Blocks are sometimes administrative management units or groups of units. Sometimes the block is a designation of more geographic than organizational or operating entity. Where topography exerts considerable influence, a grouping of lands in a particular area, or a drainage, might logically be designated as a block. This may happen when a forest is established by piecemeal purchase. For example, a large paper company may own lands in a particular state that naturally block up in two or more areas. The state ownership as a whole might be designated as a district or operating unit, with holdings within the state grouped into blocks.

COMPARTMENT AND LOGGING CHANCE

Within a block (if the designation is used) or within an administrative unit or working circle, the compartment is the primary unit of subdivision. Compartment size is highly variable. It may range from perhaps 5 acres to several thousand, depending on circumstances.

The need for and utility of a compartment is essentially a function of the intensity of management practiced. It is a practical necessity under intensive management but may not be needed when extensive management is initiated. The compartment designation is consistently used in the national forests of the United States. How they can be and are employed is well described by Gross (1950) :

> The compartment is an excellent planning unit by which the provisions of the management plan are localized. It is useful in developing adequate transportation, in allocating the annual cut, in achieving adherence to cutting cycles and cutting budgets, in planting, insect and disease control, and in other management activities.
>
> Minor drainages usually constitute compartments, although in areas of relatively easy topography, sections or other land units may be used. Any compartment may contain a variety of types, stands, and age classes. Size will vary with character of topography, methods of logging, and to some extent, with timber stands. Often compartments will constitute natural logging units. Under intensive management it may be desirable to maintain records of volume, growth, timber cut, planting, timber stand improvement, etc., by compartments. Thus, the basic data for the working circle are broken down into units more easily comprehended.

A logging chance designates a natural cutting unit. It is usually defined by a combination of topography and transportation factors and may suffice for identification of areas within a block or other large unit. For example, in the United States a large western industrial company, operating in terms of tree farm units, divides each unit into blocks defined by major drainage lines. Within each block, spur roads and secondary logging roads tributary to one main arterial route are serially numbered. Individual settings (i.e., the area within yarding distance of a spar tree along these roads) are also identified by number with respect to the road system. By this system, the source of logs can be identified from the time felling is done until they reach the mill. In thinning and stand improvement operations, the location of the area treated is identified by the road number and setting along the road. To the degree that the logging chance constitutes a natural and permanent working unit, it becomes a compartment. A compartment structure consequently may evolve from one or more of these natural logging units.

STAND OR SUBCOMPARTMENT

All the forest subdivisions discussed up to this point are employed primarily to identify land units on the ground for administrative purposes. The application of silviculture on the ground also requires that specific and often rather small areas be distinguished by silvicultural characteristics and treatment needs. Forestry can be and is organized in large units, but it must be applied stand by stand and often group by group and tree by tree. For this reason, no consideration of forest subdivision is complete without recognition of the stand as the inescapable silvicultural application unit.

How to give systematic recognition to the individual stand is often a problem in management. A stand, as its definition indicates, is a homogenous forest condition or a situation, arbitrarily defined, that can be recognized on the ground. From the standpoint of management, the significant point is that one stand exhibits some significant difference from other adjoining stands in treatment needs. There may be several stands present in a single compartment, each requiring individual consideration.

A stand is not a forest type as commonly classified. The latter is a broader designation emphasizing species composition and ecological status. A stand represents a particular forest condition within a type. Even when types are subdivided by standard age, size, and stocking classes, they do not serve as a basis for specific management planning. General forest types or arbitrary stand designations of this kind give inadequate recognition of specific forest conditions and treatment needs.

Stands are essentially temporary; they are subject to change over the years. Their occurrence in unmanaged forests is often highly irregular in relation to topographic features, to survey lines, or to transportation routes. The existence, number, and distribution of stands initially present in an area may bear little resemblance to what is desired.

Under intensive management, stand conditions requiring substantially different silvicultural treatment may be recognized as subcompartments. The subcompartment then becomes the silvicultural application unit. To the extent that it is practicable or desirable, it also may be a record-keeping unit. With a compartment system, any particular stand within it can be readily located. Boundaries of subcompartments (or stands) should be considered as semipermanent to be changed as stand conditions are modified under management. A frequent aim is to consolidate and unify stand conditions within a compartment to permit application of area treatments and generally to simplify management.

LEGAL LAND DESCRIPTIONS AS FOREST SUBDIVISIONS

Discussion of compartments and of subcompartments or stands in relation to larger forest subdivisions naturally brings up the question: Where and how do legal land descriptions fit into a plan of forest subdivision? The question can also be reversed: How does forest subdivision fit in with legal land descriptions, which are the basis of land ownership? Timber and timberlands are bought and sold, taxes are paid, and other responsibilities and privileges of landownership are measured in terms of legal land descriptions.

In the United States the major portion of the commercial forest land area is covered by the rectilinear township and range land survey. The remainder is covered by metes and bounds surveys defining specific tracts and subdivisions. In either case, lands can be legally described only in terms of official land subdivision units. Under the rectilinear surveys, these are numbered sections 1 mile square (640 acres) and subdivisions thereof of which the square 40-acre tract, or the lot in irregular sections, is the smallest usually recognized. By reference to the grid of township and range lines (at 6-mile intervals) the location of any section is exactly described. Timber estimating is commonly done and volumes recorded in section, quarter-section, and often 40-acre units.

American foresters commonly think of timber stands and specific land areas in relation to legal land subdivisions. With a map showing topographic and land culture features in relation to survey lines, any area can be readily located. Forest-type surveys are almost universally superimposed on a land survey base. Because of their exactness and widespread use, legal land descriptions are a method of land identification par excellence. They also give convenient units for the systematic keeping of maps and other land records.

Legal land subdivisions, because they define ownership units, often have considerable forest significance in areas that have been cut over. This is particularly true when, in the process of building up a forest property, lands are purchased from various owners. Past ownership and use often has much to do with present forest condition. For this reason, stand conditions are frequently related to legal land subdivisions.

Legal land subdivisions, which almost universally exist and have meaning irrespective of management, are consequently a major consideration in forest subdivision. For many landowners, and particularly where ownership is not well consolidated, legal land subdivisions are the only land unit recognized. To put it another way, they are recognized whether other units are or not. In effect, they serve much of the identification function of a compartment and it is important to recognize this point. If there were no public land survey offering an excellent system of land identification, then some other kind of compartment designation would be much more widely used. In fact, where land survey lines are lacking, a compartment designation is practically mandatory. Forest types or stands, to the extent they are recognized, are often considered a subdivision of a land survey unit. Records of areas treated, stand inventories, volumes cut and sold, etc., are commonly kept by land survey units. Data by individual stands within land survey units can be segregated in the same way as subcompartment records are separated in a compartment. This can be rather easily done if cruise data as taken in the field are identified by types or stands as is often done.

The obvious disadvantage to the use of legal descriptions as forest subdivisions is that they are entirely arbitrary and bear no necessary relation to topography or to natural forest cover types. In mountainous areas they usually have little or no relation to transportation routes either. Where lands are well consolidated, land lines tend to become less important as areas can be identified by natural features such as drainages or in relation to an existing road system. The more intensive the management, the more there is need to work in terms of natural and logical forest units. Where ownership is scattered and management extensive, land survey units furnish a fairly adequate means of stand identification and often suffice. When subdivision is carried down to the forty, the arbitrary nature of these units in relation to natural stand boundaries becomes less important, since stands of substantial size can be approximately defined by 40-acre units. In cutover forest areas and particularly where the topography is easy, there is some tendency for stand boundaries to follow survey lines anyway as a consequence of past landownership and use.

In any event, legal land subdivisions exist, they are units of ownership, and public land lines are the primary basis for forest surveys. As such, they can never be ignored in subdividing a forest and in the keeping of forest records. They may or may not be actual operating units. In many situations, they serve the basic identification function of a compartment fairly well. As management becomes more intensive and the need apparent, logically bounded compartments can be established and the use of land survey units largely confined to uses in connection with taxation, assessment, land purchase, sale or trespass, where legal identification of land areas is necessary.

the working group and cutting series

In developing regulatory controls for a forest area and in devising overall plans for cutting, there is frequently need for the systematic consideration of groups of stands requiring similar treatment. Suppose, for example, that a forest management unit, whether it be an administrative unit or a working circle, contains two kinds of forest conditions: those that are to be managed under an even-aged plan and those that are to receive uneven-aged treatment. A forest area containing well-defined and permanent hardwood and coniferous types is an example. As brought out in Chaps. 7, 8, and 9, there is no practical way simultaneously to regulate and organize a forest according to an even-aged and an uneven-aged framework of management; each demands separate consideration. Another illustration is two or more forest types requiring even-aged treatment that differ markedly in species composition and require different rotations. They cannot effectively be handled as a single unit in calculating an allowable annual cut or in working toward a desirable age-class distribution. For this reason it is frequently necessary to group stands requiring the same general silvicultural treatment and rotation as a working group. This may also be necessary in organizing the handling of uneven-aged stands where different cutting cycles should be applied because of varying forest conditions.

If the entire forest administrative unit can be handled under the same regulatory framework, then the working group obviously is the same thing as the unit, and there is no need for the working group designation. The existence of several fairly distinct conditions necessitating different treatment is, however, a common situation on large forest properties. Here, as many working groups should be recognized as there are significantly different stand conditions requiring separate regulatory treatment. No rule can be given. In general, the fewer separate regulatory working groups recognized the better, but such grouping should not be carried to the point where really important differences are obscured. In initiating management, it is usually better to start with relatively few groups and then to subdivide them as experience shows this to be desirable.

It should be emphasized that a working group is established for technical reasons and may or may not be a permanent land designation on the ground. The component parts of a working group may be considerably dispersed over the forest so far as actual location is concerned. Recognition of such groups should be regarded as an aid in applying regulatory and silvicultural analysis and made only when and where it serves a useful purpose. The use of working groups is most logical where organization for sustained yield is a major objective. To organize a large forest area including widely dissimilar forest conditions into a producing unit, recognition of working groups becomes almost a practical necessity. If regular annual or periodic cuts are of less urgency, then there is less need for use of working groups, since stands can be kept productive by treating each in accordance with the silvicultural procedures and managerial policies applied on the forest.

Within a working group, there may be certain parts that should be considered separately. An example would be a fairly large area of overmature timber included in an even-aged working group. On this area, it may be necessary to give special attention to the order and distribution of cutting to best obtain regeneration and to reduce losses through windthrow, insects, disease, or other agencies causing loss in the forest. The arrangement of cutting in a particular sequence is termed a cutting or felling series. The need for recognition of a cutting series depends on circumstances. It may be a very critical factor, as in planning strip or group cuttings for the natural regeneration of spruce, for example. In other situations the sequence of cutting may have no particular significance so far as silvicultural consequences are concerned. This is a point to be determined on the ground; but in no event can the order and distribution of cutting on the ground be ignored.

12

forest inventory control

It is axiomatic that continued management of a forest area requires a large amount and continuing flow of varied and usable information. This is true for any forest use and certainly so for timber production, the specific concern here. Ways and means of getting and using such information are of major importance.

Inventories are as old as forestry and are made for many purposes. In the initial stages of timber management, such inventories are of the stock type, placing primary emphasis on how much merchantable timber and other currently available resources there are. As practice develops, emphasis changes from merely cutting a stock of existing timber to organization of forest areas for continued production (Chap. 1). Inventory information needed accordingly shifts from a stock to a production or flow-type inventory needed to guide continuing and increasingly intensive management, area by area.

The dictionary definition of the word "inventory" basically means a listing, an itemization of goods, materials, or other stock in a business. This is the normal meaning to a businessman. Used in forestry, the term has to take a broader meaning primarily because a tree is both a factory and a utilizable product with no clear distinction between the two. Indeed, the central problem of timber management is to make this distinction, to decide which trees should be reserved as growing stock (the factory) and which should be cut at a particular time (the product). For this reason, forest inventory means more than a mere enumeration of merchantable products. It includes information on the dynamics of the factory, on growth, quality, treatment needs, and many other things that go beyond a listing of what there *is* at a given time. The term "forest survey" as defined by the Society of American Foresters (1958)[1] approximates this broader meaning. Addition of the word "control" connotes that the inventory information is built into and used as a control in the organizational framework for continuing management. Forest inventory control consequently means and is directed to the gathering of information needed to serve the purposes of management. It does not mean collecting data for its own sake or being enamored by the wonders of modern statistical techniques. This cannot be emphasized too strongly. Purposes must always come first and procedures second.

The purpose of this chapter is twofold. It is, first, to present in broad review total forest information needs for continuing management. This is needed to give overall perspective so that specific needs can be appraised. These needs include information not obtained from the forest trees and associated vegetation as well as that from these sources. Second, it is to give principal methods of getting information from surveys directly based on the forest itself. These are of most immediate concern to the forester, and the focus of the chapter is primarily upon them. Throughout, the emphasis is on getting information to meet the needs of management, primarily for timber production. Administrative, mensurational, statistical, and computational methods and techniques are included only to the extent necessary; any full treatment of them as applied to the forest is beyond the scope of this book.

total forest information needs of management

Total forest information needs of management can usefully be grouped into three general categories:

1. That exterior to the forest itself in origin. This includes landownership and other pertinent information obtained from sources often far removed from the forest.

2. That coming directly from the growing forest and associated ecosystem. These are forest surveys of various kinds.

3. That arising from the administrative operation of a forest property—operations information.

The nature of each of these three general categories of information sources will be reviewed.

---

[1] This definition is: "An inventory of forest land to determine area, condition, timber volume, and species, for specific purposes such as timber purchase, forest management, or as a basis for forest policies and programs." Because of its wide usage, "survey" is sometimes used in this chapter as an alternative to "inventory."

INFORMATION EXTERIOR TO THE FOREST

A large and varied amount of information is needed that does not come from the forest itself. Though difficult to categorize neatly, it is surely important. The following listing of major items will characterize the group:

1. *Landownership data.* Titles, deeds, leases, easements, acquisition, sale, exchange, adverse claims, boundaries, and other records concerning the establishment and maintenance of land title and control. Includes information on other ownerships intermingled with or otherwise significant to management of the property.

2. *Physical facilities and land data.* Transportation facilities by rail, road, and water that are available and needed in the future; topographic, drainage, basic soil, and geological information; character and location of buildings and other improvements; power, communication, oil and gas lines.

3. *Markets and timber supply.* Outlets for different kinds and sizes of forest products, prices and trends; timber supply in the area as it affects price and availability; competitive situation in general.

4. *Labor supply.* Kind and quantity, seasonal trends, wage trends, unionization, applicable laws.

5. *Political and public relations situation.* Relationships with local, state, and national government; private organizations. Land taxes often a major item.

6. *Administrative and financial organization.* How the organization was established, methods of finance and accounting. Few large industrial organizations are concerned with only timber; woodlands are usually a part of a large production complex. Public organizations also usually have other than forest interests, and their statutory and organizational nature may importantly affect forest operating practices.

7. *Other forest uses.* Increasing pressures for other than timber uses are often of major concern in forest land management.

8. *Weather and climate in general.* May deeply affect timber and other forest operations and necessitate close study.

9. *Protection.* The situation and needs regarding protection against fire, insects, and disease.

10. *Engineering and equipment.* Construction and maintenance of facilities in general; design and use of equipment; boundary line and other surveying needs, aerial photos, etc.

This is a heterogenous listing showing the kind and variety of information needed that does not come from the forest itself. Many of the items may be of critical significance in a particular forest situation. It is not possible here to do anything more than indicate their importance.

INFORMATION FROM THE FOREST

Information from the forest is obtained from various kinds of surveys. The listing here excludes that from research and is limited to major categories directly concerned with timber production.

1. *Area data.* Forest land areas by forest type, age, and stocking classes, and other items that may be needed.

2. *Timber volume data.* Volumes in cubic feet, board feet, cords, or other appropriate units by species, size, merchantability standards, quality, etc. These data are subdivided by area classifications as may be desired.

3. *Stand data.* Information about specific stands including such items as stocking, age, site, and per-acre stock and stand tables by species or species groups.

4. *Individual tree data.* Information classified by species including diameter, height, age, vigor, product suitability, rate of growth, etc.

5. *Forest dynamics or "change" data.* Included here is information that gives forest, stand, and tree changes with time. Increment and mortality are principal items (Chap. 4).

As with forest information exterior to the forest, this listing is not complete and is very condensed. It does, however, include the principal kinds of forest-centered information with which the forester is concerned.

OPERATIONS INFORMATION

Information arising through the operation of the forest business is another major and important source of data used in management often not considered in relation to inventories. It comes from the forest but is not obtained by forest surveys. Any continuing organization must establish a schedule of reports, a system of records, and other operating procedures. These are designed to measure performance and give managerial control. Although administrative management as such cannot be considered here, a review of items relating fairly directly to forest operation will indicate their significance in yielding information needed for management. These include:

1. *Cutting budgets.* Most organizations establish a procedure for the preparation and scheduling of cutting by periods and by location (Chap. 13).

2. *Cutting reports.* Close check is kept on the progress of cutting with frequent reports. These are especially important in industrial organizations with a mill to supply. Accurate and current data are essential on all timber supply sources.

3. *Timber cutting administration.* This includes marking or otherwise designating timber for cutting, establishment of boundaries, timber estimate and appraisal, preparation of cutting or sale agreement, timber scaling or otherwise measuring products cut, and supervision. Procedures for such work are prescribed and reports are required yielding much performance information.

4. *Site preparation and planting.* Budgets are prepared; time, cost, and area records are kept; and plantation success is measured.

5. *Noncommercial cultural operations.* Plans and budgets are prepared and progress currently reported for release cuttings, removal of low-value trees, and the like.

6. *Receipts from timber and other forest goods and services sold.* Accurate and itemized records are necessary.

7. *Work-load planning.* Certain things have to be done at certain times. Careful manpower and equipment-use scheduling are necessary.

8. *Personnel time and activity cost reporting.* It is necessary to account for people's time. Most organizations keep rather detailed activity cost records.

9. *Special time, cost, and other operations studies.*

10. *Vehicle and other equipment.* Records are kept of equipment allocation and use, maintenance, and costs. Equipment control is a large subject in itself and extremely important in many organizations.

11. *Inspection.* A schedule and procedure for inspection must be established.

The above indicates the wide range of operations information. It is necessary for legal and tax purposes, upper-level management, and for administrative control. What often seems an amazing volume of paper work is employed in the operation of a large forest as in almost any other kind of organization.

Broadly speaking, surveys yield information from the forest that must be combined with performance data and administrative planning to get work done on the ground. For example, a survey may indicate a need for site preparation and planting. Performance data from operating experience, and research, are necessary to determine methods and cost. Finally, the job must be budgeted, financed, scheduled, organized, and executed through the administrative organization. The complementary nature of forest survey and operations information in getting the job done is apparent.

The practicing forester must expect to spend a substantial amount of time working with operations information. He should appreciate its importance and to the fullest extent possible design procedures to obtain such information with a strict eye for its usefulness. Like forest survey procedures, it is a means and not an end.

forest inventories

There are three general kinds of inventories applied on forest lands:

1. Independent sampling systems
2. Permanent sampling systems
3. Unit area systems or stand description

All are important, have their place, and are widely used. To only limited degree is one kind a substitute or an alternative for another; they should be regarded as essentially complementary. Independent inventories, as considered here, are primarily designed to get a certain body of information at a given time. They may be repeated and often are, but usually there is no commitment that they will be precisely remade. Permanent sampling systems are aimed to give a continuing and consistent flow of forest information. Identical areas and trees are remeasured, although often supplemented by temporary samples. Uniformity in measurement standards and procedures are major characteristics, because these surveys are specifically designed to be repeated. Unit area or in-place inventories are designed to give on-the-ground forest information by individual stands to guide their treatment. These surveys are periodically repeated.

Procedures followed and uses of each kind of inventory are given in the following sections.

INDEPENDENT SAMPLING SYSTEMS

From the standpoint of obtaining the maximum amount of data at a given time, for a particular purpose, and at minimum cost, a well-designed independent sampling system is in general the most efficient. Full choice is possible in the selection of the sampling design to get the specific information desired from a single sample with maximum efficiency. For example, if forest soil or cover types are distributed in recognizable strata that differ significantly in variability or value, as is often the case, sampling error and costs can be reduced through stratified sampling in obtaining information at a desired level of accuracy.[1]

Full choice of sampling methods or combination of methods is also possible. Strip sampling, line plots, systematic plot grids of various proportions, random plots, double sampling, and different kinds of restricted ran-

[1] For specific information on sampling designs and methods, see Schumacher and Chapman (1948), Spurr (1952, 1960), Bruce and Schumacher (1950), Cochran (1953), and other references listed in the Bibliography. General treatment of sampling theory applied to forestry is not possible here. Treatment is here limited to appraisal of kinds of methods together with their advantages and disadvantages.

dom sampling may be employed if suitable to the particular purpose. In addition to area plots, Bitterlich angle count or point sampling is widely employed. Also used is point sampling of the type designed to obtain occurrence data, i.e., whether a quadrat or other point is occupied or not (Chap. 2).

Aerial photos are useful primarily in getting area information (Spurr, 1960, and others). Supplemented by ground checking, good aerial photos can be interpreted to define many forest types, major soil types especially when associated with geological formations or vegetative cover types, stand size and density classes, nonforest areas, etc. Tree height and crown diameter can be measured with considerable accuracy from good photos, and through these measurements gross timber volumes can be estimated with rather low accuracy, sometimes sufficient for reconnaissance purposes. In general, anything that can be seen from the air can be interpreted from aerial photos of adequate scale, quality, and photographic technique. Aerial photos are very useful in locating sampling points selected by some acceptable statistical means; photos and ground sampling are efficiently combined in many ways.

Full use can be made of machine computation as is true with most other kinds of surveys. Anything that can be put into number code form, which includes most forest observations, can be handled by computation equipment. What kind of equipment to use is a matter of adequacy, availability, and cost.

Some examples will illustrate different kinds of independent forest inventories.

A Planting Survey. Assume it is desired to determine areas in need of site preparation and planting on a forest district to guide planning and budget preparation. If available, recent aerial photos of good quality would be the best starting point. From them, as well as from general familiarity with the district, areas that may need site preparation and planting can be located and their area fairly accurately determined. Ground reconnaissance would then be necessary, and probably most possible sites would be visited. In accordance with whatever standards and policies are established regarding acceptability of natural regeneration that may be on the ground, soil types, existing forest or other vegetative cover, use of available site preparation and planting equipment, planting priorities, etc., a specific estimate of the job could be made. Continuity of such surveys is not much of a problem, particularly if the planting is to be done fairly soon. If not, the survey probably would have to be repeated anyway, at least in part. Surveys of this type are common for prescribed burning, stand improvement, and similar jobs. A good type map would serve much the same purpose as aerial photos. Treatment areas would be shown on compartment or other unit forest maps in any event.

A Timber Sale. An area is designated for cutting; the need is to prepare it for cutting. Aerial photos again would be useful in showing the terrain, the location of timber of different type and density, etc. A good type, stocking, and age-class forest map would serve the same purpose. The intensity of timber estimate needed would depend on timber value, variability, and means of selling. If the timber is to be sold by tree sale (by direct estimate of volume in the standing tree with no subsequent scaling), the estimate would normally be made as the marking is done by measuring every tree to be cut or by taking a sample, for example, measuring every fifth or tenth tree. If the payment for timber is to be made by scaling after cutting, the estimate would need be only accurate enough not to affect significantly area costs for roads, etc. that may have to be constructed to remove the timber (Chap. 18). Logging roads, if additional ones are needed, would be planned. If the area is to be cut by the owner, tree or log measurement needs would be different, but some intermediate scaling is often necessary because felling, skidding, and loading are often done on a piecework contract basis.

As in all sampling problems, needed sampling accuracy depends on the use to be made of the information. Depending on the volume, area, value, and variability of the timber stand, sampling intensity could run from 5 to 100 percent. Complete enumeration is not as expensive as might be thought and is applied on areas supporting high timber values.

A General Reconnaissance of a Large Forest Area. This is a problem encountered anywhere in the world where planning is initiated on large, undeveloped, and little-known forest areas. Development of a specific sampling design and survey plan is a complex job; only the major outline of it can be indicated here. A first question is accuracy needed. For large units of a quarter million acres or so, the sampling intensity to yield data of adequate total accuracy would probably require that only a fraction of 1 percent of the area be sampled. A second key question is what degree and accuracy of land survey data are available to permit adequate area determination. In some countries, establishment of considerable ground control may be necessary to establish satisfactory base maps. A third question is what forest information is already available to give some idea of forest types, densities, conditions, and value that will be encountered. Aerial photos are practically indispensable in helping to answer most of these questions. Few major surveys are undertaken without them, and a major initial job may be to get suitable photo coverage.

With these questions and needs met, the job is then to design the survey. This includes decision on sampling methods, specific data to be obtained, organization of crews, and execution of the field work. Computation and summarization of data and preparation of necessary maps is another major job, planning for which starts with the design of the survey, the preparation of recording forms, etc. For a large job, coding to permit use of punch cards and machine computation is advantageous, saving much time and cost in the office job.

For a survey like this, continuity is not a controlling consideration; the purpose is to give a basis for initial planning, for doing first things first, and making a beginning toward management. It can be expected that future surveys will be different in purpose, design, and intensity.

Recurrent Independent Inventories. For various reasons, there is need to make independent inventories of large forest properties at periodic intervals. This is done on a large scale by national or regional surveys in a number of countries and also by individual owners. The survey may be made for the entire area at one time or distributed by years covering a portion each year or perhaps currently sampling the entire area each year on a cumulative basis. In any event, the samples are independent in that identical areas are not revisited.

It is true that independent inventories increase the sampling error of differences between them if they are repeated, in comparison to sampling systems designed to be repeated with remeasurement of permanent plots a major feature. Specifically, the point is that when an independent inventory is repeated, the full sampling error of both surveys enters into the estimate of the significance of difference between the two, not just that due to differences when identical samples are remeasured.[1] However, if the sample from independent surveys is large enough, total differences of management significance in growing stock volumes, species, composition, and the like are obtained that may suffice. Further, there is a continuing check on the validity of the sample; a new sample of the forest is taken with each survey, which avoids large reliance on perpetuation of an initial sample.

Examples of independent surveys could be continued indefinitely; those mentioned indicate the wide range possible from small and limited surveys to very large and complex jobs. All have in common the characteristic of organizing a survey to get a particular job done. They are efficient, have served, and do serve well as a basis for forest planning.

PERMANENT SAMPLING SYSTEMS

Development of management on a permanent production basis logically leads to methods of obtaining a continuing flow of information from the forest to guide it on an equally systematic and permanent basis. The devising and application of such methods underwent much development in about the 1950s in the United States and Canada, concomitant with the great expansion and intensification of forestry application during this period. Few things have been so eagerly grasped, and seldom has Ameri-

---

[1] Hall, (1959) gives a good discussion of the effect of independent and identical plot surveys on the significance of differences as applied to forest surveys.

can talent for exploiting procedures been so well illustrated as in the development of permanent forest sampling systems.[1]

There were a number of contributing factors:

1. The limitations and inefficiency of independent surveys in measuring tree and stand changes over time as mentioned above.

2. The need to get unified and consistent forest data for a property as a whole for management planning. Forest managers were chronically confronted with a mass of mismatched survey data for parts of a property that were taken at different times with varying completeness and measurement standards and that frequently concentrated attention mainly on currently merchantable timber volumes, which are of limited utility in permanent production planning.[2]

3. A natural human yearning for a "system" that would wrap up all forest data needs for continuing forest management in a neat package. There was need to be "businesslike," to be able to present up-to-date information of known accuracy and consistency acceptable to executive management.

4. Major developments in mensuration, statistical methods, aerial photogrammetry, and computational methods enabling much better and more prompt data collection and processing at reasonable expense.

5. A certain fascination for permanent samples coupled with a belief, often not justified, that their careful measurement at periodic intervals will give all or most of the answers needed.

6. Some echoes of the *méthode du controlle* or "check method" devised by the French forester Gurnaud and principally developed by Biolley (1920). See also Meyer (1942), Huber (1952), and Knuchel (1953). This is essentially a system of 100 percent enumerations made at regular intervals, upon which information the management of the forest unit is largely based. In some major respects, American methods are a large-scale sampling version of the same thing. Also inherited in part from the same source is an undercurrent of ill-defined assumption regarding application of uneven-aged management, which these systems have some tendency to imply and best serve.

The basic characteristic of permanent sampling systems is the stress on continuity. This is achieved primarily by measurement of permanent

[1] These systems are frequently termed "Continuous Forest Inventory," or CFI for short. Mr. C. B. Stott of the U.S. Forest Service has made major contributions to their development. However, the term as specifically used is retricted in that it assumes certain techniques and usually complete reliance on permanent samples. There is also a tendency to apply it as a catchword to almost any kind of repeated survey, which can lead to confusion.

[2] It should be recognized, however, that, insofar as a single sample is concerned, an independent survey can yield exactly the same information as may be obtained from surveys designed to be subsequently repeated.

samples. Temporary samples can be and often are used in conjunction with them to gain in total efficiency and to strengthen the sample on certain items. Many combinations are possible using correlation and related techniques. For example, some samples may be remeasured and from them, by use of correlation, much continuity or "change" data can be obtained from similar samples in the system that were established but not remeasured. Remeasurement of permanent sample trees and plots and repeated forest surveys are old. It is their combination with modern sampling techniques and integration into a permanent system of wide application that is relatively new.

There are two general groups of such systems. The first is well illustrated by the National Forest Survey conducted by the U.S. Forest Service. It is designed to cover all forest areas regardless of ownership and to give uniform forest resource statistics for major forest regions and the nation as a whole. Initially, it was conducted on an independent survey basis. Increasingly, however, the need for consistent, localized, and more accurate information on changes in forest area and timber conditions significant in forest production has shifted emphasis to system continuity employing permanent samples though supplemented by temporary samples.

The second is used by public and private agencies directly concerned with timber production. Although national survey data are widely used in management planning by both public and private agencies, the specific purposes of continuing management are seldom adequately served. In the United States, national forest inventory work is coordinated with the national survey but with additional data often obtained at a higher sampling intensity to serve timber management needs. The same is true in greater or less degree with some other public and some private agencies. Industrial owners have established permanent sampling systems independently, although their data usually can also serve national survey needs.

An illustrative permanent sampling system. The following presentation of the major elements of a permanent sampling system is patterned after industrial practice in the United States but is generally applicable to other ownerships. The system described here is based entirely on permanent samples. As stated previously, temporary samples can also be used. However, these combinations add considerable complexity, and the essential principles and features of a permanent system can be best illustrated and understood by considering only permanent sampling.

P U R P O S E S   No system can be efficiently designed without clear formulation of the purposes it is to serve. Most such systems are aimed to give forest information useful in planning and conducting management on fairly large units, usually over 100,000 acres. As such, they are primarily a head-office control and planning tool designed to give an overall forest data basis for such things as determination of the cut and allocation of cutting budgets to administrative field units, consistent information on volume and character of growing stock, total needs for timber stand improvement work, and total depletion and growth for use in income tax accounting and similar total forest bookkeeping purposes. These purposes are assumed here.

Accuracy follows from purposes; essentially it is a matter of administrative decision. Levels of accuracy desired usually run from 5 to 10 percent on a 20 to 1 probability (approximately 2 standard deviations) for totals, most commonly of timber volumes. It should be emphasized that sampling accuracy is controlled by sampling intensity relative to the area sampled. As data are subdivided by areas, or by subcategories of data such as species groups, types, etc., sampling error mounts rapidly. Within a given sampling intensity it is manifestly impossible to be equally accurate for all categories. Choices have to be made; the normal practice is to gage accuracy for certain items adjudged to be of major significance.

SAMPLING METHODS   In comparison to independent sampling surveys, permanent systems impose some special restrictions. Since data are in large degree obtained from permanently located points or plots, it is important that they be located with care so that they can readily be found again for remeasurement. Further, a major assumption underlying the use of permanent systems is that cutting and other forest work is to be done over sampling locations *exactly* as if they were not there. This is difficult to ensure, and bias due to differential treatment can be extremely serious. In large degree, one has to accept the initial sample, however good or poor it may be, and live with it. Plots can be added or dropped, but the fact remains that the continuity aspects of the system are largely tied to permanent stations, and their sampling integrity must be maintained if they are to continue to represent the area as a whole.

For these reasons of continuity, unstratified sampling is normally employed. Some strata, like permanent hardwood types, can be separated from conifer types and recognized in sampling. Beyond this, forest conditions change, and an efficiently stratified initial sample may become poorly stratified over time. To ensure maximum representativeness, systematic square-grid sampling is most often employed.[1]

Most commonly, a single area plot or point is measured at each sampling station. Cluster sampling—the taking of several subplots that together

---

[1] The statistical issues of systematic versus random sampling cannot be gone into here. Systematic square-grid sampling normally gives the best mean value since all parts of an area are proportionately represented. The estimate of error correspondingly tends to be high, because the full variability of the population is well represented. In practice, errors of systematic samples are commonly calculated as if they were random, recognizing that the true error is usually somewhat less than the error calculation shows—an element of conservation.

constitute a full observation—is also often employed to give a more stable observation and to give a measure of stand variability. Also, from three to five samples fairly near together—say at five chain (330-ft) intervals—are sometimes taken in a series but regarded as independent observations. The reason is that much of the field inventory cost is in travel to sampling stations. This can be much reduced by taking several plots fairly close together. If forest types are in small units and distributed in approximately random fashion—as is true in much of the Lake States, for example—the loss in information gained can be more than offset by taking a few more plots at a saving in total cost.[1]

Various sampling methods are employed. A circular area plot of $\frac{1}{4}$ or $\frac{1}{5}$ acre (the latter most frequent) is common as are variable plot sizes. The latter means that a larger plot, say $\frac{1}{5}$ acre, is used to measure commercial-size timber, a smaller concentric plot for saplings and poles, and a still smaller one, perhaps 1 to 4 milacres, to measure reproduction.

The ultimate and theoretically perfect answer to variable plot sizes is to select sample trees by use of the Bitterlich angle gauge point sampling system. Here, there is no plot area as such, although the size of the area sampled is controlled by varying the angle used. Each tree included by the angle gauge is in effect a plot; trees are selected in proportion to their basal area. In addition to its efficiency in estimating basal area per acre, the Bitterlich system provides a means of selecting trees for measurement that will yield the maximum amount of information with minimum number. The method can be used instead of area plots, but both are sometimes used together. For example, the angle gauge may be used to select the larger trees for measurement; type and condition classification may be determined on a larger area basis; and a smaller fixed area may be used for reproduction measurement for which the angle gauge cannot be employed.

How many plots? No specific answer to this complex question is possible. The problem is more difficult with permanent systems than with an independent survey, because the sample must be applicable not only when the system is installed but also in the future when forest conditions and forest area may change. Assuming a particular sampling system, and willingness to pay for a specified level of accuracy, the number of sampling stations basically depends on the variability of the forest and its area. Areas can be determined. Some estimate of population variability is consequently necessary. This is obtained from previous survey data for the property that may be available and from experience of other owners in similar types. Tables giving approximate variability to be expected have been prepared for a number of forest types and regions.

Sampling intensities are low with permanent systems because of cost and the fact that acceptable accuracy for large areas can be obtained with a small but efficiently designed sample. Intensities in practice usually range from about 0.1 down to 0.03 percent. In terms of ⅕-acre plots, this means that a single plot represents 200 and 667 acres, respectively. Some intensities are higher, and some are lower depending on the area involved, variability, cost, and desired accuracy. If forest variability remains the same, the higher the accuracy desired the more samples must be taken. Within a given forest region, variability tends to increase with area sampled but not proportionately. For this reason, and because of the nature of sampling errors, the larger the area, the fewer samples per unit of area are needed to yield a certain accuracy; the increased number needed levels off as total area in a sampling unit is increased.

Although several methods are used, a common and efficient method of locating sampling stations is to make a template of transparent material by putting pin holes in it at whatever square spacing is decided upon. For example, if a 0.04 percent sample is desired and ⅕-acre area plots are to be used, one plot would represent 500 acres (0.2/0.0004) and a sample would be taken every 4,667 ft on a square pattern.[1] Holes on the sheet would be spaced accordingly by whatever map scale is used. If the map were 1 in. to the mile, the corresponding spacing on the template would be 4,667/5,280, or 0.884 in. The template is then placed on the forest sampling unit map, at random usually, and plot locations pricked with a needle on the map. Points falling within the ownership are taken. Location may also be done directly on aerial photos following the same general technique. A standard template can also be prepared with a large number of pin holes, so that the template can be used for different map scales and plot intensity. In any case, the point is located without bias, and its position is scaled off in relation to survey corners or with respect to permanently identifiable features shown on the photo. The essential requirement is that no choice in specific location be left to the field crew, except as rules may be prepared in advance to cover action if a plot location falls too close to a property line, on a road, in a lake, etc., and cannot be taken. If there are additions or deletions to the property, sampling points can be added or dropped by use of the grid the same as initially.

Other methods of plot location are also used. Sometimes a template is used only to select the land survey unit within which a sample is to be taken. The sampling station is then arbitrarily located in relation to survey corners.

MEASUREMENTS TAKEN   Responsibility for what forest information to take and what standards of measurement to use rests squarely on the forest manager. Statistical analysis of data can add nothing to what was in it to start with. Careful study of management needs is necessary so that data taken will be significant and useful. There is a tendency to take almost everything that might be useful, based on the argument that

[1] With 43,560 sq ft per acre, this is calculated as $\sqrt{500 \times 43,560} = 4667$.

additional field data often costs little more and modern computational procedures give much choice in subsequent analysis, also at comparatively little additional cost. This tendency can be carried too far, however, when it is forgotten that every additional item of field information taken increases geometrically the number of classifications possible and does add to the time required and complexity of the job as a whole.

A key principle is that measurements must be precise and consistent. With low sampling intensities, large "blow-up" factors are correspondingly necessary in converting sample to area data; small measurement errors become very important, especially if there is any consistent bias.

A closely related principle is that information should be based on direct and objective measurement as much as possible. It must constantly be kept in mind that the sample is to be remeasured, usually by different people. Variation in standards and definitions cause much difficulty in interpretation following remeasurement. Strict comparability of data—a major objective—is reduced. More or less subjective observations like tree vigor, crown class, amount of defect, are useful but also hard to repeat consistently, since they are based on judgment rather than direct measurement. Changes in measurement standards also cause much difficulty. For example, if utilization standards and volume tables are changed, a large job of adjustment is entailed, some of which can be done only with great difficulty, if at all, because field measurements may be involved, such as merchantable height estimated 5 years ago, that cannot be directly replicated. For such reasons, measurement of total tree height, some absolute upper tree diameters that define basic tree form, and cubic measurement are preferable to estimation of merchantable heights based on currently utilized top diameters and board foot or other imprecise volume units. Absolute measurements can be converted to current merchantability units, but not the reverse.

In American practice, there is diversity in the obtaining of area information. Areas by types, condition classes, etc. can be taken from sampling frequency data or from line survey intercept distances. For example, if half the samples or half the distance traversed falls in one type, the statistical inference is that half the area is also in that type. Interpretation of aerial photos (with ground checking) is more accurate, especially for variable stand conditions, and is most used for area control.

Field measurements, commonly made for individual samples, are listed below, though it should be understood that not all these items are necessarily taken in a single inventory.

Plot data (for sample station as a whole) [1]

> Sample number—districts or other major forest units are often numbered in series

[1] The term "plot" is used here for convenience. It means any sampling location whether it be a fixed or variable area plot, Bitterlich point sampling, cluster sampling, or some combination of methods.

Location (by legal subdivision)
County and state
Compartment, district, forest unit, etc.
Date measured and field crew
Forest type—many classifications used
Forest condition—mature, immature, etc.
Stand age—overstory and understory (if present), sawtimber, pulp-
    wood, etc.
Stocking or density—various units and classifications employed
Reproduction—amount and species
Site—usually by site index
Slope—in percent
Soil—several classifications used
Ground vegetation—by key species groups or a general prevalence
    classification
Topographic situation—swamp, flats, bottomlands, uplands, etc.
Stand treatment indicated—kind and urgency
Stand injury—fire, insects, disease, wind, etc.
Last cutting—date and character
Tree data (for individual trees)
Plot number—for identification
Tree number—serially by plots
Species—by individual species usually, but sometimes a few are
    grouped
Diameter at breast height—normally to tenths of inches
Form point—an upper diameter measurement to establish tree form
Total height—feet
Used length—by products to some merchantable top diameter
Tree grade or quality—sometimes by logs
Tree use—pulpwood, pole, sawtimber, etc.
Vigor—good, fair, poor, etc.
Growing stock class—from good to cull, etc.
Tree class—by tree position in stand, risk class, etc.
Increment—from borings
Mortality—by causes
Damage—by causes
Tree status—primarily for analysis identification used with remea-
    surement data. Shows whether tree is dead, cut since last measure-
    ment, new tree growing into measured size class, tree missed pre-
    viously, erroneously measured, etc.

For a particular inventory, the plot and tree data adjudged significant
are decided upon. Both are normally recorded on a separate card or sheet.
Every detail must be thoroughly thought through. All measurements are
reduced to a numerical code. Number data like plot number, tree diameter,

and tree height are recorded as such. Classification data, such as species, type, site, vigor, mortality, etc., must be reduced to numerical classes or items. A tremendous amount of information can be compressed into a field code. Its preparation requires much knowledge, analysis, and ingenuity and is crucially important; the utility of the whole system rests directly on the meaningfulness of the field data taken.

TRAINING AND ORGANIZATION OF FIELD CREWS   Careful and thorough crew training is scarcely less important than development of a measurement code. A high level of accuracy and consistency is impera- tive. It must be inculcated by training in the use of the code and maintained by systematic inspection and checking.

Two-man field crews are most common, though three are sometimes used. As to kind of personnel used, there is considerable diversity in practice. Some organizations wish to conduct inventory work separately from regular operating personnel because of their continuing work load and also because of a feeling that if they know too much about the sample plots and their location they may tend to be biased regarding forest treatment, which must be carried on entirely independently of the plot's existence. In such situa- tions, sampling work is done by outside personnel, often forestry students at least in part. Other organizations, and with what appear to be stronger reasons, wish their field personnel to know the sampling system thoroughly in order to understand the results. It is also believed that inventory work is one of the best possible means of making men stand- and tree-conscious, of helping them to learn, look for, and see significant forest conditions. For these reasons, the work is done largely by regular personnel with some temporary assistants.

PLOT LOCATION AND ESTABLISHMENT   Plot location infor- mation is given to the field crew in the form of a pinpoint location on a map or photo. Bearings and distances to the position from a known point of departure are scaled off in advance of field travel. The key consideration is that establishment of the actual point on the ground is wholly arbitrary; field crews have no option in selecting it or moving it a few feet because of convenience, because "it seems better," or for any other subjective reason. Strict rules of action are specified in advance for situations in which the point must be moved for any reason.

It is of first importance that the sample point be located so that it can be readily relocated for remeasurement despite cutting and other stand changes, road construction, and the like.

There are two general practices in this respect stemming from the basic fact that stand treatment must be applied precisely as if the plot were not there. The first is to conceal visual evidence of the plot insofar as possi- ble so that field personnel will not be aware of it. In this situation, sampling point center (or a reference corner if rectangular area plots or a multiple sample system is used) is located by a permanent stake driven flush at least with the forest litter surface. Necessary witness trees are located by bearing, distance, species, and other descriptions; but the trees are not visibly marked. Similarly, the locations of individual trees in the sample are identified by a map, or by the sequence in which they are measured from a specified departure point (as north). If numbered, the numbers are placed on the stump just at or below the litter level so that they are not readily visible. No bearing lines are blazed or other markings used around these "hidden" plots.

The second practice is to establish unconcealed or "open" plots. This means that travel lines to the plot, witness trees, plot boundaries, and measurement trees are plainly marked. The idea is that plots are much easier to find if visibly marked and that field personnel can be trained to avoid bias in applying treatment to the area. Opinions vary, but the trend is toward hidden plots. There is much technique in sample location and tree identification that cannot be gone into here.

FIELD MEASUREMENT AND RECORDING OF DATA   The field crew is equipped with the data code and accompanying field forms.

There are two general practices used in recording data. One commonly used, especially in industrial practice, is to record directly on code cards, so that data later may be transferred to permanent punch cards by machine methods which require no visual transference of data from field sheets to punch cards. There are at least two types of these cards in use, as illustrated by the "mark sensing" and "port-a-punch" systems shown in Fig. 12.1. On the mark sensing card, which provides 27 data columns, a special black graphite pencil is used, the results of which are illustrated in Fig. 12.1*A*. By electrical contact, data from these cards automatically can be transferred to permanent punch cards. With the port-a-punch card (Fig. 12.1*B*), there is a small rectangular perforation cut nearly through around each number. In the illustration the same numbers are punched out as on the mark sense card. This punching is done in the field with a special stylus and card case. Forty columns of data can be recorded on these cards, and they will endure a fair amount of machine handling. The use of portable equipment by which permanent cards are directly punched in the field is also employed to some extent, especially in research.

The other field practice is to record manually on field tally sheets and, after checking, transfer the data to permanent punch cards in the office. There is debate as to whether field tally sheets or machine cards are preferable, all things considered; there are adherents to both. The argument for field sheets is that they are easier to correct, are better to use in bad weather, entail considerably less bulk to carry in the field, and that manual card punching from them is not unduly expensive.

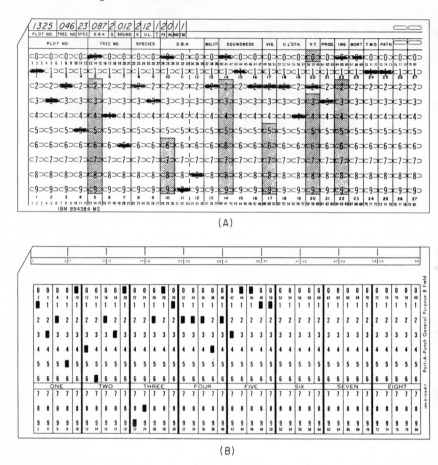

FIG. 12.1. SAMPLE FIELD INVENTORY RECORDING FORMS.

Regardless of the method by which field data are recorded, strict standards of accuracy and consistency are essential. The data code must be thoroughly understood and qualitative items like tree vigor and condition classes uniformly interpreted. This requires careful checking and field supervision. Field sheets or cards should always be checked before leaving the plot for omissions, inconsistencies, or other errors. Cards are also subsequently checked, and there are various methods of detecting incorrect field recording, for example, tree products that do not come from a certain species, diameters too small or too large for the tree height. Many such errors can be corrected through knowledge of the data, although revisiting the plot may be necessary—and this can be very expensive. Instruments employed and their use are matters of mensuration that cannot be covered here.

DATA COMPILATION Methods of analyzing field data is a large and complex subject involving expert mensurational, statistical, and computer techniques. Machine methods are assumed here, though it should also be recognized that this work has been and can be done by hand methods, although they are much slower. In order to give a picture of the job as a whole, discussion here is focussed on what is done rather than on the details of how to do it.

The data from the field are punched on cards, and further sort checking is done by machine to reveal detectable errors. Data may then be put on magnetic tapes, depending on equipment used.

Various computational extensions of the field data are then made and the results punched on the cards. With electronic computers, this is done by programming using tapes without card punching. Basal area and volume are computed for individual trees. Volumes may be in cubic, cord, board foot, or other units. Gross and net volumes for the total tree and for the mechantable portion are usually determined. This work is done in various ways and requires expert mensurational techniques. Mostly, it is done through formula and machine methods. Reduction factors are used to convert basal area, volume, tree counts, and other quantitative measurement data to a unit-area basis. Quantitative data of this sort are summed and totals transferred to plot master cards (for machine work) and "blow-up" factors used to convert basal area and volume per acre, etc. to totals for sample unit as a whole and for all area segregations.

Specific procedures in analysis depend in large degree on the kind of equipment used. There are two general kinds: accounting and electronic computer systems. With accounting machines, the punch card is the entire medium for data handling; the machines will sort, count, add, subtract, multiply, divide, and then print off the data in whatever tabulation sequence is desired. The process is detailed and requires flow charts indicating the many sorts, punching of supplementary card decks, and other machine operations.

With electronic computer systems, the process is much different and, in total outline, simpler. The machine is fed the coded field data on the same punch cards. The machine is then programmed to make the necessary computations of volume, etc. and to make the indicated sorts and summaries in a few operations and at unbelievable speed.

There are three general points to bear in mind about computation. The first is that the responsibility for deciding what tabulations are to be made and their usefulness remains firmly with the forester. A great many tabulations can be made; the real question is to decide which and why.

The second is that with the use of computers, especially electronic computing systems, the volume and complexity of computation itself is no basic problem. Impossibly laborious jobs, from the standpoint of hand methods, can often be done in minutes at a fraction of the cost of handwork.

Basically, the forester has been emancipated from the drudgery and limitations of computation and can concentrate on forest data needs.

The third is that the mechanics of machine computation are complex. With electronic systems, particularly, programming is highly technical. Although the forester can and should know what the computers can and cannot do and their basic operation, he cannot become an expert in their use and remain a forester. Where and how to get the expert help fully to exploit the possibilities of machine computation at reasonable expense is, in fact, often a real problem.

REMEASUREMENT   Remeasurement of the sample to reveal accurately forest and individual tree changes is one of the major advantages of a permanent sampling system. Timing is a first decision. The usual practice is to remeasure at 5- to 10-year intervals. A question here is whether to remeasure the complete system at one time as nearly as possible—which is commonly done—or systematically to remeasure a part of the samples each year during the remeasurement cycle. This can be done either by measuring major sections of the total area or by measuring a sample of plots for the entire area each year. This question also applies to the scheduling of initial establishment. If some plots are remeasured each year, then total results are not given for any one point in time. Instead, one has a sort of cumulative moving average, which has some advantages in evening out climatic and other fluctuations and also in distributing the work load by years.

Also necessary are decisions whether to add or to drop permanent plots needed to give adequate "change" data and whether to add temporary plots to strengthen the sample in certain categories. Through regression techniques, it is possible to measure part of the samples and get much of the information that would be obtained had all of them been remeasured. There are many statistical possibilities for gaining increased efficiency.

The field remeasurement job is essentially the same as before except for some added complications in relocating plots, finding all trees, and in maintenance of tree identification, witness trees, etc. New trees come into the sample and some go out, and the reasons must be ascertained. Some problems derive from the fact that in remeasurement errors are found that were not previously detected. Species may be incorrectly identified; trees may have been missed in the first measurement; plausible measurements turn out to be wrong; and similar discrepancies develop that entail corrections of previous as well as current data. Field crews are provided with basic data from the last measurement data to check against. These data are indicated at the extreme left top of the sample card shown in Fig. 12.1*A*.

It is also important that remeasurement crews be on the alert to detect and, if possible, evaluate any indication of bias in forest treatment in connection with plots that may affect the validity of the sample. An obvious case would be a cutting operation that surrounded but did not include the sample area. Unceasing vigilance is necessary to keep the sample units truly representative of the forest.

The computation job is also complicated by the fact that remeasurement data have to be directly related to previous data. This means that data from discontinued and new plots have to be segregated from remeasured plots, that measurements of identical trees have to be matched for two or more growth periods, etc. It is amazing how many details and problems can arise in the handling of remeasurement data.

UNIT-AREA INVENTORIES

Neither independent nor permanent sampling systems localize information by small land units such as a compartment or a particular stand. Samples can only *represent* an area. By increasing the sampling intensity, data of a desired level of accuracy can be obtained for any size of area. The cost also increases rapidly, and the fact remains that the samples still do not directly describe any particular area. The application of on-the-ground operational management requires in-place information about the condition of individual stand units and their specific treatment needs. As management has become more intensive, forest information of this nature becomes increasingly necessary.

These needs have led to another type of survey which can be termed a "unit-area inventory." There seems to be no generally recognized term in the United States. This kind of work is called stand description, compartment description or prescription, management reconnaissance or cruise, and area scouting. The term "unit-area inventory" seems more broadly descriptive and is employed here.

Procedures vary, but all have in common the purpose to locate and describe specific areas for on-the-ground management purposes. There is nothing new in principle about these inventories. What is new about them are the systematic procedures followed in periodically collecting forest information on large areas and the particular uses made of the information in management. A further and important point in common is that data for each stand are obtained at a level of accuracy consistent with use needs. Basically, a direct population estimate is made for each unit, and information is approximately as good for one as for another. Consequently, unit stand data can be grouped for a compartment or for any size of forest area desired and have about the same management significance, although total accuracy increases somewhat with larger groupings. This is in sharp distinction to sampling surveys, the accuracy of which is always directly related to the size of the area sampled.

Another point of difference from sampling surveys is in the way personnel are used. Sampling surveys are a procedural job; all observations and measurements are defined, and the work must be done in strict conformance with the specifications. Very little is left to skilled judgment, and the work is often, if not usually, done by other than those directly responsible for the management of the area sampled. With unit area surveys, there is much need for skill and experience in estimating and judging stand data and conditions and, if practicable, the work is best done by the men responsible for the management of the tract. This gives field personnel an excellent opportunity to gain close knowledge of their forest area. There is also the knowledge that they must act on the results of the survey and are held administratively accountable for its validity.

The basic procedures are as follows:

1. Individual stands are visited, identified by location, and mapped down to a minimum area—usually about 10 acres. A stand is defined as a reasonably homogenous unit regarding silvicultural condition and treatment and consequently differs significantly from adjoining stands in these respects. Standardized type breakdowns are usually not used, although broad type designations are often used for classification purposes.

Aerial photos are usually used in this work. Recent photos of high quality are needed; infrared photography is especially good. Mapping is often done directly on the photos or on a transparent overlay. Aerial photos can also be assembled in controlled mosaics of usable accuracy and copies reproduced for field use. The trend is strongly toward use of an aerial photo base which, with forest and type data added, becomes the operating base and may replace separate and expensive drafted stand maps.

2. Within each stand, estimates are made of timber volume, size, condition classes, species, density, silvicultural needs, etc. Diagnostic tree classifications may also be made. Accuracy and methods of estimation depend on the situation. No permanent sampling is done, but temporary plots or Bitterlich angle-count samples may be taken. The intensity of such sampling may be specified or left to judgment; some stands may require considerable internal sampling to get sufficiently accurate figures. In others, ocular estimates, perhaps backed by a few samples, may suffice. The main requirement is that the stand be sufficiently traversed and sampled so that its situation can be appraised within a range of accuracy adequate to make significant management decisions.

3. The treatment needs of each stand are appraised. This means the need and priority for harvest cutting, thinning, stand improvement, site preparation, planting, protection, and other forest operations during a period, usually the next 5 or 10 years. This is the heart of the job, and experienced judgment is essential. A recommendation for treatment may be prepared in the field, or emphasis may be on describing conditions with a definite prescription made later. If the work is done by experienced person-

nel, it seems preferable for the man to make a recommendation in the field when he is directly looking at the stand. Recommendations can always be changed later when the situation for the administrative unit as a whole is assembled and analyzed.

4. Field estimates and recommendations following a specific procedure are placed on record cards which, along with the aerial photos or maps, are a guide for field operations as well as a basis for making various summaries needed in cutting budget and other administrative unit planning work.

5. Each stand is revisited and the survey repeated at periodic intervals. The work is consequently going on all the time. On a 5-year cycle, a fifth of the stands would be visited each year. This is truly a continuing inventory. It is different from independent and permanent sampling surveys, which are usually done at periodic intervals. Stand boundaries are checked at each visit. Because of cutting or other treatment, some stands can be combined with adjoining ones. Some stand subdivisions may be necessary, but the trend is toward stand consolidation within compartments as impermanent differences between stands are evened out through management.

An illustrative unit-area inventory. An example will be helpful to illustrate more specifically how the work is done and uses made of the data. The following is condensed from the procedures followed by a large southern paper company. This company bases its operational management primarily on this work and has had long experience with it. They call it stand description, and this term will be used in developing the example. A sample field sheet is shown in Fig. 12.2.

Aerial Photos and Stand Delineation. The most recent photos available are used—normally not less than 5 years old, and the newer, the better. The unit forester,[1] equipped with a pocket stereoscope, takes the photos into the field along with the old photo interpreted to show previous stands. He checks the boundaries of the stands and makes changes, corrections, and combinations of stands where desirable. Age, species, and density, particularly as they affect harvest cutting, are the basic factors used in separating stands. Stands, as described, are numbered consecutively by compartments.

Location and Identification. Each stand is identified by state, county, tract (as regards acquisition), unit, and compartment. Loading point is shown so that the stand can be identified as being in a specific company railyard, barge landing, or truck loading area. Mileage zones are shown for further transportation information.

Stand Data. The following information is obtained and entered on

---

[1] The unit, under the charge of a technically trained forester, is the basic administrative field division of the company. The area averages about 25,000 acres.

STAND DESCRIPTION

UNIT *Youngstown* COMP *16*   LOAD PT. *0*   ZONE *1*   STATE *3*   COUN. *3*

TRACT *27 – 3 –12*   DEED NO.   MAP NO.

ACRES   DATE *1955*   ESTIMATOR *Hoard*

T I M B E R

ST NO	ACRES	TYPE	SITE	SPECIES DESCRIBE MOST IMPORTANT STORY	DEN	AGE	HT.	AVG DIA.	TOTAL CORDS /AC.	TOTAL MERCH BF/AC	RAD GRTH 10 YEARS
8	369	1–3	50	P Shortleaf Pine H	0.2	50	45	4-6-8	0.5		

NEXT USABLE STAND			REMARKS – GOOD – 1 FAIR – 2 POOR – 3		
SPECIES	AGE	DEN	FIRE CONTROL	3	
SLP	4	1.0	LOGGING COND.	3	
			ACCESSIBILITY	3	D/W to Roads 115, 103, 30
PHOTO #			REGENERATION COND	1	
4L –79, 128			DRAINAGE	3	
			OPERABILITY	3	

	1	2	3	RECOMMENDATIONS	1	2	3	
PINE PULPWOOD	2			PLANTING	2			OTHERS
PINE SAWTIMBER	2			DRAINAGE	2			
HDWD. PULPWOOD	2			HAZARD RED	2			
HDWD. SAWTIMBER	2			SANITATION	2			
NON COM. THINNING	2			OTHERS				
HARDWOOD CONTROL	2							
SEED BED PREP.	2							

COMMENTS			STAND TOTALS	VOLUME TO BE CUT
Stand on a large flat. Overstory extremely poor;	PINE CORDS	185	
composed mostly of small, suppr. slash pine, not fit	PINE MBF.		
for seed trees. Some seed trees of better quality in	HDWD. PULP		
NE¼ of stand.	HDWD. N PULP		
	HDWD. M.B.F.		

RECOMMENDATION CODE IN COLUMN 1 ENTER 1 (ONE) FOR YES OR 2 (TWO) FOR NO. IN COLUMN 2 ENTER ONE OF THE FOLLOWING CODE NUMBERS IF YES. 1 - CLEAR CUT, 2 - SEED TREE, 3 - REMOVE OVERSTORY, 4 - THINNING, 5 - SALVAGE, 6 - REMOVE SEED TREES, 7 - FIRE, 8 - MECHANICAL, 9 - HAND.

PRIORITY CODE   ENTER IN COLUMN 3 IF COLUMN 1 IS YES   1. URGENT,   2. SHOULD BE DONE IN RECOMMENDED YEAR, 3. SHOULD BE DONE BUT COULD BE DELAYED.

FIG. 12.2. STAND DESCRIPTION FIELD INVENTORY FORM.

the field form (Fig. 12.2), which should be referred to as the data are described.

> Areas are obtained from the photo by a dot grid count. Individual areas are balanced to check with the total for the compartment, which is the control.
>
> General forest type and topography in code numbers are entered in the type column.
>
> Site is recorded by a code fraction of species over height growth in 50 years, e.g. $\frac{20}{95}$ means a site index of 95 for loblolly pine (species code is 20).
>
> Major forest story by key species. This is the story that will be actively managed until the next major harvest cut. Species in the most im-

portant story are listed in order of predominance, the top line in the form for pine, the bottom line for hardwoods.

Stand density in tenths; 1.0 is fully stocked in basal area for the age and site.

Average age of the most important story for pine and for hardwoods separately.

Average height of the most important story for pine and for hardwoods.

Average diameter of the most important story for pine and for hardwoods.

Cords per acre of pine for the total stand are estimated excluding all merchantable sawtimber trees 13-in. dbh and larger. For hardwoods, total volumes of pulping and nonpulping hardwoods shown separately by a fraction, e.g. $7/3$, which means 7 cords of pulping and 3 cords of nonpulping hardwoods per acre.

Board feet per acre for the total stand are estimated for pine and for hardwoods.

Average radial increment for the last 10 years is obained from increment borings in dominant and codominant trees of the most important story.

Species, age, and density are estimated for the next usable stand, if there is one. A well-developed and stocked understory is an example.

Remarks.   A general rating of good, fair, or poor (following some guide lines) is made for fire control, logging conditions, accessibility, regeneration conditions, drainage, and operability.

Five-year Recommendations.   Recommendations are made only for a 5-year period, because the stand will be redescribed every 5 years. They apply to the entire stand, not just the most important story. The silvicultural treatments considered and the code followed are shown in Fig. 12.2. Four stands can be recorded on some field sheets.

Keysort Cards.   Information obtained for each stand is typed on a Stand Description keysort card shown in Fig. 12.3. On the back of the card, cumulative treatment of the stand can be listed by date, treatment, volume cut, and acres. The unit forester checks this information and then punches it in the code shown on the circumference of the card. Use of these cards is a major feature of this stand description system. They are both a visual record and a sorting device. The typed information gives a concise picture of the stand; a great deal of management information is assembled. The punching provides a quick means of sorting with no more equipment than an ice pick.[1]

---

[1] It should be noted that the stand description data could all be coded and put on punch cards for machine computation. This is a definite possibility. However, the keysort cards have the advantage of presenting easily readable data, and they can be readily sorted without machines. For a small forest unit, the hand sorting and tabulating job is not unduly burdensome.

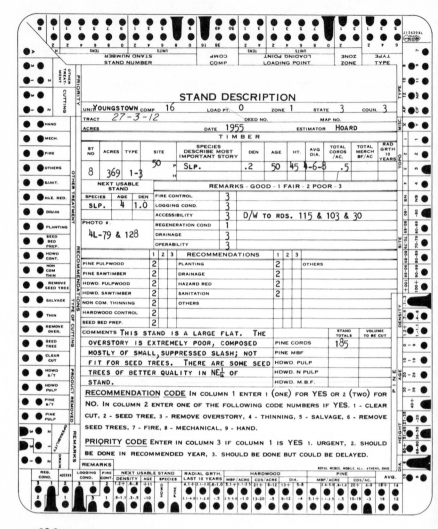

FIG. 12.3. STAND DESCRIPTION KEYSORT CARD.

Information in this form is extremely useful to the unit forester as a base for planning his field work, making reports, and preparing budget estimates. For the unit, or any part of it, he can, for example, readily sort out all cards for which a certain treatment is recommended. He can then study them individually in relation to the map and get a very clear picture of what is needed that can be expressed quantitatively. This information backs up and amplifies his personal knowledge of the unit. Further, the shock of personnel changes is much softened by this systematic collection of operating data in highly usable and cumulative form.

Stand Maps. An acetate (transparent) sheet the size of the aerial photo is used to show stand boundary lines and cutting areas. Another acetate sheet is used to show other cultural treatments such as hardwood control, seedbed preparation, etc. These acetate overlays will be kept with the aerial photo, and it is expected that they will tend to eliminate the need for separate stand maps.

Stand Description Analysis. A considerable number of tabulations can be made from the stand description data for various purposes. These data can be summed for a unit and for larger administrative units of the company.

Following is a listing of some of the tables that are made:

Pine and hardwood type area by topography
Recommended pine type cutting by kind, volume, and area
Recommended cultural treatments
Volume and acreage by age class
Acreage by site and age class
Pine density by age class and area
Hardwood types by site and area

This stand description system is thoroughly integrated into company forest land management operations, which are largely based upon it.

forest information needs of management in summary

A broad array of information is needed in forest management. Grouped by sources it includes that obtained essentially exterior to the forest itself, information arising through the administrative operation of a forest property, and that which must come from the forest itself through the medium of surveys. These should be thought of as an interconnected system and not as discrete parts. The overall aim should be to use them all in harmony and balance in managing a forest property.

Major emphasis here has been given to inventories to supply information from the forest, not that they are necessarily most important in viewing the total picture, but because they are the most directly concerned with the subject of this book, namely, techniques of forest land management emphasizing timber production. Independent and permanent sampling inventories and unit-area inventories have been presented emphasizing forest uses and basic procedures. The emphasis has been on what is obtained rather than how. With sampling inventories in particular, techniques are formidable, and a book could be filled with them.

All these inventories have their place, advantages, and limitations.

From the standpoint of getting most kinds of forest data representing an area at a given time and for a particular purpose, independent sampling systems are the most efficient and flexible. There are no limitations on methods and techniques that can be employed. Their major limitation is that they are not efficient in measuring periodic changes in the forest. Rather high intensity sampling is necessary to yield such data, and they are expensive.

Where continuity is important, for example in maintaining overall forest "bookkeeping" for large areas, and where accurate and economical measurement of tree and forest changes by time periods is a major consideration, permanent sampling systems are indicated. In such situations, they are the most efficient in getting a large amount of consistent forest information applicable to fairly large areas. Too much is sometimes expected of them. They offer real problems in ensuring the continued representativeness of a low intensity sample as the forest changes over time. A key point is that forest treatments must be applied over individual samples exactly as if they were not there. Physical and statistical problems of system maintenance are rather formidable. Permanent sampling systems are not a substitute for controlled research in yielding stratified information on tree and stand growth needed in determination of desirable growing stock under management.

No sampling system, except at high expense, can give localized in-place information needed to guide operational management which requires the identification and treatment of particular stands. To obtain this sort of information a unit area stand description and analysis is needed. Basically, this is not a sampling system, but a direct estimate of population data of sufficient accuracy to guide management decisions. Data are of approximately equal accuracy for whatever size of unit is recognized.

To only a limited degree are these three kinds of inventories alternatives. They should be regarded as complementary since they fill different needs. Experience has shown that, as management becomes more intensive in its ground application, unit-area inventories are necessary whether or not permanent or independent sampling systems are employed to give overall control. As management becomes more systematized, as compartments are established and stabilized, and as irregular stand conditions are evened out through treatment, relative dependence on unit area analysis is likely to increase and that on sampling systems to decrease. In a managed forest, total information on growing stock volumes is not particularly useful, though it may look impressive on balance sheets. What is important is sound forest knowledge, which in large degree must be research-based, applied to the getting of maximum continued production area by area. As better forest information becomes available, permanent sampling systems are likely to be reduced in intensity to give only that level of information needed for total forest control. For large areas, the sampling intensity for such purposes can be very low.

The practicing forester needs to have a good general grasp of inventory methods but remember that they are a means rather than an end. He should apply them with singleness of purpose to serve management needs.

Finally, the large importance of information arising through the continued administrative operation of a forest property must be given full recognition. Much of the performance data necessary in order to apply continuing management is obtained by means of various reports and records. The close interrelations among all sources of forest information become very apparent in considering timber management planning and plans (Chap. 13).

13

timber management planning and plans

A forest is a continuing thing. The building up of a regulated and productive forest is a complex problem usually requiring many years to work out; but once established it is perpetual in nature. The forest can be modified and changed in many ways, but unless destroyed, it goes on indefinitely in one form or another. Decisions made and action taken currently may have effects and consequences felt many decades into the future. To look and plan ahead for periods of time that may span several human generations is a characteristic and commonplace of the forestry profession, generated by the nature of the resource with which foresters work. A high degree of responsibility and stewardship is essential. Few foresters can reap what they sow and see the full fruition of their work.

At the same time, a practicing forester necessarily must live and work in the present and ply his profession in full exposure to the ups and downs and dynamics of a constantly changing economic society. It is not enough to plan well for the future and to appraise its uncertainties. The present must also be faced with all the exigencies that go with it. The necessity of providing for the continuation of a slow-changing and immobile resource and at the same time making it responsive to current requirements is a central problem of the forest manager, requiring vision, imagination, and flexibility in high degree.

The necessity for both long- and short-range planning in specific terms is best exemplified in planning for timber production, the subject of this chapter. Timber crops take a long time to grow, but like other people, foresters come and go. There is large need for continuity and reasonable consistency in the operation of the forest that requires planning. Such planning is not for the beginner or amateur. It requires experience, much judgment, wide knowledge, adequate supporting data, and authority to make it effective. It necessitates the integration of a wide range of mensurational, silvicultural, and business skills and knowledge. Fundamentally, it combines the purposes of management with the productive capacity of the forest. Both are conditioned and influenced by the economic framework as regards markets and other circumstances within which the forest business must operate.

No plan for timber production should be thought of as "set" and immutable but, instead, as an operating base that must be sufficiently flexible to meet changing conditions and yet provide a sufficient framework for forest continuity. One of the best arguments for having a plan is that it can be changed intelligently as need arises.

history of american timber management plans

Planning for timber production is older than the profession of forestry. Management plans, or working plans as they are often termed, have had a long history. They were developed mainly in Europe, where they assumed rather formidable proportions tending to be formal, rather rigid documents, certainly nothing to be spoken of lightly. It is perhaps unfortunate that considerable tradition and formalism has grown up around a management plan as an entity, as a specific document, that has tended to obscure and divert attention from the need for forest planning as a continuing function regardless of the particular form the resultant plan may assume. As a matter of fact, plans can and do take many forms, but the traditional concept is of a specific and rather formal document, revised from time to time, that constitutes, more or less come what may, the master plan of operation for a forest property. In at least earlier European practice, the dominating consideration was the technical regulation of the cut, with profitability of the enterprise often a secondary consideration. It must also be remembered that management plans, historically speaking, have been developed almost entirely on public lands.

To a very large degree, the management plan has been regarded as the end-all of forest regulation, and its preparation has been the key consideration in any technical treatment of the subject. If there were no formal working plan or definite commitment to prepare one, the presumption often was that there could be little forestry worthy of the name.

The tendency for regulation, and even forest management as a whole, to revolve around timber management plans is evident in early textbooks prepared in the United States. The first was "Theory and Practice of Working Plans" by Recknagel, published in 1913. It is essentially a book on timberland regulation to use as a guide in preparing working plans and is based almost entirely on European experience; there was no real experience with American management plans at that time. Management plans occupied a prominent position in Roth's "Forest Regulation," first published in 1914. A very thorough analysis and presentation of essentially European regulatory techniques as it was thought they might be applied in the United States is given in Woolsey's "American Forest Regulation," published in 1922. While the emphasis is on regulatory methods, they are implicitly regarded as the heart of forest management, with management plans as their ultimate and final medium of expression.

The first American management book came in 1919 (Recknagel and Bentley, 1919, and later, Recknagel, Bentley, and Guise, 1926) and is much broader in subject matter coverage, including, in addition to regulation and working plans, extensive material on tree and forest measurement, growth and yield, and some material on forest finance and organization. Chapman's "Forest Management," first published in 1931, emphasizes regulation of the cut and preparation of management plans but only as a part of a much broader treatment of the land management and business aspects of forestry. In Matthews' "Management of American Forests" (1935), emphasis is on the practical business management of forest lands for timber production, with particular stress on initial surveys and reports as necessary first steps in management planning. Regulatory techniques are recognized as of central importance but formal management plans are given little attention; at the time his book was published, the need for them in the United States was largely in the future, particularly regarding privately owned properties.

As indicated, there has been a gradual swing in American textbook treatment from management plans as the end-all of regulation and even forest management as a whole, to a broader concept, emphasizing business management, with timber management plans occupying an important role but constituting only a part of the total picture.

Attempts to prepare management plans preceded the practice of forestry in the United States. The initial body of forest information with which the first foresters of this country faced the tremendous problem of dealing with the vast, complex, and largely unknown forests of the country at the turn of the century was almost purely European in origin. The concepts and ideas of management plans were inherited along with the rest. That much of this technical heritage did not apply to American conditions would seem to go without saying. But this was not so apparent in 1900 as in 1950, and the early foresters attempted application of forest practices and planning of an intensity scarcely exceeded since.

The first management plans were prepared by the old Division of Forestry, later the Bureau of Forestry, of the U.S. Department of Agriculture, between 1898 and 1905 before the organization of the U.S. Forest Service.

The work was done for private forest landowners in an attempt to interest them in the practice of forestry. For examples and discussion of these early plans, see Pinchot, 1898; Graves, 1899; Hosmer and Bruce, 1901; Olmstead, 1902; Sherrard, 1903; Chapman, 1905; Reed, 1905; and Pinchot, 1947. The technical workmanship and presentation of these plans is excellent and has hardly been improved on since. As documents, they are superb and they showed a realistic appreciation of the situation. They did much to interest at least some people in the possibilities of forestry. But with few exceptions they were failures from the standpoint of being actually applied. It would perhaps be more accurate to speak of them as management *proposals* rather than as plans. The difficulty, as revealed by hindsight, was that these plans, or proposals, preceded the existence of a general climate conducive to the practice of forestry.

In the early days of American forestry, the U.S. Forest Service was the only organization in the country capable of and interested in making management plans for Federal or for any other forest landownership. The earlier history of plans in this country consequently revolves largely around Forest Service work. With the organization of the Forest Service in 1905, emphasis shifted from preparation of plans for private owners to plans for the national forests, and this work has been given emphasis ever since.

A good many national forest plans have been prepared over the years, but until around 1950 comparatively few have been actively followed or exerted much influence in day-to-day management practice. As with the old Bureau of Forestry plans, they tended to be ahead of their time although they constituted a necessary step in the development of American forestry. The influence of the European prototype was strong and there was a necessary period of experimentation in developing plans suitable to American conditions. In a study of early management plans in this country, Barrington Moore (1915), expressed the situation as follows:

> Conditions peculiar to America make this experimentation a necessary part of the normal growth of plans . . . . But the experimentation was wholly unconscious. Every man making a plan sincerely felt he was drawing up the provisions which should and would guide in handling the area with which he was dealing. It was not until the plan had been criticized, cut up, revised, and finally put in the files for use in drawing up a plan along entirely different lines that the author began to understand that his work was merely a step in the development of working plans, not a plan in itself.

Moore's sentiments have been echoed many times since. Some of the principal reasons why many of these earlier plans, whether for public or private lands, have not been particularly successful in application may be summed up as follows:

1. There was too much emphasis on the needs and rights of future generations and not enough on the necessities of the present generation.

As has been brought out, the real problem is to meet the present and still care for the future.

2. There was lack of appreciation of the economic position of the lumberman.

3. There was insufficient inventory, growth, silvicultural, and related forest information to furnish a solid technical foundation.

4. Markets were in general inadequate to support the degree of utilization needed to effectuate plans; an allowable cut figure was more of a goal than a reality (Chap. 6).

5. There was the lack of business training on the part of foresters. This again stemmed largely from the European tradition, initially strong in American forest education, wherein business training was regarded as of minor importance.

6. Overly long reports gave emphasis to unimportant details and insufficient attention to important ones.

7. There was lack of real need for formal plans and of opportunity for them to be followed; the time was not yet ripe for timber growing.

8. The plans failed to take local conditions realistically into account; they were too academic.

9. Attempts to regulate the yield by mathematical formulas were over-emphasized, and not enough attention was given to silvicultural conditions and problems on the ground.

These points are not listed in castigation of management plans generally, nor of early Forest Service plans in particular, but as a part of sketching the general evolution of plans in this country.

There was a tendency to include all forest uses and needs in the earlier plans. That is, they included such items as: road and other improvement plans; protection against fire, disease, and insects; and much silvicultural and mensurational information. As forest land management techniques became better developed and as more emphasis was given to other than timber uses, planning for these separate activities tended to be handled separately but with due regard to relative priority and correlation. Protection against fire is a good illustration. It was early recognized that fire control was of too great importance and ramification to be included as a part of a timber management plan. The same, in general, is true of general forest transportation planning, of forest protection against insects and diseases, recreation and wildlife uses. National forest timber management plans at present are confined rather closely to timber but are carefully correlated to other land uses as they relate to timber production. The same general practice is followed on most other publicly owned lands. In industrial forest holdings, timber production is usually the controlling aim, and there is less need for separate land use plans.

A plan for timber production is consequently a complete forest land use plan only if timber is practically the only use. Where there are other important uses in a general forest area, as is often the case, it is important to recognize that a timber management plan is only a part of a total land management plan. Multiple-use management plans prepared by the U.S. Forest Service are examples of total forest land use planning, integrating all separate forest uses and activities.

who prepares timber management plans?

With the preceding background in mind, it will be helpful to consider who prepares plans and the general status of the work. Emphasis is centered here on the United States and Canada, which are very large countries of great forest diversity. Experience here has, however, many parallels in other countries.

UNITED STATES

In the United States, there are three major groups of forest owners concerned; Federal, state, and private. Each will be briefly considered.

Federal lands. Of the Federal agencies, the U.S. Forest Service has been engaged longest in timber management planning. Within about 186 million acres administered, there are approximately 425 working circles, and the objective is to have a plan for each. The detail and coverage of these plans naturally varies widely with circumstances. They vary from rather intensive and complete plans that management opportunities justify, to more extensive plans, sometimes essentially policy statements, applied to situations in which organized timber production is in its initial stages. Up to the mid-century point, the majority of timber management plans for large properties were prepared on the national forests. These plans are the best known, because they are the most numerous and are widely distributed.

Several other Federal agencies also own and manage large forest areas and are concerned with timber management plans. Chief among these are the Bureau of Land Management and the Indian Service of the Department of the Interior. These agencies encounter needs for and problems in connection with timber management planning substantially similar to those of the U.S. Forest Service.

States, counties, and municipalities. A number of states own substantial forest land areas, some of which are sufficiently consolidated to permit their management as definite operating units. They are concerned with the orderly management of their forested lands, usually for multiple use, and some states have prepared formal timber management plans. Progress toward effective timber management has been slow for a number of reasons.

The scattered nature of many state holdings is one reason. The fact that most forest lands were cut over and in very poor condition when acquired making a long rehabilitation period necessary is another. It is also true that inadequate financial and administrative provision has been made for a timber management organization. The pressing and critical need to strengthen protection against fire on state and on private lands, which is primarily a state responsibility (Davis, 1959), and public demands for more recreation and wildlife are additional reasons.

In addition to about 21 million acres of state-owned forest lands, there are approximately 8 million acres in county, municipal, school, and various semipublic local organization ownership. About 80 percent of these lands are in Minnesota and Wisconsin. These lands are of all kinds and conditions and are used for a variety of purposes. On most, however, timber growing is a major use. Few such areas have specific timber management plans, and most of those extant have been prepared with cooperative assistance from various state and Federal agencies. There is considerable need for timber and other forest land planning on many of these areas, as their use is frequently intensive.

Private lands. With three-fourths of the commercial timberlands of the United States in private ownership, it is obvious that the major share of the timber management job is on these lands. The situation on these lands is extremely diverse, as was brought out in Chap. 1.

As a part of a large program of cooperation, a considerable number of management plans of one sort or another have been prepared for private lands with state and Federal assistance. A few of these are for industrial holdings, mostly prepared with the help of the U.S. Forest Service, the Tennessee Valley Authority, and a number of states. By far the greater number are for small holdings, mostly on farms. The Forest Service and Soil Conservation Service of the U.S. Department of Agriculture are the principal Federal agencies giving technical assistance to private forest landowners. The Tennessee Valley Authority also does this work within its territory in cooperation with state agencies. All state agencies carry on extensive work of this nature, with cooperative financial assistance from the Federal government. In all this cooperative work it must be recognized that, while much of the technical impetus comes from public agencies, the private owner makes the final decision as to whether any plan is followed. As a consequence, many timber management plans that have been prepared are essentially proposals, often with high educational value, but are not necessarily plans in actual use.

The larger industrial owners naturally do a great deal of careful timber management planning; very large investments in timberlands and dependent processing plants are involved. Few, however, prepare formal written plans, and those that exist are not generally available. The timber business is competitive like any other, and no private company is likely to release detailed information on its policies, plans, and operations, and there is no requirement to do so. In some instances private timber operations are too much in developmental stage for formal plans to have much meaning and value. General operating policies and plans may be sufficiently well known within an organization so that specific written statements are not considered necessary. Companies are more likely to concentrate attention on direct action, on acquisition, on the assembling of adequate inventory information, and on plans for cutting operations on particular tracts than on preparing formal management plans. Further, and more importantly, there is a strong tendency for industrial managers administratively to integrate timber management planning, along with inventories, into the regular forest operating program, with the result that there is no separate plan as such. This point is further discussed on p. 307. For these reasons, there is much timber management planning but not many plans as such in industrial forestry.

CANADA

The situation is very different in Canada (Davis, 1960). Public ownership is dominant, about 93 percent of the total productive forest area, but it is practically all owned by the provinces, who are largely autonomous in their administration of it. The Federal government owns little land and is primarily concerned with policy, cooperation, and research.

Because of these differences in forest land ownership and administration, organization for sustained yield and the preparation of timber management plans is also different. The general pattern is as follows:

1. Large areas of public (Crown) lands are leased to large timber companies. They are termed "forest management licenses," "Tree Farm licenses" (in British Columbia), and "lease" or "limit" lands. Both privately owned and public lands are managed in conjunction with a specific sustained-yield objective. These licenses, though having termination dates, are intended to be continuing provided their provisions are followed. The recipient accordingly has reasonable assurance of tenure and is expected to manage these public lands on a permanent basis as if they were his own. The large pulp and paper industry of Canada is built on this basic plan. Leases of hundreds of square miles are common; some include several thousand square miles.

As a part of the lease requirement, the timber company is required periodically to prepare timber management plans for provincial approval. The provinces issue detailed specifications for these plans, which are confidential between the company and the province. There is no parallel to this situation in the United States.

2. In several provinces, British Columbia and Ontario especially, sustained-yield units of public lands are established that in a general sense are counterparts of the national forests in the United States, although leased

lands may be included. The units are managed for sustained yield by th
respective province with stumpage sold to individuals who, as on the na
tional forests, have limited land management responsibilities. Timber man
agement plans for the unit are prepared by the provinces. Organizatio
of these areas as permanent public operating units is comparatively recent
     3. Farm woodlot licenses. In British Columbia, small tracts not ex
ceeding 640 acres or 10,000 cu ft in annual yield may be permanently lease
to a farmer for farm use and supplemental income. This is a sustained-yiel
unit in miniature. A simplified management plan is normally required fron
the licensee.

     The objective is to get all commercially valuable Crown lands unde
sustained-yield organization be it through long-term leases to large operators
public working circles, or small individual leases. As indicated, timber man
agement planning and plans are largely controlled by the provinces.

purposes and principles of timber management planning and plans

Why be especially concerned about preparation of timber managemen
plans? The question is not academic. A first and fundamental reason i
that some sort of plans resulting from planning work are an administrativ
necessity. Very large values are involved in forest lands and in the supplyin
of dependent processing plants. All the many parts of a forestry enterpris
come together in the process of planning for continued timber production
     A second major reason is that this work forces and focuses analysis
Planning and preparing plans makes one think the problem through, fac
up to what is entailed, and make decisions. The process can be more val
uable than the particular plans that may result.
     A third and very practical reason for having systematic procedure
and plans is that they cushion the shock of personnel changes. Like othe
people, foresters come and go, but the forest goes on. If much of wha
foresters know and intended is accumulated under their hats rather thar
on paper, much valuable information can leave with them. Personne
changes can be expensive and disruptive to the continuity of forest opera
tions and are a problem to both public and private organizations.
     A fourth reason is to give evidence of stewardship. This is a poin
of particular force with public agencies; there are sound policy reasons fo
having something tangible to show that the public objectives of managemen
are being served. Closely related is the reason that many organizations an
individuals are deeply concerned with the available supply of public timber
They have the right and need to know the allowable annual cut (Chap
6), which is the major item of economic information given in a timbe
management plan.

Continuing from reasons for doing this work, there can be stated some principles of successful timber management planning that have wide application.

1. The major emphasis should be on *planning* as a continuing function rather than on plans as such. The word "plan," and particularly a timber management plan, often tends to conjure up mental concepts and images that arouse misunderstanding and even opposition. There is a tendency for planning to stop when a plan is prepared. When a management plan is mentioned, a forester tends to think of some rather formal model, because frequently that is the only sort of a plan he has actually seen or read about. He may say he is against plans, when he really means he is against a particular kind of a plan as applied to his situation and problem. He may be quite right, but he hardly can be against planning and plans in general. Whether recognized as such or not, written or not, there is a plan of some sort for any property managed for continued timber production purposes. There has to be; the only question is what kind of plan.

2. There must be a need commensurate to the level and kind of planning employed. For example, in a situation where protection, application of reasonably effective silviculture, and close attention to utilization is all that is practicable, an intensive regulatory plan will lie unused no matter how skillfully it is prepared. There have been many examples of plans prepared at a level out of step with the realities of the situation, when a different, and usually much simpler, plan of operation would have sufficed.

3. Successful plans develop out of experience; it is an evolutionary process. "Effective plans cannot be drawn up all at once out of a clear sky, so to speak" (Moore, 1915. There have been many attempts to do this, but the results have not been good. Years of background experience and several attempts are normally required to evolve a plan that is an effective instrument for use.

4. Planning may be done at all levels; there is no set pattern. Planning should be strictly in terms of a particular situation and purpose, and any written plan resulting should reflect that situation. Models are helpful but not binding; inhibitions should be avoided. An extensive, essentially pre-management plan to initiate management on an area is just as much a plan as an intensive plan for a well-regulated property.

Initial field examinations and analyses of the possibilities of managing forest properties for continued production should be regarded as a natural and indispensable aspect of management planning. Before detailed inventories are undertaken and investments made regarding hitherto unmanaged areas, a necessary first step is to explore the situation fully and appraise what is needed and can be done. Preparation of initial reports on the basis of extensive surveys, reports that summarize the essentials of the present and prospective situation and give a basis for initiating action, have occupied and occupy a prominent position on both public and private lands in many parts of the world. They call for the utmost in professional skill, balanced judgment, good organization and presentation, and frequently salesmanship as well. An initial survey and examination follows the same general outline and framework as any other kind of management planning but is adapted, of course, to meet the particular need. The resulting report is, in effect, an initial management plan. As management progresses, there should be a logical transition from more or less preliminary estimates and conclusions and so-called stopgap plans toward more solidly based management plans.

5. Existence of a plan implies acceptance and use. This is often forgotten. Applying this test, a great many plans that have been prepared are not actually plans at all but merely proposals that may or may not become operative. This is why the work is extremely responsible; the whole forestry business is affected by it.

6. There must be a close relationship between preparation of a plan and those who are to apply it. This principle has been violated many times but not with good results. A plan is a guide but no substitute for a skilled man on the ground. An office-prepared plan handed to the field organization for application is seldom successful. There must be good liaison and understanding all along the line. The more the man responsible on the ground can feel it is his plan the better.

7. A plan can be no better than the technical skill, data, and thought that go into it. It is not difficult to prepare a plan that looks good on paper. The test is the substance behind it and its utility in meeting real needs on the ground.

8. There must be flexibility to meet the dynamics of a constantly changing situation and at the same time to give reasonable provision for forest continuity. This is not easy to accomplish. There is often a tendency to emphasize forest continuity and to give inadequate attention to current needs. Application of regulatory techniques can lead one into very long-range and sometimes overly rigid calculations that may have little reality. Attempts to base the current annual cut on long-range increment calculations involving stands many years from maturity may lead to this, for example. As was brought out in Chap. 6, the real problem and art of regulation is to achieve a satisfactory compromise between present and future needs.

9. There must be provision for continuity of the plan itself. Many have been prepared with the elements of success in them but have failed in practice because no workable mechanics were devised to keep them alive.

a check list for timber management planning

In thinking through the job of management planning and the preparation of plans, the most helpful approach is to develop a check list of things

1at must be considered and some decision reached regarding them. The ollowing has been prepared for this purpose. Some of the items will not e important in a particular situation; sometimes the problem is to deter-1ine that they are not important. But regardless of the kind of ownership, 1ey must all be considered and decisions reached before a specific plan 1n be prepared.

1. *Purposes of Management.* As has been emphasized, this is the 1arting point. What is wanted? What land, timber, financial and operating olicies either are in effect or are to be put into effect? Unless purposes 1d policies are clearly understood, no sensible plan can result. The desire f a forest owner to embark on a permanent timber-growing program may 1gically necessitate additional investments in timberland and improvements, dministrative reorganization, and changes in operating policies and capital ructure of a far-reaching nature that have not hitherto been faced or 1arified. These matters apply to an individual owner, a forest manager 1resenting the needs of a timber-growing program to the executive man-1gement of his company, or to a public forester. Key policy issues must e settled before detailed planning is in order.

2. *Markets, Labor, and General Economic Situation.* The essential 1eed is to identify which of these factors are important in a given situation 1d to evaluate them. If the purpose is to produce stumpage to sell, a 1orough job of market forecasting and analysis of utilization trends may e necessary. Development of a timber sale program may be an important 1d indispensable part of putting a management plan into operation. This 1pplies to public and private owners alike. If the purpose is to supply wood 1 a company-owned mill, the matter of markets may be largely predeter-1ined by the purposes of management. The purpose and function of com-1any-owned lands must be understood. Production from such lands often 1ust be considered in relation to procurement from other lands in meeting 1tal processing plant requirements. Owned lands are often in part regarded 1 insurance in meeting mill requirements; they may have a special strategic 1alue. When the procurement situation is favorable, timber available for 1utting on these lands may be to some extent reserved for future need. 1abor supply and various community considerations may or may not be 1nportant. The list of things that may be considered under this heading 1an be expanded.

3. *Forest Organization and Subdivision (Chap. 11).* It may be neces-1ary to organize and establish effective administrative units and additional 1rest subdivisions. This may have to precede specific management planning, 1ough in general it is a part of it.

4. *Accessibility.* This is always a consideration, often a critical one. 1he need for construction of roads and other transportation routes may e the controlling problem and require intensive analysis and planning. In 1her situations, accessibility may not be a factor at all.

5. *Correlation with Other Forest Land Uses.* On public lands, th
is a major matter. Timber, water, wildlife, recreation, and other uses an
interests may have to be fitted carefully together with compromise and a
justment necessary. On private lands, this is usually less of a problem b
may be important.

6. *Protection against Fire, Insects, and Disease.* As all foresters knov
these factors may be and often are of great importance. While action plar
regarding them usually cannot be included in a timber management plar
their present and probable future effect on production must be appraised.

7. *Silviculture.* Although a plan is not the place for a detailed expos
tion of the silviculture applicable in a particular situation, silvicultural ma
ters must be given frank and careful consideration. They are often of d
cisive importance and affect every other aspect of management. It is utter
useless to make regulatory prescriptions for a form of management to whic
the forest will not respond. It is equally bad to ignore the existence
decadence and other factors which may profoundly affect the schedule
cutting. From a management planning standpoint, the essential thing is t
take account of the really important silvicultural factors and to make sur
they are faced. The plan should include the essentials of decisions reache
regarding cutting methods, regeneration methods, and the like. The bod
of available silvicultural data and experience upon which these decisior
are based cannot be included.

8. *Inventory Information.* The necessity for having adequate fore
and related information was stressed in Chap. 12. In some instances, rathe
extensive data are all that are really necessary. In other situations, rathe
detailed and accurate inventory data are required. Both too much and to
little money and energy can be spent in getting forest information in relatio
to need; there can be no general rule. Sometimes so much time is sper
on getting and organizing necessary resource data that there is not enoug
left for constructive analysis of what it means. There is a tendency to thin
that getting resource data together is management planning, whereas it
only a necessary basis for planning.

It often happens that management planning has to be done on th
basis of general forest surveys that do not yield adequate forest informatio
As a result, planning is adjusted to fit available data. The situation shoul
be reversed and forest surveys designed from the start to yield the informa
tion needed in management planning.

Information on growth is closely allied with inventory work and ofter
though not necessarily, obtained as a part of the job. Since in the lor
run forest yield depends on growth, it is inescapable that management plar
ning include searching analysis of growth. As was brought out in Chap
4 and elsewhere, the major impact of growth information in managemer
is in design of the management structure. Growth considerations come t
focus particularly in the determination of the rotation and in the estal
lishment of a cutting regime that will give the character and level of growin

ock that will provide maximum yield in harvestable growth under the eco-
omic conditions prevailing.

Provision for getting adequate inventory information, including data
n growth, is a logical part of a managment plan.

9. *Regulatory Framework.* A timber management plan must include
ecific consideration concerning how, and to what degree, forest continuity
to be maintained. This basically requires deciding how much, where,
hen, and how fast to cut. As was brought out in Chaps. 6, 7, 8, and
, there is a considerable body of techniques available on determining the
ut and in regulating the forest, and it is through their application that
rest continuity is achieved. Continued forest productivity does not neces-
arily require that an approximately equal annual yield be obtained from
particular forest tract. This can be accomplished by effective application
f silvicultural measures only; the degree of sustained yield desired from
given forest property is essentially a matter for managerial decision. A
mall owner content with irregular yields but following productive silvicul-
ural practices would have little interest in methods for regulating the cut
ith a high degree of uniformity. He can rely directly on inventory and
rowth data plus a silvicultural prescription. For a forest supplying a mill
r sustaining a community, regulation of the cut to provide a sustained
ield on an annual basis is extremely important. Whether or not some for-
ula or specific technique is applied is not the point; more than often
t is not, especially in a forest that has been under management for some
ime. The point is that a regulatory framework suitable to the purpose is
n essential item in the preparation of any plan of management.

10. *Provision for Plan Continuity.* If continuity of the forest is impor-
ant, so is continuity of planning. This is often overlooked or not given
dequate attention. It is not enough merely to say that a plan will be revised
n 5, 10, or more years. Just *how* it is to be kept alive as an operating
ool needs to be given careful thought and provision. The whole framework
f management planning should consciously be designed for continuity from
he start. The objective should be so to arrange things that this is natural
nd almost automatic.

Continuity is achieved by administrative means. There are two of them
f particular importance here. The first is the establishment and mainte-
ance of an adequate system for getting continuing forest information
Chap. 11). If a realistic schedule is established for conduct of surveys
nd analysis of the results, much of the problem of continuity is met. The
esultant flow of data, ensured by administrative direction, does much to
orce systematic planning revision. As better information is obtained, it is
ut to use in improving operating practices. A plan should include specific
rovision as to how a continuing supply of needed data is to be obtained.
These provisions should also be revised as experience indicates.

The second means is through the normal processes of current adminis-
ration. A procedure and schedule is established for the making of reports,

the keeping of records, the preparing of maps, and the like. Things lik
cutting budgets, cultural operations, inspections, etc. are regularly mad
It is through such procedures that management planning is implemente
and kept current. Their design is consequently an important part of pla
ning. A constant aim should be to build planning into operational procedu
so that continuity is enforced by the administrative system and that revisic
is made whenever better information and the purposes of management s
dictate.

One general caution should be observed: keep things as simple an
direct as possible. The development, in a first burst of enthusiasm, of a
elaborate inventory control system and operating procedures which are fir
in theory but which break down in practice and cannot be kept up a
no better, and in some respects worse, than no system. A broken-down sy
tem tends to sour everybody on the subject and represents wasted mone
as well. Procedures should be built up carefully and deliberately with a cor
stant eye for practicality and simplicity. It must constantly be remembere
that management and management planning is a cumulative thing an
never finished. Continuity is the essence of the matter.

11. *The Cutting Budget.* Management planning is never complet
unless it is carried to a schedule specifying which stands are to be cu
when, and how for some period in the immediate future. In many respect
development of cutting budget, complete with timber-marking specification
is the acid test of effective planning. It is the vital connecting link betwee
regulatory planning and the forest; it is the physical tie to action on th
ground. All of the many adjustments, compromises, and integrations tha
may be necessary in developing a forest production schedule come togethe
and find final expression in the cutting budget, which defines what is t
be done on the ground.

Common practice is to establish a total cutting budget for periods c
5 to 10 years, usually coinciding with or being a multiple of the plannin
period for which an allowable cut is determined (Chap. 6). More extende
projections are also made for long-range planning purposes. Provision i
also normally made for cutting more or less of the planned budget volum
perhaps 5 to 10 percent, to give flexibility for meeting market change
forest exigencies or other factors requiring current adjustment of the cu
The attempt is made to balance out these adjustments in total volume ove
the allowable cut planning period as nearly as possible.

Within this total cutting budget, the job of the forest manager i
charge of an administrative operating unit or working circle is to plan th
cut by years and to designate specific areas for cutting in desired sequence
Here is where unit area surveys (Chap. 12) are particularly useful. A spe
cific schedule of cutting is prepared for at least a year in advance. Usually
it is made for 3 to 5 years and annually revised. By this procedure, a fores
manager always has a cutting schedule for several years ahead, althoug

that for the next year is the most definite. This work is necessary to prepare areas for cutting and to schedule road development and related work.

structure and form of plans

From the foregoing, it is clear that there can be no single form or outline for timber management plans. Depending on need and circumstances, what constitutes an adequate plan may vary from a statement of policy and purpose together with some summary forest area, type, and volume figures on a few sheets of paper, to a bulky collection of maps, tabulations, and written material backed by much inventory data. In basic terms, a plan should be thought of as an expression, an embodiment, of management planning brought to focus at a particular point in time and applicable for a particular period. The specific form it takes is a matter for the forest owner to decide in view of his purposes of management; it is more helpful to think of function rather than of form. A forest owner may practice intensive forestry, do efficient and effective planning, have his resource data and maps in good shape, and know precisely what he is doing and why, and yet have no specific management plan as such that can be given out for inspection.

Why is this so? A helpful answer to this question can be given by recognizing two general approaches to the process of expressing the substance of timber management planning in written form. They are a documentary and what may be termed a "built-in" approach. A documentary plan is the traditional kind. It means a specific and dated report that in one place brings together what is considered key information regarding the policies and procedures for timber production on a property for a specified period. When one speaks of a "plan" as a document, this is what is normally meant.

A "built-in" approach means that the substance of a plan is embodied in the policies and operating procedures of the organization and is not brought together in any single document identified as the management plan. These two approaches are related and should be regarded as differences in general direction rather than as discrete methods. Elements of a documentary and a "built-in" approach are always present; it is a matter of emphasis.

In a large organization, private or public, a considerable amount of administrative manual, handbook, and related procedural material is prepared that is drawn upon and applied to a particular working circle or other planning unit but which cannot and need not be restated in a specific written plan. This is particularly true of large public organizations, which normally prepare plans in a documentary sense. It is important to recognize that such plans do not include much of the policy, silvicultural, total forest land use, and operating information and practices upon which they are based. Fully to understand the timber management function, one must study

the nature and purposes of the organization as a whole. Where private
owners are under no compulsion to prepare a plan as such, as is true in
the United States, the trend is toward a "built-in" approach.

As has been pointed out (p. 305), the vital need for continuity of
planning is achieved by administrative means. In this sense, no documentary
plan can be complete in itself. There is always related administrative
material that must be considered.

Despite these considerations, there are good reasons, which have been
brought out, why the results of timber management planning should periodically be brought to focus and assume some documentary form. Such a plan
serves as a useful guide post along the route of progress. The following
is aimed to facilitate preparation of such plans.

In analyzing the process of reducing management planning to written
form, the job can be divided into three fairly distinct parts.

Background and Foundation Material. This includes the purposes of
management, accessibility to markets, social and economic considerations,
description and history of the forest, major silvicultural and protection situations and problems, basic management methods applicable, need for integration with other forest uses, and similar material. This kind of information
does not change rapidly, is not a part of a specific timber-growing action
plan, and logically can best be prepared and applied to rather large forest
units. On the national forests, such foundation materials are prepared for
the forest as a whole and apply to all working circles or districts within
it if more than one is recognized. The need for written foundation material
naturally varies widely. There is no particular reason why a small private
owner should prepare it; presumably he knows his own situation. A large
corporate owner may or may not be interested Its situation and general
policies may be well known within the organization through other media.
Public owners often feel the need for such material since it helps to crystal-
lize and focus thinking for the multipurpose forest land management job
they have to perform.

Forest Information. This includes information about the forest itself
(Chap. 12), its area, stocking classification, conditions, growth, cutting history and records, etc. These are the basic factual background and embody
the results of forest inventories. The inventory data and/or system itself
should be handled separately from the plan—this is likely to be rather bulky
material—but the key summaries are a natural part of the plan. The same
in general applies to operations information. The material itself is not a
part of the plan, and much of it does not apply. But the results that do
and specification of procedures to get the information neeeded are a logical
part. There can be no sharp dividing line between maintenance of forest
information and the management plan. The records themselves, if kept up
to date in good shape, can be applied directly in field management. Fundamentally, it is a purpose of management planning to see that this can
be and is done.

The Regulatory Plan. This is the most indispensable part; it defines what is to be done. It grows out of and follows the management design adopted. The crux is the regulatory procedure applied which determines the allowable cut by years or other periods of time. This part should also define action policies regarding silvicultural and protection needs as directly relating to timber production, specify correlation with other uses, provide for application of regulatory controls, and include a cutting budget. This part need not be long or include any more description and explanation than is necessary for coherence. It should be regarded as a working tool to guide field action rather than as a piece of writing. If a general area and volume allotment procedure is applied (Chap. 6), the periodic cutting budget and schedule, together with the inventory and growth data upon which they are based, may be all that is really necessary. The periodically revised budget *is* the plan.

In connection with timber management planning and in the operation of any extensive forest business, special studies and analyses are made from time to time to give answers to particular problems. These are essential to any alert and progressive business. Such material should be cross-referenced as appropriate but not regarded as a part of the plan. To include such material tends to make it less effective as an operating instrument.

illustrative outlines of timber management plans

The best way to indicate the form timber management plans may take is to give the outlines, by major captions, of a few actual plans. The following are illustrative of several different kinds of American plans, public and private.

Timber Management Plan for the Cannel
Meadows Working Circle, Sequoia and
Inyo National Forests, California

This is an example of a working circle plan applying to the timber production use of 604,000 acres of national forest land of which 194,000 acres are classed as productive forest land. Recreation interests in the area are very strong.

Title and approval sheet

Map of working circle

Summary of plan—area, timber volume, allowable cut, sustained-yield capacity, cutting budget and sales program, control records, date of revision.

Management plan

    Objectives, silvicultural and community support

    Sales policy

    Forest regulation—assumptions, rotation, cutting cycle, growth and mortality, methods of cutting, growing-stock objectives, calculation of allowable cut, unregulated annual cut

    Forest development—transportation, planting, timber stand improvement, disease and insect control, fire control, land exchange

    Coordination with other uses—recreation, wildlife, water, grazing, mining

    Cooperation—Federal, state, private

Supporting data
   History
   Land description—boundaries, zonal subdivisions, relation to other working
      circles
   Physiography—topography, soil, climate
   Economy—population of communities, industries
   Detailed timber data (10 tables)
Maps

Timber Management Plan for the
Lower Michigan National Forests

This is an example of a national forest plan wherein the material is divided
into two distinct parts: (1) a basic data and policy section covering the national
forest as a whole and applying to five working circles; (2) management plans for
each of the working circles. The outlines for the overall basic data section and
for one of the working circles are given below.

BASIC DATA AND POLICY STATEMENT, LOWER MICHIGAN NATIONAL FORESTS

Summary tables—area (national forest and other), volume, growth, allowable
   cut by area and volume.
Basic data—history, ownership status, physiography, forest description, social
   and economic aspects.
Forest management—protection, reforestation, timber stand improvement.
Administrative correlation—recreation, wildlife, grazing, fire, watershed protection, acquisition, roads, state and private forestry, research.
Management policies
Appendix—approved policy statements covering reforestation, timber stand improvement, marking and management guides, commercial sales, sales at cost,
   free and administrative use, roadside and water front restrictions, sale area
   betterment, slash disposal, instructions for maintenance of plan records,
   growing-stock levels by timber types.

TAWAS WORKING CIRCLE PLAN

Summary
Introduction
Cutting budget (essentially two tables)
Description—boundary, ownership, topography, soil and climate, forest cover,
   area by timber types and size classes, volume, stocking and stand condi-
   tions, growth of timber types, results of past management.
Management objectives
Regulation—method of cutting by major types, allowable cut by acres and
   volume, rotation, cutting cycle, and operable acreage.
Sales policy
Administrative correlation (by uses)
Cooperation
Management plan maintenance
Next revision

A Preliminary Plan for Sustained-yield Forest Management Prepared
in Cooperation with the Hassel and Hughes Lumber Company.
By the Tennessee Valley Authority and the Tennessee
Department of Conservation

As the title indicates, this is a preliminary plan. It is aimed to explore the
opportunities for sustained-yield management, to serve the need for a preliminary

period of management, and to point the way to a second period of management. The written part, exclusive of the Appendix, is fairly short (17 single-spaced typed pages), and emphasis is on clear and direct presentation to meet this initial need.

Introduction

Opportunities for sustained-yield management—management possibilities of the present timber stand, financial aspects of management, future possibilities.

Management recommendations—forest fire protection, consolidation of holdings, capital improvements, cutting practices, records, development of future plans.

Summary

Appendix—inventory methods, growth predictions and methods, type and condition sample map, sample ledger sheet, sample stock and stand table, key map to tract location.

Timber Management Plan by a Timber Company

This plan was prepared by a company for its own use and covers nearly a quarter million acres purchased in a single block. A permanent sampling system was promptly installed for the tract, and the supporting forest information is largely drawn from the initial measurement data. These gave a consistent planning foundation for the entire property. This plan was the basis for formulation of an initial management program for the property. The major captions follow:

Policy statement—the purposes of management

Forest information—types, age, condition, quality

Cutting methods—basic silvicultural methods

Cutting plan—priorities by areas and stand conditions, allowable cut, 5-year cutting schedule and budget.

Access roads—present, mileage, needed road plan and mileage, improvement and maintenance.

Markets—analyses of present and potential outlets for different classes of material.

Methods of logging operation—possible alternatives.

As these few samples show, variations in how to present a written management plan are many. In the United States and around the world there are numerous forms of specific plans, and it is fruitless to try to cover the range in total. As stated before, it is the situation and need that governs and not the particular form. In addition to the above examples, all of which represent fairly large properties, plans of one sort or another have been prepared for many small holdings as a part of farm forestry work. In general, they are a simplified version of the same general thing but are adapted to the particular situation and need of the owner. Formal plans prepared by private owners on their own initiative and entirely for their own use are few and normally are not available for general distribution.

In the final analysis, it is not the existence of a formal plan that counts but the quality of forest management being practiced. Written plans are only a means, although in many instances a necessary means, to an end—effective forest management.

part 3   *forest valuation*

*How to regulate and organize a forest property to make
it responsive to the purposes of management is given in
Parts 1 and 2. While the emphasis was on the forest as
a biological entity, it was fully recognized that financial,
or more broadly economic, considerations determine what
can be done within the capability of the forest. Money is
never unlimited, and financial choices must be made.
Part III deals with valuation, which is regarded as an
indispensable tool of management in seeking the best
financial choice under existing conditions. It begins with
valuation principles, investment, and interest with particular
reference to forestry. A three-chapter sequence follows
dealing with the evaluation of forest land and its growing
stock, slumpage, and of the individual tree. This material is
brought together and applied in analyses of financial
alternatives and with consideration of damage appraisal.*

14

valuation principles

An understanding of some valuation fundamentals is necessary to place their applications to forestry in clear perspective. It should be clearly recognized that valuation is basically an expression of economic principles applied to certain problems of business finance and cuts deeply into these fields. Some aspects are more or less peculiar to forestry, but, for the most part, they should be regarded as variants of more general business situations. Many problems of engineering economy are closely similar to those in forestry.

values

A first essential in considering valuation is to understand what it means. The key word is "value," a word of many meanings and correspondingly diverse applications that require discrimination. A dictionary definition is an excellent point of beginning in grasping its many usages:[1]

> A fair return or equivalent in goods, services, or money for something exchanged.
> The monetary worth of something: marketable price.
> Relative worth, utility or importance: degree of excellence.
> A numerical quantity assigned or computed.
> Something intrinsically valuable or desirable.

Worth is a closely related word. Both mean "the quality of being useful, important or excellent. Worth applies to what is intrinsically or enduringly excellent, meritorious or desirable, value may suggest the immediate estimation of the worth of something to an individual or in a particular situation."[1]

[1] Webster's Seventh New Collegiate Dictionary, 1963.

The above definitions of value can be summed up under two general meanings. The first expresses the utility of something, its power, directly or indirectly, to satisfy the needs or desires of human beings. This is often termed "value in use." Air, for example, has a large value in use but normally no market value, since it is not scarce in a general sense, although millions are spent to condition or to control it. An individual may prize a certain thing highly as an heirloom, even though there may be no market for it. Value in use is not necessarily dependent on either scarcity or sale value. The second meaning, and the normal economic usage, is value in exchange, meaning the amount of other commodities, commonly represented by money, for which a good can be exchanged in the open market, i.e., value as measured by market price. For something to have value in exchange, it must have attributes of both utility and scarcity in some degree.

In forestry, there are many values in use, some of which can be measured fairly completely in market-determined monetary terms and some of which cannot. Aesthetic, sentimental, recreational, and water values associated with forest lands are, for example, known to be large and often of decisive importance in determining forest land use but are imperfectly and incompletely measurable in monetary terms. This fact does not lessen their importance but does make their valuation difficult. Other values, as that of a forest product of standard grade and specifications, such as lumber, can be rather readily expressed in dollar-exchange terms at a given place and point of time, even though such a value does not necessarily measure what it is really worth to a user in any general or even economic sense.

The degree to which forest values can be expressed in monetary terms at a given time is something like a spectrum in that there are all intergradations with no sharp dividing lines. It is inaccurate to speak categorically of tangible and intangible, direct and indirect, or market- and nonmarket-determined values for this reason. Few values are wholly either tangible or intangible, it is a matter of degree. These terms are useful to label extremes or general bands in the value spectrum but should be thought of as relative designations rather than as definite categories.

MARKET VALUE

Measurement of monetary values is necessarily closely associated with the idea of a market, a mechanism for their establishment. It is consequently important to be clear on what is meant by market value. The idea of a market rather naturally conjures up a mental image of people with something to sell mingling with those interested in buying at some common meeting ground more or less equally accessible to all. As a result of bargaining, prices are agreed upon and goods and money change hands. This is indeed the classical concept of a market and of market price establishment and calls attention to the basic ingredients of goods or services available for sale, some avenue or means for making them known to prospective buyers, and the element of negotiation or bargaining in setting the price based on factors of supply and demand. While in a modern technological society the processes of marketing and price determination are often exceedingly complex, the concept of a market value remains and is of basic importance in valuation as a basing point in determination of monetary values.

As might be anticipated, market value is not easy to define. The most direct and basic definition is the maximum amount of money obtainable for a good or property under prevailing market conditions, or, more bluntly, what something can be sold for. This definition places the emphasis on the fact of sale rather than on the conditions under which it is made. Sales can be and are made under conditions not measuring a "fair" or "reasonable" market value. There may be fraud, lack of adequate information on the part of either buyer or seller, duress, or undue pressure to sell at a disadvantageous time or place. Sales made under such conditions, while indubitably constituting and often influencing market prices, may not be indicative of any reasonable or stable market value.

Mertens (1958) in "The Law of Federal Income Taxation" gives an accepted definition expressing conditions under which a "fair" market value can be established as "the price at which a property would change hands in a transaction between a willing buyer and a willing seller, neither being under compulsion to buy nor sell and both being reasonably informed as to all relevant facts." In general, an appraiser is primarily concerned with estimating on the basis of a fair market value. This is particularly true with appraisals made for legal purposes, as in the settlement of claims, in which the central purpose is to establish a reasonable, middle-of-the-road value fair to all. While a buyer and a seller naturally hope for an especially favorable price in accordance with their respective interests, both have to recognize that under competitive conditions, an actual sale price is likely to be at a level approximating a "fair" market price and thus tend to estimate values accordingly.

In the case of real estate, and timberland is one form of it, the following definition by Henderson (1931) is particularly significant: "The market value of a property at a designated date is that competitively established price which represents the present worth at that date of all the rights to future benefits arising from ownership, and considering its highest and best use." The fact that a property value is essentially a forecast of the future is emphasized by the following statement by the famous jurist Oliver Wendell Homes [*Ithaca Trust Co. v. United States* 279 U.S. 151 (1929)]:

> But the value of a property at a given time depends on the relative intensity of the social desire for it at that time expressed by the value it would bring in the market. Like all values, as the word is used by the law, it depends largely on more or less certain prophecies of the future; and value

is no less real at that time if later the prophecy turns out false, than when it comes true.

The significance of market value in valuation work is that it represents a monetary integration, for the most valuable use to which a property or good can be put, of buyer and seller interaction, and of all factors affecting value. Not all values can be entirely expressed in monetary terms and this must be recognized. But to the extent values are expressible in dollars, a well-established market value is a standard or basis for comparison in all valuation work. As has been brought out, the essentials of a valid or "fair" market price are lack of fraud or undue pressure, adequate information by both buyer and seller, and the existence of some market mechanism. If transactions for a particular good or property are few and irregular, a market price cannot be said to exist, since there is no established market.

nature and purposes of valuation

Valuation as a term means the act or procedure of estimating the value of something. Appraisal means about the same thing and the two words are often used synonymously, although appraisal is commonly applied to valuation in a specific instance. For example, one may speak properly of the valuation of stumpage in general and the appraisal of a tract of timber in particular. Similarly, watershed values may be evaluated in general but the value of the land for a particular reservoir site or of a tract of land for watershed use may be estimated by appraisal. Broadly, valuation is concerned with all values whether measurable in dollar terms or not. The specific purpose of valuation, as considered here, is, however, to estimate values in monetary terms as consistently, fully, and accurately as possible.

Valuation, being a search for value, must be broad and flexible in its application and techniques. It is not an exact science, and a practitioner should not be deluded by the apparent precision of mathematical computations or the seeming finality of an appraisal from an authoritative source. There is an element of judgment in all appraisals. The need is to measure within a significant limit of accuracy those things that can be measured so that the area of uncertainty can be made as small as possible. There is ample scope for judgment in valuation work but it should rest on the best facts obtainable and not be offered as a substitute for them.

Value depends on use. If a person has no use for a property or a good either to resell or to use oneself, it has no value to that person regardless of what it might have to others. As uses change, values can be expected to change. It is perfectly possible and logical for the same property or good to be appraised for different purposes with widely differing results. A particular piece of land may have little value for timber production but, because of its location, have a fairly high value as a motel site. In northwestern

Montana, certain lands of medium to poor site quality supporting Douglas-fir stands have been found to be worth more for Christmas tree production than the best quality timberlands in the area for sawtimber production. Anyone who has dealt with real estate values cannot but be impressed by the tremendous change in value that may accompany changes in current or prospective use. A large reason why values of cutover timberlands in the United States were so low in the 1930s was that few people at the time either appreciated their potentialities for timber growing or had any plans for so using them.

In addition to changes in value accompanying change in use, a large element of negotiation, even of a poker-playing type, often enters into determination of value where buying and selling are involved. This is particularly true with real estate. A seller will consider the values germane to him in setting his price and he is more or less influenced by past costs as well as earnings. He has a price he hopes to get and a minimum below which he will not sell except under compulsion. A buyer likewise considers values pertinent to him. Past costs and earnings are of interest only as a basis for prediction as he is concerned with future earnings or other returns under his projected plan of use which may be quite different from that followed or envisaged by the seller. While he would like to buy as cheaply as possible, he has a maximum price above which he will not willingly go. If the seller and buyer price ranges have a common area, a sale may be negotiated. The final price is a compromise between buyer and seller interest. It should be emphasized that price in a particular instance does not necessarily match with any one person's estimate of value, "fair" or otherwise.

The difference between buyer and seller point of view is well illustrated by the familiar instance of an owner selling his home. He is quite conscious of what he paid for it and what improvements he has made. He may also have various sentimental or other attachments influencing his idea of value. He may be unclear as to how or why depreciation should be figured. The viewpoint of the buyer is quite different. He is not at all concerned with what the house originally cost, with what subsequent improvements may have been made, or in any factors of past use except as they may affect the future. He is interested solely in the present condition and future utility of the house and its cost in relation to other houses he might buy. In the final analysis, it is the current and prospective supply and demand situation that governs.

Differences in viewpoint as affecting value are particularly evident when private and public interests are considered. In private business, most values directly considered are measured in monetary terms, even though various nonmonetary considerations involving so-called intangible values often influence business decisions. Private individuals or nonbusiness private groups are interested in values of all sorts. They are often as much concerned with intangible or indirect values as with those directly expressible in monetary terms. Sentimental, aesthetic, or other rather intangible values are often dominant considerations. The establishment of memorial forests is a good illustration. While the total range of values that may be considered is wide, value interest in a particular instance is usually rather limited.

The public is concerned with practically all values and has the widest range of value interest as applied to a particular thing like an area of forest land. While often engaged in business ventures and always concerned with monetary values, the public has a larger and broader interest in values, often indirect in nature, that contribute to the general welfare. In a democratic society, the general function of government is to protect common interests and to supply those services and facilities promoting social welfare that private enterprise cannot safeguard or provide. In a field so deeply and broadly affecting many interests as forestry, wide differences between public and private viewpoints and interests as regards values involved and their measurement are both natural and to be expected.

There are three underlying and closely related problems common to most appraisals. First, the point of view, purpose, and values germane in a particular situation must be identified. This is often a difficult problem in itself. Valuation must be for a purpose and, as has been indicated, purposes and consequently results may be expected to vary widely. A key question to be answered in valuation work is who is to receive the value. This may make a great deal of difference in the values to be considered and in the appropriate methods to use. Value must be appraised in relation to something and cannot be an independent or abstract entity. Second, the appropriate methods or procedures applicable must be defined; i.e., how the appraisal is to be made. Third, the values involved must be measured. Problems of measurement are often especially difficult. The values germane in a particular appraisal problem may be known and the general methods appropriate to its solution may be well understood, but successful appraisal prevented by inability to measure values believed to be significant.

Appraisals are made principally for the following purposes:

1. To determine or guide price in transfers of title, as purchase or sale, exchange, or estate settlement.

2. To determine or describe property pledged as security.

3. To determine compensation, as for damages, proceedings under eminent domain, or insurance settlement.

4. To establish a base for tax purposes.

5. For many managerial purposes. Valuation is employed by both public and private owners as a means of gauging investment alternatives, determining sound operating methods, and generally in arriving at sound business decisions.

Valuation is an indispensable tool of many uses in forestry. The first four uses of appraisal, as listed above, involve external relationships; something outside the business. Of these, its usefulness in guiding or setting price is perhaps the most obvious. The fifth use, as a managerial tool, should not be overlooked by the forest manager, as it offers one of the most fruitful opportunities for application of valuation techniques. Many decisions can be aided by a careful and searching financial evaluation of different alternatives possible. Although precise answers are frequently not obtainable, comparative values can usually be determined within a range of accuracy sufficient to guide sound decisions. Various considerations are involved and considerable long-range estimation is often necessary. Nevertheless, with care, skill, and some imagination, comparative financial returns can be estimated within a significant range of accuracy. Analyses of this type are given in Chaps. 17 through 20.

bases for valuation

There are three possible bases for valuation: (1) cost value (based on historical cost, replacement, or restoration), (2) income value (the estimated present net worth of all future costs and returns expected), and (3) market value. In most applications of valuation methods, the objective is to estimate or to determine present value. Sale, exchange, compensation for damage, etc., are normally negotiated on the basis of present value. Similarly, when a forest manager wishes to gauge alternative financial choices, costs and benefits are normally equated to the present.

COST VALUE

Historical costs tend to be tangible and definite and are often favored for this reason by accountants and courts as a basis for value determination. From the standpoint of an investor, past costs are of great importance since they necessarily are the basis upon which the return on the investment is measured. As a guide to present market value, however, past costs are a poor measure. In the first place, past costs are often not as tangible as may be thought. A processing plant may be built, rebuilt, and extensively remodeled at various times, and it becomes difficult to determine what capital investment has actually been made. The line between new construction and heavy maintenance is often hazy. Questions of depreciation and carrying costs also enter in and may be difficult to resolve.

With an operating property like a factory, carrying costs like taxes and normal maintenance are not a part of cost value but are regarded as currently liquidated costs offset by benefits of ownership. The situation is different with an investment property such as a tract of forest land planted to trees or a real estate development, both having in common a substantial investment made in expectation of returns that may be received considerably in the future. To the investor, certainly, the initial land purchase cost, taxes, administrative and developmental expenditures are all a part of the investment cost and would be normally carried at interest less returns received to estimate the total investment at a particular point in time. Specific treatment of expenditure items in cost value estimation consequently depends on circumstances.

In the second place, past costs may bear little relation to present value because of appreciation or depreciation, present or prospective changes in use, or because past costs were out of line to begin with. A property may have been acquired at an excessively high or low cost and neither circumstance have any bearing on its present value. Patent or other monopoly controls may be another important factor. A productive business with high earning power may be established with a comparatively small capital outlay because of patents or other circumstances giving some monopoly on supply.

Replacement or restoration costs are often a good measure of present values from the standpoint of evaluation of damage in that they indicate the cost of putting something damaged back into its original condition. They are also frequently a good measure in determining a fair or reasonable value of a processing plant or other improvements for income tax, insurance, or general accounting purposes. Applied to forests, however, these costs have relatively little application for the basic reason that timber cannot be directly replaced. It can be restored only by growth over a period of time, and there is no guarantee that the new timber will be of the same kind, quality, volume, or value. A stand of timber destroyed by fire does not necessarily naturally restock to the same species composition, stocking, and general quality; usually it does not. Even a young plantation destroyed for one reason or another often cannot be replanted to produce a fully equivalent stand; it may be better or worse.

INCOME VALUE

An income value is the estimated present net worth of all future earnings or other returns (less costs) expected from a property. Lacking an established current market value, which integrates all such earnings or returns and also reflects buyer and seller interaction, there is no recourse but to make a direct estimate of expected net returns. In an operating business, present earning are significant only to the degree that they indicate probable future earnings which may be greater or less. A mine nearly worked out or a liquidating timber business the year before the mill must shut down for lack of timber would not have much value even though current earnings were high. In a continuing business, such as a forest operated for sustained yield, present net earnings are often the best and sometimes the only basis for predicting probable future earnings. They are at least a sound point of beginning, and a buyer will increase or decrease what he will pay according to his judgment as to the probable trend of future net earnings.

What is termed business "good will" is a value growing out of past reputation and performance. While intangible in so far as direct measurement is concerned, it may have a very tangible bearing on earnings expected in the future and hence be an important item in estimating the present value of a business.

Since the volume of earning must be measured both by amount and duration, interest necessarily enters in, as it is the only tool available to measure the importance of the passage of time. If the duration of annual income flow is expected to continue indefinitely, the present capital value is indicated by dividing the annual net income by what is considered an equitable rate of interest. If future earnings are estimated to be of limited duration or to begin at some future date, the income or capital value is their present worth as obtained by discounting them at some rate of interest. See Chap. 16 for methods of computation.

MARKET VALUE

Where established and applicable, market prices are an excellent and realistic guide to value. They have the great advantage of summing and integrating all factors affecting monetary value. Market prices as a guide to forest values are essentially comparative. If the product or good is well standardized as to quality and measurement, the comparison is close. The current market value of a deck of logs or of pulpwood along a railroad siding can, for example, be estimated with considerable precision in terms of price obtainable. In the case of real property, the difficulty with market price as a measure of value is that no two properties are quite alike and the comparison to "going" prices is approximate only. The price received for one farm is only indicative of the value of the farm adjoining, even though the two may be closely similar in most respects and identical in area. This is especially true of forest properties. There are many factors of location, site quality, timber stocking, and other factors that affect market value.

Whether the comparison is close or not, market prices exert a profound influence. If a parcel or two of land change hands at a lower figure than has been common hitherto, and almost regardless of the reason, there is a strong tendency for market values of generally comparable properties to be depressed. The same is true, only in reverse order, of occasional high sale prices. Similarly, where market values have not been established, a few initial sales have a large precedent effect on subsequent prices. Extreme prices influence real estate values out of proportion to their frequency of occurrence.

15

interest and investment

Operation of a continuing forest business requires large and relatively permanent investments. Once made, investments in land, timber, and processing plants are not readily convertible into cash for investment elsewhere. Few businessess require such long-range planning and commitment to the future as one concerned with building up and maintaining a forest for continuous production. A managed forest property of 25,000 acres yielding approximately 10 million board feet a year on a sustained basis may well represent an investment of 2 to 3 million dollars in land, timber, and forest improvements. The capital investment in a pulp and paper plant may easily be from 30 to 50 million dollars or more, and other processing plants are proportionately expensive. A small logging contractor owning three or four trucks, a couple of tractors, and other necessary logging equipment may have a capital investment in equipment of upwards of $50,000, not to mention working capital needs for labor and other current expenses.

Investment and accompanying cost charges are a major driving force behind business operation. The return to capital is urgent. Depletion and carrying costs of excessive investments in timberlands have been the cause of rapid and destructive liquidation of the forest resource. While capital investment may be a force that destroys natural resources, it also makes their productive management possible. Capital wisely invested in developing productive forest properties receives a fair rate of return over long periods of time, longer than in the case of many other investments.

The forest manager is accordingly much concerned with matters of investment and interest. They play a large part in valuation problems and are a day-by-day business fact of life.

the concept of interest

As pointed out, operation of a forest business requires a large amount of capital as defined in the sense of an aggregation of economic goods used to promote the production of other goods, instead of being valuable solely for immediate enjoyment. Accumulation of this capital, as reckoned in monetary terms, necessarily requires saving, a postponement of present enjoyment for a future benefit. In industrial countries a great deal of saving is necessary, whether voluntary or not, to accumulate the tremendous amount of capital necessary to operate a technological society. Individuals or nations save to the extent they recognize the resultant benefits and are able to do so.

Capital in monetary form is an extremely usable commodity; it can be used to buy things, initiate productive enterprise, and yield additional income. Its use over a period of time is accordingly worth something to the user, and the owner likewise expects some return for it. The concept of interest stems from this basic fact; it is the return to capital. Interest is the rental price of money, the reward for waiting. Except when money appreciates in value through a decrease in price level, this reward is not received merely by holding money and waiting. Money buried in the ground will not sprout interest though it may be worth more (or less) in purchasing power when it is dug up. It is not automatically entitled to any return. Interest, as a specific payment for the use of money, arises only when it is used, *i.e.,* borrowed. A miser gets no monetary income from his money. His return comes from the physical pleasure of ownership—and complete liquidity.

Another way to look at interest is that the rate employed gives a measure of the importance of the time element involved. The future always carries less weight than the present; a promise to pay a dollar some years hence is seldom worth a dollar, cash in hand, now. The degree to which the passage of time is discounted or valued is measured by the rate of interest; the higher the rate, the more heavily the future is discounted, and vice versa. Consequently, to the extent that time is important in financial matters, consideration of interest as a measure of it is logically inescapable. Interest furnishes an indispensable means of comparing at a common point in time values which arise at different points in time. For example, through interest computation, it is possible to compare the value of a payment made now with one to be made at some time in the future at a common point in time, usually but not necessarily the present. Similarly, the value of a sum available now can be compared with its estimated value at some future time. In much the same way, the present value of a series of payments due at stated times in the future can be determined. Interest is indispensable as a means for making financial comparisons when the time element is involved.

The rate of interest furnishes an expression of time preference. If an individual's time preference is nil, it means that he would just as soon receive a dollar at some time in the future as now. If it is high, it means that he values present income and gratification more highly than the prospect of additional income in the future. Because of the limited span of human life, individual time preference is usually fairly high, sometimes extremely so. This fact shows up repeatedly in the selling of standing timber by an owner. The offer of immediate cash often overshadows acceptance of a plan of management offering much larger total returns and a good return on the investment over a period of years. Rejection of such a plan is not entirely a matter of time preference, however. The owner may also question the validity of the plan or be unable to execute it.

Individual and organizational time preference varies greatly. With individuals, it varies from person to person and for the same person, depending on age, degree of education and maturity, level of income, current personal wants in relation to income, and other circumstances. A man with urgent current need for cash to meet a family emergency has a high time preference overshadowing other considerations. People living at a subsistence level on the land will often destructively utilize natural resources to meet present needs. Corporations, or other forms of continuing business organization, ordinarily have a lower time preference than individuals though the same general forces are operative. Government has a still lower time preference and in general the larger the political subdivision, the lower it is. The Federal government with a national responsibility takes the longest view and tends to have the lowest time preference. Even so, it is not realistic to assume that time preference, even for the Federal government, is zero. There can even be circumstances under which time preference may seem to be less than zero, *i.e.,* the present is discounted in favor of the future. Where national security is involved, a government may be forced to adopt measures of current frugality reversing and overriding normal economic forces. Individuals may, for various personal reasons, and particularly during times of great stress and uncertainty, emphasize the future even more than the present in both financial as well as other matters.

The easiest and most direct way to approach interest as a business matter is through the familiar process of borrowing money. When money is borrowed, a price is set for its use which is termed interest. Interest begins to accrue as soon as the money is made available. The flow of services from its use is theoretically continuous. Because it is not practical to pay interest daily or for very short periods, longer periods are normally set with interest payable at the end of them. Since interest is paid for the use of money, it logically follows that it can be due and payable only *after* the money has been used for some period. Strictly speaking, interest cannot be paid in advance; there can be no such thing as prepaid interest, even though financial organizations sometimes discount the present value of a note by deducting interest not yet due.

Normal business practice is to define the rate of interest as the rental price for 1 year. Thus a 5 percent rate means a $0.05 rental charge for $1 at the end of 1 year and that the total debt at the time is $1.05. Lacking specific agreement to the contrary, a stated rate of interest always means a yearly rate. If $100 is borrowed, interest at a predetermined rate is due every month, 3 months, 6 months, or 1 year, depending on what the contractual payment period is. Paying interest is simply a matter of paying rental on the use of money in the same way as one pays rent for use of a house. For example, on $100 at 5 percent, one would pay $5 in interest at the end of 1 year if it is to be paid annually. The payment would be $2.50 every 6 months if such were the interest payment period agreed upon. The principal of $100 remains intact, and the rental process continues as long as the owner is willing to loan the money and the borrower to use and pay interest on it.

So long as interest is paid when due, there can be no accumulation or compounding of principal. If interest is not paid when due, a question then arises as to whether it should be regarded as an accumulated bill payable and separate from principal or as an addition to the principal. If what is termed simple interest is applied, the amount of the principal remains constant, whether interest is paid when due or not, and interest is always figured on this amount. In the $100 example above, if $5 were not paid at the end of 1 year, the interest bill would be $10 at the end of 2 years, $15 after 3 years, and so on. The principal would remain $100.

There are many reasons, whether by contract or because of other circumstances, why interest is not or cannot be paid when due but accumulates over a period of time. Forestry is full of examples where the return on a particular investment is necessarily deferred. An investment in a plantation or a stand of immature timber may yield little or no current income out of which interest can be paid. The time-sequence nature of timber production has repeatedly been emphasized. The frequency of such situations explains why foresters have always been concerned with the problem of interest accumulation as a large factor in forest investment.

Returning again to the example of $100 borrowed at 5 percent, suppose that the $5 is not paid annually but allowed to accumulate for a number of years. The owner of this $100 may quite correctly take the position that he could reinvest the interest due him each year and make 5 percent on it too. Interest due is capital in his view in exactly the same way as the original $100. By the fact that interest is not paid when due, he is deprived of the opportunity for productive use of this additional capital. Consequently, interest due *is added to the principal* and interest figured on an increasing total capital sum. The process of adding interest to the initial capital is called compounding and interest accumulated on such a basis is termed compound interest. While compounding can be carried to extremes and beyond the realm of business reality, there is no fallacy to such a process. It is inherent to the nature of capital. Unless there is stipulation to the contrary, deferred interest is normally compounded.

the rate of interest

A commercial rate of interest is made up of several fractions or elements. While these fractions are not separately labeled or often recognized in practice, it is important to know what they are and how they affect the "going" rate (Guttenberg, 1950). The subject is approached here from the standpoint of an investor with money to lend.

PURE OR RISK-FREE INTEREST

The average rate yielded by invested capital, without inclusion of risk or the costs of investing it, is often termed pure or economic interest. It represents, on a long-term and stable basis, the average return to capital investment in a given society. If capital could move with complete freedom, the rate theoretically would be the same all over the world. For various reasons this is not so, though there is a tendency in that direction. Economic rates reflect the overall supply and demand situation for capital. As more capital is accumulated, the rate tends to fall unless demand keeps pace. These rates are stable and change very slowly over the years. The tendency in the United States, as in other countries, is for the pure rate to fall gradually; it has decreased between 2 and 3 percent in the last 200 years or so. The best measure of a "pure" rate is that paid by a stable government on its securities. In the United States it ranges between 3½ and 4½ percent depending on the market and kind of security.

RISK FACTOR[1]

All investments are not equally safe. In most enterprises, the investor runs the risk of losing some or all of his invested capital or of not getting all the interest due him. Some fields of investment, mining for example, are commonly regarded as inherently risky. A liquidating timber enterprise has earned a similar reputation based on experiences of past years. In fact, one of the financial problems in forestry has been to demonstrate and sell

---

[1] "Risk" as used here is closely akin to "uncertainty" in that neither all possible outcomes nor their probability of occurrence are considered as specifically determinable. This is distinct from risk in an insurance sense, where probabilities are estimated on an actuarial basis. In practice, risk and uncertainty are not consistently separable.

the idea that forest investments in properties managed for sustained yield are good business risks.

In accordance with the risk that is considered to be involved in a particular kind or class of investments, an additional factor for the risk assumed may be added to the pure rate. Such risks are not insurable; if they were, an insurance premium could be paid and the element or risk converted to a direct cost and largely eliminated as a risk so far as the individual investor is concerned. Since business investment risks are noninsurable, the investor can only make a judgment estimate as to how much the rate should be increased to compensate him for the risk assumed. If the enterprise is considered risky, he will demand a high rate or refuse to invest his money. There is no precise way to determine what part of an investor's capital may be lost; here is where the indispensable and critical factor of individual judgment enters into investment.

While the loss to an individual investor on investments of a certain class cannot be determined with certainty, the *likelihood* of loss can be estimated as a guide to a reasonable risk rate. The problem and its solution can best be illustrated by an example. Suppose a man has $80,000 available to invest. He can get 4 percent on Treasury bonds with no risk and essentially no investment cost. This represents a "pure" rate to him. He contemplates investment in a field where his judgment or general experience indicates that the chance of losing both capital and interest on it is about 1 in 30, or 3.3. percent. This can be interpreted either as 1 investment in 30 going entirely bad, or the average investment failing to pay out in this ratio. The question is: What rate of interest must be charged to keep the capital intact and yield an average net return of 4 percent?

The solution can be worked out as follows:

Annual net interest expected at 4%............	$3,200
Average capital loss at 3.3% of $80,000........	2,640
Total required annual income.................	$5,840

Since it is assumed that 3.3 percent of the capital is annually lost and bears no interest, the average annual interest-bearing capital is $80,000 — 2,640, or $77,360. The rate necessary to replace lost capital and yield 4 percent net is consequently $5,840/$77,360 or 7.55 percent. In this instance, the investor would certainly want this much and undoubtedly more for him to go to the trouble of making the investment as compared to buying government securities.

The problem can also be readily expressed in general formula terms:

$$E = \frac{P + R}{100 - R} \times 100$$

where E = effective rate consisting of pure rate plus risk rate
P = pure rate in percent
R = risk rate expressed as a percent of expected annual loss of total capital invested

To illustrate in the present example:

$$E = \frac{4.0 + 3.3}{100 - 3.3} \times 100$$
$$= \frac{7.3}{96.7} \times 100$$
$$= 7.55\%$$

While it may be logical for risk to be estimated in an actuarial sort of way as illustrated here and added to the pure rate, this is not the only or necessarily the most accurate way to estimate risk where interest is compounded over fairly long periods. The actual risk does not necessarily occur uniformly or cumulatively as is assumed when it is regarded as a part of the interest rate. Handled in this way, it may give a disproportionately large allowance for the real risk involved. In appraising investments, it is often sounder practice to use a fairly "safe" rate and then estimate risk separately and strictly on its own merits. This matter is further discussed on p. 332.

COST-OF-HANDLING FACTOR

It takes time and money to investigate possible investments, make loans, obtain and handle payments, make reinvestments, and generally look after an investment business. International mobility of capital is in part limited by the various costs of making foreign investments. The same is true, though to a lesser degree, within a country. Individual investors often cannot or do not wish to take the time and care it takes to place and handle investments. Such services are furnished by banks and investment companies. Building and loan associations and investment trust companies are excellent examples. They must charge a somewhat higher rate on investments they make than they can pay to their members. The difference is used to pay administrative and other overhead costs. This is a direct illustration of the cost of handling being considered a part of the rate. Such services can and often are paid directly on a fee or commission basis in which case they are not reflected in interest rates. Whatever the arrangements, cost of handling is always a factor to consider in the rate of return on investment.

INDUCEMENT FACTOR

To induce investors to enter new or particular fields of investment, something in addition to pure interest, cost of handling, and risk allowance may be necessary. If there were no promise of additional profit, investors would tend to keep their money in well-established fields where the channels of investment are well known and convenient. There is competition for available capital as for other commodities. In the case of capital, competition is waged primarily by offering a higher rate of interest. Considerably higher than the "going" rates may be necessary to overcome inertia and induce capital to enter a new field even though there is no additional risk involved. Such competition naturally tends to increase interest rates, other things being equal. Risk and inducement are, however, hard to separate. A new and untried field of investment is likely to be considered more risky whether it is or not, and profits are likewise assumed to be less certain. Questions of probable profit are exceedingly important in a field like forestry where investments, once made, may be and often are committed for many years.

length of investment period and the rate of interest

The length of the investment period has considerable influence on the rate of interest. Purely on a cost-of-handling basis, loans made for a short period of time as a few months or years, usually cost more per dollar invested than do loans continuing for a number of years. One reason is that the frequent necessity to reinvest may entail some loss of time between investments and hence loss of interest earnings. Another is that it costs more per dollar invested to collect interest payments, supervise investments, and the like. With the same rate of interest and risk, an investor handling short-time financing, say in loans for a year or two or less, will ordinarily make less per year than if his investments had an average life of 10 years or more. This explains in part why a higher rate is commonly charged for 90- or 180-day financing than for a 15-year mortgage, with the security first class for both.

The idea of liquidity is also related to time. Other things being equal, people prefer to have their money in liquid form and require inducement in the form of interest to lose liquidity by investing money where they cannot get at it readily. Buying readily marketable 20-year bonds is a very different thing from putting money in an enterprise from which it cannot readily be extracted for 20 years. A higher rate of interest would normally be demanded for the latter, even if the risk is estimated to be no greater. Liquidity as well as the duration of the loan must be considered in gauging interest rates.

Risk may or may not be directly related to time. Investments of either long or short duration may be more or less risky and for entirely unrelated reasons. The most risky period in the life of a forest plantation is usually during the first few years following initial establishment. The risk from fire is by no means constant. It changes with the age of the stand, its treatment as well as that of surrounding stands, the attitudes and practices of people regarding forest fires, and the effectiveness of protection given against fire. These things cannot all be foreseen at the time an investment in planting or in the purchase of existing timber stands is made, although some estimate is naturally made.

Inclusion of a large risk element in an interest rate may give an unreasonably large allowance for risk if the investment is compounded for long periods. As an extreme example, interest on $1,000 amounts to $339,302 in 100 years at 6 percent and to $50,505 at 4 percent. This latter rate constitutes a fair return on stable investments and possibly could be received on the average over a long period. The difference between the two of $288,797, occasioned by the change from 6 to 4 percent, is a tremendous allowance for the risk that may be involved and assumes that it is constant and geometrically cumulative throughout the period. In forestry practice, it is common to make at least a partial allowance for risk by applying reasonable conservatism in estimating costs and returns. To the extent this is done, it is manifestly incorrect to allow for risk a second time in the interest rate used in accumulating costs and returns or in capitalizing net income.

What is sometimes called the fallacy of compound interest, by which is meant the mathematical capacity of a sum at even a modest rate of interest to grow to astronomical and meaningless proportions over a long period of time, is simply an expression of the fact that absolutely safe and effortless investments over long periods of time do not exist. There are wars, depressions, political upheavals, technological changes, and other social and economic phenomena that profoundly affect the return on investments. The *average* actual return on investments over a long period is much less than a going commercial rate and may be less than a pure or economic rate as measured by government security or financing rates.

For these reasons, the equitable rate of interest to use in valuation work must be selected with due consideration to the length of time involved, the purposes, and the realities of the situation. There is no formula to determine the proper rate to use. For long-term investments, about 20 years or more, a fairly low rate of 4 to 6 percent is usually used, particularly when the major purpose is to use interest as a measure of the importance of time. Such a rate includes the pure rate plus some allowance for cost of handling and a little risk.

In appraising public works, there is no logical reason to apply a pure rate only, as is sometimes advocated, merely because this rate is approximated by government securities. There are risks in public as well as private undertakings. Also, the business aspects of public undertakings must be considered. In some respects, and recognizing that public time preference tends to be low, it is more logical to use no rate of interest at all than to use a very low rate that has no business and little economic significance. A common practice is to estimate a benefit-cost ratio without interest as a point of beginning. A ratio of 1 indicates that costs will at least be matched by benefits and that the higher the ratio, the better the project. Such ratios for two or more projected undertakings can validly be compared only if the time element for costs and returns is substantially the same. If different, they can be directly compared only by including interest.

If interest is included, and other considerations are equal (which they often are not), that undertaking showing the highest rate of return on the investment is, relatively, the most desirable in so far as it is measurable in monetary terms. Whether any or all of the projects constitute sound investment, public or private, is another matter.

In using interest in forest valuation analyses, the rate should be selected with great care, for it has a major influence on the results. There is some tendency to underappreciate the importance of what may seem to be a small change in rate. For example, an increase from 5 to 6 percent represents a 20 percent increase in the price of borrowed money. No rule can be set for what rate to use; this depends on the purposes and circumstances. For investments within the normal time span of business practice, a rate approximately equal to the going rate for comparable undertakings should be used if meaningful business comparisons are to be made.

In many situations, it is much more helpful to design the analysis to solve for a rate rather than arbitrarily to assume one. Comparisons are most directly and meaningfully made on the basis of rate of return received. Solving for the rate does make the arithmetic more difficult but is often well worth the trouble. Techniques for rate solution are given in Chap. 16 and are applied in later Chapters, especially Chap. 20.

interest on the investment as a cost

Since interest is recognized as the price for the use of money, the question frequently arises as to the extent to which interest on capital invested in a business should be regarded as a cost. Does it logically follow that interest on all capital invested in a business should be determined and regarded as a cost? Payment of interest on borrowed money is clear enough; there is a contract and definitely a bill to be paid. What about owned funds—those supplied from internal sources? It can hardly be argued that the source of a dollar affects its utility.

From the standpoint of the economist, interest on all invested capital is certainly a cost of production and a price-influencing factor in the long run, regardless of the source of the capital. It is also clear that, in comparing costs of production of different businesses and in price determination analysis, ignoring interest on owned capital may lead to misleading results.

From the standpoint of the cost analyst, interest on all capital invested is certainly a factor to be reckoned. For example, suppose it is desired to compare the costs of two methods of skidding. Without regard to interest on investment the following comparison is obtained:

Cost	Method A	Method B
Direct cost per M (including depreciation)...	$3.30	$3.55

On this basis, it would be concluded that Method A was the less expensive. Suppose however, that Method A necessitates much more investment in equipment than Method B. Including interest on the investment as a cost, the comparison then becomes:

Cost	Method A	Method B
Direct cost (including depreciation).........	$3.30	$3.55
Interest on investment....................	0.55	0.25
Total cost per M......................	$3.85	$3.80

It now appears that Method B has a slight cost advantage over Method A. Clearly, interest should be taken into account in determination of comparative costs, and the source of the capital obviously has no bearing.

What about interest on the investment from the standpoint of the capital owned by an individual proprietor? Should he reckon it explicitly in his accounts and if so, how? Here is where the controversial aspects of interest as a cost center.

> . . . it is the function of accounting to show expenses from the point of view of some particular person, group of persons, or business entity, rather than from the point of view of the theorist who is studying the problem of price determination in a given market area, and is defining cost from the standpoint of the buyer. In fact if all *price-influencing costs* (assuming they might be determined) were included in operating expenses there never would be any net income except in the case of concerns realizing true differential profits, since normal entreprenurial rewards are as clearly price-influencing factors as pure interest. Most business concerns, moreover, are not continuously in the focus of the price-making forces which are operating in the market, and hence are not interested, immediately, in effective economic costs; they are only concerned with their own costs[1]

It must be remembered that the individual business is a *determinant* of the return to capital in enterprise. A return cannot be assumed; it must be earned. If the owner or stockholder is not satisfied with what return he gets, he usually can, in time, take out his capital and invest it elsewhere. But while invested, he has to take what return the business earns, and there is no sound basis for distinguishing between "normal" interest on the invest-

---

[1] "The Accountant's Handbook," W. A. Paton, editor, pp. 144–145, The Ronald Press Company, New York, 1949.

ent and profit. Proprietorship capital is not entitled to return in any exclu-
ve or preferential sense even though the proprietor certainly expects to
't at least a reasonable return. Whether he does or not is another matter.
or managerial purposes it may be desirable to segregate that part of net
perating return constituting what is adjudged a proper rate of return on
vested capital, the rest being profit from entrepreneurship. Such a sub-
diary calculation can readily be made if the facts of investment are known,
ut the desirability of so doing hardly constitutes an argument for explicitly
cording interest on the investment in the books.

If an attempt is made to use interest on owned capital as a cost, some
ifficult problems arise. One of them is that the proper investment base
to use may be difficult to determine for the business as a whole or more
articularly for different departments. Another is to determine what rate
hould be used. Money may be borrowed at various rates. At what rate
hould interest on owned capital be figured? Should it be computed on
he basis of average rates of return on reasonably secure investments in
he area or on the basis of pure interest rates strictly representing the return
to capital? The latter would not be meaningful, since it represents a rate
owhere to be found in private business. If any arbitrary average rate is
sed, there would still be the illogical situation of using one rate for owned
apital and another rate or rates for borrowed capital.

Essentially, interest on owned capital in a business is not a cost to
, but an opportunity foregone. As long as capital is invested in forest lands
nd other property, it is not available for investment elsewhere. Counting
nterest on it in effect anticipates a profit that may or may not be realized.
mputed costs of this nature are not recognized in income taxation for this
eason. In comparing producion costs between different business units, the
ost of capital employed is a factor regardless of source. It is for this reason
hat trade associations, for the information of their members, often include
nterest on owned capital in cost classifications to place all on a common
asis in estimating production costs and profit margins.

In summary, interest on owned capital is certainly an economic cost
f production, and its use is necessary in cost analyses. It cannot, however,
e included in proprietorship accounting.

16
the arithmetic of interest

Effective use of compound interest in financial calculations necessitates a thorough knowledge of its mathematical structure and computation. In this chapter the principal formulas useful in interest calculations are listed
together with the nature of the problem they can be used
to solve. Each formula is then derived and its use illustrated.

symbols and formulas used

The following symbols in common usage are used in all
formulas given here:

$1 =$ \$1 or unit of principal invested and
receiving interest

$a =$ amount of equal annual or periodic
payment

$n =$ number of years or interest-bearing
periods

$i =$ interest on \$1 for 1 year or other
specified interest-bearing period expressed as a decimal figure

$t =$ interval in years or number of interest-bearing periods between periodic payments

$V =$ value or amount of sum of money

$V_0 =$ value of sum of money when placed
at interest, or after it has been discounted to its present value

$V_n =$ value of sum of money with interest
n years hence

V_1, V_2, etc. $=$ value of sum of money after 1, 2, or
indicated number of years of interest
bearing periods

PRINCIPAL COMPOUND INTEREST FORMULAS

Formula number	Nature of problem solved	Formula
1	Single payments Future value of a single sum	$V_n = V_0(1 + i)^n$
2	Present or discounted value of a single sum due n years hence	$V_0 = \dfrac{V_n}{(1 + i)^n} = V_n \dfrac{1}{(1 + i)^n}$
3	Value of $(1 + i)^n$ or i, the rate of interest, when V_0 and V_n are known	$(1 + i)^n = \dfrac{V_n}{V_0}$
3a	Alternative form for direct solution for i	$i = \sqrt[n]{\dfrac{V_n}{V_0}} - 1$
4	Terminable equal annual payments (or payments made every interest-bearing period) Future or accumulated values: Future value of a series of terminable annual payments	$V_n = a \dfrac{(1 + i)^n - 1}{i}$
5	Amount of an annual payment or annuity that will amount to a specified capital amount, V_n, at the end of n years (sinking fund formula)	$a = \dfrac{V_n}{\dfrac{(1 + i)^n - 1}{i}} = V_n \dfrac{1}{\dfrac{(1 + i)^n - 1}{i}}$ $= \dfrac{i}{(1 + i)^n - 1}$
6	Present or discounted values: Present value of a series of terminable annual payments	$V_0 = a \dfrac{(1 + i)^n - 1}{i(1 + i)^n}$
7	Amount of an annual payment or annuity that will pay off a specified capital sum, V_0 in n equal annual installments (installment payment formula)	$a = \dfrac{V_0}{\dfrac{(1 + i)^n - 1}{i(1 + i)^n}} = V_0 \dfrac{1}{\dfrac{(1 + i)^n - 1}{i(1 + i)^n}}$ $= V_0 \dfrac{i(1 + i)^n}{(1 + i)^n - 1}$
8	Terminable equal periodic payments Future value of a series of terminable periodic payments made t years apart	$V_n = a \dfrac{(1 + i)^{nt} - 1}{(1 + i)^t - 1}$

PRINCIPAL COMPOUND INTEREST FORMULAS (*Continued*)

Formula number	Nature of problem solved	Formula
9	Present value of a series of terminable periodic payments made t years apart	$V_0 = a \dfrac{(1 + i)^{nt} - 1}{[(1 + i)^t - 1](1 + i)^{nt}}$
10	Infinite number of payments. Capital value of a permanent annual income the first payment of which is due 1 year hence.	$V_0 = \dfrac{a}{i}$
11	Capital value of a permanent periodic income.	$V_0 = \dfrac{a}{(1 + i)^t - 1}$
12[a]	Value of an increasing or decreasing arithmetical series. The accumulated amount, at the end of n years, of the increases or decreases in a series of payments that increase or decrease annually in equal amount. The first payment is made at the end of the second year of the period n.	$V_n = g \dfrac{(1 + i)^n - ni - 1}{i^2}$ g = amount of first payment and amount of annual increase

[a] From Matthews (1935).

The formulas given are arranged in such an order that the identifying captions included may be used as a key in selecting the right one to use. The first step is to get clearly in mind the nature of the problem to be solved. This can be most helpfully done by asking a series of questions about the problem and checking the answers against the key. Is a single payment or a series of payments involved? If a series, is it terminable, that is, to continue for a specified period only, or is no termination set and the serie of infinite duration? Are payments made annually (or for every interest bearing period if other than one year, as in the case of payments com pounded quarterly or monthly), or are they made periodically? Is a future value desired, or is the problem one of determining the present value o a series of payments due in the future. By asking these questions in the order given, selection of the right formula to use in solving problems involv ing the use of the $(1 + i)$ formulas (formulas 1 to 11, inclusive, or combina tions built on them) is greatly facilitated. Formula 12 involves a specia situation. The first 11 formulas are derived and all 12 are individually illus trated in the following sections. Solutions for formulas 1, 2, 4, 5, 6, and are given in standard compound interest tables for different values o i and n.

derivation and illustration of compound interest formulas

SINGLE PAYMENTS

The problem to be solved is the amount n years hence of a single sum invested now with interest not paid currently but accumulated and added to the principal. The accumulation of interest on the original unit of capital invested is determined as follows:

1. At the end of the first year the amount (V_1) of initial capital plus interest is $V_1 = 1 + i$, or $(1 + i)$.

2. At the end of the second year, $V_2 = (1 + i) + i(1 + i)$, or $(1 + i)^2$.[a]

3. At the end of the third year, $V_3 = (1 + i)^2 + i(1 + i)^2$, or $(1 + i)^3$.

4. At the end of n years, $V_n = (1 + i)^{n-1} + i(1 + i)^{n-1}$ or $(1 + i)^n$.

The expression $(1 + i)^n$ consequently gives a factor by which any sum invested can be multiplied to determine its value at the end of a specified period. Thus, in general,

$$V_n = V_0(1 + i)^n \tag{1}$$

Values for $(1 + i)^n$ are given in compound interest tables (see Appendix) and are most readily obtained in this way. They can, however, be computed on a slide rule having logarithmic scales or from tables of logarithms.

By simple rearrangement of terms,

$$V_0 = \frac{V_n}{(1 + i)^n} = V_n \frac{1}{(1 + i)^n} \tag{2}$$

This formula gives the present value V_0 of a sum V_n due n years hence. It introduces the idea of discount, which can most simply be thought of as interest accumulation in reverse. This is in accordance with the dictionary definition of the prefix *dis*—meaning reversal or undoing. The present value of any sum due n years in the future can be determined by dividing by the value of $(1 + i)^n$ or through multiplication by the value of the fraction

---

[a] Note the following algebra:

Let $x = (1 + i)$. Then the amount or sum at the end of the second year is

$$V_2 = x + ix$$
$$V_2 = x(1 + i)$$

Since $x = (1 + i)$, then $x(1 + i) = (1 + i)(1 + i)$ or $(1 + i)^2$. The same relationship holds for any other year or for n years.

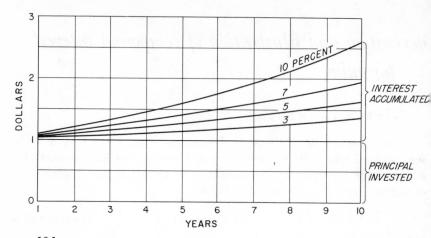

FIG. 16.1. ACCUMULATION OF A SINGLE PAYMENT.

$1/(1 + i)^n$. Discount factors in this latter form are given in compound interest tables. The process of deriving present from future values is termed discounting. As indicated, discount logically and mathematically follows from interest accumulation.

To solve for the value of $(1 + i)^n$ or i,

$$(1 + i)^n = \frac{V_n}{V_0},\tag{3}$$

or

$$i = \sqrt[n]{\frac{V_n}{V_0}} - 1\tag{3a}$$

The easiest way to determine the value of i is to use a compound interest table and determine by inspection the value of i most nearly corresponding to the value of $(1 + i)^n$ for the number of years involved. By interpolation, the value of i can be closely determined. The value of i can be computed directly by taking the nth root of the V_n/V_0 ratio by use of a slide rule or logarithmic tables and subtracting 1 as shown in formula 3a.

The general nature of compound interest accumulation is illustrated in Fig. 16.1. As shown, the higher the rate of interest and the longer the period, the greater is the accumulation of interest upon a unit of investment. For high rates and for long periods, the accumulation can obviously attain astronomical proportions that bear no relation to the actual productivity of capital invested in enterprise.

Examples: 1. What is the value of $100 at end of 10 years at 5 percent? In this instance, $V_n = V_{10}$. Then

$$V_{10} = \$100 \times (1.05)^{10}$$
$$= \$100 \times (1.629)$$
$$= \$162.90$$

2. What is the present value of $100 due 10 years hence at 5 percent?

$$V_0 = \$100 \times \frac{1}{(1.05)^{10}}$$
$$= \$100 \times (0.6139)$$
$$= \$61.39$$

3. What is the interest rate on an investment of $100 that will amount to $162.90 at end of 10 years?

$$(1 + i)^{10} = \frac{162.90}{100} = 1.629$$

In a table of compound interest values, this value of $(1 + i)^{10}$ is found to correspond to an interest rate of 5 percent when $n = 10$. The value of i may also be determined by direct solution for i as indicated in formula 3a.

TERMINABLE ANNUAL PAYMENTS

Future value of a series of annual payments.   Instead of a single payment or sum, what would be the value, with interest, of a series of equal annual payments at the end of a specified period or time? This is a common problem in forestry and elsewhere. Suppose fire protection costs are paid annually for a specified period. What is the value of this *series* of payments, with interest at the end of n years when the last payment is made? If these fire costs did not have to be paid, the money spent presumably could have been reinvested at interest elsewhere.

Life insurance provides another common example. Suppose one is paying annually into a retirement fund. All interest on the payments is impounded and added to principal. How big is the total retirement fund at the end of the premium-paying period just after the last premium is paid? It is out of this accumulated retirement fund that a life annuity may be purchased.

The problem can be worked out a payment at a time employing formula 1 and the basic mechanics of the operation can be best understood by so doing. Suppose 5 annual payments of $100 each are made with interest at 5 percent. What is the total value just after the fifth payment is made? The process is shown in Table 16.1 and graphically illustrated for a 10-year period in Fig. 16.2.

The total of $552.56 is the accumulated value of the five payments just after the last one is made. Note that while there are five payments made there are only four interest-bearing years. No interest is received on the last payment. Interest on the first payment is due only after one year; thus there can be only four interest-bearing years before the fifth and final payment is made at the end of the series.

**TABLE 16.1. ACCUMULATION OF ANNUAL PAYMENTS
(INTEREST AT 5 PERCENT)**

Order of payments	Number of years payment draws interest	Value of $(1 + i)$ for the number of interest-bearing years indicated	Amount of payment	Accumulated value of payment
First.......	4	1.2155	$100	$121.55
Second.....	3	1.1576	100	115.76
Third......	2	1.1025	100	110.25
Fourth.....	1	1.0500	100	105.00
Fifth.......	0	1.0000	100	100.00
Total....	..	5.5256	....	$552.56

Computation of interest separately on each yearly payment (a) is obviously a tedious process if a number of years is involved. The job can be shortened by derivation of a formula to give the end result in a single computation. The basic problem to solve is the summation of a geometric series, of five terms in this particular instance. A geometric progression is a series of numbers such that the quotient of any term of the series divided by the preceding term is always the same.

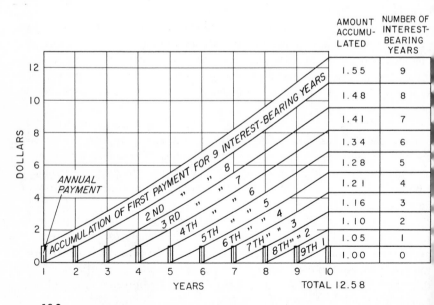

FIG. **16.2.** ACCUMULATION OF ANNUAL PAYMENTS.

Referring to Table 16.1, the amount, or sum V_5 of the five separate payments or terms in the series, beginning with the last, is

$$V_5 = a + a(1 + i) + a(1 + i)^2 + a(1 + i)^3 + a(1 + i)^{4*} \qquad (a)$$

A second equation (b) may be obtained by multiplying through by $(1 + i)$, as follows:

$$V_5(1 + i) = a(1 + i) + a(1 + i)^2 + a(1 + i)^3 \\ + a(1 + i)^4 + a(1 + i)^5 \qquad (b)$$

Equation (a) may then be subtracted from Eq. (b):

$$
\begin{array}{lll}
V_5(1 + i) & = & a(1 + i) + a(1 + i)^2 + a(1 + i)^3 + a(1 + i)^4 + a(1 + i)^5 \\
V_5 & = & a + a(1 + i) + a(1 + i)^2 + a(1 + i)^3 + a(1 + i)^4 \\
\hline
V_5(1 + i) - V_5 = & -a & \qquad\qquad\qquad\qquad\qquad\qquad\qquad\quad + a(1 + p)^5
\end{array}
$$

Combining and factoring,

$$V_5[(1 + i) - 1] = a[(1 + i)^5 - 1]$$

Then

$$V_5 = a\frac{[(1 + i)^5 - 1]}{(1 + i) - 1}$$

Since 5 is the number of payments in this particular series and the series is perfectly general in form, it may be written for any number of terms or number of payments n as

$$V_n = a\frac{(1 + i)^n - 1}{(1 + i) - 1} = a\frac{(1 + i)^n - 1}{i} \qquad (4)$$

This formula gives the future or end value, with interest, of a series of equal payments. Value of $[(1 + i)^n - 1]/i$ for specified values of i and n are commonly obtained from compound interest tables or may be computed from $(1 + i)$ values. The payment period is not necessarily one year. It may be monthly, quarterly, semiannually, or any uniform period. Interest is often compounded semiannually.

Examples: 1. What is the value of 5 annual payments of $100 each at 5 percent just after the last payment is made?

$$V_5 = \$100 \times \frac{(1.05)^5 - 1}{0.05}$$

$$= \$100 \times \frac{1.276282 - 1}{0.05}$$

$$= \$100 \times 5.5256$$

$$= \$552.56 \text{ exactly as calculated a payment at a time in Table 16.1}$$

* Note that the ratio or relationship between any two consecutive terms is constant as it must be in a geometric series. Thus

$$\frac{a(1+i)}{a} = (1 + i), \frac{a(1 + i)^3}{a(1 + i)^2} = (1 + i), \text{ etc.}$$

2. What is the value of a series of payments of $10 made monthly at 6 percent for 5 years just after the last payment is made? There are 5×12 or 60 monthly payments and the monthly rate is $\%_{12}$, or $\frac{1}{2}$ percent. Then

$$V_{60} = \$10 \times \frac{(1.005)^{60} - 1}{0.005}$$
$$= \$10 \times 69.77003$$
$$= \$697.70$$

Value of an annuity. It is often desired to determine the size of annual payment necessary, with interest, to amount to a specified capital sum in a given period. That is, solution is made for the annual payment a instead of V_n for an assumed annual payment. Formula 4 can readily be rearranged to solve for a:

$$a = \frac{V_n}{[(1 + i)^n - 1]/i} = V_n \frac{1}{[(1 + i)^n - 1]/i} = V_n \frac{i}{(1 + i)^n - 1} \qquad (5)$$

Solution of the expression $i/[(1 + i)^n - 1]$ defines the amount of an annuity whose compound amount is 1. These values or factors are given in annuity tables for various rates of interest. The amount of the annual payment necessary to accumulate any V_n value can consequently be determined by multiplying the desired V_n value by the annuity factor for the number of years and interest rate involved. This formula is often called the sinking fund formula since it provides the mechanics for determining how much to save annually, assuming it can be invested at interest, to provide a given sum n years hence.

Example: Suppose it is desired to save $500 at the end of 5 years and money can be invested at 5 percent. How much must be saved annually if 5 equal annual payments are made?

$$a = \$500 \times \frac{0.05}{(1.05)^5 - 1}$$
$$= \$500 \times 0.180975$$
$$= \$90.49$$

How this works out is shown in Table 16.2 in about the same way as payments, interest earned, and principal earned would be shown by an investment company in a statement to a customer. Note that the 5 annual payments of $90.49 with interest amount exactly to $500 when the last one is made.

Present value of a series of annual payments. The present value of a series of annual payments may readily be determined by discounting the end or V_n value back for n years.

TABLE 16.2. ACCUMULATION OF AN ANNUITY OR
SINKING FUND
(INTEREST AT 5 PERCENT)

Balance brought forward	Payment at beginning of year	Total amount of fund at beginning of year	Interest earned during year
0	$ 90.49	$ 90.49	$ 4.52
$ 95.01	90.49	185.50	9.27
194.77	90.49	285.26	14.26
299.52	90.49	390.01	19.50
409.51	90.49	500.00	
Total.......	$452.45	....	$47.55

Referring to formula 2,

$$V_0 = \frac{V_n}{(1 + i)^n} \qquad (2)$$

Substituting the value of V_n as given in formula 4 in the above equation gives

$$V_0 = a \frac{[(1 + i)^n - 1]/i}{(1 + i)^n}$$

which reduces to

$$V_0 = a \frac{(1 + i)^n - 1}{i(1 + i)^n} \qquad (6)$$

Example: Assume a contract to pay $100 a year for 5 years with interest at 5 percent, the first payment to be made at the end of 1 year.

$$V_0 = \$100 \times \frac{(1.05)^5 - 1}{0.05(1.05)^5}$$
$$V_0 = \$100 \times \frac{1.27628 - 1}{0.05(1.27628)}$$
$$= \$100 \times 4.3295$$
$$= \$432.95$$

This formula also indicates the size of a capital fund which if invested at a specified rate of interest will provide a series of equal annual payments for n years, the first one being made at the end of the year. The mechanics of the process are illustrated in Table 16.3. Note that in this case no compounding takes place; no interest is paid on interest. A capital fund is invested at interest and payments are made from this fund. It illustrates the general rule: If interest is paid when due there can be no compounding, only simple interest. Note also that in this case there are not only five pay-

TABLE 16.3. EQUAL ANNUAL PAYMENTS FROM A CAPITAL SUM
(INTEREST AT 5 PERCENT)

Capital amount at beginning of year (Jan. 1)	Interest earned during year	Total amount of fund at end of year (Dec. 31)	Annual payment made at end of year	Balance of fund at end of year (Dec. 31)
$432.95	$21.65	$454.60	$100	$354.60
354.60	17.73	372.33	100	272.33
272.33	13.62	285.95	100	185.95
185.95	9.30	195.25	100	95.25
95.25	4.75	100.00	100	0

ments but five full interest-bearing years, whereas in Table 16.1, used in developing formula 4, there were only four interest-bearing years and total elapsed time. Both are in accordance with the business facts of life. In regard to formula 6, consider the situation if an article is bought on time, or installment financing. A certain amount is paid down with the balance due in periodic payments. The financing contract is written in terms of the unpaid balance only and payments on it do not begin until *after* one month, or one year, or whatever is the payment period. Formula 6 shows what sum would have to be invested *at the time of purchase* to handle these installment payments and hence indicates its present value.

Present value of an annuity. As indicated above, it is often desired to determine what amount of annual payment is necessary to pay off a given capital sum in a specified period. This is the familiar problem of installment buying. Formula 6 can be readily rearranged to solve this problem as follows:

$$a = V_0 \frac{1}{[(1+i)^n - 1]/[i(1+i)^n]} = V_0 \frac{i(1+i)^n}{(1+i)^n - 1} \tag{7}$$

The term $[i(1+i)^n]/[(1+i)^n - 1]$ indicates the amount of an annuity whose present value is 1. These values are given in annuity tables. They can be multiplied by any value of V_0 to get the amount of the annual payment necessary to pay off a debt in n years at i percent.

Example: Suppose one owes $500 to be paid off in five equal installments, with interest at 5 percent, the first payment being due 1 year hence. What is the annual payment?

$$a = \$500 \times \frac{0.05(1.05)^5}{(1.05)^5 - 1}$$
$$= \$500 \times 0.230975$$
$$= \$115.4875$$

TABLE 16.4. PRESENT VALUE OF AN ANNUITY
ILLUSTRATING INSTALLMENT FINANCING
(INTEREST AT 5 PERCENT)

Balance brought forward beginning of year	Interest due at end of year	Annual payment at end of year	Amount of payment credited to principal
$500.00	$25.00	$115.49	$ 90.49
409.51	20.48	115.49	95.01
314.50	15.73	115.49	99.76
214.74	10.74	115.49	104.75
109.99	5.50	115.49	109.99
Total.......	$77.45	$577.45	$500.00

How this works out is illustrated in Table 16.4 in financial statement form which is helpful in understanding exactly what happens. The following relationships should be noted:

1. The present value of $115.4875 per year for 5 years is necessarily $500. To illustrate:

$$V_0 = \$115.4875 \times \frac{(1.05)^5 - 1}{0.05(1.05)^5}$$
$$= \$115.4875 \times 4.32948$$
$$= \$500$$

2. The compound amount of the five annual payments at the end of 5 years is

$$V_5 = \$115.4875 \times \frac{(1.05)^5 - 1}{0.05}$$
$$= \$115.4875 \times 5.525631$$
$$= \$638.14$$

This is the same thing as $500 compounded for 5 years, thus:

$$V_5 = \$500 \times (1.05)^5$$
$$= \$500 \times 1.27628$$
$$= \$638.14$$

The size of the debt if no payments were made would have to be the compound amount of the original debt and necessarily checks with the compound amount of the annuity.

A variation of this problem of paying off a debt, that follows from the relationships given above, is how much principal would be left after a specified number of payments have been made. Assume, for example a

$10,000 debt being paid off at the rate of $1,000 per year. What would be the balance of principal after 10 years, with interest at 6 percent?

The formula is

$$V_n = V_0(1 + i)^n - \frac{a(1 + i)^n - 1}{i}$$

and the solution is

$$V_n = \$10,000(1.06)^{10} - \$1,000 \frac{(1.06)^{10} - 1}{0.06}$$

$$= \$17,908.48 - \$13,180.79$$

$$= \$4,727.69$$

Note that this formula is simply a combination of formulas 1 and 4. The first part gives the value of the debt if nothing were paid and the second part subtracts the compounded amount of what has been paid. This is the amortization formula used by Meyer in a problem of allowable cut determination (Chap. 6).

TERMINABLE PERIODIC PAYMENTS

Future value of a periodic series. Instead of payments or incomes being due every year, or whatever the payment period is, they may come at periodic intervals, for example, every 10 years. The solution follows the same pattern as developed for formula 4 except that n number of payments are made t years apart. The value of $(1 + i)$ is $(1 + i)^t$ in this instance and the total period is consequently nt years which is the same as n in previous formulas. The first form of formula 4 as derived on p. 343 can accordingly be rewritten.

$$V_n = a \frac{(1 + i)^{nt} - 1}{(1 + i)^t - 1} \tag{8}$$

Example: A property yields $100 every 10 years for 50 years. What is the value, with interest at 5 percent, at the end of 50 years of these five equal payments just after the last one is made?

$$V_{50} = \$100 \times \frac{(1.05)^{50} - 1}{(1.05)^{10} - 1}$$

$$= \$100 \times \frac{11.4674 - 1}{1.6289 - 1}$$

$$= \$100 \times 16.6440$$

$$= \$1,664.40$$

Present value of a periodic series. The present value or sum of a periodic series is obtained in exactly the same way as in formula 6, namely, by discounting the end of V_n value back nt years which is the total elapsed time. The formula consequently becomes

$$V_0 = a \frac{(1 + i)^{nt} - 1}{[(1 + i)^t - 1](1 + i)^{nt}} \tag{9}$$

Example: What is the present value of five payments of $100 each made at 10-year intervals at 5 percent?

$$V_0 = \$100 \times \frac{(1.05)^{50} - 1}{[(1.05)^{10} - 1](1.05)^{50}}$$

$$= \$100 \times \frac{11.4674 - 1}{(1.6289 - 1)11.4674}$$

$$= \$100 \times \frac{10.4674}{7.2118}$$

$$= \$100 \times 1.4514$$

$$= \$145.14$$

Note that this present value can also be determined by discounting the end value of a series of periodic payments. In the preceding example this was $1,664.40 at the end of 50 years.

$$V_0 = \frac{1.644.40}{(1.05)^{50}} = \frac{1.664.40}{11.4674} = \$145.14$$

NONTERMINABLE PAYMENTS

Yearly payments. The yearly income from a regulated forest has no set termination date; in theory at least such income is realizable indefinitely. Obviously then, there can be no end future value but there is a present capital value. How is it determined? Formula 6 gives the present value of a series of terminable annual payments.

$$V_0 = a \frac{(1 + i)^n - 1}{i(1 + i)^n} \qquad (6)$$

The value of n becomes infinity (∞) in this instance. Substituting ∞ for n, the formula becomes

$$V_0 = a \frac{(1 + i)^\infty - 1}{i(1 + i)^\infty}$$

This can also be written

$$V_0 = \frac{a}{i} \left[\frac{(1 + i)^\infty - 1}{(1 + i)^\infty} - \frac{1}{(1 + i)^\infty} \right]$$

Since the numerator and denominator of the first term in the brackets, $\frac{(1 + i)^\infty - 1}{(1 + i)^\infty}$, approaches infinity at the same rate, its quotient is 1. The value of the second term in the brackets is zero, since a number divided by an infinite number is zero. Consequently, the last term of the equation enclosed by brackets reduces to $1 - 0$, and the equation becomes

$$V_0 = \frac{a}{i} \qquad (10)$$

In words, this formula says that the value of a property that will yield a certain annual return indefinitely is equivalent to a capital sum yielding this annual income at a specified rate of interest. Thus, a property yielding an income of $1,000 annually with interest at 5 percent has the capital value.

$$V_0 = \frac{\$1,000}{0.05} = \$20,000$$

It should be noted that as the interval lengthens the difference between the present value of a terminable and an infinite series of incomes becomes rather small. For example, the present value of $100 a year for 60 years at 5 percent is

$$V_0 = \$100 \times \frac{(1.05)^{60} - 1}{0.05(1.05)^{60}} = \$100 \times 18.9293 = \$1,892.93$$

The capital value of $100 a year indefinitely is $100/0.05, or $2,000. A promise to pay the $100 indefinitely is worth only a little over a hundred dollars more than a promise to pay it for 60 years. This corresponds with business experience; all promises extending into the future become more or less indefinite.

Periodic payments. Suppose an income is to be received at periodic intervals indefinitely. This is the situation on a particular tract of forest land managed to give a return every cutting cycle or rotation period. Using formula 9 and following exactly the same procedure as employed in developing formula 10, the equation becomes

$$V_0 = a \frac{(1 + i)^{t^\infty} - 1}{[(1 + i)^t - 1](1 + i)^{t^\infty}}$$

which reduces to

$$V_0 = \frac{a}{(1 + i)^t - 1} \tag{11}$$

Examples: What is the capital value at 5 percent of an infinite series of $100 payments received every 10 years, the first one due 10 years hence?

$$V_0 = \frac{\$100}{(1.05)^{10} - 1} = \frac{\$100}{1.6289 - 1} = \$159.01$$

Note that $159.01 at 5 percent for 10 years would amount to $159.01 $\times$ 1.6289, or $259.01. At the end of 10 years the $100 payment could be paid, leaving $159.01, and the process can go on indefinitely.

TERMINABLE PAYMENTS INCREASING OR DECREASING IN ARITHMETICAL SERIES

Situations sometimes arise in which a series of increasing or decreasing payments are made, and it is desired to determine their total amount with interest. An example is a property on which annual taxes or other costs are expected to increase more or less regularly over time and can be expressed as an average gradient of yearly increases or decreases. Another example is a piece of equipment that is depreciated by a regularly declining yearly amount.

Formula 12[1] can be used to calculate the increase or decrease due to such a gradient.

Example 1. Assume an annual payment of \$100 that increases regularly for 5 years at \$10 per year beginning with the second year. Interest at 5 percent. The payments per year are consequently \$100, \$110, \$120, \$130 and \$140, the last payment coming at the end of the fifth year. Using formula 12 with the annual payment g of \$10, the compound amount of the increase only is

$$V_n = \$10 \frac{(1.05)^5 - (5 \times 0.05) - 1}{0.0025}$$
$$= \$10 \frac{1.276282 - 0.25 - 1}{0.0025}$$
$$= \$10 \times \frac{0.026282}{0.0025}$$
$$= \$105.13$$

If there were no increase, the compound amount would be

$$V_n = \$100 \frac{(1.05)^5 - 1}{0.05}$$
$$= \$100 \times 5.52563$$
$$= \$552.56$$

The total payment or V_n value is consequently \$105.13 + \$552.56, or \$657.69 which, with a short series like this, can readily be checked by direct computation as shown in Table 16.5. This V_n value can, if desired, be converted to an equivalent annual series by multiplying by the annuity or sinking fund factor $i/(1+i)^n - 1$ (formula 5) as follows:[2]

$$\text{Equivalent annual value} = \$657.69 \frac{0.05}{(1.05)^5 - 1}$$
$$= \$119.03$$

Exactly the same procedure is applied for a decreasing series, only the situation is reversed. Assuming \$100 again with an annual reduction

---

[1] An equivalent formula is given by Grant and Ireson (1960) p. 52:

$$V_n = \frac{g}{i} \frac{(1+i)^n - 1}{i} - \frac{ng}{i}$$

[2] Grant and Ireson (1960) give a formula for computing only the gradient and converting to an annual series in one operation as follows:

$$\text{Equivalent annual series} = \frac{g}{i} - \frac{ng}{i} \left[\frac{i}{(1+i)^n - 1} \right]$$

TABLE 16.5. COMPOUND AMOUNT OF ANNUAL PAYMENTS
INCREASING IN ARITHMETICAL SERIES
(INTEREST AT 5 PERCENT)

Year	Total amount			Increase or decrease only	
	Payment	Years to accumulate	Amount	Payment	Amount
1	$100	4	$121.55		
2	110	3	127.34	$10	11.58
3	120	2	132.30	20	22.05
4	130	1	136.50	30	31.50
5	140	0	140.00	40	40.00
Total...	....	...	657.69	...	105.13

of $10 per year, the annual payments are $100, 90, 80, 70, and 60.
Consequently

Total amount if no decrease = $552.56
Amount of decrease　　　 =　105.13
Total amount paid, V_n　　 = $447.53

This amount can readily be checked by direct computation as was done
in Table 16.5.

Example 2. The above procedure can be combined with an initial capital cost to figure an annual cost schedule. For example, assume a piece
of equipment costing $10,000 with a life of 10 years and with no salvage
value. Annual costs for operation, maintenance, taxes, and insurance are
$300 the first year and increase $50 per year thereafter for 10 years. What
is the average annual cost at 5 percent? The answer comes in three parts:

1. Yearly capital cost. This is the annual value of an annuity that will pay
off $10,000 in 10 years (formula 7)

$$\$10,000 \times \frac{0.05(1.05)^{10}}{(1.05)^{10} - 1} \qquad = \$1,295.05$$

2. Yearly cost without gradient increase　=　300.00
3. Yearly cost of increase in annual operating cost. By formula 12, the value of the
$50 increase for 10 years is $2577.90.
Converted to an equivalent annual series
(following procedure illustrated in foregoing example)　　　　　　　　　　　 =　204.95
Total annual cost　　　　　　　　　 = $1,800.00

nominal and effective rates

The solution of many valuation problems requires determination of the rate. The following illustrations will be helpful.

YEARLY PAYMENTS

As stated in Chap. 15, valuation problems involving costs and returns received at different points in time are often best solved by determining the rate rather than assuming one. The basic equation of equivalence for solving such problems is that at some rate of interest (positive or negative) costs equal returns.

Examples: 1. A SINGLE PAYMENT. $1,000 is invested in a security that was sold after 10 years for $1,750. What rate of interest was earned? According to formula 3

$$(1 + i)^n = \frac{V_{10}}{V_0} = \frac{\$1,750}{1,000} = 1.75$$

By reference to a book of compound interest tables giving $(1 + i)$ values to a tenth of a percent (see Appendix) the following figures are obtained:

For 5.7 percent, $(1.057)^{10} = 1.741$
For 5.8 percent, $(1.058)^{10} = 1.757$

By interpolation, the earned rate is 5.75 percent

2. DISCOUNTED NOTES. A sum of $1,000 is borrowed at 6 percent, but a year's interest is deducted at the time the loan is made, and the borrower receives $940. What is the effective rate? Since only $940 was actually received, the $60 interest applies to this amount. The effective rate is consequently

$$ {}^{60}\!/\!_{940} = 0.0638, \text{ or } 6.4 \text{ percent} $$

3. ANNUAL PAYMENTS. Capital is paid into a business at the rate of $1,000 a year for 10 years. At the end of this period, the share of the business bought by these 10 capital payments is sold for $14,000. What rate of return was made? In this case $V_n = V_{10} = \$14,000$.

From formula 4

$$\$14,000 = \$1,000 \frac{(1 + i)^{10} - 1}{i}$$

Transposing,

$$\frac{(1 + i)^{10} - 1}{i} = \frac{14,000}{1,000} = 14$$

By reference to an appropriate compound interest table giving values for $[(1 + i) - 1/i$, 10-year values of this factor are:

At 7 percent = 13.8164
At 7½ percent = 14.1471

By interpolation of the calculated factor of 14, the effective rate is 7.3 percent.

4. SINGLE AND ANNUAL PAYMENTS COMBINED. A piece of forest property is purchased for $10,000 and $200 a year are paid in taxes for 10 years. At that time, the property is sold for $22,000. What rate of return has been made on the investment, all costs considered? There are two items to accumulate: the original investment and the annual carrying charges. Stated in formula terms, the problem is as follows:

$$[\$10,000 \times (1 + i)^{10}] + \left[\$200 \frac{(1 + i)^{10} - 1}{i}\right] = \$22,000$$

At 6 percent, $10,000 × 1.7908 + $200 × 13.1808 = $20,544
At 7 percent, $10,000 × 1.9672 + $200 × 13.8164 = $22,435

Since the $22,000 is between these two figures, the rate must be between 6 percent and 7 percent. By interpolation, it is approximately 6.8 percent. A solution for the rate in examples 3 and 4 is possible only by a series of successive approximations as illustrated. A solution to any desired degree of accuracy required can readily be programmed on a computer when a series of such problems are involved.

PAYMENTS MADE MORE OFTEN THAN ONCE A YEAR

While it is customary to state interest rates on an annual basis, there are many circumstances in which interest is due (or compounded) at semi-annual, quarterly, monthly, or other intervals. A question then arises as to the meaning of a stated interest rate in relation to an annual rate which is the normal basis of comparison. The following definitions should be observed:

1. The *effective* rate is measured on an annual basis. It is mathematically defined as equal to $(1 + i/m)^m - 1$ where m = number of times interest is due or compounded per year and i is the nominal rate.

2. The *nominal* rate is an annual rate divided by the number of times interest is paid during a year. For example, a 6 percent nominal rate is $^6/_4$ or 1½ percent if due quarterly, or $^6/_{12}$ or ½ percent if due monthly.

Examples: 1. QUARTERLY, MONTHLY, AND CONTINUOUS PAYMENTS. Assume $1,000 is borrowed at a stated annual rate of 6 percent, but payments are due quarterly or every 3 months. What is the effective rate? The quarterly payment is 60/4 or \$15 and the quarterly rate is $6\!\!/\!\!4$ or 1.5 percent. The quarterly payments compound for a year are

$$\$15 \times \frac{(1.015)^4 - 1}{0.015} = \$15 \times 4.0909 = \$61.36$$

Obviously, the borrower is not getting the use of \$1,000 for a year at a price of \$60. The effective annual rate is 6.136 percent. This can be determined directly by the formula given on p. 354.

$$\text{Effective rate} = \left(\frac{1 + 0.06}{4}\right)^4 - 1 = (1.015)^4 - 1 = 0.06136, \text{ or } 6.136 \text{ percent.}$$

If compounding were made monthly, the effective rate would be

$$\left(1 + \frac{0.06}{12}\right)^{12} - 1 = 1.06168 - 1, \text{ or } 6.168 \text{ percent}$$

If compounding was made at half-month intervals the effective rate is

$$\left(1 + \frac{0.06}{24}\right)^{24} - 1 = 1.06176, \text{ or } 6.176 \text{ percent}$$

Rather obviously, the effective rate levels off as the number of compoundings increase. It reaches a limit defined by Pe^{rn} in which P is the amount invested, e is the base of natural or Naperian logarithmus, and r is the nominal rate. An assumption that the flow of money use is continuous is known as continuous compounding. It is used to some extent in financial calculations. In forestry, where one normally deals with rather long-time intervals and relatively low rates, continuous compounding seems to have little application and its use would not affect any practical decision. Annual costs are primarily affected and it is true that many of these do occur more or less continuously through the year although items like taxes and insurance tend to be paid only once or a few times a year. The end-of-period convention (normally end-of-year) as expressed in standard compound interest tables is much easier to use than continuous compounding, also a convention, and neither necessarily describe how cash actually may flow in a business. If there is particular reason to treat a particular cost differently from other items, it can be done.

2. SOLVING FOR A MONTHLY RATE. Sometimes a capital sum is borrowed to be repaid at a certain payment schedule with the interest rate not stated. Local finance companies are a familiar illustration. The following is taken from a current advertisement encouraging a person to pay up back bills (and finance a vacation!) in one loan. For \$851.11 in cash actually received, 36 monthly payments of \$33 are required. What is the effective

rate? This is a problem of the present value of an annuity (formula 7). Substituting known values

$$\$33.00 = \$851.11 \left[\frac{(1 + i)^{36} - 1}{i(1 + i)^{36}} \right]$$

By transposing, the formula in brackets consequently equals \$33.00/851.11, or 0.03877 when $n = 36$. Interpolation from compound interest tables indicates a monthly rate between $1\frac{3}{4}$ and 2 percent or approximately 1.9 percent. The effective annual rate is consequently

$$(1.019)^{12} - 1 = 0.254, \text{ or } 25.4 \text{ percent}$$

17

valuation of forest land and of the timber stand

Land and the timber stand upon it are the basic capital of any timber production enterprise. Since investments are heavy, relatively permanent, and entail in full the many responsibilities of landownership, the valuation of land and of growing timber is of first importance. It is a part of the broad field of real estate valuation. The long-range nature of timberland investments makes careful and searching application of valuation techniques particularly important. Applicable market values often do not exist and where they do often give imperfect and incomplete expression of investment values for forest production purposes.

Historically, timberland market values have been based almost entirely on the conversion value of the timber stand currently in existence upon the land with little regard for the possibilities of continued production of forest crops. Cutover lands have commonly been bought and sold on the basis of an arbitrary residual value often based on some other use, such as agriculture. With the development of many timber-growing enterprises entailing large forest investments, competition for timberlands has developed and recognition of their value as the basis for continued production has slowly emerged. As a consequence, timberlands increasingly are appraised, bought, and sold on the basis of their continuing productive capacity in addition to the value of currently standing timber. The application of sound valuation methods based on land productivity is consequently of increasing importance as a guide for the establishment of market prices permitting sound forest investment, and for many managerial purposes.

valuation of forest land

"Land is the one enduring asset of a permanent forest business" (Matthews, 1935). The great importance of site quality upon forest productivity has been stressed in Chap. 2 and elsewhere. It is the inherent vigor of the site that determines the potential productivity of the forest. Site quality remains approximately constant, irrespective of the character, condition, or quality of the timber stand currently occupying the area, except when land use practices have caused soil erosion, impoverishment, or development of undesirable soil texture or structure. In acquisition for forest production purposes, the basic quality of the land is consequently of the utmost importance. This is most immediately apparent when purchase of bare land, as that withdrawn from agriculture, is considered. There is no timber stand to appraise, and agricultural values have no meaning except as affecting market values. It is the quality of the land for forest growth that is being purchased. Similarly, because of past forest mismanagement, an area may support a timber stand of little current value. Perhaps the present stand is more of a liability than an asset and should be so regarded in valuation. But if the site is good, the land will respond to treatment. Bare or poorly stocked forest lands are increasingly being purchased for forest production purposes, making estimation of their value of great practical importance.

As with any other kind of land use, the value of land for forest uses necessarily stems from the forest crops or other services it can produce. Forest land may and often does have value for other than forest uses of one kind or another and must be appraised accordingly. The treatment here, however, is of timber production.

A land value for timber-growing purposes does not have a separate and distinct marketable existence except where there is no, or only a negligible amount of, growing stock present. Where there is a substantial growing stock present, land and timber values are usually considered together although in many transactions a separate land value is recognized and assigned a value. Forest land has a value and the fact that it often does not have a separate and distinguishable market price does not invalidate either the existence of such a value or minimize its fundamental importance. As competition develops, market values of land as such will tend to approach the economic worth of the land for timber production.

FACTORS DETERMINING FOREST LAND VALUE

Since forest land takes its value from the crops it produces, estimation of this value necessarily requires measurement of these crops over a considerable span of time. The problem, in basic outline, is to determine the future income value or contribution of the land itself. Four controlling factors are involved: (1) site quality, (2) the kind and intensity of management practiced including its cost, (3) the market value of the product, and (4) the importance of the time interval involved as measured by the rate of interest employed.

While potential productivity is determined by site, the volume and quality of timber actually produced is influenced tremendously by the kind and intensity of management practiced. The degree and promptness of regeneration, species composition, stocking, and growth can be largely controlled by the silvicultural practices applied. Depending on how it is handled—or mishandled—a given site may produce crops ranging from practically none at all to those approaching its biological potential. The cost of forest practices naturally must be considered in relation to their efficacy.

Closely related to the practicable level of forest practice is the value of the product produced. This entails not only an estimate of what the products will bring in the market, but also the cost of getting the products to the market. Accessibility factors are often of controlling importance in determining the value of the timber crop as it stands in the forest.

Finally, the growing of timber takes time and usually a lot of time in relation to the length of most productive processes within the range of business experience. Some measure of the effect of the time intervals involved on value is necessary. This brings up the question of what rate of interest should be employed in bringing the various expenditures and receipts incurred and received at widely differing times to a common point in time as is necessary in valuation. The time preference of individuals or groups is one important factor involved. Public owners have a relatively low time preference, logically indicating the use of a fairly low interest rate in considering public undertakings. Industrial owners, who must operate in full exposure to competitive business pressures, have a higher time preference and can be expected to apply a rate related to alternative investments.

While there are many formulas for interest computation, there is no formula for determining what rate should be used in a particular situation. The rate employed exerts a large and often overshadowing influence on estimation of forest land values because of the long time periods usually involved. In many situations the valuation problem helpfully can be framed to solve for a rate instead of assuming one. Factors affecting equitable rates for long- and short-time investments should be borne in mind as brought out in Chap. 15.

ESTIMATION OF FOREST LAND VALUE
FOR AN EVEN-AGED STAND

The most direct way to approach estimation of forest land value is to start with a piece of bare land and visualize establishment of a forest

360   *forest valuation*

TABLE 17.1. COSTS AND RETURNS PER ACRE FROM AN EVEN-AGED
SOUTHERN PINE STAND MANAGED FOR PULPWOOD
PRODUCTION, PRODUCTION ON A 30-YEAR ROTATION
(INTEREST AT 5 PERCENT)

Receipt or expenditure item and assumptions made	Value per acre	Formula for accumulation with interest	Value of interest factor	Amount of receipt or expenditure item at rotation age
Receipts:				
Major harvest at age 30, 37 cords at $6.50 per cord	$240.50	....	....	$240.50
Thinning at age 15, 2 cords at $3.00 per cord	6.00	$(1.05)^{15}$	2.0789	12.47
Thinning at age 20, 3.5 cords at $4.00 per cord	14.00	$(1.05)^{10}$	1.6289	22.80
Thinning at age 25, 7 cords at $5.00 per cord	35.00	$(1.05)^{5}$	1.2763	44.67
Total receipts at rotation age	....	....	....	$320.44
Expenditures:				
Site preparation and planting in year 1	30.00	$(1.05)^{29}$	4.1161	123.48
Annual costs for taxes, protection, and administration	1.75	$\dfrac{(1.05)^{30}-1}{0.05}$	66.4388	116.27
Total expenditures at rotation age	....	....	....	$239.75
Net value at rotation age	....	....	....	$ 80.69

stand upon it. This is the actual situation encountered when unstocked land is placed in forest production. In simplest outline, a stand is grown to maturity, harvested, and a new stand again established with no set termination date to the timber production process. This holds true for any particular spot of land whether a simple one-cut even-aged system is applied, or some form of a shelterwood plan involving a number of cuttings. In any case, a particular plot of soil can yield a forest crop or crops during a rotation period and periodically thereafter.

The capital value or present worth of a continuing series of net periodic incomes is given by the formula (formula 11, Chap. 16)

$$V_0 = \frac{a}{(1+i)^t - 1}$$

In the case of forest land, the periodic interval t is the rotation, assuming that all receipts, less expenditures, are equated to this age at the interest rate i. Hereafter in this chapter r will be used to indicate that the interval involved is a rotation. The symbol a represents net income received at rotation age. Since V_0 is the present capital value of a series of continuing periodic net incomes obtained from the land, it indicates the land value which is designated as L_e, meaning land expectation value.

If there were no timber production costs and receipts were all received at rotation age only, L_e values could be determined by the simple capitalization process indicated by the above formula. Receipts are seldom received all at one time, however, and they are not net; expenditures are also incurred at various times. To apply this formula, receipts and expenditures pertinent to a particular schedule of management must all be brought to a common point in time, rotation age, so that net income can be determined and capitalized. Since interest is employed as a measure of the importance of time, this means that each item must be carried with interest, where necessary, to rotation age.

The process can best be illustrated by means of an example. The receipts and expenditures from an acre of an even-aged loblolly pine managed for pulpwood production on a rotation of 30 years are estimated in Table 17.1, and their value at rotation age is determined, assuming interest at 5 percent. This net value, determined by the difference between receipt and expenditure items, is estimated at $80.69 per acre. Capitalization of this value received once every 30 years represents the contribution from the land itself as economic rent. Consequently,

$$L_e = \frac{\$80.69}{(1.05)^{30} - 1} = \frac{\$80.69}{3.3219} = \$24.29 \text{ per acre}$$

Calculations of this type can be presented in general formula form as follows:[1]

$$L_e = \frac{Y_r + T_a(1 + i)^{r-a} + T_b(1 + i)^{r-a} + I\left[\dfrac{(1 + i)^r - 1}{i}\right] - C(1 + i)^{r-a} - S_a(1 + i)^{r-a} - e\left[\dfrac{(1 + i)^r - 1}{i}\right]}{(1 + i)^r - 1}$$

[1] The formula was first developed by Faustmann (1849) and often bears his name. However, as formulated, the treatment of establishment costs is in error as it is assumed that they are always compounded for a full rotation period. This is mathematically incorrect, as pointed out by Davis (1965), because it assumes the stand is established simultaneously with determination of the land value itself which cannot be so. A more serious objection is that there is often some delay in stand establishment and costs in more than one year may be necessary. The cost or costs should be entered in the formula when they actually occur. See Chaps. 7, 10, and 20 for the financial consequences of a delay in regeneration.

where L_e = land expectation value
   Y_r = yield at rotation age
T_a, T_b, etc. = net value of thinnings or other cuttings made at respective age a
   I = annual receipts received, as from lease of grazing or hunting privileges
   C = cost or costs of stand establishment by planting or otherwise at age or ages a
S_a, S_b, etc. = net cost of stand improvement cuttings made at respective age a
   e = annual expenses, as for taxes, fire protection, administration, etc.
   r = length of rotation, years
   i = rate of interest expressed as a decimal

Expressed in this expanded form, the formula is a rather formidable thing chiefly useful to frighten students. It should be recognized that its specific form will change with the number and kind of receipt and expenditure items involved, of which there may be many or only a few depending on the production schedule applied.

It is better to think of the determination of L_e values as a procedure, following a general account-book pattern of receipt and expenditure items as shown in Table 17.1, rather than as a specific formula. The basic form of the formula and the fact that it is the capitalization of a permanent periodic net income should, however, be kept firmly in mind. The long numerator of the expanded formula is only an itemization of net periodic income necessitated by the fact that there are various receipts and expenditures coming at different times, that must uniformly be brought to rotation age with interest so that net income at that time can be determined and capitalized.

Presentation of the process in formula form does, however, suggest some simplification of the computation procedure. Annual or periodic receipt or expenditure items that come at the same time are direct offsets to each other and the difference only needs to be considered. In the illustration given, the annual expense is $1.75. Since this item presumably will be continued indefinitely, it can more simply be represented by a capital sum E sufficient to pay these net expenses annually out of interest. Consequently, $E = e/i$.[1] The capital value E is then subtracted after the rest of the items involved have been capitalized. The general formula can consequently be rewritten as

$$L_e = \frac{Yr + T_a(1 + i)^{r-a} - C(1 + i)^{r-a} - S_a(1 + i)^{r-a}}{(1 + i)^r - 1} - E$$

---

[1] The algebra of this can be easily demonstrated. Considering the annual expense item only, as given in the expanded formula, its capitalized value E from the formula is determined as follows:

$$E = \frac{\dfrac{e(1 + i)^r - 1}{i}}{(1 + i)^r - 1} = \frac{e(1 + i)^r - 1}{i(1 + i)^r - 1} = \frac{e}{i}$$

If it should happen that annual income exceeded annual expenses, E would be an addition rather than a subtraction.

When net income estimated at rotation age is divided by $(1 + i)^r - 1$, the result indicates the capital value of an indefinite number of such incomes, each received r years apart. If the income is to be received for only one rotation period, the divisor would be $(1 + i)^r$ only, following the usual procedure for discounting the value of a single payment due r years in the future. The -1 makes all the difference between a single and a permanent periodic income and it is helpful to appreciate just what this difference is and means.

In terms of the illustration given in Table 17.1, the present value of a single net income of $80.69 due 30 years hence is

$$V_0 = \frac{\$80.69}{(1.05)^{30}} = \frac{\$80.69}{4.3219} = \$18.67$$

The present value of a permanent periodic income, or L_e value was $24.29, or $5.62 more. This difference, which amounts to 30 percent of the single rotation value, represents the present value of all future rotations after the first. How this works out can be illustrated as follows. The $5.62 compounded for 30 years to the end of the first rotation is necessarily $24.29 ($5.62 \times 4.3219 = \$24.29$), the land value at that time. If this value is compounded for another 30 years, the result is 24.29×4.3219, or $104.98. Out of this amount, the net income of $80.69 from the timber for a rotation can be paid leaving the land value of $24.29 and the process can go indefinitely. While this may seem a bit theoretical, the practical aspect is the fundamental point that the land is the only residual value at the end of a rotation when the final harvest is taken. Timber grows and is cut; only the land has a continuing value, which emphasizes its basic importance.

In the illustration given here, the difference between a single and a permanent periodic income was 30 percent, which is substantial, and the ratio becomes higher as the rotation is shortened. In general, the longer the rotation and the higher the interest rate, the less difference it makes; for rotation over about 50 years the difference is small. Unless, however, one wishes to assume that there is no residual land value after a single rotation, it is logical to include it, as is done by using the $(1 + i)^r - 1$ divisor.

SIGNIFICANCE OF FOREST LAND VALUES

When the mechanics of calculating L_e values are understood, as illustrated above, the question remains: what do they mean? There is a tendency to give them either too little or too much weight. It must be clearly recognized that an L_e value is a calculated figure entirely controlled by the data used in its determination. Its estimation includes all the four factors affecting forest land values. Anything affecting receipts and expenditures can be included in the calculation. Site quality and the intensity and kind of management are integrated in the physical level of productivity estimated. The costs of management are embodied in the costs assumed. Market and accessibility factors enter into the net stumpage prices used. The importance of the time element is represented by the rate of interest used. All these factors may vary widely with circumstances, and there can consequently be as many L_e values as there are possible assumptions. For this reason, L_e values should not be thought of as anything fixed or immutable, but always in relation to the particular assumptions upon which they are determined. That these assumptions may seem difficult to make and of a long-range nature only serves to point up the nature and practical difficulties of making a direct estimation of a land value for a crop of such long duration as timber.

L_e values are extremely sensitive to the rate of interest employed. The higher the rate, the lower the land value for a given production schedule. For the schedule given in Table 17.1, the land value at 5 percent was $24.29. At 3 percent it would be $108.79, and at 6 percent only $5.46 for exactly the same receipts and expenditures. With fairly high rates, and especially for long rotations and/or poor sites, L_e values are commonly negative. Undue importance may be attached to this fact. A negative L_e value is not necessarily conclusive evidence that "forestry does not pay"; it merely indicates, for the assumptions made, that a forest could not economically be built up on bare land, even if the land was free. There is an element of business unreality attached to any long-range compounding of interest. The shorter the period, the more realistic the L_e value becomes. Such calculations for periods of about 40 years or less are within the realm of business experience and have considerable practical significance.

The process of making L_e calculations focuses attention on the estimation of costs and returns of building up a forest on bare land. To the extent that these estimates and the rate of interest employed are realistic, an L_e value indicates the contribution of the ingredient land itself and what could be paid for it on an investment basis at the rate assumed. As such it is of basic importance in estimating true economic worth for timber production. Under competition, the market value for bare forest land will tend to approach an L_e value calculated at a "going" rate of interest. Such land often has been purchased at far less than its economic value, at least as revealed by hindsight. The fact that this is so accounts in part for the very large profits that have been made on some forest land purchases. Undervaluation of immature timber stands already on the land is another and often larger factor. As land and growing timber values have become better appreciated and demand has increased, their market value has increased accordingly. L_e calculations are consequently a guide to forest land value, indicating ceiling prices that could be paid on an investment basis.

As brought out in Chap. 10, estimation of L_e values gives a useful guide to the desirable length of the rotation. Emphasis is placed on the rate of return on the investment. The rotation so determined will be that for which the marginal return on the investment is at the rate assumed in the L_e calculation. Determination of a meaningful rate is, accordingly, the crux of the problem. Depending on the rate used, the rotation of highest L_e value will be shorter than maximum mean annual forest rent which sets a mathematical limit on longer rotations and usually not much less than the culmination of mean annual increment in cubic feet which tends to set a practical limit on shorter rotations.

The general level of L_e values calculated on reasonable business rates is of broad regional significance. It indicates whether a forest once destroyed can be rebuilt on anything approaching a business investment basis. If forest lands with a good growing stock including a desirable range of age and size classes can be purchased very cheaply, a profitable business may be carried on, even though L_e values, based on a reasonable rate of return, may be low or even negative. But if the forest is destroyed and an attempt is made to build up a new one, the significance of the low L_e values becomes painfully apparent.

The situation is analogous to the business circumstance of buying a factory at far less than it actual construction cost. With the advantage of a cheap factory, a profitable business may be carried on at least for a considerable time that would be impossible if it had to carry a full investment cost. If, however, the plant is destroyed, so is the business as it cannot be rebuilt on a normal investment basis.

valuation of timberland

In contrast to land values, which are relatively timeless, the value of the timber stand upon the land increases as the stand grows. Land does not grow; it remains. With even-aged management, the initial value is that of the land itself. Following establishment of a new stand, its value increases to a maximum defined by economic maturity—the rotation age or time of major harvest. At some intermediate age there may be a timber value (as determined by stumpage valuation, the subject of the next chapter), but it is less than the value at economic maturity. Valuation of a growing timber stand is a widespread problem. Such timber lands are bought and sold in anticipation of an increasing future value; many managerial decisions are based on estimates of these values. How can these values be determined?

As in any valuation problem of this nature, there are three general approaches possible: (1) current market value based on comparable timber-lands, (2) cost, or (3) income value. In some areas, market prices for grow-ing timberlands are fairly well established. The setting of an actual market price is, of course, a matter for buyer and seller negotiation. Timberland buying (or selling) is an art that cannot be imparted in a textbook. For the most part, however, well-established market prices for timberlands of varying site quality, age, and stocking do not exist.

The determination of cost values of a stand at a given age is funda-mentally a matter of looking backward to answer the question: What has been invested? It is a natural approach for an owner since it provides a measure for the degree of success or failure of the investment made. It is also an important basis in the event of damage when questions of loss incurred must be faced (Chap. 21). Immediate replacement or restoration is physically impossible with timberlands because of the time element neces-sary to grow another stand.

Income values, in contrast, look ahead to estimated future returns. Essentially, their determination is a matter of estimating the present net worth of all future incomes (less costs) that reasonably may be expected.

ESTIMATION OF COST AND INCOME VALUE FOR AN EVEN-AGED STAND

Methods of estimating cost and income values for even-aged stands follow logically from those used in land value determination except that the focus is on the stand and either actual or assumed land values are used. The mechanics are essentially the same.

The problem of determining a cost value is to estimate, for a stand of given age, the net present worth, at some assumed rate of interest, of all past expenditures. To illustrate, the value at age 15 of the same stand for which a land expectation value was determined (Table 17.1) is deter-mined as shown in Table 17.2. All the receipt and expenditure items are the same except for the addition of the actual purchase cost of the land. As indicated, the accumulated value of these costs is $132.74 which answers the question: How much have I invested per acre, with interest, in this particular tract of land? Note that this is a value for land and timber to-gether as a physical entity and only past expenditures and receipts are considered.

A rental value for the land could be used and the value of the growing stock only determined. For example, if the $20 land cost is considered as a rental at 5 percent as are other costs, the annual charge would be $20 × 0.05 or $1 per year. The accumulated value of this rental in 15 years would be $1 × $\frac{(1.05)^{15} - 1}{0.05}$, or $21.58, which is exactly $20 less than the accumulated land value of $41.58 in Table 17.2. The value of the growing stock only is

TABLE 17.2. COST VALUE PER ACRE OF AN EVEN-AGED
SOUTHERN PINE STAND AT AGE 15
(INTEREST AT 5 PERCENT)

Receipt or expenditure item	Value per acre	Formula for ac-cumulation	Value of interest factor	Value at age 15
Expenditures:				
Purchase cost of land........	$20.00	$(1.05)^{15}$	2.0789	$ 41.58
Site preparation and planting.	30.00	$(1.05)^{14a}$	1.9799	59.40
Annual costs...............	1.75	$\dfrac{(1.05)^{15} - 1}{0.05}$	21.5786	37.76
Total expenditures............	......	....	....	$138.74
Receipts:				
Thinning at age 15..........	6.00	....	....	6.00
Net value at age 15............	......	....	....	$132.74

^{a} This item is carried for $r - 1$ years for the reasons given in connection with the L_e
calculation, p. 361. The land cost is, by its nature, a beginning-of-year value. That
is, the land is first obtained and then a stand subsequently established, which by the
normal convention of interest is paid for not earlier than at the end of the first year.
If the stand is established in the first year without losing a growing season, 15 years
of growth are obtained as assumed here. The annual cost is paid at the end of the first
year and at the end of the last year; so there are 15 payments.

accordingly $132.74 − 20, or $112.74. Any actual rental cost could be used
although rentals of this kind are relatively few.

The computation can be presented in formula form as was done in
the case of the L_e calculation, but there is no virtue in so doing as the
precise form of the formula changes with the particular cost and value
assumptions. It is clearer and easier to focus attention on the individual
items involved and their presentation in financial statement form as
illustrated.

Income values are determined following the same general procedure
except that the viewpoint is forward and only future receipts and expenditures are included. Table 17.3 gives the income value for the same 15-year-
old stand as in Table 17.2, assuming a 30-year rotation. The assumptions
are again the same as in Table 17.1, except for a different estimated land
value at the end of the rotation. Note that in estimating an income value
a termination date for the stand has to be assumed. In this situation, a
land value can logically be estimated separately from the timber value, since
such a value, which represents all future values, would exist at the end
of the rotation when the major crop is harvested. The bare land could
presumably be sold as such or again used for timber production. In any
event, it is an element of value at that time to consider in exactly the
same way as an expected future timber value.

TABLE 17.3. INCOME VALUE PER ACRE OF AN EVEN-AGED SOUTHERN
PINE STAND AT AGE 15, ROTATION 30 YEARS
(INTEREST AT 5 PERCENT)

Receipt or expenditure item	Value per acre	Formula for discount	Value of interest factor	Value at age 15
Receipts:				
Estimated land value at rotation age..............	$ 30.00	$\dfrac{1}{(1.05)^{15}}$	0.4810	$ 14.43
Major harvest cut at rotation age................	240.50	"	0.4810	115.68
Thinning at age 20.........	14.00	$\dfrac{1}{(1.05)^{5}}$	0.7835	10.97
Thinning at age 25........	35.00	$\dfrac{1}{(1.05)^{10}}$	0.6139	21.49
Total receipts...............	....	....	....	$162.57
Expenditures:				
Annual costs.............	1.75	$\dfrac{(1.05)^{15} - 1}{0.05(1.05)^{15}}$	10.3797	18.16
Net value at age 15.........	....	....	....	$144.41

It should be emphasized that cost and income values are determined
by independent calculations. The first considers what has happened. The
second considers what it is expected will happen. Estimated future cost
and returns will seldom be at the same level as past costs; management
methods and the whole picture may have changed. Each estimate is made
strictly on its own merits.

It would consequently be extremely unlikely in an actual instance that
cost and income values for the same stand and calculated at the same time
would be the same. There is no reason why they should be. If the estimated
income value substantially exceeds the cost value, it merely means that cost
have been low in relation to expected income and that a good investment
has been made. If cost value exceeds income value it means that, according
to the estimates, a poor investment has been made. For either case, it is
the income value that exerts the greater influence on establishment of market
ket price, bringing out the fundamental fact that the real basis for an appraisal
praisal of any property is expected future earnings or services that may
be obtained from it. It is the future and not the past that casts the heavier
vote.

RELATIONSHIP BETWEEN COST AND INCOME VALUE

Even though cost and expectation value determinations are separate
calculations, there is a fundamental relationship between them through the

land value which is the one element common to both. For the illustrations given, cost value per acre was estimated at $132.74 (Table 17.2) and income value at $144.41 (Table 17.3). Exactly the same assumptions were employed as were used in the determinations of a land or L_e value (Table 17.1), except that estimated actual cost or market values for the land were assumed.

If the calculated L_e value had been used as the land value in both cases, the cost and income values would have been identical as can readily be demonstrated. In the cost value computation of Table 17.2, a land value of $20 was used whereas the calculated L_e value is $24.29.

TABLE **17.4.** COST AND INCOME VALUES PER ACRE OF AN EVEN-AGED
SOUTHERN PINE STAND AT AGE **15** WHEN ROTATION IS **30** YEARS
(INTEREST AT **5** PERCENT)

Receipt or expenditure item	Value per acre	Formula for accumulation or discount	Value of interest factor	Value at age 15
		Cost value		
Expenditures:				
Land value (L_e)............	$ 24.29	$(1.05)^{15}$	2.0789	$ 50.50
Site preparation and planting	30.00	$(1.05)^{14}$	1.9799	59.40
Annual costs..............	1.75	$\dfrac{(1.05)^{15} - 1}{0.05}$	21.5786	37.76
Total expenditures...........	....	....	....	147.66
Receipts:				
Thinning at age 15.........	6.00	....	....	6.00
Net value at age 15...........	....	....	....	141.66
		Income value		
Receipts:				
Land value at rotation age...	$ 24.29	$\dfrac{1}{(1.05)^{15}}$	0.4810	11.68
Major harvest cut at rotation age.....................	240.50	$\dfrac{1}{(1.05)^{15}}$	0.4810	115.68
Thinning at age 20.........	14.00	$\dfrac{1}{(1.05)^{5}}$	0.7835	10.97
Thinning at age 25.........	35.00	$\dfrac{1}{(1.05)^{10}}$	0.6139	21.49
Total receipts................	....	....	....	$159.82
Expenditures:				
Annual costs..............	1.75	$\dfrac{(1.05)^{15} - 1}{0.05(1.05)^{15}}$	10.3797	18.16
Net value at age 15...........	....	....	....	$141.66

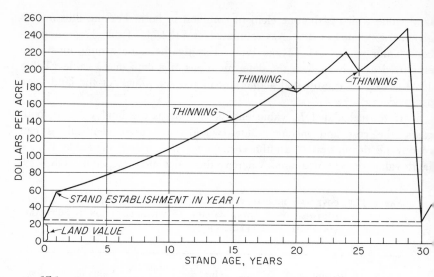

FIG. **17.1.** LAND AND TIMBER VALUES DURING A 30-YEAR ROTATION.

Using this figure, the accumulated value at age 15 is $24.29 × $(1.05)^{15}$, or $50.50. Substituting this figure in Table 17.2 brings the total cost value to $141.66. For the income value, an estimated market value of $30 was used. Using the L_e value instead and discounting for 15 years gives $24.29 × 1/$(1.05)^{15}$, or $11.68. Substituting this figure reduces the total income value to the same $141.66. When all other assumptions are the same, the L_e value is the connecting link that equates cost and income values.

While similar assumptions undoubtedly would not be made in estimating current values in an actual case, nor would an L_e value necessarily be used, an understanding of the conditions under which cost and income values are the same casts considerable light on the entire structure of cost, income, and land value relationships and is useful in comparative production cost and return analyses. To show the whole structure, cost and income values at age 15, using an L_e land value, are brought together in Table 17.4. Using the same data, similar computations were made for all other stand ages as shown in Fig. 17.1.

Figure 17.1 brings out some significant points. At the beginning of the rotation, or at age zero, the cost or income value is the land value only, or $24.29 in this instance. There is no other value. No costs have been incurred, and since no action has been taken to establish a stand, there is no timber income value other than the land value itself. At the end of the rotation when the stand is harvested (all values are calculated as of the end of the year), a land value again appears, indicating the value of the land at that time for continued forest production.

As long as there is a timber stand occupying an area, land and timber are physically merged. This is evidenced by the fact that standing timber is legally regarded as real estate, a part of the land. A land value is always latently present, but it cannot physically and actually appear as a separate item until the stand is removed.

It should be emphasized that forest land values are determined on the premise that bare land is to be used for forest production; the value estimate indicates what the land only is worth for such a purpose based on the value of the crop it can produce.[1]

A cost or income value for a timber stand can only be calculated when there is a timber stand on the ground. The land value included in the calculation, whether based on actual past cost or expected future value, is in no different category than any other item of cost or income. It is simply an element of value to include along with others. If the land value used fairly represents the productivity of the soil, cost or income values for an even-aged stand consequently represent the value of the land and timber not only for the current rotation, but also for all future rotations. The value of the forest land for future production beyond the current rotation is the land value at the end of the rotation.

Another point brought out by Fig. 17.1 is the fact that when intermediate costs or returns are involved, as is usually the case, the increase in net value during a rotation is not a smooth curve. Each expenditure or receipt item makes a deflection in the curve when they are made or received. From a cost value standpoint, an expenditure is simply not in the picture at all until it is made. When made, the cost enters the accumulating investment stream, creating a rise in the curve. The reverse results when intermediate receipts are received. For example, the income thinnings made at ages 15, 20, and 25 each lowered the curve, since the value of this income partially offset accumulated past costs. From an income value standpoint, at the beginning of the year before an income was received, the full value was expected. At the end of the year in which it was received, it is no longer a factor. Similarly, a cost item, as for prunings, is included in expectation value determination only if it is to be made in the future. As shown in Fig. 17.1, the total value rises during the rotation to a peak reached at the end of the rotation just before the final crop is harvested. At the end of the twenty-ninth year, the total value rises to $250. Just *before* the end of the final or thirtieth year, the full value of the final cut plus the land value is received or becomes available. By the

[1] If timberland is to be used for other than forest production purposes, the situation changes depending on contemplated use, and both land and timber are valued on different bases. If the land is to be cleared, the timber is worth only what it can be sold for at the time. If trees, or some of them, are wanted, as in recreational use, they might add substantially to the total market value of the tract whether or not any of them are cut with a net stumpage value.

end of the year when the crop is removed, the value drops to the continuing land value only.

In practice, one certainly would not expect to be able neatly to plot a curve for either cost or income values for a period as long as an entire rotation. Cost and income items would surely change, including the underlying land value. The general pattern of increasing total value with age and the effect of intermediate cost and income items on this accumulating value are significant, however. Fig. 17.1 brings out these relationships clearly by showing the logical consequences of the particular management assumptions employed. It also illustrates the complementary nature of cost and expectation value approaches when an L_e land value is used. It is evident that in the early life of the stand there are mainly expenditures only, whereas receipts peak at the end of the rotation. The analysis also points to the importance, when making managerial comparisons, of using a land value that represents fairly the contribution of the land. If not an L_e value, calculated in consonance with the assumptions made in determining the cost or income value, it at least should be one approaching a fair market value. Use of a bargain purchase price in cost value determination, or of an inflated selling price in income value estimation, would both indicate values out of line with true investment values and distort a managerial analysis.

INCOME VALUES FOR UNEVEN-AGED STANDS[1]

The nature of uneven-aged stands necessitates some modification in the application of cost and income value concepts. In the first place, a cost value cannot meaningfully be determined. An even-aged stand, as a practical matter, is never developed directly on bare land. No one could establish a few trees on an acre one year and additional trees every few years thereafter literally to build up an uneven-aged stand. Such stands can only develop over time, and while they may have a current market value, they have no definable point of beginning as do even-aged stands. Calculated values must, accordingly, be based on income values only.

In the second place, a land value never exists separately from the timber value unless the stand is all cut, in which case there is no longer any uneven-aged stand. Land and timber necessarily go together.

In an uneven-aged stand, there is a combination of site quality and growing stock that produces receipts either annually or periodically, depending on the length of the cutting cycle. Certain expenditures are also necessary to produce these returns. There are two elements of permanently productive capital involved, the land as measured by its site quality, and the reserve growing stock, instead of the land only as in the case of even-aged management.

[1] Refer to Chaps. 8 and 9 for uneven-aged management. Treatment here is limited to *stands* that can be considered as uneven-aged.

If the cut is annual, the value of the land and timber together can be estimated as being the capitalized value of the net annual income. For example, an acre that on the average yields 450 bd ft per year worth $30 per M, and costs $2.50 to protect and administer, has a capital value at 5 percent of $\dfrac{(0.450 \times \$30) - \$2.50}{0.05}$, or $220 per acre. Growing stock and land values cannot realistically be separated.

If incomes are received on a periodic basis, the value of the tract is the capital value of a permanent periodic income in exactly the same way as an L_e value is determined, except that land and timber are valued together. The capital value is accordingly defined as follows:

$$V_0 = \frac{Y_c - e\left[\dfrac{(1 + i)^t - 1}{i}\right]}{(1 + i)^t - 1} \quad \text{or} \quad V_0 = \frac{Y_c}{(1 + i)^t - 1} - E$$

where V_0 = capital value
Y_c = yield per cutting cycle (net stumpage value)
e = annual expenses
i = rate of interest expressed as a decimal
t = number of years in cutting cycle
E = capitalized value of annual expenses, or e/i

To illustrate, assume that $125 worth of forest products, per acre, can be cut every 10 years and that annual costs for protection, administration, etc. are $2.50 per acre per year. Interest is assumed at 5 percent. The capital value of the land and timber producing this income is then

$$V_0 = \frac{\$125 - \$2.50 \times \dfrac{(1.05)^{10} - 1}{0.05}}{(1.05)^{10} - 1} = \frac{\$125 - \$31.44}{1.6289 - 1}$$

$$= \frac{\$93.56}{0.6289}$$

$$= \$148.77 \text{ per acre}$$

This is the capital value of a permanent net income of $93.56 received every 10 years, the next payment coming 10 years hence. It represents the productive value of land and timber together just after a cyclic cut is made. As pointed out in connection with the development of formula 11 for periodic payments in Chap. 16, this capital sum of $148.77 is an amount that will provide for making payments of $93.56 every 10 years in perpetuity. In 10 years, the amount of the capital fund will be $148.77 $\times$ (1.05)^{10}, or $242.33. The net income of $93.56 is then deducted, leaving $148.77, and the process starts over again.

If the stand has a net capital value of $148.77 just after a cyclic cut, it obviously increases in value during the cycle as the stand approaches its next cyclic cut. The value for each year during the cycle is calculated in Table 17.5.

TABLE 17.5. INCOME VALUE OF AN UNEVEN-AGED STAND BY YEARS
DURING A 10-YEAR CUTTING CYCLE ACRE BASIS
(INTEREST AT 5 PERCENT)

Year (end)	Receipts[a]		Expenditures[b]		Net value
	Years to discount	Discounted value	Years to discount	Discounted value	
(1)	(2)	(3)	(4)	(5)	(6)
1	9	$ 176.47	9	$17.77	$ 158.70
2	8	185.29	8	16.16	169.13
3	7	194.57	7	14.47	180.10
4	6	204.28	6	12.69	191.59
5	5	214.50	5	10.82	203.68
6	4	225.23	4	8.87	216.36
7	3	236.47	3	6.81	229.66
8	2	248.30	2	4.65	243.65
9	1	260.74	1	2.38	258.36
10	0	148.77[c]	0	0	148.77[c]
Total...		$2,094.62		$94.62	$2,000.00

[a] Capital value of land and timber from all future cuts of $148.77, plus value of current cyclic cut of $125, both at end of cutting cycle.

[b] Annual cost of $2.50 per acre.

[c] Capital value of land and timber from all future cuts at end of year. The value of the current cut is nominally received just before the end of the year so is not included. The annual cost is also paid just before the end of the year and is not included either.

The structure of the table needs a bit of explanation. Note that it is a discounted income value calculation the same as Table 17.3 except that the values for the end of each year of the cycle are determined instead of for only one. The figures in column 3 of Table 17.5 are based on the sum of two end-of-cycle receipt items. One is the continuing capital value of land and timber together, $148.77, which represents all future values. The other is the value of the current cyclic cut, $125, which is nominally received just before the end of the cycle. The sum, $273.77, is then discounted to give the value by years during the cycle. For example, in the fifth year of the cycle, this amount is discounted for 5 years, or $273.77/1.2763 = $214.50. There is only one expenditure item, that for accumulated annual costs, which is treated in the same way.

A point to be emphasized is that the above valuations are all based on the assumption of continued management of a stand according to a specific plan and well illustrate the fact that values depend on uses contemplated. Values would be different if some other plan of use was intended.

Whether or not the values estimated are a good guide to current market value depends on the accuracy of the estimates and how closely they approach intended use. If, for example, the aim is to liquidate the stand at a certain time during the cycle, the value would be merely the current stumpage value of the timber at that time plus the land value for whatever use to which it might be put.

valuation of the regulated forest— the going concern

All the land and timber valuations hitherto have dealt with a specific stand producing an annual or periodic income. What about the value of a continuing business based on a forest organized for sustained yield? This is a common business situation and a major aim in timber management. Receipts in more or less equal amounts are received each year and expenses are currently paid. The difference represents the yearly operating net income or loss, as the case may be.

EVEN-AGED MANAGEMENT

Consider, for example, a regulated even-aged forest with costs and incomes per acre as were assumed in Table 17.1 for calculation of an L_e value. Since the rotation is 30 years, a 30-acre unit with all age classes present will represent such a forest. On this forest, there would be the following annual incomes and costs:

Receipts:		
Major harvest cut at age 30 on 1 acre......	$240.50	
Thinning at age 15, 1 acre...............	6.00	
Thinning at age 20, 1 acre...............	14.00	
Thinning at age 25, 1 acre...............	35.00	
Total receipts.........................		$295.50
Expenditures:		
Site preparation and planting, 1 acre.......	$ 30.00	
Net annual costs, $1.75 per acre on 30 acres	52.50	
Total expenditures.....................		82.50
Net annual income......................		$213.00

This net annual income is received on 30 acres. The capitalized value of the 30-acre unit, again using 5 percent, is accordingly $213.00/0.05, or 4,260, and the average per acre is $142. This is the value of land and growing stock together as a producing entity, as estimated by capitalization at this rate of interest. It measures what a forestry business, operating on the continuing basis assumed, is worth per average acre as an investment proposition on the basis of its current earning capacity. An acre is reestablished, and an investment is consequently made on that particular acre that cannot be realized for many years to come. At the same time, however, a final cut is made on another acre that was established in the past and upon which the benefit of that past investment is now realized. Costs and returns are consequently simultaneous in an offsetting sort of way.

On the face of it, this simple capitalization process seems to ignore the effect of compound interest and the fact that each unit in the regulated forest has a separate cost or income value as shown for a sample age in Table 17.4. The same question can be raised regarding the concept of forest rent as a rotation determinant (Chap. 10) which should be recognized as a continuing or "going concern" calculation.

There is no alchemy to the concept of a "going concern" that violates or eliminates the effect of time or of interest accumulation. One way to grasp the point is to refer to the derivation of the annual capitalization formula on p. 349 and see that it is the present value of a series of annual incomes with no termination date. If, in the above illustration, the cost (or income) value of each of the 30 units ranging from age 1 to 30 were separately calculated, using the L_e land value, the sum of these would be exactly \$4,260. Use of the L_e value gives, as has been emphasized, not only the value for a single rotation but for an indefinite series of succeeding rotations as well.

This point is important and merits explicit demonstration. Because calculation of 30 individual units for a 30-year rotation is tedious, an illustration will be given for a model forest of just 5 units of area. The case is, however, perfectly general, and the specific procedure can be applied to any cost and return assumptions or length of rotation (Davis, 1965).

If one wishes to rationalize in forestry terms, consider some kind of super tree (or Christmas trees) that can produce a financial crop in 5 years.

The receipts and expenditures assumed, their accumulated value at rotation age, and annual receipts and expenditures from a regulated "forest" of 5 units are given in Table 17.6. As shown (column 4), the net value at rotation age is \$28.92. The L_e or land expectation value is consequently

$$\frac{\$28.92}{(1+i)^5 - 1} = \frac{28.92}{0.4693} = \$61.62 \text{ per unit of area}$$

The "going concern" or capitalized value of the net annual income for 5 regulated units (column 5) is

$$\frac{\$45}{0.08} = \$562.50$$

Table 17.7 gives the complete structure of income and cost value calculations by individual years. As shown in column 20 the total is $562.50 which checks exactly with the "going concern" or capitalized net annual income from the 5 units. The table also shows calculations by beginning and end-of-year values illustrating the point made on p. 370 that there is only the land value at the beginning and end of the rotation. This table is useful as a general model for such calculations since it shows the exact treatment of individual items in consonance with the end-of-year assumption upon which compound interest tables are based. For example, note that with cost values the improvement cost of $10 (column 10) has been paid sometime *during* the second year, nominally just before the end, so yearly interest is not due on it at the end of the year. Also, since it has been paid, it is not included at all in the income value calculation for the end of that year—which only looks ahead. As an item of technique, note that with income values all items are carried to rotation age and the net income for each year is discounted back to its age (columns 18–20). In table 17.3, each item was discounted separately. These are alternative methods; the former was used in Table 17.7 for illustration and because it eliminated two columns in this instance.

TABLE 17.6. COSTS AND RETURNS FROM A REGULATED FOREST
MODEL MANAGED ON A 5-YEAR ROTATION
(INTEREST AT 8 PERCENT)

Receipt or expenditure item	Value per unit	Years to accumu- late	Value at rotation age	Annual receipts and expenditures from regu- lated forest
(1)	(2)	(3)	(4)	(5)
Receipts:				
Final harvest at age 5........	$100	0	$100.00	100
Intermediate harvest, age 3...	10	2	11.66	10
Total receipts.................	....	...	$111.66	110
Expenditures:				
Establishment cost, year 1[a]...	30	4	40.81	30
Improvement cost, year 2.....	10	3	12.60	10
Annual costs...............	5	5	29.33	25
Total expenditures............	....	...	$ 82.74	65
Net value at rotation age.......	....	...	$ 28.92	45

[a] Assumed establishment will be completed before the growing season so 5 years of growth will be made.

TABLE 17.7. INCOME AND COST VALUES BY YEARS FOR A 5-YEAR FOREST MODEL (INTEREST AT 8 PERCENT)

INCOME VALUES

Year	Land value (L_e)	Final harvest cut	Intermediate cut, yr. 3			Total income at r age	Annual costs			Establishment cost, yr. 1			Improvement cost, yr. 2			Total costs at r age	Net income at r age	Years to discount	Net income value for year
			Amount	Years to accumulate	Value at r age		Amount	Years to accumulate	Value at r age	Amount	Years to accumulate	Value at r age	Amount	Years to accumulate	Value at r age				
(1)	(2)	(3)	(4)	(5)	(6)	(7)	(8)	(9)	(10)	(11)	(12)	(13)	(14)	(15)	(16)	(17)	(18)	(19)	(20)
B-1[a]	$61.62	$100.00	$10.00	2	$11.66	$173.28	$5.00	5	$29.33	$30.00	4	$40.81	$10.00	3	$12.60	$82.74	$90.54	5	$ 61.62
E-1[a]	61.62	100.00	10.00	2	11.66	173.28	5.00	4	22.53				10.00	3	12.60	35.13	138.15	4	101.55
E-2	61.62	100.00	10.00	2	11.66	173.28	5.00	3	16.23							16.23	157.05	3	124.67
E-3	61.62	100.00				161.62	5.00	2	10.40							10.40	151.22	2	129.64
E-4	61.62	100.00				161.62	5.00	1	5.00							5.00	156.62	1	145.02
E-5	61.62					61.62										0	61.62	0	61.62
Total[b]																			$562.50

COST VALUES

Year	Land cost (L_e)			Establishment cost, yr. 1			Improvement cost, yr. 2			Annual cost			Total costs	Final harvest income	Intermediate income, yr. 3			Total incomes	Net cost value for year
	Amount	Years to accumulate	Cost	Amount	Years to accumulate	Cost	Amount	Years to accumulate	Cost	Amount	Years to accumulate	Cost			Amount	Years to accumulate	Income		
(1)	(2)	(3)	(4)	(5)	(6)	(7)	(8)	(9)	(10)	(11)	(12)	(13)	(14)	(15)	(16)	(17)	(18)	(19)	(20)
B-1[a]	$61.62	0	$ 61.62										$ 61.62					0	$ 61.62
E-1[a]	61.62	1	66.55	$30.00	0	$30.00				$5.00	1	$ 5.00	101.55					0	101.55
E-2	61.62	2	71.87	30.00	1	32.40	$10.00	0	$10.00	5.00	2	10.40	124.67					0	124.67
E-3	61.62	3	77.62	30.00	2	34.99	10.00	1	10.80	5.00	3	16.23	139.64		$10.00	0	$10.00	$ 10.00	129.64
E-4	61.62	4	83.83	30.00	3	37.79	10.00	2	11.66	5.00	4	22.53	155.82		10.00	1	10.80	10.80	145.02
E-5	61.62	5	90.54	30.00	4	40.81	10.00	3	12.60	5.00	5	29.33	173.28	$100.00	10.00	2	11.66	111.66	61.62
Total[b]																			$562.50

[a] B indicates the beginning and E the end of year. At any time except the end of the last rotation year, the value for the end of one year and the beginning of the next year are identical. Thus E-1 = B-2, etc.

[b] Total from B-1 to B-5 or E-1 to E-5, inclusive.

UNEVEN-AGED MANAGEMENT

The capital value of a regulated forest managed on an uneven-aged basis is determined in the same general way as for even-aged management only the process is simpler. Some cultural work like pruning may be done currently on an annual basis. It cannot be identified by stand age, since stands are of mixed ages, and hence applies to the area as a whole as an annual cost. Harvest cutting and thinning operations are made simultaneously when a cyclic cut is made. Assuming a 10-year cutting cycle and the same receipt and expenditure data used on p. 373, the capital value per acre based on a sample area of 10 acres (1 acre for each year of the cutting cycle) is estimated as follows:

Receipts:
    Net stumpage value of cyclic cut made on 1 acre.............. $125.00
Expenditures:
    Annual costs of taxes, administration, protection, and an annual
      budget for stand improvement work not done as a part of the
      cyclic cut, $2.50 per acre................................. 25.00

Annual net income... $100.00

Again using 5 percent, the capital value of this net annual income is $100/0.05, or $2,000 on 10 acres, or $200 per acre for land and timber together as a continuously productive entity. Note that in Table 17.5 giving values for individual years in the cutting cycle the sum of the 10 years is exactly $2,000 giving a check on the arithmetic and explicitly relating values for individual years with a "going concern" for the same operating period—a cutting cycle in this instance.

In conclusion, this chapter has developed and demonstrated methods for estimating forest land and timberland values on the basis of their continued capacity to produce wood under a timber-growing production schedule. As shown, time is a major factor, really a dimension, in all of the calculations. This is inescapably true as timber can be grown only over time. This fact necessitates the use of interest as a means of estimating the importance of the passage of time. Interest is always more or less difficult to understand fully and to rationalize. But it cannot be escaped in timberland valuation. It is perfectly true that, in practice, no one attempts to keep historical cost and return records on individual stands duly recording interest accumulation. Forest land and timber stand valuations are none the less an indispensable managerial tool in appraising the relative desirability of silvicultural and other management alternatives and in giving a basis for market value determination. The mechanics are worth mastering so that they can be meaningfully applied.

18

valuation of stumpage

Stumpage is timber in unprocessed form as it is found in the woods. Normally, it means standing unsevered trees, whether live or dead, but the term can also be applied to timber that is wind-thrown or cut in connection with right-of-way clearing, as long as it is in place and not cut up into logs or other merchantable units.[1]

The valuation of stumpage is important to almost everyone in the timber business. It is the raw material of the forest from which all wood products are derived. Not only is stumpage a commodity frequently bought and sold in the daily conduct of a forest business, but it also has special significance to the landowner as the source of his timber income. Stumpage prices consequently directly influence the profitability of timber growing as a business. As brought out in Chap. 17, the value of forest land and growing stock stems from the net value of the products harvested. Since stumpage values so vitally affect his business, it is important for the practicing forester to have a thorough grasp of the methods employed in their estimation whether he is concerned with growing, selling, or buying timber.

---

[1] Timber is also cut by the owner and taken to a market point accessible to buyers such as roadside, streamside, railroad, or other delivery point and sold there as logs, bolts, or other timber units. This is general practice in Europe but not in the United States and in many other areas. It adds the cost of cutting and market point delivery to the stumpage value and simplifies the selling process. In the United States and Canada, as well as in many other large forest areas, timber is preponderantly sold as stumpage. Appraisal of logs and individual trees is given in Chap. 19.

nature of stumpage appraisal

The purpose of stumpage appraisal is to estimate, at a particular point in time, the value of standing timber available for cutting on a particular area. Both buyer and seller are equally concerned although from different points of view. The buyer wants to know how much he can afford to pay for the timber and make what he considers a satisfactory profit on his processing operation. The seller is cost-conscious and naturally wants to cover his timber production costs, if they are known, and make a profit besides. He must also take into account what the material is worth to a buyer who must process the timber and sell the products under current price levels and market conditions. It is both possible and normal for the seller and prospective buyers to arrive at different estimates of the value of a particular tract of timber. With competition, the actual selling price is determined by buyer-seller negotiation following the usual processes of market price establishment. The relative influence of buyer and seller depends on their respective financial strengths and the current supply and demand situation.

While negotiation and competition is usual, selling prices are often set by appraisal, which makes the process of special importance. The U.S. Forest Service, for example, is charged by law to sell timber at "not less than the appraised value" (Act of June 4, 1897). When timber is offered for sale and competition does not develop, it may be sold at the appraised price. The same is true of public agencies generally; an appraised price is set to protect the public interest. Under certain conditions, as in small sales and under specific enabling legislation such as the Federal Cooperative Sustained Yield Act (Mar. 29, 1944, cited as Public Law 273 of the Seventy-eighth Congress), public timber is sold at an appraised or otherwise established price without competition. Private owners, for various business reasons, may and often do negotiate with a single buyer and arrive at a price without open competition. In legal proceedings, what is adjudged to be a fair price for timber may be established by appraisal with no element of competition entering in.

Both as a guide in establishment of market price and in determination of price where there is no competitive bidding, appraisal is of fundamental importance. There is some tendency to deprecate the importance of careful appraisal because of a feeling that it is sufficient to be alert and sensitive to going market prices. Where an active stumpage market exists for timber of approximately the same quality and accessibility, there is much truth to this view, so far as current buying and selling is concerned. It is also true that competition, when present, will protect the seller's interest and make accurate appraisal less essential. It is well to remember, however, that appraisal is a guide to judgment and as such exerts an important influence on market price. This fact becomes apparent when there is a change, present or prospective, in cost-price relationships. An alert seller or buyer will be aware of these changes and employ them to his advantage. Market price will follow and will be based upon buyer and seller reappraisal of the changed situation. Appraisal is in effect going backstage to see how the scenes are arranged.

In essential outline, the problem of stumpage appraisal is simple. The value of standing timber is calculated as the difference between the selling value of the products produced from it and the stump-to-market processing costs, including an allowance for profit and risk. It should be particularly noted that the value of stumpage is considered a residual item, a difference. The cost of growing the timber itself does not enter in directly at all. Instead, the appraisal process determines what is available to cover the costs of timber production.

Why is this so? Why is stumpage value, the return for so vital an enterprise as timber growing, calculated as a residual item? Stumpage appraisal follows the same general pattern as that for any other raw material. Basically, the demand for such is derived from the products that can be made from it. Consider a farmer, for example. He owns or rents land, buys seed, puts in a crop, tends it, and finally offers the produce for sale in the market. Does he present the buyer with an itemized statement of his cost plus what he considers a reasonable return for his effort and expect this to be the selling price? Not at all. The price he gets is determined by the current supply and demand relationship. A wholesaler, for example, cannot offer more for the produce than what can be retailed on the market plus what he considers a necessary margin for profit and handling costs. If the market is good, as they say in popular terms, the farmer may make a handsome return for his effort. If the market is bad, i.e., the effective demand in relation to supply is weak, he may scarcely get his seed cost back, to say nothing of a return for his season's work. In addition, he has to assume the risks of crop failure and general bad luck. His actions affect market price only through their effect on supply; he has no control over demand except as he also acts as a consumer. In no case do his particular costs of production enter directly and immediately into the establishment of the market price of his product.

In the long run, however, the costs of production do affect market prices. In a case where the farmer consistently does not receive what he considers an adequate return for a product, he will plant less of it, shift to some other crop he estimates will pay better, or quit farming and try some other occupation. In any event, the supply of the particular crop will be reduced, which, along with demand, controls prices. While fluctuations in many farm product prices are controlled by public action in various ways and risks are partially insurable, the basically residual situation of the farmer with respect to current produce prices in a competitive market remains. A producer is continually squeezed between costs of production on one side and selling prices on the other, both of which are set by the interaction of forces for the most part beyond his immediate power to control. He may, however, influence demand through advertising, and billions are spent annually to do this.

While the timberland owner is basically in the same situation as the farmer, there are three notable differences: (1) he normally is under less immediate pressure to sell at any particular time (his crop will not spoil in the woods if held a few extra years); (2) his crop takes much longer to produce, and he has correspondingly less control over current supply; (3) he normally has much less knowledge of what it costs to produce it. The first is a saving feature of forestry as it gives the owner considerable flexibility and bargaining strength in the current merchandizing of his products. The second offers a difficult problem in adjusting a rather inelastic supply to effective demand at a price that will cover cost of production. Although the amount cut can currently be adjusted within fairly wide limits, timber can neither be overcut nor withheld from the market indefinitely on any economic basis. The general level of growing stock and volume of timber available for cutting cannot be changed in any short period of time. The forces which brought about the present supply were of a long-time nature, and a general change involves equally deliberate processes.

There is a tendency for changes in demand to operate contrary to the timber grower's best interest. For example, if demand increases and seems symptomatic of a general upward trend, there is a tendency to overcut and deplete growing stock when it should be built up for greater production. If demand slackens, there is a tendency to accumulate growing stock, further aggravating an excess of supply in relation to demand at the current price level (Zivnuska, 1949; Vaux, 1949). Because of the long-time nature of the timber-growing process, it is not possible to get close adjustment of supply to demand at a particular price level as would be possible in the case of a product that can be manufactured and put on the market in a matter of months.

As to the third point, it must be remembered that, at least up to the present time, by far the major proportion of timber cut worldwide was not consciously "grown" by anyone. It just grew. Consider the case of virgin timber, which essentially means old-growth timber uninfluenced by man's purposeful action. Nobody grew it, and actual costs of production do not exist. Ownership was established by right of government or by purchase. In neither case have timber production costs been incurred beyond those for taxes, protection, and capital investment. The same general situation prevails on much of present forest areas supporting second-growth stands. It is only as existing stocks of virgin and other more or less "wild" timber become or threaten to become scarce that conscious timber growing is seriously considered. Such timber growing is increasingly being undertaken by private owners, with some public assistance, because an appraisal of present and prospective effective demand for timber products in relation to supply indicates that they can be sold at a price that will cover production costs and make timber growing a profitable undertaking.

The many factors affecting prices of wood products both on a short- and long-range basis cannot be analyzed here. Stumpage supply is one of them, and, in the long run at least, prices will have to cover the cost of growing it. In appraising a particular tract of timber, however, the appraiser must base his calculations on selling prices as they are and go on from there. So far as establishment of a current market price for stumpage is concerned, it makes not a particle of difference whether the timber is of virgin or timber-farming origin. The appraisal process and the immediate price-influencing forces are exactly the same.

In summary, the current value of stumpage is determined by the difference between the value of the products sold and the cost of processing them out of the standing tree plus a margin for profit and risk to the processor. Stumpage prices are of particular interest to the landowner since they constitute the return for growing the timber and as such determine the profitability of the enterprise. Costs of timber growing do not directly enter into stumpage appraisal but influence finished product and stumpage prices through their long-range effect on timber supply.

general problems of stumpage appraisal

While stumpage appraisal is simple in general outline, it is complicated in its application. Standing timber is not a standard commodity like a ton of steel plate of certain specifications. No two timber stands are quite the same in quality, accessibility, and other factors, and wood products are sold in a multitude of shapes, sizes, forms, and grades for many uses.

Six general and recurrent problems of appraisal should be given consideration before going into specific appraisal methods. They are: (1) the purposes of seller or buyer and conditions of sale; (2) determination of derived product selling value; (3) determination of production costs; (4) division of the conversion return between a margin for profit and risk and stumpage; (5) problems of measurement; (6) evaluation of time effect where stumpage purchased is cut and processed over a substantial time period.

PURPOSES OF SELLER OR BUYER
AND CONDITIONS OF SALE

With stumpage, as in any appraisal, results depend on purposes and plan of use. For the seller or landowner in general, cutting is the crucial and final act of the timber production process and must be considered in relation to his purposes of management; he is the one who determines what timber is to be cut. As regards its sale, the purpose of most owners is to get the best price possible in the market. With many, however, the situation is not that simple.

In the United States, most industrial owners do not directly cut their own timber. More often they cut through contractors or sell stumpage, although often with the expectation of buying it back in the form of cut logs or pulpwood to supply their processing plants. These companies deal with a network of established timber buyers who cut and sell timber in round and unprocessed form, many of them more or less dependent on company stumpage although essentially independent as business operators. The company is under no compulsion to solicit bids and sell on the open market. It is often in their business interest to sell directly to individual buyers at a negotiated price that is adjudged to give a fair return to the company and also give the buyer a reasonable profit; they want to keep him in business. Some companies also help the buyer in the financing of equipment and in other ways.

Public owners also must consider various limitations on market value determination that affect appraisal. They are concerned with public policy, and their transactions are basically public information; they usually have limited authority for direct negotiation with individuals. The U.S. Forest Service is the largest seller of stumpage in the United States, and in some areas, notably the West, private forest industry is highly dependent on this timber source. As previously stated, the Forest Service is committed by law to sell at not less than an appraised value, and they also solicit competitive bidding. As officially stated: ". . . the appraised value is based on the operator of average efficiency and is aimed at a market value which will interest sufficient purchasors to harvest the allowable cut offered for sale" (U.S. Forest Service, n.d., F.S. Handbook 2423.12). The aim is to give a profit margin sufficient to maintain business operations over the long run and to give also an appraised stumpage value approximately equal to current market value considering lumber market trends (FSH 2423.13). The Forest Service also establishes minimum stumpage values, by regions and species, below which they will not sell. In view of these conditions and limitations, it is impossible consistently to equate appraised and current market value, especially considering that much timber is sold at above the appraised price.

In summary, most stumpage sellers, numerically, wish to get the highest price possible on the current market, and if an active market exists, they will get it through competitive bidding. With public agencies, and with some large private sellers, this objective is tempered by policy and business considerations, making the total objective more nearly conform to the economic concept of a functional price, which essentially means one that will accomplish a desired purpose in selling a commodity.

As regards conditions of sale, it must be recognized that in selling stumpage a contract is made and a buyer enters upon the property of an owner to cut timber. This can be a disruptive operation. The seller, in addition to wishing a fair price for the timber to be cut, must consider the cutting in relation to his purposes of management. Normally, he will designate the area and the particular trees to be cut. He will also specify when and how they shall be removed and the condition in which the cutting area shall be left. A number of restrictions may be imposed to protect trees not to be cut from unnecessary damage, to specify utilization standards, to guard against erosion, to minimize damage to other forest land values such as recreation or wildlife, and to specify the location and construction of roads and their improvements that may be built in connection with timber cutting. The listing of conditions of sale that may be imposed by the seller can be long and varied.

To the buyer, these conditions of sale are essentially costs of cutting the timber as will be discussed later. They are introduced here to emphasize the close relationship of timber cutting to the operation of a forest property and to the fact that it is difficult and often not possible fully to include the cost of these sale conditions in an appraisal. They also emphasize that cutting operations should be considered area by area and owner by owner. Differences in conditions of sale are often important (differences between the sale of private, state, and federal timber, for example) and can cause controversy and frequently misunderstanding in relation to stumpage appraisal.

DETERMINATION OF PRODUCT SELLING VALUE

Since stumpage value is derived from the value of products made from the timber, determination of their selling value is the logical point of beginning in making an appraisal. The selling value must be based on products that actually can be produced and sold from the area being appraised. In general, the price should be that actually received by buyers for the most valuable products obtainable at the earliest stage of processing or manufacture for which a free market exists and costs of production can be segregated. For a small logger or pulpwood contractor, the log or pulpwood price received at the mill, or wherever his handling of the timber stops, is the point of beginning as far as he is concerned. It is the correct procedure if there are established log or pulpwood market prices (with necessary transportation cost adjustment for actual point of delivery). In the case of a sawmill operator who sells rough lumber on the market, the prices he receives for lumber in this form are the base. If the lumber is dried and planed, the basis is finished lumber market prices in the area, weighted by the dimensions and grades that can be produced from the stumpage under consideration.

Complications occur where the buyer may sell several different kinds of primary products such as pulp chips, veneer logs, and transmission poles in addition to sawed products. These are further compounded in the case of integrated producers who manufacture and sell a variety of products both unfinished and finished from sawed timber, chips, or veneer, since joint costs are involved that can only arbitrarily be segregated by products sold. In practice, selling prices for primary products such as standard lumber grades and pulp chips, for which market price and cost can be obtained, are established on a fairly arbitrary basis, although a question may remain as to what these primary products are really worth to the manufacturer.

This question is particularly significant in the pulp and paper industry because of the wide variety of products sold and the complex pricing structure. It is impracticable, if not impossible, to appraise pulpwood on the myriad of products made from it. However, pulpwood is a marketable commodity, and market prices for it are established. The pricing mechanism, at least in the United States, consists of a mill offering prices based on its judgment of what is sufficient to get the quantity of wood it needs. Prices so established are consequently adjusted to the local pulpwood supply-and-demand situation.

It is evident from the above that determination of a proper and fair selling price applicable in a particular situation offers many and complex technical problems. In addition to the items mentioned, there is the problem of getting good current price information. Should it be from the past 3 months, 6 months, 1 year, or 3 years? Also, how well will price information, no matter when it was collected, apply to the period during which the timber actually will be cut? In this connection, and regarding stumpage appraisal in general, there must be sober recognition that pricing is a complex matter; books are written about it, and there are no final answers. Stumpage is an inherently difficult commodity to appraise.

DETERMINATION OF PRODUCTION COSTS

All costs directly necessary to the production of the product sold should be included. These do not, however, include costs of income taxes, interest on invested capital, or the cost of the stumpage itself. These items are, however, considered in determining a proper allowance for profit and risk, which will be discussed later. Accurate cost determination is difficult. No two tracts of timber are exactly alike. Such items as the size, condition, and quality of the timber, the difficulty of logging and accessibility, can vary widely from tract to tract. Similar kinds of problems are encountered in determining manufacturing costs. The equipment and general efficiency of the operator may result in large cost differences. Should one appraise in terms of a particular operator, or for the most efficient or average operator in a position to buy the stumpage? These are difficult questions, and the answers given to them depend on the purposes of the appraisal.

The determination of applicable logging and milling costs runs the gamut of logging and milling engineering. It is beyond the scope of treatment here, where emphasis is on appraisal methodology and on the use rather than the techniques of determining specific costs. It should be clearly recognized, however, that in practice the timber appraiser can expect to spend a major portion of his time estimating costs and that this work requires much knowledge, skill, experience, and judgment.

DIVISION OF THE CONVERSION RETURN
BETWEEN PROFIT AND RISK AND STUMPAGE

The difference between selling prices and related cutting and processing costs is termed the "conversion return." This is the key figure in any analytical timber appraisal.[1] The amount of this margin is essentially a matter of determinable fact, although, as pointed out, there are many technical problems as well as differences in point of view between buyer and seller that affect its determination.

The second and central problem is to divide this conversion return between an appropriate return to the buyer for profit and risk and return to the seller for stumpage. In fact, analytical methods differ primarily concerning how the conversion margin is divided. Methods of so doing are discussed later.

There obviously has to be a return to the producer for profit, including return on his investment, and for noninsurable business risks involved in processing and selling the timber. The residual of the conversion return is stumpage and goes to the timber owner. It must be clearly recognized that a stumpage value determined by any appraisal is an estimate from some point of view. If the timber is sold at appraised value, or this value accepted in timberland purchase, it becomes a market price. Otherwise, it is only a base from which actual market price is established by buyer-seller interaction. One must always distinguish sharply between a value estimate and an actual price as obtained in the market.

PROBLEMS OF MEASUREMENT

Stumpage appraisal is complicated and made more difficult because trees and the various products made from them are inherently difficult to measure and because of the fact that, world-wide and often within countries, there is great variation in the measurement units used. Standing trees are sold and stumpage prices are expressed in forest units, of which the board

[1] By an analytical appraisal is meant one that makes a full analysis of the tree-to-market production process in estimating a stumpage value. This is distinct from methods based directly on current stumpage market values or other approaches that do not include all costs and selling prices.

foot as measured by one of several log rules, cubic measure, and stacked measure, such as the cord, are the most common. Qualitative tree and log grades are often applied. Cut timber may also be sold by the piece, lineal foot, pole unit (by size classes), weight, and as bolts of various sizes and descriptions. Felled trees are handled in the woods, sometimes in tree lengths but mostly in pieces such as logs or pulpwood bolts. Logging costs are somewhat variously figured by the tree, piece, lineal foot, board foot, cubic measure, or cord according to circumstances and local practice. Relating logging costs to these units can be difficult.

Processing and selling units are still different. In lumber manufacture, the board foot, lumber measure, is almost universally employed in the United States and Canada. Sawmill and subsequent processing costs and selling prices are consequently expressed in lumber measure, and, as is well known, the number of board feet measured in log scale and actual lumber or mill scale may often differ widely owing to defect, sawing and manufacturing methods, scaling practice, and to the peculiarities of the log rule employed. Determining the difference between log and lumber board foot scale and making the conversion are continual problems in appraisal.

In the veneer and plywood business, the finished product is measured in square feet for sheets of varying thickness and number of plys, but logs are commonly bought log scale by the board foot or by cubic measure, which necessitates establishment of conversion factors. In the United States, pulpwood is widely bought and sold by the cord, of which the 128 cu ft stacked cord is the standard for comparative purposes, although various sizes of "units" are employed in the field. Cubic measure, such as the "cunit" of 100 cu ft, and weight are also employed. Pulping material is frequently bought in the form of chips. In the western United States, pulpwood is mostly bought on log scale. Although pulpwood is cut and handled using cord, piece, cubic, weight, and sometimes board foot units, the resultant pulp in the mill is measured in tons, necessitating more conversions.

These problems of measurement and conversion, being what they are, constitute a complicating factor in stumpage appraisal. Although they do not affect basic procedures, they are a common source of error and difficulty and necessitate that the appraiser thoroughly understand mensurational units and techniques.

THE TIME ELEMENT

Since timber is uncut at the time it is appraised, stumpage valuation is basically a forecast of what it will be worth when cut and processed. If conditions are not likely to change, as when the sale period is short or business conditions are stable, present or near-present costs and prices are clearly the best basis. If, however, the timber is to be cut and processed over a period when prices are expected to rise or fall significantly, the fact that an appraisal is a value forecast can become very important to buyer and seller alike. Current costs and prices obtained over a period are normally used, but some adjustment for estimated trends may also be necessary.

Both public and private agencies selling timber collect selling price and cost data for use in appraisals. Average selling prices, sometimes expressed in index number form, are often compiled for a calendar year. They may be adjusted for the current quarter or some such period as may be used as a base in making an appraisal. Adjustments may also be made in costs. Provision for redetermination of stumpage, as in long-term sale contracts running several years, is made for the same reason. The practice of basing appraisals on average current costs and selling prices explains why it is, even when adjustments are made, that appraised prices are usually below, often substantially, offered prices in times of rising market value and equal to or slightly above them with a declining market.

Another aspect of time that affects stumpage values is the way in which it is purchased. For example, it is one thing to buy 10 years' supply of timber at one time and assume the risks, capital and other costs that may be involved, especially if the contract gives the right to cut all merchantable timber on an area. It is another thing to buy approximately the same amount of timber on a pay-as-cut basis with provision for rate renegotiation but have the seller assume the risks on uncut timber.

methods of stumpage appraisal

The preceding discussion has presented the nature of stumpage appraisal, has given some of the major problems involved, and has cleared the way for specific consideration of appraisal methods. There are two general groups of methods, direct and analytical.

DIRECT METHODS

With direct methods, stumpage value is determined in comparison to current stumpage market prices in the areas, though usually with some adjustment for timber quality and logging costs to improve the comparison. The simplest approach is not to appraise at all but to put the timber on the market and rely on competitive bidding or direct negotiation to establish price. Where an active market exists, and stumpage in a price area is not greatly dissimilar, such an approach can give a final and fair answer. Market price underlies all appraisal and is the final arbiter of value.

More commonly, however, the buyer or seller will consider timber quality and logging costs specifically relating to the timber being sold and adjust the offering or asking price and negotiate accordingly.

ADJUSTED STUMPAGE APPRAISAL IN SOUTH CAROLINA
A good illustration of an adjusted direct approach to stumpage appraisal, intended primarily for general use of small independent sellers, is given by Anderson (1961). It is specifically applicable to pine sawtimber marked for partial cuttings in South Carolina. It is based on a regression analysis of variables affecting the price actually paid on 93 sales distributed throughout the state and made during a 10-year period. This sample was supported by a study of a much larger number of sales made over the same period to obtain the average trend of state prices. This information was used to relate prices paid on the 93 sample sales to average prices paid at the time they were made. The state forestry service periodically publishes average stumpage prices received, but these are not always currently available.

Of the variables studied, four were found to be significant in this situation and were used in making estimating equations. They were as follows:

1. Average volume per marked tree
2. Distance in miles to the nearest adequate mill
3. Number of bids received
4. Geographic location (by counties)

Two simple estimating procedures were developed from these variables.

1. *Using the State Average Price.* A table was prepared giving, for a range of average state prices, the base stumpage price paid for different average volumes per tree marked. A second table was prepared giving by counties plus or minus adjustment factors by road distance in miles to the nearest mill.

To give an illustration, assume the average state price is $35 per thousand bd ft; for a particular tract offered for sale the average volume per market tree is 120 bd ft, the location is Richland County, and the distance to the nearest adequate mill is 3 miles. From the first table and for a state average of $35, the base price for trees averaging 120 bd ft is $34.30. From the second table, the adjustment is minus $1.90 giving an estimated stumpage value of $32.40 per M bd ft. This is an estimate only, and a seller is advised to get three bids if possible and to be hesitant about accepting an offer of more than $5 below the estimate (based on observed variability in the estimating equations).

2. *Using the Local Average Price.* Current average state prices are not always available. In this case, the seller should, by local inquiry (ignoring county lines), ascertain a local "going" price, the average volume per tree of timber sold, and the distance to the nearest mill. Assume in this case, the average price is $34, the average volume is 160 bd ft per tree, and the distance to the nearest mill 5 miles. To make an estimate of stumpage value in this situation a third table was prepared giving price indicators by average volume per tree marked and by haul distances.

Using the same tract information as in the first illustration, the estimation procedure is as follows:

Price indicator for the offered tract (120 bd ft average volume per tree,
  3 miles from nearest mill)................................. $7.40
Price indicator for average tract in the locality (160 bd ft per tree, 5 miles
  from nearest mill)... 8.40
Difference... $1.00

Since the average local price is $34 and the price indicator for the offered tract is smaller than that for the average tract, the difference is subtracted indicating a stumpage value of $33.

The procedure given here is useful because logging conditions are closely similar over the state, most tracts are readily accessible, and the average volume per tree cut fairly well represents timber quality differences. Volume cut per acre was not found to be significant in this study.

DIRECT STUMPAGE APPRAISAL BY A STATE AGENCY A related and more complete approach is applied by a state forestry organization selling stumpage in the Lake States.[1] By law, a presale appraisal must be made. All timber is sold by one of the following methods:

1. By comparison to nearby and recently advertised sales of timber similar in quality and logging cost. May be applied to sales of less than $200 in total stumpage value.

2. By use of average stumpage rates by species and product for the county during the past year. Also used only for sales of less than $200.

3. By use of timber stumpage factors. This method is applied to all advertised sales and to all sales over $200. Smaller sales may be advertised. Based on thorough study of logging operations in the state from stump to mill or other market point, factors of individual logging costs, marketability, and quantity and quality, are expressed as percentages of total cost. What is considered a fair margin for profit and risk is included. These percentages or factors are prepared for average, excellent, and poor conditions with each item included specifically defined. An average prudent timber operator is assumed. Average stumpage selling prices are also determined by tree species and by county (and for state or county forest areas) and revised annually. This is done for sawlog and for cordwood sales separately.

Use of this method of appraising sawlog and cordwood stumpage, as applied to average conditions, is illustrated in Table 18.1. Note that a margin for profit and risk is included and that the ease or difficulty of selling stumpage (marketability), quantity, and quality of timber are also evaluated. Estimated factors are all related to the average factors and selling values. The factors for poor and excellent conditions are 0.50 and 1.50, respectively. They are defined in the same way as average factors to

[1] Unpublished material, courtesy of the Wisconsin Conservation Department.

TABLE 18.1. APPLICATION OF STUMPAGE FACTOR ADJUSTMENT
METHOD IN STUMPAGE APPRAISAL

Line	Item	Sawlogs		Cordwood	
		Average factors	Factors estimated for yellow birch	Average factors	Factors estimated for balsam fir
1	Felling and bucking.........	0.08	0.08	0.36	0.32
2	Skidding...................	0.11	0.10	0.22	0.22
3	Road construction and maintenance....................	0.03	0.03	0.05	0.05
4	Hauling (including loading and unloading).............	0.18	0.20	0.32	0.30
5	Marketability..............	0.10	0.18	0.05	0.03
6	Quality and quantity........	0.50	0.55		
7	Total factors..............	1.00	1.14	1.00	0.92
8	Base stumpage value[a].......	....	$46.00	....	$5.20
9	Estimated stumpage value...	....	$52.44	....	$4.78
10	Minimum advertised value[b]..	....	$44.57	....	$4.06
11	Volume...................	....	20 M bd ft	....	200 cords
12	Minimum total value........	....	$891.40	....	$812.00

[a] As given in table of average stumpage selling values for a particular county in Wisconsin.

[b] State practice is to advertise sales at a minimum rate of 85 percent of appraised value.

Line derivation; 1 to 8 and 11 given, 9 = 7 × 8, 10 = 9 × 0.75, 12 = 10 × 11.

establish a practical range of conditions encountered. The person selling the timber has the responsibility of adjusting the factors to fit specific conditions.

The method requires much background information regarding logging conditions, timber marketability, and quality, plus good local selling price data kept current. Having these data, application of the method is simple and systematic yet allows considerable scope for use of experience and judgment.

The practice of appraising stumpage by use of adjustment factors directly related to current selling prices is fairly generally applied, especially to small sales, by both public and private timber owners, although the detail and specific methodology varies.

The appraisal process can be further simplified, at least from the seller's standpoint, by the seller cutting the timber himself and delivering it to roadside or some other point readily accessible to buyers where the timber can be segregated by size, species, and quality if necessary. In this situation, he can rely directly on bid prices, provided there is a reasonably established and active market. The buyer does, of course, have to make some appraisal to guide his offered prices.

Another and very different direct approach, sometimes advocated, is to estimate stumpage value as a percentage of selling price of lumber or other primary products derived from the timber. This is direct and simple enough, and there is a statistical association between product selling price and stumpage. However, logging and log transportation costs particularly can vary quite independently of product selling prices. The conclusions reached by following this approach could indicate the same stumpage price for timber differing widely in production costs. Also, this approach ignores the residual nature of stumpage value in an appraisal.

ANALYTICAL METHODS

Application of analytical methods requires that the logging, processing, and marketing of timber from a particular area be analyzed in detail. There are two general methods. One is the investment method. The other is a more general approach that centers on determination of the conversion return, which is the difference between selling price and production costs, and on its division between a margin for profit and risk and stumpage.

Investment method. The investment method was developed to meet situations in which heavy investments were necessary to log and mill large bodies of timber and capital costs were a major consideration. It was applied in the United States by the U.S. Forest Service to meet a fairly common circumstance of past years, that of cutting a large body of timber for which a processing plant had to be built and extensive railroad, road, logging camp, and other development costs incurred. In recent years a straight investment approach is seldom employed except in special situations such as are found in Alaska. The distinguishing feature of the method is that the margin for profit and risk is based on the investment. Determination of the investment necessitates long, detailed, and complex calculations of total and average investment and of necessary working capital. In addition, estimates of other production costs and selling values have to be made as in any analytical appraisal. General use of the method has largely been discontinued because of (1) the difficulty of making meaningful investment and working capital requirement calculations; (2) the fact that most timber is logged using existing improvements and taken to established mills for which investment costs applicable to a particular body of timber cannot realistically be determined; (3) questions as to the logic and validity of basing a profit and risk margin exclusively on the capital investment; (4) development of the broader and more flexible conversion return analysis procedure.

For these reasons, the method will not be developed here. The subject is treated in the current Forest Service Manual (U.S. Forest Service). The most detailed presentation, although old, is given in "Instructions for Appraising Stumpage on National Forests" (U.S. Forest Service, 1922). See also Matthews (1935) and Chapman and Meyer (1947).

Division of the conversion return. The most complete analytical approach to stumpage appraisal is to determine the conversion return and then divide it between return to the buyer for profit and risk and return to the seller for stumpage. Expressed symbolically, the relationships are:

Conversion return $= R - C$
   (including M and S)

and

Stumpage value $= R - C - M$

where R = product selling value
   C = production costs including depreciation
   M = margin for profit and risk including capital costs
   S = stumpage value

Determination of an appropriate conversion return is essentially a matter of fact; questions of method depend on the knowledge, skill, and purposes of seller or buyer. Each can arrive at somewhat different results. Very obviously, an analytical approach is an interdependent system. All errors, uncertainties, or differences of opinion regarding selling values or production costs directly affect the conversion return and hence the amount available for profit and risk allowance and for stumpage.

The division of the conversion return is a competitive matter with all the forces of market price establishment coming to focus upon it. There is not nor can there by any fixed ratio or procedure for dividing the conversion return. Here is where judgment and all facets of practical business come into play. There is no single ratio any more than there is a rule to tell what rate of interest to use in investment problems. The setting of a stumpage value, either by appraisal or actual market negotiation, is an arbitrary matter, and this should frankly be recognized. Business is not an exact science, and estimation or determination of a stumpage price is a cold-blooded business matter. Application of judgment is essential.

Procedures for dividing the conversion return can be grouped into what is termed the "overturn method" and the use of certain business ratios.

OVERTURN METHOD   By the overturn method, the margin for profit and risk is calculated as a percentage of production costs exclusive of stumpage. This approach is useful when the investment is nominal, the period is short, and when the risks of the enterprise largely attach to production costs. A simple appraisal of pulpwood stumpage value in the Lake States is illustrative of its application. Estimated selling prices and production costs per cord are as follows:

Selling price of unpeeled pulpwood delivered on railroad cars at woods siding (contract price)	$18.25
Production costs:	
Fell, limb, and buck	$4.85
Skidding and draying	2.00
Loading on trucks and unloading on cars	1.62
Truck haul, woods to railhead (labor plus truck cost)	3.85
Total direct production cost	$12.32
Conversion return	$ 5.93
Margin for profit and risk at 15% of direct production cost	1.85
Indicated stumpage value	$ 4.08

In this instance, the selling price is fixed by contract and assumed not subject to risk. The pulpwood is hauled over existing roads; therefore, no investment in roads is necessary. A power saw and hand tools only are involved in cutting, and their investment cost is relatively small. Trucking costs are fairly well standardized for such operations. The pulpwood operator is assumed to work as a member of the crew and gives direct supervision. The margin of $1.85 per cord represents the return to the operator for his initiative, responsibility, and effort and also serves as an allowance to cover noncalculable risks such as bad weather, accidents, and the like. There is no formula for determining whether the allowance is fair and reasonable or not. This is a matter to be decided on the basis of experience and judgment gained from similar situations.

If a public agency owned the timber and made the appraisal, the stumpage would probably be offered for sale at the indicated price. Under competition, a higher price might be obtained, but unless an operator could get the wood out at less than estimated cost, the higher price would necessarily mean a reduced margin for profit and risk. If a prospective buyer made the appraisal, the margin would be based on what he felt was needed to make a reasonable return on the job, and the indicated stumpage price would indicate about how much he was willing to pay. A lower price would mean more profit and margin for risk and naturally would be preferred.

Applied in this instance, the overturn method is a reasonable approach, simple and straightforward, and is widely applied in appraisals of this nature. In more complex situations, however, the method has weaknesses which should be pointed out.

Calculating the margin on production costs only ignores selling price, which may be a major source of risk and uncertainty in an appraisal. In the above illustration, the selling price was fixed by contract and not subject to risk. If, however, sawlogs are cut and made into lumber sold on the open market, lumber prices may change from those estimated in the ap-

TABLE 18.2. ILLUSTRATION OF OVERTURN METHOD WITH
        DIFFERENT SELLING PRICES
        (PER THOUSAND BOARD FEET)

	Tract A	Tract B
Selling value......................	$90.00	$65.00
Total production cost................	45.00	45.00
Conversion return..................	$45.00	$20.00
Margin at 15% of cost..............	6.75	6.75
Indicated stumpage.................	$38.25	$13.25
Total cost to producer (cost plus stumpage)..	$83.25	$58.25
Margin on total cost................	8%	12%

praisal and be a major source of risk. The point can be illustrated by a simple example. Consider two tracts of sawtimber trees having the same production costs but different product selling prices (Table 18.2), which naturally affect stumpage values—a cost to the producer. It is hard to justify the higher margin on total cost (production cost plus stumpage) given for Tract B, as compared to Tract A.

For these reasons, the overturn method is limited to appraisals in which production costs are in fact the major variable and source of risk and therefore a reasonable basis for determining the margin for profit and risk. Used in other situations, the valuation basis is unsound and can lead to erratic and inequitable stumpage value estimates.

USE OF BUSINESS RATIOS   Use of certain commonly used business ratios, guided by judgment, is the most comprehensive and flexible method of dividing the conversion return. Three interrelated ratios are commonly recognized and are defined as follows: [1]

R = product selling value
C = production costs, including depreciation
M = margin for profit and risk, including capital costs
S = stumpage value
P = profit ratio
O = operating ratio
Q = selling value ratio or return to sales

1. *Profit Ratio.* This is the margin for profit and risk divided by production costs plus stumpage, or $P = M/(C + S)$ and consequently

[1] A valuation factor or ratio determined by dividing stumpage by the conversion return is sometimes recognized and used. While such a factor has some attraction because of its simplicity, it does not rest on any sound valuation basis. There is no consistent reason why stumpage should be any particular proportion of the conversion return.

$M = P(C + S)$. Because it includes stumpage, the ratio also measures the effect of selling price. This is evidenced by the fact that, by substitution and algebraic manipulation,[1] M can be expressed in terms of selling value (R) and P as follows:

$$M = \frac{PR}{1 + P}$$

Also $P = \dfrac{M}{R - M}$

The first equation is particularly useful, for it permits direct calculation of the margin for profit and risk from an assumed profit ratio and a given selling value without first defining stumpage, which is the residual value to be determined. Once this margin is known, stumpage value is obtained by subtracting it from the conversion return.

   2. *Selling Value Ratio.* This is the margin for profit and risk divided by the selling value. Thus:

$$Q = \frac{M}{R} \quad \text{or} \quad M = QR$$

Also $Q = \dfrac{P}{1 + P}$

The selling value ratio expresses a significant relationship useful in making comparisons. Data for its computation are readily available, because in income statements gross sales R and net earnings M before income taxes are given, and production costs do not have to be analyzed. The margin can also be directly determined without assuming a stumpage value by the relationship $M = QR$.

   3. *Operating Ratio.* This is production costs divided by selling value, or $O = (C + S)/R$. This ratio shows how many cents of the sales dollar go for costs. The margin for profit and risk in terms of the operating ratio is $M = P(1 - 0)$.

   In application, the margin for profit and risk, and consequently the indicated stumpage value, is usually computed from an assumed profit or selling value ratio. A numerical illustration will make the relationships clear.

----

[1] The derivation is as follows:

By definition

$$P = \frac{M}{C + S} \quad \text{and} \quad S = R - C - M$$

Substituting for S,

$$P = \frac{M}{C + R - C - M} = \frac{M}{R - M}$$

Then

$$M = PR - PM \quad \text{and} \quad M + PM = PR$$

Consequently

$$M(1 + P) = PR \quad \text{and} \quad M = \frac{PR}{1 + P}$$

assume a product selling value R of \$65 and production costs C of \$45. assuming a 12 percent profit ratio

$$M = \frac{PR}{1+P} = \frac{0.12(\$65)}{1+0.12} = \frac{\$7.80}{1.12} = \$6.96$$

ince the conversion margin is \$65 — \$45, or \$20, the indicated stumpage alue is \$20 — \$6.96, or \$13.04.[1] The corresponding selling value ratio $Q = M/R = \$6.96/\$65 = 0.1071$. Starting from an assumed selling ratio f 0.1071 (using the same figures for comparison), $M = QR = 0.1071$ (\$65) = \$6.96 as before.

In appraisal practice, the profit ratio is usually used because of its onvenience in appraisal work as explained above. The selling ratio is faored by economists, since it can more accurately and readily be derived rom business data and because profits basically flow from sales and are ot a consequence of costs (Weintraub, 1958). In practice, it makes no lifference which is used, since one can be directly derived from the other s demonstrated above. Profit ratios provide a direct means of cutting the Jordian knot of dividing the conversion return between profit and risk and tumpage. With a conversion return figure, as is developed in a full analytial appraisal, use of a profit ratio gives an immediate answer and directly ocuses attention on the economics of the problem. The question becomes: Vhat is an equitable profit ratio?

Answers to this question are not simple. Analysis of gross profit ratios, s given by Weintraub (1958), shows that they vary significantly between inds of businesses and for a number of reasons. Available data indicate nuch variation within the lumber and pulp and paper group as a whole, s would be expected. Nonetheless, there is considerable internal consistency vithin certain classes of businesses in this group as is true in others. It s clear that a single profit ratio cannot be used for the timber industry s a whole and further that it must be changed with business conditions.

At this point, it is well to examine just what is included in the margin or profit and risk; it is rather a conglomerate. It measures gross income efore income taxes and includes not only these but also entrepreneurial rofit to the operator, return on invested capital, and an allowance for oninsurable business risks. In studying timber appraisals made by the U.S. orest Service, the Worrell Committee (U.S. Forest Service, 1963) suggested that it would be helpful to divide the margin into two parts, (1) n average and fairly stable figure to maintain an operator of average effiiency over the long term and (2) an allowance for noninsurable risk. The atter figure can be varied for specific timber appraisals in accordance with udgment as to the particular risks involved. Such a practice is followed y the British Columbia Forest Service.

---

[1] Stumpage may also directly be calculated by the formula

$$S = \frac{R}{1+P} - C$$

The U.S. Forest Service, which makes extensive use of profit ratio in connection with timber appraisals, sets profit ratios on the basis of market value evidence, experience, and judgment. The ratios vary by forest region and often by species in the same appraisal. They can also vary by individual appraisals on the basis of estimated risks, unusual capital costs, or other considerations. The aim is to use them as guides, aided by judgment, in making an equitable division of the conversion margin.

sample appraisal

With the general nature and methods of stumpage appraisal in mind, it will be helpful to consider a specific example. The following is taken from a timber sale report and appraisal made by the U.S. Forest Service in the Douglas-fir area of the Pacific Northwest. It is illustrative of an analytical appraisal of selling value and production costs leading to the development of the conversion margin and its division between profit and risk and stumpage.

No one appraisal can exemplify all appraisal problems, although this example includes a good cross section. The forest situation naturally varies from area to area and by forest types and regions. Specific appraisal techniques also vary by appraising agencies. Although this example is made by the seller, a similar appraisal could be made by the buyer to guide his offering price.

GENERAL INFORMATION

AREA AND PURPOSE OF CUTTING   The cutting area includes 498 acres in 11 separate units plus 47 acres in road right-of-way clearing made outside the cutting units to give access to them. The timber is overmature Douglas-fir and mixed conifers. The cutting follows the management plan for the general area and is aimed to clearcut the 11 units, although some patches of natural reproduction are saved. The period of cutting is estimated to cover four full operating seasons which normally run from May 1 to October 31.

INVENTORY   The area was cruised by log grades estimated in the standing tree. The standard error of the mean is estimated at ±5.8 percent of the mean with a coefficient of variation of 51 percent. The estimated volumes to be cut (in thousands of board feet) are:

Douglas-fir............................	12,400
Pines (mostly western white pine)........	1,900
Shasta red fir and Noble fir..............	4,500
Hemlocks and other conifers.............	5,200
	24,000

The average volume per acre, all species, is 48.25 M bd ft.

LOGGING AND PROCESSING   The topography is rather rough and steep requiring some care to prevent erosion. Approximately 321 acres must be cable-logged. Approximately 177 acres may be tractor-logged under dry-soil conditions, which will help to save clumps of young timber.

Following a careful analysis of alternatives, the tract is appraised for timber

TABLE 18.3. SELLING VALUE AND MANUFACTURING COSTS
(M FEET LOG SCALE)

Item	Doug-las-fir	Pines	Shasta and red fir	Hem-lock and others	Total (weighted)
Selling value:					
Lumber and veneer.....	$108.19	$129.51	$ 98.30	$ 86.57	$103.34
Chips and peeler cores..	1.65	0	3.35	3.35	2.21
Total..............	$109.84	$129.51	$101.65	$89.92	$105.55
Manufacturing cost......	$ 38.54	$ 45.21	$ 46.07	$37.20	$ 40.18

processing by the mills in Roseburg, Oregon. This is an important matter; realism in selecting a proper point of appraisal is a key consideration.

To log the timber, it will be required that the operator construct 5.3 miles of Huge Butte Road, 1.3 miles of Lava Creek Road, and 0.8 miles of Upper Loafer Creek Road to specified Forest Service utilization road standards.

SELLING VALUES AND MANUFACTURING COSTS

Selling values and manufacturing costs were estimated from data collected by the Forest Service. The job was done by the species groups shown by log-grade volumes as estimated in the cruise. Peeler or veneer logs and sawlogs were estimated separately by log grades and weighted by volume. The results per M are given in Table 18.3.

LOGGING COSTS

Logging costs were estimated for all species together on the basis of costs and adjusted from average data for the region collected by the Forest Service. All are in log scale.

Stump to truck   Cost per M

Felling and bucking (including snag falling $0.30)........... $ 3.35
Yarding and skidding (including spur roads)............... 5.95
Loading on trucks.................................... 1.55

Total... $10.85

Log transportation

Logs are hauled an average of 79.1 miles to Roseburg. Cost based on detailed estimates by road classification and distance with allowance for defect (defective logs cost as much to haul as sound ones) and necessary log handling. Cost per M...... $17.59

Road maintenance. Detailed estimate of necessary road maintenance, rock crushing and spreading, and related costs to be incurred by the operator......................... $ 1.80

Total log transportation cost per M........................... $19.39

Administrative costs (based on general experience data)

General logging overhead............................... $2.52
Depreciation... 1.13

Total cost per M... $ 3.6~

Contractual costs

Slash disposal. Mostly done by the Forest Service and based
on detailed estimate of total costs of work to be done........ $1.11
Erosion control. Seeding of road-cut banks and fill slopes..... 0.08
Fire protection—special costs........................... 0.17

Total contractual costs per M.................................. $ 1.3~

Total logging costs (excluding roads) per M........................... $35.2~

UTILIZATION ROAD CONSTRUCTION

The cost of constructing necessary roads is often a substantial part of the total
logging cost necessary to get out the timber. In this appraisal, a total of 7.4 miles

TABLE 18.4. APPORTIONMENT OF ROAD CONSTRUCTION COSTS
BY SPECIES GROUPS

Line	Item	Douglas-fir	Pines	Shasta and red fir	Hemlock and other conifers	Totals
1	Volume, M bd ft.......	12,400	1,900	4,500	5,200	24,000
2	Selling value, per M....	$109.84	$129.51	$101.65	$89.92	
3	Manufacturing and logging, per M..........	$ 73.79	$ 80.46	$ 81.32	$72.45	
4	Conversion value without roads............	$ 36.05	$ 49.05	$ 20.33	$ 17.47	
5	Profit margin, per M...	$ 11.77	$ 13.88	$ 10.89	$ 9.63	
6	Indicated stumpage without roads........	$ 24.28	$ 35.17	$ 9.44	$ 7.84	
7	Minimum stumpage rates...............	$ 3.00	$ 3.00	$ 2.00	$ 2.00	
8	Net stumpage apportionment base, per M..	$ 21.28	$ 32.17	$ 7.44	$ 5.84	
9	Total net stumpage value...............	$263,872	$61,123	$33,480	$30,368	$388,843
10	Percent by species.....	67.86	15.72	8.61	7.81	100.0
11	Prorated road costs....	$71,602	$16,587	$ 9,085	$ 8,241	$105,515
12	Road cost per M.......	$5.77	$8.73	$2.02	$1.59	$4.40

Derivation by line numbers: 4 = 2 − 3; 5 calculated from profit ratio of 0.12 (see
text p. 399); 6 = 4 − 5; 7 set by Forest Service; 8 = 6 − 7; 9 = 1 × 8; 11 =
$105,515 × species group percentages (line 10); 12 = 11 ÷ 1.

of road is to be built by the operator to Forest Service standards. This necessitates that detailed road engineering specifications, with cost estimates, be prepared by the Forest Service as a part of the appraisal, which, when the timber is sold, become a part of the sale contract. The detail of the estimates cannot be given here. The total estimated cost of the roads is $105,515, which, divided by the total volume to be cut of 24,000 M, gives an average cost per M of $4.40.

The next job is to apportion this cost by species groups.[1] This was done in this case on the basis of total value by these groups as measured by their total indicated stumpage value exclusive of road costs. This was done in this appraisal except that the minimum stumpage rates the Forest Service sets were arbitrarily subtracted and the road cost prorated on the balance. The procedure followed in the appraisal is given in Table 18.4.

APPRAISAL SUMMARY

The different parts of the appraisal are brought together in Table 18.5 giving the conversion return (line 7). A profit ratio of 0.12 was assumed for all species and the margin for profit and risk and indicated stumpage value calculated as shown. The profit ratio could vary by species, if it is adjudged that there are significant differences between them. Logging costs are estimated as the same for all species, for they are handled together in this instance. In other situations they could be different, for example, in an operation where pulpwood or poles were logged, handled, and sold separately. In this instance, the indicated stumpage value includes an allowance for needed stand improvement work under the Knutsen-Vandenberg Act (K-V money), but it does not affect the appraisal process and is not segregated here.

Total values are shown to give a better picture of the financial magnitude of the operation as a whole, which unit values per M do not. They will be discussed later as will the adjusted amortization of the road construction costs given in the lower part of Table 18.5.

With the completion of the appraisal, the next job is to sell (or buy) the timber. This involves seller-buyer negotiation in setting the actual price and in coming to agreement on various conditions of logging, utilization, scaling, mode of payment, etc. A sale contract is drawn up specifying these conditions. The relative strength of seller and buyer varies with circumstances in these matters. In sale of public timber, the buyer may have little option on sale contract provisions; in some situations, a good deal. However these matters may be arranged, the seller does the necessary on-the-ground preparation for cutting, such as designating the sale area, trees to be cut, and road locations if these are specified. He also supervises the cutting and logging operations as regards contract provisions.

Exactly how the contract is written and the sale administered are matters of large importance and often complexity, but they cannot be treated here. Essentially, they concern administration rather than the principles and methods of appraisal, which are the focus here.

[1] This is a joint cost situation since the roads serve all species. Road construction standards and costs do not differ on account of individual species. Allocation of such costs by species can only be done arbitrarily but is necessary here because stumpage values by species or species groups are needed for practical purposes. Allocation by species value is a reasonable basis in this situation since the overall objective is to get timber on the market recognizing species value differentials.

TABLE 18.5. APPRAISAL SUMMARY (LOG SCALE)

Line	Item	Per M board feet					Total[a]				
		Douglas-fir	Pines	Shasta and Noble fir	Hemlock and other conifers	Total all species (weighted)	Douglas-fir	Pines	Shasta and Noble fir	Hemlock and other conifers	All species
1	Volume to cut, M bd ft	12,400	1,900	4,500	5,200	24,000	12,400	1,900	4,500	5,200	24,000
2	Selling value	$109.84	$129.51	$101.65	$89.92	$105.55	$1,362,016	$246,069	$457,425	$467,564	$2,533,074
3	Manufacturing costs	$38.54	45.21	46.07	37.20	40.18	477,896	85,899	207,315	193,440	964,550
4	Logging costs	35.25	35.25	35.25	35.25	35.25	437,100	66,975	158,625	183,300	846,000
5	Road construction costs	$ 5.77	8.73	2.02	1.59	4.40	71,548	16,587	9,000	8,268	105,515[b]
6	Total production costs	$ 79.56	$ 89.19	$ 83.34	$74.04	$ 79.83	$ 986,544	$169,461	$375,030	$385,008	$1,916,065
7	Conversion return	$30.28	$40.32	$18.31	$15.88	$25.72	$375,472	$76,608	$82,395	$82,576	$617,051
8	Profit ratio	0.12	0.12	0.12	0.12	0.12					
9	Margin for profit and risk	$11.77	$13.88	$10.89	$9.63	$11.31	$145,948	$26,372	$49,005	$50,076	$271,401
10	Indicated stumpage value	$18.51	$26.44	$7.42	$6.25	$14.41	$229,524	$50,236	$33,390	$32,500	$345,650

Adjustment for amortization of roads on 80% of volume

Line	Item										
11	Adjusted road cost	$ 7.22	$10.91	$ 2.52	$ 1.98	$ 5.50					
12	Adjusted conversion return	$28.83	$38.14	$17.81	$15.49	$24.62					
13	Margin for profit and risk	$11.77	$13.88	$10.89	$ 9.63	$11.31					
14	Adjusted stumpage value	$17.06	$24.26	$10.89	$ 5.86	$13.31					

[a] Slight discrepancies in some figures due to rounding of species unit values.

[b] From appraisal estimate.

Derivation by line numbers: 1 from cruise; 2, 3, and 4 from appraisal estimates; 5 from line 12, Table 18.4; 6 = 3 + 4 + 5; 7 = 2 − 6; 8 assumed; 9 computed on basis of profit ratio in line 8 as illustrated p. 200; 10 = 7 ...

special appraisal problems

The preceding presentation of stumpage appraisal methods should make clear the point that there is no standard method applicable to all situations. This applies to both direct and analytical methods. The latter, which requires analysis of all relevant selling prices and related production costs leading to determination of the conversion return and its division, is the more basic and certainly the more difficult approach. It gives the specific information from which a seller or a buyer can base judgment as to what a particular supply of stumpage is worth as a guide in price establishment.

There are a number of more or less special problems of appraisal that should be considered. Six are discussed here with particular reference to analytical appraisals.

EFFECT OF INACCURACIES IN SELLING VALUES AND PRODUCTION COSTS

Because an analytical appraisal is an interdependent system, all inaccuracies in selling values and production costs are reflected and relatively magnified in the indicated stumpage value. This is illustrated in Table 18.6 using some assumed selling value and cost data. As shown, a 10 percent increase in selling values increases the stumpage value 44 percent, and the same percentage increase in production costs decreases stumpage 35 percent. The margin for profit and risk is affected only by changes in selling values (see p. 398).

TABLE **18.6.** EFFECT OF DIFFERENCES IN PRODUCTION
COSTS ON STUMPAGE VALUE

Item	Appraisal data	10 percent plus difference in selling value	10 percent plus difference in cost
Selling value....................	$65.00	$71.50	$65.00
Production cost..................	45.00	45.00	49.50
Conversion return...............	$20.00	$26.50	$15.50
Margin for profit and risk with 12% profit ratio....................	6.96	7.66	6.96
Indicated stumpage..............	$13.04	$18.84	$ 8.54
Total difference in dollars.........	0	5.80	−4.50
Difference as percent of appraisal data.........................	...	44	−35

This interdependence within the appraisal system naturally places much emphasis on accuracy in selling value and cost determination. Because any stumpage value desired can be obtained by juggling the profit ratio, there is sometimes a temptation to use it to correct for known or suspected inaccuracies in the appraisal estimates. This should not be done. The profit ratio is not an adjustment factor and has economic validity only when it is selected and used to give a fair margin for profit and risk in view of the actual circumstances of the situation. Stumpage is then properly a residual.

It should also be noted that when a stumpage price is fixed by appraisal or otherwise and there is no question about the validity of costs and selling values, the margin for profit and risk becomes the residual value.

EFFECT OF TIMBER VOLUME ESTIMATES ON UNIT COSTS DERIVED FROM GENERAL COSTS

In making an appraisal, costs are normally expressed in unit terms, as so much per M bd ft, per cubic foot, per cord, or similar units. This offers no difficulty with direct costs, which are incurred only if a particular tree or log is cut or handled. General costs, those that are incurred whether or not a particular volume is handled, are in a different category.[1] Unit costs based on costs of this type are affected by the volume actually cut. The road construction item in the sample appraisal is a good case in point. Here, a total of $105,515 is estimated for construction of utilization roads to make the timber accessible. Most of these roads have to be built before any of the timber can be removed from the forest. The average cost per M of $4.40 allowed in the appraisal was determined by dividing the estimated road cost by the estimated total volume of 24,000 M bd ft. If this volume is actually cut and the road cost estimate is correct, there is no problem. As is well known, however, timber volume estimates and road construction costs may be high or low for a variety of reasons.

Assume, for example, that the road cost estimate is correct but that 15 percent more timber is actually cut during the sale period (4 years in this instance). The volume is consequently 24,000 × 1.15, or 27,600 M. At $4.40 per M, this means that $121,440 is allowed to the buyer for building the road, whereas the actual cost of the road is estimated at $105,515. The difference, $15,925, goes to the buyer as a potential addition to profit. The situation would be reversed if the sale undercut the estimate or the road cost more than expected.

In an attempt to meet this situation, the U.S. Forest Service often amortizes road costs against a part of the timber estimated to be cut in the appraisal; 80 percent of it is a common figure. This was done in the sample appraisal. All volumes were reduced 20 percent and the total road

---

[1] See p. 412 for a discussion of cost classification.

cost of $105,515 was prorated by species and unit costs determined following the procedure shown in Table 18.4. The results are shown in lines 11–14 of Table 18.5, and the timber was advertised for sale, with proper explanation, at the adjusted stumpage value (line 14). After the road cost has been amortized by cutting 80 percent of the estimated volume, the stumpage rate will be increased by the adjusted road cost per M (line 11) for the balance of the cutting, because a road cost is no longer included.[1]

The purpose of this adjustment is to protect both buyer and seller against variations between timber estimate and the amount cut. By initially reducing the stumpage rate, it gives the buyer increased working capital to finance road construction. Acceleration of road amortization could be increased beyond the 80 percent used here. One could go to 100 percent as has been suggested (U.S. Forest Service, 1963). The most direct and clear way to implement maximum acceleration is to make the appraisal without including the cost of permanent utilization road costs at all. The buyer is then credited in his stumpage account for timber cut until the amount equals the estimated road construction cost. Beginning at this time, the stipulated stumpage price is paid on the balance of the timber.

General costs are affected by the accuracy of the timber volume estimate in other ways too. Some of these costs, such as general administration, taxes, insurance, and fire protection are essentially controlled by time, as by the month or year. They are also shown in the appraisal as a cost per unit of estimated volume of timber to be cut. If the volume estimate is either high or low but the timber can be cut in about the same total period of time, the total amount of these general costs remains about the same. Consequently, if the volume cut is above the estimate, the buyer gains since his unit costs are reduced in relation to those allowed in the appraisal. If the volume cut is below the estimate, his unit costs increase, and he loses, insofar as general cost estimates are concerned.

If the length of the cutting operation is extended or shortened because of error in timber estimate or for other reasons, general costs controlled by time are likewise affected, but the relationships are not simple and the actual effect on each cost item should individually be scrutinized. Some direct costs would also be affected, as in the case of bad weather or breakdowns. The margin for profit and risk includes a general allowance for contingencies, but it should be reiterated that the profit ratio is not to be used to adjust for known or suspected errors in either selling values or production costs.

The central point of this discussion is that general costs must be con-

---

[1] How this works out can readily be demonstrated. In Table 18.5 (line 10) the indicated average stumpage value is $14.41, including a $4.40 road cost. Without the road cost the stumpage would be $18.81 (the margin for profit and risk would not change). The adjusted stumpage value (line 14) is $13.31, and this increased by the adjusted road cost of $5.50 (line 11) also equals $18.81.

sidered in relation to the total volume cut. Errors in either will affect, although in different ways, the accuracy of unit costs used in appraisal.

USE OF MARKET AND BIDDING EVIDENCE

Because the evidence of the market place is the final judge of validity, it is logical and natural to use it in appraisal. With direct methods of stumpage appraisal, the use of market evidence is straightforward and relatively simple. Appraised stumpage prices are based on market values adjusted for the particular situation. Competitive bidding or direct negotiation between a buyer and a seller determines the actual price.

In the case of analytical appraisals, the situation is more complex and there is a problem in how to use actual transaction evidence fairly and effectively. If an analytical appraisal is to be made at all, the work must be done thoroughly and consistently, letting the answer, regarding indicated stumpage, come out as it will. If an appraisal is made with a preconceived notion of what the stumpage price should be (and any appraiser knows that the indicated stumpage value can be made to conform) there is no real purpose in doing the job—except, perhaps, to execute some prescribed procedure. It is also clear that any analytical appraisal, made by either seller or buyer, is necessarily based on assumptions about levels of production costs, selling values, and profit ratios that are based on certain producers or groups of producers. How then can transaction and bid evidence be used?

The answer depends primarily on market conditions, the way in which the stumpage is offered for sale, the situation of individual buyers, and conditions of sale. There are these four major points to consider. First, regarding market conditions, stumpage is by its nature a commodity of fixed geographic location. The actual number of buyers or sellers concerned with stumpage sales in a particular area, consequently, may be few, and one cannot assume the convention of a free and open market. Consider, for example, the not infrequent situation in which the Federal government, a state, or a large corporation owns the timber upon which a certain buyer is dependent for his livelihood. Under such circumstances there is not free competition for a particular tract. If there are two or three possible buyers, there can be competition among them but not between sellers.

The second point concerns how the stumpage is offered for sale. In the case of many public agencies, the U.S. Forest Service, for example, it is offered for sale at not less than an appraised price, which is designed to estimate a fair market value for buyers of average efficiency (a difficult thing to determine). Lower bids, that otherwise might have been made, are therefore excluded, and such bidding is consequently not representative of an open market.

Third, individual buyers may, for various reasons, bid more than the appraised price and often do. Such reasons include greater than average efficiency and consequently lower costs, ability to get higher product selling values than estimated, particular need for timber to keep a mill operating, strategic considerations to suppress competition, and other business reasons. The operator may also be in error regarding his cost and return situation.

If production costs and selling values are considered equitable in a given situation, then the conversion return is also fixed by definition. If prospective buyers of the stumpage bid over the appraised value, it is obvious that a smaller part of the conversion return goes for profit and risk, and the indicated profit ratio is consequently reduced. Application of profit ratios so derived from bid evidence to appraisal of generally similar timber consequently reduces the profit ratio and increases the indicated stumpage value. In effect, this means basing appraised stumpage values on the higher bidders, whose situation is better than that assumed in the appraisal, which is designed for average operators. It cannot be assumed that these higher bidders are accepting a lower margin for profit and risk, although this could be true.

A simple example will be helpful. Assume a selling value (R) of $100, a conversion return of $30, and a profit ratio (P) of 12 percent. The margin for profit and risk (M) is then $PR/(1 + P) = 0.12(100)/1.12 = \$10.71$. The indicated stumpage price is accordingly $30 — 10.71, or $19.29. Assume a bid of $24 for the stumpage, which indicates a margin for profit and risk of $30 — 24, or $6. Solving the above formula for P and using the same appraisal data gives $P = M/(R — M) = 6/(100 — 6) = 0.0638$, or 6.38 percent instead of the 12 percent used in the appraisal.

The general result of applying profit ratios so derived from bid evidence to other appraisals of generally comparable timber is accordingly to reduce the profit ratio and profit margin and consequently to increase stumpage. Basing adjustment of the profit ratio on the median of bids made above appraised price is less extreme than using only the highest bid, but the trend is the same; full market evidence as obtained by bidding is not included.

There are no simple answers to this problem. If appraised prices are consistently overbid, then a question is certainly raised concerning the validity of the appraisal as a guide to a fair market price. Costs and selling values should be reconsidered as well as the profit ratio. In any event, it is clear that bid evidence, although certainly significant, must be used with care and discretion; an admixtire of judgment is inescapable. The market, as always, is the final arbiter of actual price, but how the market operates must be considered.

Fourth, and as has been previously mentioned, conditions of sale as specified in the cutting agreement may have an effect on stumpage prices not fully reflected in the appraisal. In the sample appraisal given, the operator is required to build some utilization roads at substantial cost. In extreme cases in the Pacific Northwest, a stumpage buyer may be as much a road builder as a logger. Other conditions of sale regarding how the timber is to be cut or utilized may also make a significant difference to the buyer, for example, differences between Federal, state, and private stumpage sources.

DIFFERENCES IN SPECIES VALUES

In many situations, the timber offered for sale is composed of several species of quite different value. How to handle these differences, where all species should be cut together, is a recurrent problem. Where species are cut into different products, as some for pulpwood and some for sawtimber, and these products are cut and handled separately, logging costs can be segregated. If such is not the case, segregation is difficult, and they may all have to be lumped, as was done in the sample appraisal given, even though some logging cost differences may exist. Manufacturing costs are also often difficult to segregate by species. Selling values usually can be segregated fairly well.

A more difficult valuation problem is what to do when appraisal indicates that some species have very low or negative stumpage value but when, particularly from the standpoint of the seller as well as of the practical realities of cutting, all species should be removed.

The answer depends basically on the kind of logging costs involved and the situation of the buyer. If a species can carry all direct costs of logging and manufacture and give a positive return in comparison to selling value, it will contribute something to general costs, and ordinarily it would pay the buyer to handle it for this reason. If not, it can be cut only at a loss that someone must meet. Normally, it would be the seller who, for timber-growing reasons, would have to reduce the stumpage value of higher-value species sufficiently to carry them. In the appraisal, general as well as direct costs are added in obtaining the conversion return. To expose the real situation, costs must be segregated by kind.

Consider, for example, some data from an appraisal made in the Lake States including aspen, a species of often low stumpage value. Essential data per cord are:

Selling price		$ 13.00
General production costs	$3.75	
Direct production costs	8.72	
Total production cost		$ 12.47
Conversion return		0.53
Margin for profit and risk at 8%		1.18
Indicated stumpage		$−0.65

In this case, the aspen is sold as pulpwood to a mill and further manufacturing costs are not considered; only cutting and delivering the pulpwood to the mill is involved. General costs have been segregated and the full amount, prorated on the basis of volume, has been charged to aspen along with the other species included in the appraisal. The owner wishes to sell the aspen for timber management reasons. It is evident that the aspen contributes something to general costs, $3.75 — 0.65, or $3.10 per cord in this instance. Note that the margin for profit and risk would be unchanged by dropping out the general production cost item (see p. 398) as an assumed profit ratio is used to determine an indicated stumpage value.

What should be done? Stumpage is never sold at a negative value. One answer is to reduce the stumpage value of other higher-value species sufficiently to give the aspen some arbitrary positive value. It would be possible to do this even if the aspen could contribute nothing to general costs; in effect, the seller is partially subsidizing the cutting operation. An adjustment of this sort was made in the sample appraisal (Table 18.4 p. 402) by apportioning road costs to species on the basis of their total stumpage value figured without inclusion of road costs. The result, in this instance, was that the relatively high-value pines carried a charge of $8.73 per M as compared to $1.59 for the hemlock and other conifers group. The average road cost for all species, weighted by volume, was $4.40 per M.

Another answer, returning to the aspen example, is to offer it for sale at some nominal figure like $0.50 per cord with other stumpage values left unchanged. To the buyer, this means that the aspen would contribute $3.75 — 0.65 — 0.50, or $2.60 per cord, to general costs, but it would just about wipe out his profit and risk margin for this species, for there is a conversion margin of only $0.53, and paying $0.50 for aspen would leave only $0.03 for profit and risk. He might take the aspen at $0.50 for business reasons, particularly if it constituted a relatively small proportion of the total timber volume, but there is no getting around the fact that in this example aspen cannot carry all production costs. There is no easy answer to the problem of handling submarginal values in an appraisal; somebody has to pay.

IMPORTANCE OF TOTAL VALUES
IN AN APPRAISAL

Total values for all costs, returns, and other items are often not computed in an appraisal, except for certain items, but all are of significance—to the buyer especially. Such total values are included in the summary of the sample appraisal (Table 18.5). Unit values can sometimes conceal more than they reveal about the business aspects of an operation as a whole. For example, a margin for profit and risk estimated at $11.31 per M for all species and with different values for individual species may be less meaningful than the fact that a total of $271,401 is allowed in the appraisal. A buyer can better relate a total figure to his capital costs, whatever they may be, than unit values only. The risk element in the margin cannot be applied evenly to each log cut or unit of lumber or other products sold. The buyer must decide for himself where the real risks of the enterprise lie—in production costs or in selling values—and judge accordingly. Losses may occur independently in different phases of the operation and often in lump-sum amounts.

Similarly, acknowledging the fact that the total of all logging costs, road construction costs, and stumpage payments aggregate $54.06 per M for all species is not quite the same thing as recognizing that an estimated total of $1,297,165 will be spent for these items over the 4 years of the cutting operation. The timing, as well as the total amount of these expenditures in relation to receipts from products sold, gives the basis for estimation of working capital requirements.

appraisal when cutting to different diameter limits

To this point, stumpage appraisal has been considered from the standpoint of buying or selling a specified amount of timber which is to be cut from a certain area. The appraisal problem was to estimate what the particular body of timber was worth with no question about cutting more or less timber except the recognition that unit costs derived from general production costs are affected by inaccuracy in volume determination.

The problems considered here are the financial results of cutting to higher or lower diameter limits or of buying or selling stumpage on a per unit of volume or area basis. Such situations frequently arise in practice and are of concern to buyer and seller alike. Valuation methods applicable can be considered as an extension of appraisal procedures presented. Although considerable detail may be involved in a specific instance and specific techniques may vary, the essentials of analyzing such problems from a valuation standpoint can be simple presented. In economic language, they are an application of marginal analysis.

The key to the problem is to recognize that costs are of different kinds and must be considered separately. This point was brought out in connection with analysis of the effect of inacuracy in volume estimates on unit values derived from general costs, but a more complete discussion was delayed until now. A number of different cost classifications have been applied, and there is some confusion about them, particularly in terminology. In the following, emphasis is on the nature of the costs rather than terminology, although, for convenience in reference, specific designations are used (Matthews, 1948).

> *Direct costs* are those incurred only if a particular tree, log, bolt, board, or other unit is actually handled. These can be subdivided further into:

Class A. Costs which vary per M, per cord, or other unit according to timber size. Common examples are felling, bucking, and limbing when done with labor paid on an hourly basis.

Class B. Costs which are constant or fixed per volume unit. Skidding, loading, and hauling when done on contract rates are good examples.

General costs (often termed fixed or indirect costs) are costs incurred irrespective of whether a particular unit of timber is handled or not. They may be subdivided:

Class C. Costs fixed per unit of area. Roads, camps, and landings are good examples. These apply to an area as a whole and, once constructed, their cost is fixed in total amount whether a particular tree is cut or not.

Class D. Costs fixed per unit of time. General overhead, supervision, insurance, and the like are common examples.

It should be particularly noted that this classification is by *kind* of costs and not of specific cost items. A particular cost item often changes classification according to circumstances. To a buyer, for example, stumpage bought on a pay-as-cut basis is a Class B cost, but it becomes a Class C cost for the tract if bought on a lump-sum basis. Felling and bucking is basically a Class A cost since it is affected by tree size. However, if the work is done at a fixed contract rate in a particular situation, it becomes a Class B cost to the producer. The same is true of skidding, loading, hauling, and sawmilling costs. The same cost may also change classification when internal cost relationships are considered. Felling is ordinarily considered a direct cost. But in analyzing utilization of the felled products of a tree, it becomes a general cost since it is applied to the tree as a whole and is incurred whether certain logs in it are utilized or not. The actual circumstances and not the name of the cost determine its classification.

TABLE 18.7. PULPWOOD STAND PER ACRE

Dbh class, in.	Volume, cords	Cumulative volume, cords	Bolts per cord, number	Bolts per dbh class, number	Cumulative bolts by dbh classes, number
4	2	18	100	200	835
6	3	16	75	225	635
8	5	13	50	250	410
10	4	8	25	100	160
12+	4	4	15	60	60
Total..	18	...	...	835	

The effect of cost classification on stumpage values and financial alternatives can best be illustrated in terms of specific examples, following in general a pulpwood analysis developed by Matthews (1948). Table 18.7 gives the average stand per acre of a tract available for cutting. The following costs are assumed:

Class A: cut, peel, and skid........................ $ 0.15 per bolt[1]
Class B: load, haul, and other unit volume costs..... 6.40 per cord
Class C and D: roads and overhead costs............ 12.00 per acre
Selling price of pulpwood at mill.................. $16.85 per cord

APPRAISAL TO DETERMINE MAXIMUM STUMPAGE VALUES PER CORD AND PER ACRE

A first problem is to determine which diameter classes should be cut, from the seller's standpoint, to give the maximum conversion return per cord or per acre. This can be done by appraising the timber when cutting to different diameter limits, as follows (refer to Table 18.7):

---

[1] Piece rates by bolts are commonly employed in some areas. Strictly, the price per bolt should vary somewhat with size. The size range is comparatively small in most pulpwood stands, however, and differential costs are omitted here in the interest of simplicity. Their inclusion would accent diameter class value differentials but would not change any basic relationships.

1. Cut all trees 4 in. dbh and larger   Per cord
   Selling price. $16.85

   Class A cost. . . . . $\dfrac{835 \times \$0.15}{18} = \$6.96$

   Class B cost. 6.40
   Class C and D costs $12/18. . . . . 0.67
   Total production costs. 14.03
   Conversion return. . . . . $ 2.82

2. Cut all trees 6 in. dbh and larger
   Selling price. $16.85

   Class A cost. . . . . $\dfrac{635 \times \$0.15}{16} = \$5.95$

   Class B cost. 6.40
   Class C and D costs $12/16. . . . . 0.75
   Total production cost. 13.10
   Conversion return. . . . . $ 3.75

3. Cut all trees 8 in. dbh and larger
   Selling price. $16.85

   Class A cost. . . . . $\dfrac{410 \times \$0.15}{13} = \$4.73$

   Class B cost. 6.40
   Class C and D costs $12/13. . . . . 0.92
   Total production cost. 12.05
   Conversion return. . . . . $ 4.80

4. Cut all trees 10 in. dbh and larger
   Selling price. $16.85

   Class A cost. . . . . $\dfrac{160 \times \$0.15}{8} = \$3.00$

   Class B cost. 6.40
   Class C and D costs $12/8. . . . . 1.50
   Total production cost. 10.90
   Conversion return. . . . . $ 5.95

5. Cut all trees 12 in. dbh and larger
   Selling price. $16.85

   Class A cost. . . . . $\dfrac{60 \times \$0.15}{4} = \$2.25$

   Class B cost. 6.40
   Class C and D costs $12/4. . . . . 3.00
   Total production cost. 11.65
   Conversion return. . . . . $ 5.20

If the margin for profit and risk is determined by a profit ratio approach, as seems logical here, it will give a constant amount per cord, regardless of diameter cutting limit. Assuming 0.10 as an equitable ratio, the margin for profit and risk would be (following the formula given on p. 398)

$$\text{Margin} = \frac{0.10(16.85)}{1 + 0.10} = \$1.53 \text{ per cord}$$

These calculations are summarized in Table 18.8 giving the stumpage return per cord and per acre under the conditions assumed. As shown, the highest conversion return and stumpage value per cord occurs when cutting trees 10 in. dbh and larger, but the highest return per acre comes at the 8-in. limit. An owner wishing to get the greatest return per acre would consequently sell all trees 8 in. and larger. If, however, he wanted to get the greatest return per cord, he would dispose of trees 10 in. and larger only.

APPRAISAL ASSUMING FIXED STUMPAGE VALUES PER CORD OR PER ACRE

To a buyer of stumpage paying a fixed price per cord or for the timber on a tract as a whole, the situation is reversed, and the problem is to determine the most profitable diameter limit as measured by the margin for profit and risk, with the stumpage price already determined. Assume that a buyer agrees to pay $2 per cord for the stumpage but no lower diameter limit is specified. To him, consequently, stumpage becomes a Class B cost since it is fixed per unit of volume. His situation is then:

Selling price, per cord...$16.85
Class B cost, including stumpage................................ 8.40
Margin available to cover A, C, and D costs, and profit and risk, per

cord.. $ 8.45

Analyzing Class A costs by dbh classes separately:

4-in. trees have 100 bolts per cord and consequently cost 100 × $0.15, or $15.00 per cord, to cut. Obviously, he cannot afford to take them, since they will not cover even the direct cost.

TABLE 18.8. STUMPAGE VALUE PER CORD AND PER ACRE
WHEN CUTTING TO DIFFERENT DIAMETER LIMITS

Lower dbh cutting limit	Conversion return per cord	Margin for profit and risk	Stumpage value per cord	Volume cut per acre, cords	Total stumpage value per acre
4	$2.82	$1.53	$1.29	18	$23.22
6	3.75	1.53	2.22	16	35.52
8	4.80	1.53	3.27	13	42.51
10	5.95	1.53	4.42	8	35.36
12	5.20	1.53	3.67	4	14.68

6-in. trees cost 75 × $0.15, or $11.25 per cord, which still will not cover the direct cost.

8-in. trees cost 50 × $0.15, or $7.50 per cord, which will cover direct cost and contribute something to C and D costs, which will be incurred if the area is logged at all.

Eight-inch trees are consequently the smallest that can be cut and contribute to direct costs. This defines the minimum diameter limit if the objective is to get the greatest return per acre, since 8-in. trees give something to the general costs which will be incurred if the area is logged at all. It is not necessarily the desirable diameter limit if the objective is to get the greatest return per unit of volume. This limit may be and usually is higher depending on cost-volume relationships of the particular situation.

These relationships are brought out in Table 18.9, which summarizes the results of appraising to various diameter limits with stumpage regarded as a fixed cost per cord. As shown, cutting to the 8-in. limit gives the largest margin per acre, while the largest margin per cord and profit ratio occurs at 10-in. If the buyer could get plenty of timber, he would naturally prefer to cut down to 10 in. only at the stumpage price set. He should, as it gives him the highest profit ratio. If timber were scarce and he wanted to get the greatest dollar return from a particular area, he would cut to an 8-in. limit, since trees of this size will cover their direct costs and contribute something to general costs. He cannot cut 6-in. or smaller trees except at an actual loss.

Another situation to consider is the common one of lump-sum sales. That is, all timber of merchantable size designated for cutting on an area

TABLE **18.9.** MARGIN FOR PROFIT AND RISK WHEN CUTTING TO DIFFERENT DIAMETER LIMITS WITH STUMPAGE PRICES FIXED PER CORD

Item	Lower diameter cutting limits, in.			
	6	8	10	12
Per cord:				
Selling price......................	$16.85	$16.85	$16.85	$16.85
Class A costs.....................	5.95	4.73	3.00	2.25
Class B costs including stumpage....	8.40	8.40	8.40	8.40
Class C and D costs..............	0.75	0.92	1.50	3.00
Total production cost..............	$15.10	$14.05	$12.90	$13.65
Margin for profit and risk..........	1.75	2.80	3.95	3.20
Per acre:				
Volume cut per acre..............	16	13	8	4
Margin per acre..................	28.00	36.40	31.60	12.80
Profit ratio......................	0.12	0.20	0.31	0.24

is sold for a fixed sum per acre. In this case, stumpage becomes a Class C cost to the buyer since it is fixed by unit of area. Assume, for example, that he purchased all the pulpwood on the area at $30 per acre. The Class C cost then becomes $12 + $30, or $42 per acre. His position can then be analyzed as follows:

Selling price, per cord... $16.85
Class B cost, per cord.. 6.40
Available to meet A, C, and D costs and margin for profit and risk... $10.45

Analyzing Class A costs by dbh classes separately as before:

4-in. trees cost 100 × $0.15, or $15.00 per cord
6-in. trees cost 75 × $0.15, or $11.25 per cord
8-in. trees cost 50 × $0.15, or $7.50 per cord

Since the 8-in. class is the lowest that will return something to C and D general costs, smaller trees can be cut only at a direct loss. This indicates that the greatest return per acre will result from cutting to this limit. It is important to note that the size of the general cost has no bearing whatever on this fact. Whatever it is, cutting to an 8-in. limit will contribute the most per unit of area to it. Greatest return per unit of volume may or may not occur at this point, though in this particular case it does, as shown in Table 18.10.

This analysis brings out some facts of very practical significance. In lump-sum sales, the buyer often feels he must cut everything merchantable to get his money's worth. If the area available is limited, he will make the most per acre, so far as the logging operation itself is concerned, by cutting anything that will return direct costs and contribute something to general costs. Unless he is very hard up for wood as, for example, to keep

TABLE 18.10. MARGIN FOR PROFIT AND RISK AT DIFFERENT DIAMETER LIMITS WHEN THE STUMPAGE PRICE IS FIXED PER ACRE

Item	Lower diameter cutting limit, in.			
	4	6	8	10
Volume cut per acre, cords............	18	16	13	8
Selling price........................	$16.85	$16.85	$16.85	$16.85
Costs:				
Class A...........................	6.96	5.95	4.73	3.00
Class B...........................	6.40	6.40	6.40	6.40
Class C and D at $42 per acre.......	2.33	2.62	3.23	5.25
Total production costs..............	15.69	14.97	14.36	14.65
Margin for profit and risk per cord.....	1.16	1.88	2.49	2.20
Margin for profit and risk per acre.....	20.88	30.08	32.37	17.60

a mill going and the cost of partial or complete shutdown is taken into account, he will not gain by cutting anything smaller than 8-in. trees. The analysis summarized in Table 18.10 shows that, as a logging proposition, it does not pay to cut 4- and 6-in. trees, even though when cutting to these limits there is still a margin for profit and risk per acre. These trees individually lose money, as measured by their selling value in relation to direct costs, but this fact is concealed in per-acre totals.

In any appraisal where differential values exist and can be considered in cutting, they should be carefully investigated by both buyer and seller. The pulpwood example given above is highly simplified, but it illustrates the basic principles and problems involved in evaluating cutting different portions of a stand where costs of different classifications are involved. A parallel analysis based on sawtimber production would be more complex than the pulpwood example given, as more diameter classes and costs would have to be considered. The general pattern would, however, be about the same.

DETERMINATION OF RESIDUAL
GROWING-STOCK VALUES

A logical conclusion to this analysis of differential values when cutting to different diameter limits is to consider residual growing-stock values. Here is where management of a forest specifically enters the picture and stumpage appraisal as a valuation technique merges with it. Again using the pulpwood example, assume that both the timber and land are bought. The new owner now has an economic interest in the continued productivity of the land as well as in the value of the timber stand for current conversion, which is the immediate concern of stumpage appraisal.

As shown in Table 18.10, there is no gain in cutting 4- and 6-in. trees; in a sense this growing stock is free, as the owner cannot immediately profit by cutting it. If, for silvicultural reasons, it would also be desirable to leave the 8-in. trees, their investment value can be measured by comparing the margin for profit and risk per acre when cutting to 8- and 10-in. lower diameter limits, respectively. The difference (Table 18.10) is $32.37 − $17.60, or $14.77 per acre, for the 5 cords in this class. The problem then becomes one of comparing this present value with the value of these 5 cords plus 4-, 6-in., and smaller trees present as growing stock for future returns. This problem can only be solved through a management analysis of the tract, including consideration of growth. Although stumpage appraisal is most commonly thought of and applied as a technique to guide establishment of market values in connection with purchase or sale of timber, it should also be recognized as an indispensable tool of management in analyzing alternatives. This subject is further developed in Chaps. 19 and 20.

19

valuation of the tree

An interrelated group of forest valuations has been presented in Chaps. 17 and 18. The series began with valuation of forest land, the basic resource. Growing stock on the land was next considered with emphasis on the valuation of immature stands. In Chap. 18, attention was focused on evaluation of stumpage, the crop severed from the forest. Principles and methods of valuation were first applied to the common business problem of appraising stumpage as a commodity, as a specified body of timber available for cutting. The analysis was then extended to the estimation of stumpage values when there are alternatives concerning what part of the stand may be cut or left. This brought forest management choices directly back into the picture and necessarily introduced the effect of different kinds of costs, both direct and general, on stumpage values.

The purpose of this chapter is to complete the series by applying the principles and methods of stumpage appraisal to valuation of the individual tree in terms of the products it contains. Timberland, and stumpage without the land, can be bought and sold in large amounts. Timber production as a business can be and usually is organized and conducted on a large-scale basis. Management is applied, however, mainly by cutting trees. There are often many choices concerning which should be cut and which left in a particular situation and point in time. In making wise choices, knowledge of individual tree values is required.

What is the value of a tree in the woods? This is one of the most basic and practical questions in forestry. To a buyer, a tree is a storehouse of raw material. He sees in a tree, and collectively in a tract of timber, a certain quantity of logs, pulpwood, bolts, piling, and other items that can be made into salable products. Tree and timber value to him obviously is measured by what he can get for these products less the necessary costs of cutting, processing, and placing them on the market. The landowner must consider trees not only as a currently marketable commodity, but also as capital growing stock. He must appraise the value of the products presently derivable from the tree and balance this against future growing-stock values if a certain tree or group of trees is cut or not. His problem is three-dimensional, being financial, biological, and involving time. He must forecast growth of the tree in volume as well as value and make his decision as to what to cut accordingly. Silviculture and economics are necessarily fused; there is no dividing line, and the forest manager's job, as always, is to balance for the best overall result in accordance with the purposes of management.

Determination of individual tree values is consequently a problem of wide significance. Its importance in uneven-aged management has been emphasized; effective application of an uneven-aged system directly depends upon a knowledge of individual tree performance measured in both physical and dollar terms. The same knowledge of how trees grow and what they are worth is necessary in even-aged management. Several intermediate cuttings are usually made, and the objective is to get the greatest possible return from the growing stock. Every time a thinning or other cutting is made, in fact every time a tree is cut, some appraisal of tree and stand values both now and in the future is necessarily made. The determination of the rotation length is a major decision depending in large part on the product values. To the degree that trees are cut for economic purposes, there is no escape from consideration of tree values. A knowledge of how they are determined should be regarded as an indispensable tool of management.

The valuation problem is an extension and refinement of stumpage appraisal techniques, and from Chap. 18 it should be apparent that no single solution is possible. The job is simple in general outline; it is essentially a matter of estimating the conversion return of individual trees, or more specifically, the conversion return of individual logs or other units contained in the tree. The difficulties arise in the mechanics of identifying logging and milling costs and selling prices in terms of individual tree or log units. Trees, logs, and processing practices are not standard; in fact, they vary endlessly. A multitude of sizes, shapes, and grades of finished or semifinished products are involved, often complexly interrelated.

A great many logging and milling studies have been made to determine individual tree and log values, and a general body of techniques has been developed that has a more or less common pattern. Once the basic procedure is understood, it will be found that particular applications are largely variations on the same theme. The purpose here is to follow through in essential detail a sample logging and milling study, pointing out possible variations and alternatives as the analysis progresses.

A common procedure in such studies is to take a sample of trees from some cutting operation or group of them. Individual trees are described, and the logs or other products obtained from them are carefully measured and identified by trees. The logs may be estimated in the tree, but, in any event, they are checked and measured after the tree is felled. These logs are then individually followed through the various steps of logging and subsequent manufacture to the finished product in whatever form it is sold by the primary producer. Selling prices and the various costs incurred in the process are determined and brought together to determine the value of each log handled and eventually of the tree from which it came.

The job also can be done in segments and often is. A milling study can be conducted starting with logs as they come to the mill, whether identified by tree origin or not. Attention may be concentrated on certain parts of the milling operation only, such as a special study of overrun. The same can be true of the logging operation. A part of it can be and frequently is studied separately, for example, felling and bucking, skidding, loading, hauling, and the like. The main thing to bear in mind, from the standpoint of individual tree valuation, is that each step in the process is a part of a sequence of operations extending from the tree to the product sold. To determine values in the tree, the sequence must be complete.

Two general procedural choices are possible in determining individual tree values. The first is to use the tree as a whole as the basic computational unit. Some logging and milling studies are designed to determine values by tree diameter (dbh) only. But the diameter alone does not measure large quantitative and qualitative differences found in trees of the same diameter. This has led to the use of various tree classifications by which standing trees are classified or graded as a whole according to some qualitative scheme based on observable differences in form, average log-grade content, branchiness, and other external factors affecting quality and hence value. Tree classes have been developed, particularly with conifers, and frequently used with diameter in tree value studies. When one follows a tree approach, processing costs and selling values are assembled and presented by tree units. Individual logs are necessarily identified as they pass through the logging and milling process, but the results are merged into the tree unit. Log grades are often employed, but not necessarily since log and hence tree costs and values can be determined directly without using any grade classification.

A second and more basic procedure is to concentrate attention on values of individual logs described by diameter, length, and grade. With the development and increasing use of log grades, their recognition is of increasing importance. If the value of individual logs by size and grade as they stand in the tree is known, then the value of any particular size, kind, or class of tree can be determined on the basis of its log-grade structure. Determination of log values, by size and grade, is consequently a more comprehensive and widely usable procedure in establishing tree values than is use of tree classes and diameter directly by tree units. The individual log approach is followed in this chapter.

It should be kept in mind that the usefulness of log and tree value studies is proportional to the value and variability of the timber involved. For this reason, they have been largely confined to sawtimber and to products of comparatively high value. Lumber yield studies of sawtimber species are by far the most typical, and it is such a situation that is considered here.

development of a sample case

The mechanics of individual log and tree value determination can best be illustrated in terms of an integrated sample case. Sugar maple will be used as a key species in illustrating techniques. It is a species of high value widely cut into standard lumber grades throughout its extensive commercial range in the United States. Hardwood tree values tend to be highly variable, and sugar maple is a good example. Applicable hardwood log grades exist, and their use in the buying and selling of timber and logs is increasing. The case will be carried through to the tree in terms of logs measured by grade and size.

The general utilization situation in this case is that of a small logging and milling operation in the southeastern United States handling sugar maple along with a number of other hardwood species. The same general techniques apply equally to the other species; sugar maple only is considered in the interest of simplicity in presentation. The sawmill is of the circular type and cuts about 10 M bd ft per day. Lumber is piled in the yard immediately after sawing and sold on a rough green basis. The data are adapted and updated from a study of such an operation made by James (1946).

Following the normal procedure in stumpage appraisal, the starting point is the price of lumber as sold on the market. The selling price of lumber sawed from logs of different diameter, length, and grade is determined from these prices. The net conversion value of the log as it stands in the tree is determined by successively deducting the costs of milling and logging. The process is accomplished in a series of four major steps, each involving several subsidiary operations. These steps are defined and outlined as follows:

> *Step* 1. Lumber value per M by log grade and diameter. Determination of these values necessitates information on:
>
> *a.* Lumber prices by grade as received by the operator.
> *b.* Thicknesses, widths, and lengths of lumber sawed.

    c. Lumber-grade recovery from logs of different diameter and log grade.

Step 2.   Value of logs per M by diameter, log grade, and length as they reach the mill. Determination of this value requires deduction of milling costs and necessitates information on the following:

    a. Cost analysis of the various steps in milling.

    b. Time studies to determine the varying time required to saw logs of different diameters and lengths.

    c. Sawmill costs of logs (from *a* and *b* above) and inclusion of overrun or underrun to convert values from mill or lumber scale to log scale as logs are measured in the woods.

Step 3.   Value of logs per M and per log by diameter, log grade, and length as they stand in the tree. Determination of this value necessitates deduction of logging costs and requires:

    a. Cost analysis of the various steps in logging.

    b. Time studies to establish the varying time required to handle logs of different diameters and lengths.

    c. Conversion of log values per M to values per log on the basis of log volume.

Step 4.   Application of data to standing tree values. This necessitates information on the log structure of individual trees.

As the analysis progresses, it will be helpful to refer to these four major steps to maintain perspective on the job as a whole and to avoid getting lost in the various intermediate calculations necessary. Analyses of this nature require considerable detailed arithmetic and involve a series of cost determinations and operating assumptions. Although the purpose here is not to give detailed instructions on the mechanics of making logging and milling studies, the essential steps will be made clear together with sufficient detail to follow development of the key figures. It should also be kept in mind that, although this case illustrates a basic pattern of procedure, there can be many variations in specific detail to meet other situations.

lumber values by log grade and diameter

The starting point is the price received by grades for the lumber sold. Considerable choice in base is possible, depending on purpose. If the study is being made for the immediate benefit of a particular operating company, current prices actually received would be appropriate. If the study is made on a longer-range basis with fairly wide application an objective, then average prices received for a period by a single concern or by several combined would be logical. Average prices received are gathered and published by trade associations and can be used as a base. In this case, average regional prices of rough green lumber were used and adjusted to price received at the sawmill. The particular price level used here is not important in developing the illustration.

Since lumber prices vary by board thickness, but not, in the case of hardwood lumber grades, significantly by board width and length within the range of standard log lengths cut, they must be weighted by the average percentage distribution of thicknesses cut. Weighting by the thicknesses actually cut, the following sugar maple selling prices per M were used:

Lumber grade	Selling price
First and seconds............	$234.73
Select.....................	159.96
No. 1 common..............	145.45
No. 2 common..............	80.30
No. 3 common, A............	56.57
No. 3 common, B............	38.58

The next job is to apply these lumber prices to the lumber grade recovery from logs of different diameter and grade. The log grades employed are essentially those prepared by the Forest Products Laboratory of the U.S. Forest Service (1953).[1] Grade recovery information, obtained by sawing logs of various diameter and grade and determining the actual volume of lumber by grade contained in each, is given in Table 19.1. The values given are curved to smooth out irregularities due to sampling. In Table 19.2 the grade recovery information is combined with lumber price data to give lumber values per M by log grade and diameter. The mechanics of the operation for an 18-in. grade 1 log are illustrated in Table 19.3.

The lumber values per M by logs given in Table 19.2 complete Step 1 and constitute the base from which milling and logging costs are subsequently deducted to give the log value in the tree. It should again be emphasized that the specific mechanics employed will vary with the lumber grades recognized, the diameter range involved, the log grades employed, and related circumstances. The basic pattern remains of determining lumber selling prices, weighting them by lumber thicknesses, lengths, and widths to the extent these factors influence price, and applying the result to grade recovery data to get lumber value by logs.

---

[1] A discussion of hardwood log grading is beyond the scope of this presentation. The log grades employed are based on readily recognizable surface characteristics and segregate logs suitable for lumber manufacture into high-, medium-, and low-quality classes according to the lumber yields and values they will produce.

TABLE 19.1. LUMBER YIELDS BY GRADE OBTAINED FROM LOGS OF SPECIFIED DIAMETER AND LOG GRADE

Log diam class, in.	Percentage of lumber yield by grade						
	F and S	Sel.	No. 1	No. 2	No. 3CA	No. 3CB	Total
Grade 1 logs							
10							
12							
14	26	11	35	16	12	...	100
16	27	12	35	15	10	1	100
18	29	13	34	14	8	2	100
20	30	14	34	13	7	2	100
22	31	14	34	12	7	2	100
24	32	14	34	11	7	2	100
26	33	15	33	10	8	1	100
28	34	15	33	8	10	...	100
Grade 2 logs							
10							
12	...	2	38	29	22	9	100
14	3	7	39	27	17	7	100
16	6	9	39	27	14	5	100
18	9	9	40	27	12	3	100
20	10	10	40	27	11	2	100
22	11	10	41	27	9	2	100
24	12	10	41	28	8	1	100
26	13	10	41	29	6	1	100
28	14	10	42	30	3	1	100
Grade 3 logs							
10	...	...	18	45	37	...	100
12	...	...	26	43	29	2	100
14	1	2	28	42	23	4	100
16	3	3	28	41	19	6	100
18	4	3	30	40	16	7	100
20	4	3	31	40	15	7	100
22	4	4	31	39	15	7	100
24	4	4	32	38	15	7	100
26	5	3	33	38	15	6	100
28	6	3	33	39	15	4	100

TABLE 19.2. LUMBER VALUES PER M OF LOGS
OF SPECIFIED LOG DIAMETER
AND GRADE
(LUMBER SCALE)

Log diam class, in.	Log grade		
	1	2	3[a]
10	. . . . . .	. . . . . .	$ 83.26
12	. . . . . .	$ 98.01	89.50
14	$149.18	108.96	95.10
16	151.56	116.75	98.53
18	154.84	123.32	101.67
20	157.42	126.32	102.57
22	158.97	128.85	
24	160.53	131.19	
26	162.39	133.22	
28	163.88	136.12	

[a] Grade 3 logs larger than 20 in. are seldom cut of this species and so are not included.

TABLE 19.3. LUMBER VALUE OF AN 18-IN. GRADE 1 LOG

Lumber grade	Grade recovery percentage from Table 19.1	Lumber selling price per M	Weighted log value per M, lumber scale
Firsts and seconds.......	29	$234.73	$ 68.07
Select................	13	159.96	20.79+
No. 1 common..........	34	145.45	49.45
No. 2 common..........	14	80.30	11.24
No. 3 common-A........	8	56.57	4.52
No. 3 common-B........	2	38.58	0.77
Total...............	100	. . . . . .	$154.84

value of logs at the mill

The job of Step 2, in overall terms, is to determine and deduct milling costs.

COST ANALYSIS

The first step is to analyze costs. The sawmill in this case is equipped with a circular head saw, edger, trimmer, cutoff saw, and a small skidder to haul logs from the yard to the deck. The mill is operated by seven men, and usually the mill superintendent assists in addition to his management duties. Men are paid at hourly rates. Administrative and general overhead costs are low for this type of operation. The mill site is on rented land. Insurance and taxes are average for the area.

The mill operates rather steadily through the year, obtaining logs from various sources. As is well known, the pace of a sawmill is set by the head saw and particularly is this true in a small mill with no separate operating departments. Consequently, sawmill costs, per M bd ft cut in this case, are almost all controlled by sawing time. The cost per hour of operation was obtained by dividing average total yearly cost by the number of hours operated per year. Average operating time was figured on a 250-day 8-hour per day work year. Direct labor and yearly costs such as for fire insurance, taxes, and depreciation are directly added together in this instance. They are all a part of the cost of operating the mill for a given period of time.

After sawing, the lumber is piled in a yard for initial drying and sale. Two men do this work, using small carts to move the lumber from the mill platform to the yard. While there is probably some variation in yard cost occasioned by thicknesses, lengths, and widths of boards handled, the differences are small. Because of this, it is unlikely that log size is correlated significantly with yard costs. These costs are logically figured on the basis of the volume of lumber handled and hence are fixed per M. The cost per M was determined by summing all costs chargeable to the yard for a year and dividing by the volume handled during this same period.

Sawmill and lumberyard unit costs are summarized in Table 19.4. Selling costs are not included here. The mill is one of a chain under common management, and these costs are not charged to the individual mill. In most instances, however, selling costs must be figured in. They may be esti-

TABLE 19.4. SAWMILL AND LUMBERYARD COSTS
(LUMBER SCALE)

Cost item	Sawmill costs per hour of operation	Lumberyard costs per M bd ft
Wages, including social security, workman's compensation, and unemployment insurance.......	$15.34	$4.70
Other direct costs, including operating supplies, maintenance, and depreciation..............	3.06	1.05
General costs, including supervision, administrative overhead, land rent, insurance, and taxes..	3.69	2.39
Total..................................	$22.09	$8.14
Total per minute........................	$ 0.3682	

mated as a flat cost per M. More realistically, however, salesmen's commissions are based on the sale value in dollars rather than volume and hence should be deducted directly on a percentage basis from the gross lumber value per M as given in Table 19.2.

TIME STUDIES

From the cost analysis above, two kinds of cost figures were obtained, costs fixed per M and per unit of time. Those fixed per M, the lumberyard cost, do not vary by log size and can be applied directly to the log values per M of Table 19.2. The sawmill costs are expressed per hour of mill operation, which means that they vary per M in accordance with the time it takes to saw a thousand board feet of lumber from logs of varying diameter and length. To convert these hourly costs to per M costs, it is necessary to make a time study of the sawing operation, which controls the pace of the rest of the mill.

Through preliminary testing of sawing times, it was found that the various hardwood species going through the mill could be divided into two significant groups: the "hard" hardwoods, of which sugar maple is one, and the "soft" hardwoods. For each group, stop-watch studies were made of the time required to saw logs of various diameters and lengths. The volume of lumber cut was also recorded so that the time required to cut a thousand board feet could be determined. Log grade was not considered as influencing sawing time, though it undoubtedly does to some extent. If the effect was adjudged to be significant, log grade would have to be taken into account as another factor affecting costs varying by log diameter.

Table 19.5 gives the results of the head saw time study for the "hard" hardwood group, expressing output as the time in crew-minutes necessary to saw a thousand board feet from logs of varying diameter and length. For the diameter range studied, sawing time is a maximum for 10-in. logs and decreases rapidly with increasing diameter up to about 16 in. Sawing time above 16 in. continues to decrease, though at a much slower rate, until logs of about 28 in. are cut, when the time increases somewhat. As shown, the effect of log length is not pronounced except for the smaller diameter classes. The specific magnitude and distribution of these figures in this table are characteristic of the particular kind of sawmill and logs sawed. They would be different for a band mill designed to cut large conifer logs. For any kind of sawmill, however, the general sawing time pattern is recurrent. The smallest logs always take the most time to saw in relation to their volume. As larger logs are sawed, the time required diminishes up to a point and then increases because of the fact that logs are sawed larger than the equipment is designed to handle most efficiently. This trend is particularly apparent in small mills when logs oversize for the head rig equipment are handled.

TABLE **19.5.** TIME IN CREW-MINUTES REQUIRED
TO SAW **1,000** BD FT OF
LUMBER, "HARD" HARDWOOD GROUP,
BY LOG DIAMETER AND LENGTH

Log diam class, in.	Log length, ft			
	10	12	14	16
10	146	130	115	99
12	93	86	81	76
14	73	70	66	62
16	63	59	57	54
18	57	54	52	49
20	52	50	49	46
22	48	46	46	44
24	46	45	44	43
26	45	44	43	41
28	45	45	45	44
30	46	46	46	46
32	48	48	48	49
34	52	52	53	54
36	55	58	59	61
38	59	62	64	67
40	64	68	73	73

SAWMILL COSTS

The next operation is to combine the cost analysis and time study data to determine costs per M in the sawmill. To do this two things are always necessary: the cost per unit of time and the variable time required for a constant unit of volume. The cost per unit of volume is the product of the two. In this case the cost analysis (Table 19.4) showed that the cost per hour of sawmill operation was $22.09, or $0.3682 per minute. Table 19.5 gives the variable sawing time in minutes. To use a specific example, the cost per M for an 18-in., 16-ft log is the sawing time of 49 minutes times $0.3682, or $18.04. These conversions are made in Table 19.6 for the log diameter range of sugar maple occurring in this study plus a little more to show trends. It should be noted that these values apply to all log grades and in this case to all "hard" hardwoods.

VALUE OF LOGS AS THEY REACH MILL

Sawmill and lumberyard costs can now be combined and subtracted from log lumber values (Table 19.2) to give the value of logs as they reach

TABLE **19.6.** SAWMILLING COST PER M MILL SCALE
FOR "HARD" HARDWOODS
BY LOG DIAMETER AND LENGTH

Log diam class, in.	Log length, ft			
	10	12	14	16
10	$53.76	$47.87	$42.34	$36.45
12	34.24	31.67	29.82	27.98
14	26.88	25.74	24.30	22.83
16	23.20	21.72	20.99	19.88
18	20.99	19.88	19.15	18.04
20	19.15	18.41	18.04	16.94
22	17.67	16.94	16.94	16.20
24	16.94	16.57	16.20	15.83
26	16.57	16.20	15.83	15.10
28	16.57	16.57	16.57	16.20
30	16.94	16.94	16.94	16.94
32	17.67	17.67	17.67	18.04
34	19.15	19.15	19.51	19.88
36	20.25	21.36	21.72	22.46
38	21.72	22.83	23.56	24.67
40	23.56	25.04	26.88	26.88

the mill. The detail of the process is shown in Table 19.7 for grade 1 logs
12 ft long, and the completed job for all grades and lengths is given in
Table 19.8. As shown, the effect of log grade and diameter on value per
M is rather large, but the effect of log length is small.

TABLE **19.7.** DETERMINATION OF LOG VALUE PER M AT MILL
FOR **12-**FT GRADE **1** SUGAR MAPLE
(LUMBER SCALE)

Log diam class, in.	Lumber value of log per M (Table 19.2)	Sawmill cost per M (Table 19.6)	Yard cost per M	Total cost per M	Log value per M at mill
14	$149.18	$25.74	$8.14	$33.88	$115.30
16	151.56	21.72	8.14	29.86	121.70
18	154.84	19.88	8.14	28.02	126.82
20	157.42	18.41	8.14	26.55	130.87
22	158.97	16.94	8.14	25.08	133.89
24	160.53	16.57	8.14	24.71	135.82
26	162.39	16.20	8.14	24.34	138.05
28	163.88	16.57	8.14	24.71	139.17

TABLE 19.8. LOG VALUE PER M OF SUGAR
MAPLE LOGS AT THE MILL
(LUMBER SCALE)

Log diam class, in.	Log length, ft			
	10	12	14	16
Grade 1 logs				
14	$114.16	$115.30	$116.74	$118.21
16	120.22	121.70	122.43	123.54
18	125.71	126.82	127.55	128.66
20	130.13	130.87	131.24	132.34
22	133.16	133.89	133.89	134.63
24	135.45	135.82	136.19	136.56
26	137.66	138.05	138.42	139.15
28	139.17	139.17	139.17	139.54
Grade 2 logs				
12	55.27	57.84	59.69	61.53
14	73.94	75.08	76.52	77.99
16	85.41	86.89	87.62	88.73
18	94.19	95.30	96.03	97.14
20	99.03	99.77	100.14	101.24
22	103.04	103.77	103.77	104.51
24	106.11	106.48	106.85	107.22
26	108.53	108.90	109.27	110.00
28	111.41	111.41	111.41	111.78
Grade 3 logs				
10	21.36	27.25	32.78	38.67
12	47.19	49.69	51.54	53.38
14	60.08	61.22	62.66	64.13
16	67.19	68.67	69.40	70.51
18	72.54	73.65	74.38	75.49
20	75.28	76.02	76.39	77.49

The values in Table 19.8 are in mill scale or lumber scale, as it is usually termed. Sawlogs, however, are normally bought, and logging costs are reckoned in log scale according to some accepted log rule. Measurement by log scale indicates only approximately the actual board foot lumber recovery in the mill as determined here. This introduces the necessity of determining overrun (or underrun), one of the more troublesome and perplexing problems of logging and milling analyses. Overrun or underrun is the difference between log scale and mill scale. When expressed as a percentage, as is commonly done, the log scale is used as the base. The difference between log and mill scale results from a compound of the inherent nature of the log rule and scaling practice applied, the size and character of the logs sawed, the kind of lumber cut, grading practices, and the efficiency of the sawmill. The amount of overrun obtained can and often does vary substantially from mill to mill, even when the same log rule is used. Since the overrun (or underrun) obtained has a direct effect on log values, it should be checked for a particular operation, even though regional or local area averages by class of mill are available and usable as a guide. Overrun is particularly important in hardwoods because of the variable nature of the logs usually sawed and peculiarities of lumber grading.

In the study being followed here, overrun and underrun were determined at the sawmill, using gross scale by the Scribner Decimal C log rule as the base. The results, expressed as percentages, are given in Table 19.9. As shown, the percentages are highly variable by both diameter and log grade. The size and frequency of the negative percentages, indicating underrun, are somewhat surprising but result in this case partly because gross log scale was used and partly because in sawing hardwood lumber from the lower-grade logs a considerable amount of footage is lost in edging and trimming.

The mill scale values of Table 19.8 are converted to log scale by applying these overrun percentages, the results being given in Table 19.10. Since percentage overrun conversions in volume and value are tricky and some-

TABLE 19.9. PERCENTAGE OF OVERRUN OR
UNDERRUN BASED ON
LOG SCALE FOR SUGAR MAPLE
BY LOG DIAMETER AND GRADE

Log diam class, in.	Log grade		
	1	2	3
10	. . . . . .	. . . . . .	26.5
12	24.5	13.5	13.5
14	9.5	4.0	1.5
16	0.0	− 1.0	− 9.0
18	− 5.0	− 4.0	−16.5
20	− 8.0	− 5.5	−20.0
22	−10.0	− 6.5	
24	−11.5	− 8.5	
26	−12.5	− 9.5	
28	−14.0	−11.0	

TABLE 19.10. LOG VALUES PER M OF SUGAR
MAPLE LOGS AT THE MILL (GROSS LOG SCALE)

Log diam class, in.	Log length, ft			
	10	12	14	16
Grade 1 logs				
14	$125.00	$126.25	$127.83	$129.44
16	120.22	121.70	122.43	123.54
18	119.42	120.48	121.17	122.23
20	119.72	120.40	120.74	121.75
22	119.84	120.50	120.50	121.17
24	119.87	120.20	120.53	120.86
26	120.45	120.79	121.12	121.76
28	119.69	119.69	119.69	120.00
Grade 2 logs				
12	62.73	65.65	67.75	69.84
14	76.90	78.08	79.58	81.11
16	84.56	86.02	86.74	87.84
18	90.42	91.49	92.19	93.25
20	93.58	94.28	94.63	95.67
22	96.34	97.02	97.02	97.72
24	97.09	97.43	97.77	98.11
26	98.22	98.55	98.89	99.55
28	99.15	99.15	99.15	99.48
Grade 3 logs				
10	27.02	34.47	41.47	48.92
12	53.56	56.40	58.49	61.15
14	60.98	62.14	63.60	65.09
16	61.14	62.49	63.15	64.16
18	60.57	61.50	62.11	63.03
20	60.22	60.82	61.11	61.99

times confusing, a useful schedule for applying overrun or underrun data to log and lumber measure is given in Table 19.11.[1]

The highly variable percentage overrun, ranging from a substantial plus value for the smaller diameters to strongly negative values for the larger

[1] As Herrick (1946 and 1948) has pointed out, overrun and underrun can usefully be expressed directly in board foot units, in which form it is initially determined, rather than as a percentage. For example, if a 16-in., 16-ft log, which contains 144 bd ft log scale Doyle rule cuts out 190 bd ft of lumber, overrun can be expressed as 46 bd ft instead of 32 percent. Overrun expressed in board feet is much less variable by log size than are percentages in Doyle scale particularly, which gives a sharply increasing percentage as log size is

TABLE 19.11. CONVERSIONS FOR OVERRUN AND UNDERRUN

Conversion desired	Conversion formula[a]	Example[b]
Overrun:		
Log scale to mill scale..	$M_s = L_s(1 + p)$	$M_s = 1,000 \times 1.20 = 1,200$ bd ft
Mill scale to log scale...	$L_s = M_s \div (1 + p)$	$L_s = 1,000 \div 1.20 = 833$ bd ft
Log value to mill value.	$M_v = L_v \div (1 + p)$	$M_v = \$100 \div 1.20 = \$83.33$
Mill value to log value..	$L_v = M_v(1 + p)$	$L_v = \$100 \times 1.20 = \$120$
Underrun:		
Log scale to mill scale..	$M_s = L_s(1 - p)$	$M_s = 1,000 \times 0.80 = 800$ bd ft
Mill scale to log scale...	$L_s = M_s \div (1 - p)$	$L_s = 1,000 \div 0.80 = 1,250$ bd ft
Log value to mill value.	$M_v = L_v \div (1 - p)$	$M_v = \$100 \div 0.80 = \$125$
Mill value to log value..	$L_v = M_v(1 - p)$	$L_v = \$100 \times 0.80 = \$80$

[a] L_s = log scale
L_v = log value per M
M_s = mill scale
M_v = mill value per M
p = percentage overrun or underrun expressed as a decimal
[b] Assume 20 percent overrun or underrun and units of 1,000 bd ft and $100 per M, respectively.

diameters in this example, gives a rather peculiar twist to the log values per M. In mill scale (Table 19.8), a considerable increase in unit value with increasing log diameter is evident for all log grades. In log scale (Table 19.10) this trend is reversed for grade 1 logs. For the other two grades, some increase in value with diameter remains, but the trend is considerably reduced through the effect of overrun. An overrun that is high for small diameters and thereafter decreases with increasing log diameter increases the value of small logs and decreases the value of large logs. The general effect of a variable overrun is consequently to minimize the value differences associated with diameter when measured in log scale.

Overrun should be recognized as largely a phenomenon of inconsistent measurement. Unit values per M mill scale do increase markedly with increasing diameter, but this trend is partially offset by the change to log scale, which, in this case, considerably underestimates the lumber yield of small logs and overestimates that of large logs. This would not happen if logs could be scaled in the woods on a mill scale basis. The International rule accomplishes this very nearly, particularly with conifers, since the mill

---

reduced. The curve of overrun in board feet plotted over log diameter is much flatter. When overrun is determined by log diameters (and length) as in the case presented here, it makes little difference whether percentages or actual board feet are used. In making conversions based on average log diameter, however, use of an average board foot instead of a percentage figure is likely to give a more accurate answer, since it is much less sensitive to errors in estimating average log size.

scale closely approximates the log scale in most situations. The significant point is that both buyer and seller should be well informed as to the facts of overrun (and underrun). It can be, as it is in this instance, of overshadowing importance. Its accurate determination is important, since errors in its measurement may nullify precision in other phases of the work.

The determination of log values per M in log scale (Table 19.10) completes Step 2. If the study is made by a mill owner who buys logs or by a producer selling logs at roadside or some other marketing point, the analysis would stop here. Table 19.10 gives the conversion return of logs, in log scale, as they reach the mill and, consequently, the basis for an appraisal of log values. The rest of the appraisal process is to determine what part of the conversion return should go to the mill operator as margin to cover investment, profit, and risk. The rest can be paid for logs. No set formula can be given for division of this conversion return; it is a matter for estimation and market negotiation as brought out in Chap. 18.

value of logs as they stand in the tree

The job of Step 3 is to determine and deduct logging costs to obtain conversion returns of logs as they stand in the tree. The first need, as in the mill phase of the study, is to analyze the costs involved in this particular operation. Costs were not segregated by species. Time per M and hence the cost of felling and bucking,[1] skidding, and log loading vary by log size. These costs consequently must be determined per unit of time and distributed per M in accordance with the variable time required to handle logs of different size as determined by time studies. A check on log hauling and unloading showed that in this operation these costs were not significantly affected by log size and consequently could be considered as fixed per M. Board and camp costs were handled in this instance by direct charges to the men employed and consequently do not need to be considered in estimating the operation costs.

Felling and bucking was done by two-man crews using a power saw and paid on an hourly basis. Skidding was done by horses with the driver receiving some assistance from a swamper. Slopes ranged from zero up to 100 percent, averaging 30 percent. Skidding distance ranged up to 1,000 ft and averaged 167. Loading was done with a machine loader with an A-pole frame. Hauling was done by 1½-ton trucks, and a small amount

---

[1] Strictly, felling is a joint cost applicable to the tree as a whole but not to individual logs. It is different from bucking, which directly applies to individual logs. Felling cost was not segregated from bucking in this study as the two operations were handled together in the woods. Although it would be technically desirable to deduct the felling cost directly from tree values as developed later in this chapter, it is not possible to do so, and in this case it makes little practical difference.

TABLE 19.12. FELLING AND BUCKING CREW-MINUTES PER M
AND COST PER M BY LOG DIAMETER AND LENGTH

Log diam class, in.	Crew-minutes per M for log length of:				Cost per M for log length of:[a]			
	10 ft	12 ft	14 ft	16 ft	10 ft	12 ft	14 ft	16 ft
10	118	116	96	68	$10.32	$10.15	$8.40	$5.95
12	103	93	79	62	9.01	8.14	6.91	5.42
14	92	78	67	57	8.05	6.82	5.86	4.99
16	83	68	59	52	7.26	5.95	5.16	4.55
18	77	61	52	48	6.74	5.33	4.55	4.20
20	72	56	49	44	6.30	4.90	4.29	3.85
22	68	53	45	42	5.95	4.64	3.94	3.67
24	65	50	44	40	5.69	4.37	3.85	3.50
26	62	48	42	39	5.42	4.20	3.67	3.41
28	60	47	41	38	5.25	4.11	3.59	3.32

[a] The cost per crew-hour is $5.25, or $0.0875 per crew-minute. The cost per M is obtained by multiplying crew-minutes by this figure.

of road construction and maintenance was charged in with the hauling. Average costs in this instance are:[1]

Felling and bucking..................... $5.25 per crew-hour
Skidding (av slope and distance)......... 2.52 per man-hour
Log loading............................ 4.20 per crew-hour
Log hauling[2]......................... 8.40 per M, log scale
Log unloading......................... 0.43 per M, log scale

Felling and bucking, skidding, and log loading hourly costs are distributed on a per-M basis by log diameter and length in Tables 19.12 to 19.14 through application of the variable times required for these operations, also shown in these tables. In Table 19.15 these costs are combined with the hauling and unloading costs per M, which are not affected by log size in this case, to show total logging costs per M by log diameter and length.

To complete Step 3 it is only necessary to deduct these costs, which apply to log grades equally, from the log values per M at the mill (Table

[1] The techniques of logging engineering and of cost determination cannot be covered here. The amount and kind of logging costs naturally vary from operation to operation. Delay and travel time, actual working time, repairs, and maintenance are included in this example.

[2] Log hauling costs per M vary by log diameter and length, whether gross or net scale, by size of truck, road quality and gradient, and also, of course, by hauling distance. In this instance, hauling was done on a contract basis, and variable costs were not determined. Hauling was done essentially over existing roads. In other situations, road construction and maintenance may be major cost items.

TABLE 19.13. SKIDDING MAN-MINUTES PER M AND COST PER M BY
LOG DIAMETER AND LENGTH

Log diam class, in.	Man-minutes per M for log lengths of:				Cost per M[a] for log length of:			
	10 ft	12 ft	14 ft	16 ft	10 ft	12 ft	14 ft	16 ft
10	427	364	314	271	$17.93	$15.29	$13.19	$11.38
12	315	269	239	215	13.23	11.30	10.04	9.03
14	247	213	192	180	10.37	8.95	8.06	7.56
16	208	179	163	154	8.74	7.52	6.85	6.47
18	178	157	144	138	7.48	6.59	6.05	5.80
20	157	141	132	127	6.59	5.92	5.54	5.33
22	141	129	121	117	5.92	5.42	5.08	4.91
24	130	119	113	109	5.46	5.00	4.75	4.58
26	123	113	107	103	5.17	4.75	4.49	4.33
28	116	107	102	98	4.87	4.49	4.28	4.12

[a] The cost per man-hour is $2.52, or $0.042 per man-minute. The cost per M is obtained by multiplying man-minutes by this figure.

19.10). This is done in Table 19.16, giving the conversion return of logs per M, gross log scale, as they stand in the tree. Also shown is the value per log, which is obtained by multiplying the per-M value by the volume per log as given by the Scribner Decimal C log rule.

Table 19.16 gives the end result of a series of interrelated computations. It applies specifically to a particular species, sugar maple in this case, and to specified logging and milling conditions. The procedures illustrated are applicable to the situation assumed and typical in general pattern for most analyses of this type. It should be emphasized that the objective is to get conversion return information applicable to logs in standing trees. Precise methodology will naturally vary with circumstances. While it is true that most costs do vary with log diameter, length, and often grade, the differences may be small and in some situations unimportant and not worth segregating. Also, some operations may be handled on a contract basis on a flat rate for average logs. Logging methods and costs, milling practices, and certainly lumber selling prices can all differ widely. For these reasons, extreme care must be taken in applying conversion return information obtained under one set of circumstances to another.

On the face of it, determination of log values as they stand in the tree might appear to be too complex and variable a job for such data to be used generally. While there is some truth to this, and there is no escape from the need for considerable data and arithmetic in developing such values, the job in practice is not as difficult as it might seem.

Various short cuts and simplifications are often possible. Computation of lumber values per log may be facilitated by use of an average log quality

TABLE 19.14. LOG LOADING CREW-MINUTES PER M AND COST
PER M BY LOG DIAMETER AND LENGTH

Log diam class, in.	Crew-minutes per M for log length of:				Cost per M[a] for log length of:			
	10 ft	12 ft	14 ft	16 ft	10 ft	12 ft	14 ft	16 ft
10	149	125	101	77	$10.43	$8.76	$7.07	$5.39
12	89	77	65	54	6.23	5.39	4.55	3.78
14	61	53	46	40	4.27	3.71	3.22	2.80
16	46	40	35	30	3.22	2.80	2.45	2.10
18	37	32	27	24	2.59	2.24	1.89	1.68
20	30	26	22	19	2.10	1.82	1.54	1.33
22	24	21	18	14	1.68	1.47	1.26	0.98
24	21	17	14	12	1.47	1.19	0.98	0.84
26	18	14	13	11	1.26	0.98	0.91	0.77
28	16	13	11	10	1.12	0.91	0.77	0.70

[a] Average cost per crew-hour is $4.20, and the cost per crew-minute is consequently $0.07. The cost per M is obtained by multiplying crew-minutes by this figure.

index (Herrick, 1946, 1956) and much of the detail of using lumber-grade recovery data eliminated. Sawmill costs may be fairly consistent between mills of the same general class, particularly regarding trend patterns, and can be adjusted for differences in average level. Milling cost differences between species are usually small. While the handling of overrun is often troublesome, in some cases fairly broad averages are sufficient for the pur-

TABLE 19.15. TOTAL LOGGING COST PER M
BY LOG DIAMETER AND LENGTH

Log diam class, in.	Log length, ft			
	10	12	14	16
10	$47.51	$43.03	$37.49	$31.55
12	37.30	33.66	30.33	27.06
14	31.52	28.31	25.97	24.18
16	28.05	25.10	23.29	21.95
18	25.64	22.99	21.32	20.51
20	23.82	21.47	20.20	19.34
22	22.38	20.36	19.11	18.39
24	21.45	19.39	18.41	17.75
26	20.68	18.76	17.90	17.34
28	20.07	18.34	17.47	16.97

TABLE 19.16. CONVERSION VALUE PER M AND PER LOG OF SUGAR MAPLE LOGS AS THEY STAND IN THE TREE (SCRIBNER DECIMAL C LOG RULE, GROSS SCALE)

Log diam class, in.	Value per M by log length				Value per log by log length			
	10 ft	12 ft	14 ft	16 ft	10 ft	12 ft	14 ft	16 ft
Grade 1 logs								
14	$93.48	$ 97.94	$101.86	$105.26	$ 6.54	$ 8.61	$10.19	$11.58
16	92.17	96.60	99.14	101.59	9.22	11.59	13.88	16.25
18	93.79	97.49	99.85	101.72	12.19	15.60	18.97	21.36
20	95.90	98.93	100.54	102.41	16.30	20.78	24.13	28.67
22	97.46	100.14	101.39	102.78	20.47	25.03	29.40	33.92
24	98.42	100.81	102.12	103.11	24.60	30.24	35.74	41.24
26	99.77	102.03	103.22	104.42	30.93	37.75	45.42	52.11
28	99.62	101.35	102.22	103.03	35.86	44.59	52.13	59.76
Grade 2 logs								
12	25.43	31.99	37.42	42.78	1.27	1.92	2.62	3.42
14	45.38	49.77	53.61	56.93	3.18	4.48	5.36	6.26
16	56.51	60.92	63.45	65.89	5.65	7.31	8.83	10.54
18	64.78	68.50	70.87	72.74	8.42	10.96	13.47	15.28
20	69.76	72.81	74.43	76.33	11.86	15.29	17.86	21.37
22	73.99	76.66	77.91	79.33	15.54	19.16	22.59	26.18
24	75.64	78.04	79.36	80.36	18.91	23.41	27.78	32.14
26	77.54	79.79	80.99	82.21	24.04	29.52	35.64	41.10
28	79.08	80.81	81.68	82.51	28.47	35.56	41.66	47.86
Grade 3 logs								
10	−20.49	−8.56	3.98	17.37	−0.61	−0.26	0.16	1.04
12	16.26	22.74	28.16	34.09	0.81	1.36	1.97	2.73
14	29.46	33.83	37.63	40.91	2.06	3.04	3.76	4.50
16	33.09	37.39	39.86	42.21	3.31	4.49	5.58	6.75
18	34.93	38.51	40.79	42.52	4.30	6.16	7.75	8.93
20	36.40	39.35	40.91	42.65	6.19	8.26	9.82	11.94

pose, and their determination by individual species frequently can be avoided. Use of a consistent log rule like the International, which gives values close to mill scale, obviates most of the overrun problem. Values per M are not strongly affected by log length, and in some cases the detail of carrying log length through all computations can be eliminated. While total logging costs differ from operation to operation, some items, such as loading, hauling, felling, and bucking, are fairly well standardized in contract rates. It is often possible to use applicable time study data to average contract rates to obtain useful information on cost variation by log size. For example, the sawing time data given in Table 19.5 could be applied to other mills of the same type and with different average costs per minute. The same is true with other operations such as felling and bucking, skidding, and hauling. The pattern of cost variability by log size is often relatively consistent. It must be remembered that to the extent average costs are used for items known to vary significantly by log size and grade, value differences between logs and trees are concealed.

It is impossible to spell out all the possibilities for adaptation and simplification, but the point should be emphasized that, once the basic pattern and procedure is clearly in mind, it is often possible to adjust logging and milling data for one operation to apply to another without undue difficulty.

application of log values to tree values

The development of conversion return values per log as they stand in the tree (Table 19.16) completes the logging and milling phase of the job. The next step, and the reason for making the analysis, is to apply this information to trees as a useful tool in management. Several applications and procedures are possible.

DIRECT ESTIMATE OF INDIVIDUAL TREE VALUES BASED ON LOG CONTENT

The most direct application of log value information is in estimating the value of trees considered for cutting on the basis of their log-grade structure. This means that, in cruising, the diameter, length, and grade of each log contained in the tree is estimated. The necessity for and utility of log grades based on surface characteristics, such as are employed here, become immediately apparent. Data for 30 sugar maple trees are given in Table 19.17 to illustrate the kind of data required and its use. Values per log are taken from Table 19.16, interpolating for odd-inch diameters not given in this table.

While log lengths, diameters, and grades obviously cannot be determined as readily for the standing tree as for logs on the ground, they can, with some skill and experience, be estimated with surprising speed and accuracy. Most hardwoods do not contain more than two or three merchantable logs, and the bulk of the value is consequently not far above the ground level. About half of the total value is usually contained in the butt log alone. Of the 26 trees included in Table 19.17 having 3 or more logs, 51 percent of the total value is in the butt logs, 36 percent in the second logs, and only 13 percent in the third and fourth logs. The practical importance of errors in estimation of log sizes and grades consequently diminishes

TABLE 19.17. CONVERSION RETURN VALUE OF 30 SUGAR MAPLE TREES[a]

(SCRIBNER DECIMAL C LOG RULE, GROSS SCALE)

Tree no.	Dbh in.	First log Dib in.	First log Length, ft	First log Grade	First log Value	Second log Dib in.	Second log Length, ft	Second log Grade	Second log Value	Third log Dib in.	Third log Length, ft	Third log Grade	Third log Value	Fourth log Dib in.	Fourth log Length, ft	Fourth log Grade	Fourth log Value	Total tree value	Total tree vol	Conversion value per M
1	24	19	16	2	$18.32	18	10	2	$ 8.42	17	10	3	$ 3.80					$ 30.54	490	$ 62.33
2	24	18	12	2	10.96	15	10	3	3.80	15	10	3	2.68					17.44	370	47.14
3	21	17	12	1	11.59	15	14	1	12.03	13	12	3	2.20					25.82	330	78.24
4	22	16	16	1	16.25	14	16	1	11.58	13	10	2	2.22	11	10	3	$0.10	30.15	370	81.49
5	18	13	12	2	3.20	11	12	3	0.55									3.75	110	34.09
6	23	18	12	2	10.96	16	12	2	7.31	15	16	3	5.62	14	10	3	2.06	25.95	490	52.96
7	26	20	16	1	28.67	18	12	2	10.96	16	14	3	5.58	13	10	3	1.43	46.64	640	72.87
8	23	18	14	1	21.55	18	16	1	21.36	15	14	3	4.67					47.58	540	88.11
9	19	15	16	2	8.40	13	16	3	3.61	12	12	3	1.36					13.37	300	44.57
10	26	16	16	1	16.25	14	14	2	5.36	12	12	3	1.36					22.97	320	71.78
11	28	22	12	1	25.03	20	16	2	21.37	18	12	2	10.96					57.36	690	83.13
12	18	14	12	2	4.48	13	12	2	3.20	11	12	3	0.55					8.23	200	41.15
13	24	18	12	1	15.60	18	16	2	12.91	13	12	3	2.20					30.71	410	74.90
14	30	22	16	1	33.92	18	16	1	21.36					11	12	2	0.70	55.28	540	102.37
15	21	17	14	1	16.42	15	14	1	12.03	14	12	2	4.48	11	12	2	0.70	33.63	410	82.02
16	24	19	14	1	21.55	17	16	1	18.80									40.35	390	103.46
17	18	15	14	1	12.03	13	12	2	3.20									15.23	190	80.16
18	20	16	16	1	16.25	14	14	1	10.19	13	10	2	2.22	11	12	3	0.55	29.21	360	81.14
19	21	16	14	1	13.88	15	12	1	10.19	14	12	3	3.04	11	10	3	0.10	27.12	380	71.37
20	17	15	12	1	10.10	14	14	1	10.19	11	16	3	1.88					22.17	280	79.18
21	26	24	6	Cull	0.00	17	16	1	18.80	15	14	2	7.09	12	12	3	1.36	27.25	360	75.69
22	25	20	16	1	28.67	18	14	2	18.97	17	14	3	9.13					56.77	610	93.07
23	19	16	16	1	16.25	15	16	1	8.40	14	10	2	3.76					28.41	400	71.02
24	23	18	16	1	21.36	17	16	2	18.80	15	10	3	4.41	14	10	3	2.06	46.63	550	84.78
25	22	16	14	1	13.88	16	10	2	5.62	13	10	2	1.43	11	16	3	1.88	22.81	370	61.65
26	26	21	14	1	26.76	19	12	1	18.19	18	10	2	8.42	16	8	3	2.10	55.47	660	84.05
27	21	17	12	2	13.59	15	12	2	5.89	14	12	3	3.04					22.52	340	66.24
28	18	15	16	1	8.40	13	10	3	1.43	11	10	3	0.10					9.93	240	41.37
29	26	18	12	1	20.78	16	16	1	16.25	15	10	3	2.68					39.71	390	101.82
30	26	21	12	1	22.90	20	12	2	15.29	19	10	2	10.14					48.33	590	81.92
																		$941.33	12,320	

[a] Data courtesy of Southeastern Forest Experiment Station, U.S. Forest Service.

rapidly with increasing height above the ground and distance from the observer.

The worthwhileness of making a detailed quality cruise depends primarily on the magnitude of the values involved and their variability by trees. With sugar maple, the species being studied here, conversion returns per M are high, and individual tree values are highly variable. The value of individual trees, as shown in Table 19.17, warrants careful study. For example, compare trees 2 and 16, each of the same diameter, as follows:

Tree no.	Tree diam, in.	Utilized length, ft	Utilized volume, bd ft	Log grades	Conversion return
2	24	32	370	2–3–3	$17.44
16	24	30	390	1–1	40.35

Tree 16 contains 2.3 times the value of tree 2 almost entirely because of the high grade logs it contains.

Knowledge of log values by grade is of large utility in cutting up a tree into log segments that will yield the greatest total value. Referring to Table 19.16, a 12-ft, 20-in. grade 1 log is worth $20.78 in conversion return, whereas a 14-ft grade 2 log of the same diameter is worth $17.86. In cutting a tree into logs, the total conversion return can be increased substantially by taking the fullest possible advantage of the bole quality in selecting log lengths. The effect of crook, rot, blemishes, and other causes of degrade on log value can be reduced by care in the determination of log lengths.

The making of lump-sum tree volume estimates on a timber tract and applying average per-M values can result in large errors in total value when a particular sample of trees with highly variable individual values is considered. This fact explains in large part why an owner selling timber on a lump-sum basis so frequently gets far less than the market value for his timber even if the total volume involved is accurately estimated, as is often not the case. The total value for the timber quoted, and even the per-M value if separately recognized, may seem equitable enough to the owner and be accepted in situations where the market value of the timber, based on log grades, would warrant a higher price, which could be obtained if the owner knew the facts. Knowledge of the individual tree values is of equal value to a purchaser in recognizing a good buy and in avoiding overbidding.

There is an increasing tendency toward selling logs on log grade, particularly when they are of high and variable unit value. This practice logically and naturally can and is being extended to the determination of tree values. Owners frequently insist upon it, for recognition of log grades tends to get them a higher price for the timber.

The conversion return information by trees can be used directly in stumpage appraisal. The 12,320 bd ft included in Table 19.17 have an average conversion return value of $76.41 per M. Stumpage value can be estimated in accordance with the methods and considerations outlined in Chap. 18 for dividing the conversion return between stumpage and margin for profit and risk. It should be noted that the conversion returns used here are based upon particular logging and milling conditions and lumber price level. If any of these factors change, the conversion return would have to be adjusted accordingly. Frankly, this is often much easier said than done, but with skill and knowledge of the procedure upon which they were developed, it is often not difficult to adjust the conversion return values per M as given in Table 19.16, which are the basis for the log and tree values developed. It should be recalled that the conversion return is determined from the simple equation

Conversion return = selling value − milling cost − logging cost

Any change in the milling and logging cost items is directly reflected in the conversion return, which can accordingly be directly adjusted.

None of the trees in this particular sample show a negative conversion return. Sugar maple is a high-value species, and the large overrun obtained from small logs partially offsets the lower quality of lumber obtainable from them and increases the value of small trees. If smaller trees or trees of generally lower quality were included, there could be logs showing a negative conversion return. Studies with generally lower-value species often show both logs and trees to have a negative conversion value.

What a negative conversion return means should be interpreted with care. On the face of it, no margin for either stumpage or profit and risk is available, and the tree can be cut or the log handled only at a loss. This may not, however, necessarily be true. The costs upon which the conversion return is based may and usually do include some general costs fixed for the particular operation. As was pointed out in Chap. 18, p. 410, a log or tree that will return some margin over the direct costs incurred if the item is handled at all will return something toward general costs fixed in the particular situation being considered, and should be taken. Strictly, therefore, only items having a negative conversion surplus (the difference between selling value and direct costs only) are necessarily unprofitable to handle. Whether or not a particular item is unprofitable to handle consequently depends on the specific situation regarding general costs. Considerable confusion often arises in the interpretation of logging and milling studies from lack of clarity on this point.

In the particular situation considered here, practically all the costs involved are direct. The logging and milling operation had little general overhead. In this case, consequently, a negative conversion return may be taken to indicate that the log or tree involved is likely unprofitable to handle under any circumstances. If the timber was purchased at some flat rate per M, subtraction of this amount from the conversion return immediately shows the margin for profit and risk and consequently whether or not a particular tree is profitable to cut on the basis of the stumpage price established. For example, if stumpage was purchased at $45 per M, there are three trees in the group of 30 given in Table 19.17, and a considerably larger number of logs, that would return no margin for profit and risk and on financial grounds should be left if the buyer had the choice.

USE OF TREE INFORMATION AS A GUIDE TO FUTURE VALUE

Another, and in many respects probably the most useful, application of individual tree value information is its use as an aid in deciding which trees should be cut or left, weighing both present and future value. Again referring to Table 19.17, Tree 5 is 18 in. in dbh and obviously of rather low quality, since it contains two 12-ft logs of grade 2 and 3 quality, respectively, having a total conversion return of only $3.75. In contrast, Tree 20 is 17 in. in dbh but has excellent form since it has less taper, contains two grade 1 logs, and has a total conversion return value of $22.17. If it has good possibilities for future growth as evidenced by position in the stand, crown, bark character, or other evidence of vigor and growth potentiality, it should be a good tree to keep for high-value growth in the future.

The fundamental point is that the same information that permits determination of the current value of a tree of specified value and log-grade structure also gives a basis for estimating the value at some future time by taking growth into account. To use a simple example, assume that Tree 20 can grow 2 in. in 8 years with bole taper, log lengths, and log grades remaining the same except that the third log increases to grade 2. Estimating on the basis of present price levels, the value of the tree now and 8 years hence is as follows:

Logs		Logs now			Logs 8 years hence		
Position	Length	Diam	Grade	Value	Diam	Grade	Value
Butt.......	12	15	1	$10.10	17	1	$13.59
Second.....	14	14	1	10.19	16	1	13.88
Third......	16	11	3	1.88	13	2	4.84
Total....	...	...	...	$22.17	...	...	$32.31

On a simple interest basis, this 8-year growth of $10.14 is $10.14/22.17, or 45.7 percent for 8 years, or 5.7 percent annually. The corresponding compound rate is 4.8 percent.

In general, trees of the same diameter in a particular stand require about the same amount of growing space. It follows, consequently, that to the extent the rate of value growth of the growing stock can be increased by utilizing growing space with the best trees possible, total net returns will be maximized. The application of value information in determining trees to cut or to leave is essentially a comparative process tempered by silvicultural considerations. Trees must be considered not only individually but also in relation to others nearby.

Choice of trees to cut or leave can be approached through the alternative rate concept (Duerr, Fedkiw, Guttenberg, 1956, and others). If, for example, a 5 percent compound rate is considered the minimum acceptable, then trees that it is estimated will grow less than this rate should be cut, provided better trees are available to leave. The reason for this comparative proviso is that an alternative rate, rigidly followed as a guide, may deplete the growing stock to a degree that the growing space is substantially under-utilized and net returns per unit of area consequently reduced. This points to the fact that the land is the basic resource.

With even-aged management, if the net return per unit of area falls below an obtainable and acceptable level, the stand probably should be removed so a new and better one can be established.

With uneven-aged management, a growing stock is continuously left on the land except as small areas may be clearcut, in which case the specific areas so treated follow the pattern of even-aged management. In general, however, land and timber go together. For a given volume of reserve growing stock, one can increase net returns only by increasing the net value productivity of the growing stock per unit of area, often a rather slow process. This means leaving the best trees possible, and a flat alternative rate cannot be followed. The volume of reserve growing stock and related length of the cutting cycle can, however, be changed on the basis of a rate of return attainable and acceptable, following the same basic considerations involved in determining the length of the rotation. The use of rates in making such decisions is further treated in Chap. 20.

Many useful applications of the principle of combining conversion return (or conversion surplus) information with growth data have been and can be made. Various tabular, graphic, and slide-rule procedures can be used depending on purpose and data available. The usual procedure is to present annual value growth, expressed in either percentage or dollar form, by tree classes. In addition to diameter, trees are often classified by vigor (good, fair, and poor, or similar), form, general age group, species or species groups, or by increment. The latter may be expressed as number of rings in outer radial inch, radial growth in the last 5 or 10 years, or some other measure. It is important that the forest manager be able to recognize, evaluate, and use such information. To do so effectively he needs to have knowledge of their basic derivation as given here.

ESTIMATION OF VALUES BY TREE CLASSES

Another useful way to apply tree value data is in the development of tree classes which may be grouped as follows:

1. Classes based directly on utilization of the tree, which may be based on
   a. Grade of butt log only
   b. Grade of butt and second log
   c. Grade recovery from the tree as a whole with or without specific use of log grades
2. Classes based on physical characteristics of the tree

Regarding the first group, it has been found that for many species the grade of the butt log gives a good measure of the quality of the rest of the tree. Much of the total value of the tree is often included in the butt log, making this segment of the bole of large significance. The grades of the second and higher logs in the tree tend to be correlated with the butt log in a fairly consistent sequential pattern. If the tree classification is extended to include the grade of the second log as well as the butt log, the quality of the tree is rather closely defined. It has also been found that the form class of a tree is correlated with its log-grade structure. A tree having a butt and second log of grade 1 is likely to have rather small taper and consequently a relatively high form class. These relationships hold best in younger timber having not over four or five logs per tree.

Log values by diameter, length, and grade, as given in Table 19.16, can rather readily be transformed into tree grades or classes by assuming some average log-grade structure for trees of different classes. For example, a tree classification proposed by Campbell (1951, 1955) is based entirely on the classification of the butt log. Field classification consequently depends on ability to recognize log grades of butt logs in standing trees. The general utility of such tree classes depends on how well they distinguish between trees of significantly different quality and hence unit value. This has to be determined by carefully measuring a sample of trees to determine their total volume and content.

Some economic tree classifications, as by Anderson (1934), have been devised that are based on more general observable characteristics of a tree as a whole and not specifically on log grades. Anderson classified ponderosa pine trees in the northern Rocky Mountains in rather general categories based on age and growth form. The classes differ consistently in lumber grade recovery and are also readily recognizable in the field. The trend, however, is strongly toward basing tree classes developed for utilization purposes upon log grades, even though the classes established may also be described in terms of more or less general tree characteristics.

The advantage of these economic tree classes is that they are a useful and valuable tool in appraising the utilization value of a tree as a whole. It is easier to learn to recognize tree classes in the woods than it is to estimate individual log grades, diameters, and lengths in a standing tree. Marking rules can conveniently be based on tree classes in conjunction with silvicultural specifications. A disadvantage of tree classes directly based on log grades is that some average sequence of log grades must be assumed in establishing them. While this may work out well on the average, there may be considerable variation by individual trees. Where this variation is large, the sample small, and values high, it may be desirable to estimate the log-grade structure of individual trees as shown in Table 19.17. What to do depends on values involved and circumstances.

Several classifications based on observable characteristics of trees have been developed. The Keen (1943) and Dunning (1928) tree classes for ponderosa pine are good examples. They define rather specific types of trees having significantly different silvicultural as well as utilization characteristics. Tree classifications of this sort can be related to utilization through determination of average differences between classes in the yield of lumber or other products obtainable from them but are less discriminating in this respect.

20
valuation of financial alternatives

The successful operation of a forest property requires an integration of business methods and technological knowledge, which is applied to a complex biological entity, a forest, to achieve a desired result.

A forest manager continually must decide between alternative choices. Should he apply more or less intensive forest practices, such as site preparation, cleanings, thinnings and improvement cuttings, pruning, and related cultural measures? Should he plant, or rely on less controllable natural regeneration? In even-aged management, when should he keep a partially stocked or otherwise unsatisfactory stand, and when should he cut it and start over? Should he lengthen or shorten the average rotation, increase or decrease the frequency of partial cuttings, work toward lighter or heavier growing-stock levels? In uneven-aged management, should he shorten or lengthen the cutting cycle, build up, reduce, or change the structure of reserve growing stock? In harvesting the forest crop, into which products can the trees most profitably be converted? In fire control, what kind of expenditures might be most economical in reducing losses? Lastly, timber production must be weighed against other forest uses and land allocations.

There are many such questions, basically all concerned with input-output relationships. Not all of them can, by any means, fully be resolved into financial terms. Also, no forest owner or manager has complete freedom of choice; policy, social, political, and related considerations impose various restrictions. But many such questions can be reduced to financial terms and, within whatever constraints may be imposed, give a guide for decision. Financial success is directly related to the making of the best possible choices under existing circumstances.

The purpose of this chapter, building on the valuation framework given in preceding chapters, is to present a series of forest valuations to illustrate typical and recurrent problems. Timber management is assumed, but the general methods developed here have fairly general application to other situations.

analysis of financial alternatives—general

Before considering specific problems, some general orientation concerning the nature of financial alternative analysis is needed.

O B J E C T I V E S A first need in applying valuation methods to financial alternatives is clearly to define objectives. As has been repeatedly stressed, the purposes of forest management are many and vary widely between individuals, organizations, and ownership, whether private or public. For all, the idea of maximization—of something—is the common denominator. Just what is being maximized has to be defined; a mixture of financial and other objectives are often involved. Financial objectives, as are assumed here, normally center on maximization of net return, which can be defined in several ways depending on purpose.

In general terms, maximization of net return occurs when marginal cost equals marginal revenue. This measure may be applied to an enterprise as a whole or to any part of it in terms of maximizing the rate of return on the investment. The marginal cost is then the opportunity cost of the additional investment. This introduces the concept of an alternative rate, internally or externally determined, to which the desirability of a particular investment is compared. Capital budgeting is a common example; net return will be maximized when those investments are selected that promise the highest rate of return. Another common application is in deciding when to cut or to leave a particular tree based on the tree's expected rate of financial return. Those trees making or expected to make a rate of return below some acceptable figure may be cut and those above this figure, left. The same principle is applied in an economic determination of rotation length (Chap. 10). There, the rotation of maximum land expectation value is determined in relation to some rate of interest. A forest rent rotation is determined by reducing this alternative rate to approach zero, at which point the maximum net return from a property is obtained, assuming that there is no outside alternative use of capital.

The point of emphasis is that financial objectives vary, and each must be defined in accordance with purpose.

C O N S T R A I N T S   Closely akin to objectives are the constraints within which a forest manager must operate. These constraints can be of many kinds. Those relating to the purposes of management have been mentioned; they include financial policy, availability of capital, and often social and political considerations. There may also be constraints imposed by the character of forest land owned or available for purchase. Limitations on the availability of adequate input and output data are a chronic and often severe restriction on execution of financial analyses.

In many situations there are limitations on the number of forest choices available. There may be only a limited number of practical alternatives as to how to regenerate, cut, and log timber stands. Time itself is a major constraint; timber production is necessarily carried on over a rather long time sequence; operational commitments that limit opportunity for quick change have to be made. Where markets are fixed by forces external to the business, as is usually the case, financial alternatives that do not yield increased returns per unit of volume sold resolve into a problem of cost minimization, which is characteristic of the logging process.

Constraints, then, must be recognized, since they often distinctly limit the number and kinds of choices possible. It is often not practicable to consider a full range of alternatives that can be plotted as cost and revenue curves; usually, the forest manager deals with only certain segments of what theoretically may be a continuum.

U N C E R T A I N T Y   Uncertainty[1] is a large, important, and unsatisfactory subject to deal with, certainly so in forestry because of the large time element and natural hazards involved. There is a tendency, when using data mathematically in analysis, to assume that the results are accurate because the right formula and correct arithmetic are used. This is far from true; in forestry one works in a considerable area of uncertainty. Costs at a particular point in time may be accurate, although good cost data are hard to get and change with method, kind of equipment, labor efficiency, and the like. Cost accounting is a difficult subject in itself. Estimating the effect of a given input, pruning for example, on future output is more difficult. What will be the value of increased log quality 30 to 50 or more years in the future when technology, markets, etc. undoubtedly will be different? Financial forecasting is always difficult and uncertain; the whole gamut of costs and returns will almost surely change.

What should be done? One answer, commonly practiced, is to be conservative, to estimate returns at what is considered a "safe" level. Although good practice to a degree, undue conservatism results in severe and chronic underestimation; things may turn out better as well as worse then anticipated. A more desirable practice, where meaningful forecasts are desired,

[1] See p. 328. By "uncertainty" is meant those events whose outcome is not subject to actuarial prediction, although estimates may be made.

is to estimate as accurately as possible and then appraise carefully and severally the possible areas of uncertainty. It is often possible to bracket the likely range of uncertainty and analyze for high or low values as well as average (Marty, 1964). Where different alternatives are subject to about the same kinds and degree of uncertainty, the effect of uncertainty may approximately cancel out (Flora, 1964).

USEFULNESS OF COMPARATIVE ANALYSES   In many situations the key purpose in analyzing alternatives is not so much to make financial forecasts as such but to appraise relative differences between possible choices. By using best present data available, it is often possible to make comparisons to a degree of accuracy sufficient to guide decisions. One can compare the financial results of different regeneration methods, stand improvement work, and the like, with considerable confidence as to their relative desirability either within or between such groups. A comparative approach is necessary when one is working within a general production framework and wishes to test the effect of varying one factor with others held constant.

single factor analysis

The basic pattern of a single factor analysis is an investment in a particular factor of production made in expectation of a return at some future time. Other factors are held constant, so that the input and output of the particular factor investigated can be isolated and studied. Such analyses underlie and are the point of beginning for more complex and integrated analyses wherein a number of factors are considered that may interact in various ways and affect total outcome, such as the analysis of the profitability of a timber-growing business as a whole.

PRUNING EXAMPLE

There are many opportunities for single factor analysis in forestry. Take forest pruning as a common example. Pruning is done in one or more operations to remove the lower limbs from trees. The purpose is primarily to increase the future market value of selected trees and is based on the assumption that the additional clear wood grown outside the knotty core will command a premium price in the future. There are some other benefits of pruning, principally in reduction of forest fire fuel hazard and in improvement in visibility and ease of movement through young stands, that are sometimes deemed sufficient to prune most of the trees in a stand. These benefits are not, however, considered here. In any event, considerably more trees are normally pruned than will remain in the stand long enough to receive full benefit of the treatment.

Alternative applications of pruning to increase tree and stand value can be isolated rather readily. Done in stands of species, quality, and condition where such work is worthwhile, pruning does not significantly affect species composition, stocking, or rate of growth. For an individual tree, the return is received when the tree is harvested. It is also reasonable to assume that continuing forest costs, such as for protection against fire or insects, and general forest improvement and administration will not appreciably be affected.

The basic valuation method is simple, although the silviculture, mensuration, and cost determination of forest pruning are not. The essential valuation data needed are illustrated in Table 20.1 for an average tree pruned in a stand. As shown (column 2), an expenditure of $0.82 per tree harvested yields a receipt of $7.40 thirty years from the time the initial pruning is made. Assuming an interest rate of 6 percent, the net gain in present value is $0.54. It would make no difference, relatively, if expenditures were accumulated to the time when the receipt was realized. The net gain would be $0.54 compounded for 30 years or $3.10 per tree. The present is, however, a more logical time to make comparisons. In this instance, if 6 percent is considered an acceptable alternative rate, pruning is clearly desirable, since it yields a small net return above this rate.

In such situations, it is often better to solve for a rate rather than

TABLE 20.1. COSTS AND RETURNS FROM PRUNING AN AVERAGE
TREE IN A STAND

Item	Values without discount	Present value discounted at 6 percent
(1)	(2)	(3)
Expenditures[a]:		
Initial pruning to 10 ft.................	$0.49	$0.49
Pruning to 17 ft 4 years later...........	0.33	0.26[b]
Total...........................	$0.82	$0.75
Receipts:		
Increased tree value resulting from pruning in 30 years........................	7.40	1.29[c]
Net return............................	$6.58	$0.54

[a] Adjusted for a 25 percent reduction in number of pruned trees that will not be harvested and sold, therefore receiving the added value of a pruned log.

[b] Discounted for 4 years.

[c] Discounted for 30 years.

to assume one. At some rate of interest, cost equals return (Chap. 16, p. 353). In this case,

$$\$0.75(1 + i)^{30} = \$7.40$$
or $\quad (1 + i)^{30} = \$7.40/0.75 = 9.87$

By interpolation from compound interest tables, the rate is a little over 7.9 percent. This rate can be directly compared to that from any other pruning alternative expressed in the same terms.

If adequate mensurational and cost data were available, costs and returns could be expressed on a per-acre basis or in value added per unit of tree volume (cubic or board feet). The valuation treatment would, however, remain basically the same, except that pruned trees probably would not all be cut at the same time. This would be true in uneven-aged stands.

The return from pruning comes mainly from the added value of products such as veneer or clear lumber manufactured from the timber. It can consequently be expressed in terms of value added to finished products sold, to pruned logs as they reach the mill, or to the stumpage value of trees as they stand in the forest, following the same sequential pattern of valuation illustrated in Chaps. 18 and 19. Which to use depends on purpose. To the landowner who sells stumpage, this is the base, because it is what he sells and measures what he receives from his pruning investment, which is necessarily made in the forest. To a log buyer, the log is the base. To an integrated producer who both grows and processes timber, or to a community where it is desired to estimate full economic benefits resulting from value added to raw materials in manufacture, product prices would be appropriate as a base in measuring the full benefit of pruning.

In valuation work, and pruning is a good example, it is important to define carefully the basis on which cost and return comparisons are made. The basic question is always: Who gets the value and when?

DISPOSAL OF UNMERCHANTABLE TREES

In many forest areas, there are trees of low or negative value that encroach on growing space that could be utilized by much more valuable trees. Removal of these low-value trees can substantially increase total value production. Such trees sometimes can be removed commercially but more often must be disposed of by felling, girdling, or poisoning at net cost. The problem is widespread.

The following illustration is drawn from the United States where low-value hardwoods often seriously overtop and inhibit the growth of more valuable pine species. The valuation problem is similar to pruning in form except that the benefit from release does affect the remaining stand in stocking, rate of growth, and species composition. Also, the effects of the release occur over a considerable period of time, affecting thinning as well as major harvest yields. These circumstances make estimation of financial returns from treatment difficult.

Applied in an essentially even-aged stand (as regards the pine component) that is 10 years of age and managed for pulpwood production on a 30-year rotation, costs and returns are estimated in Table 20.2. In gross terms, a single expenditure of $9 per acre resulted in increased receipts of $63 coming from 10 to 20 years in the future. The returns from this kind of work are often high; without treatment, the stand may produce little net value. At 6 percent interest, the present net worth per acre was increased $14.20. It is always a bit difficult to define such a figure. Often it is called profit, but this may or may not be correct terminology. Strictly, it is a net gain remaining above a certain interest cost assumed.

The rate of return can be determined as follows:

$$\$8/(1 + i)^{10} + \$15/(1 + i)^{15} + \$40/(1 + i)^{20} = \$9$$

When one substitutes values for i and interpolates, the equation balances at a rate of 12.3 percent.

The cost of treatment is presumably rather accurate, but its efficacy in killing the hardwoods and the subsequent timing and amount of growth effects on the young pine stand may be uncertain, as are also the unit prices received for the timber. This is an instance where one might well estimate some maximum and minimum growth responses and unit prices to bracket the possible range of uncertainty and judge accordingly.

As in the pruning example, a large amount of information based on experience and research must be compressed into the relatively few key figures necessary to evaluate the results of a particular investment. This is characteristic of the valuation process, the accuracy of which is dependent

TABLE 20.2. COSTS AND RETURNS OF RELEASING A YOUNG PINE STAND FROM HARDWOOD COMPETITION ACRE BASIS (INTEREST AT 6 PER CENT)

Item	Values without discount	Discounted present value
Expenditures:		
Poisoning hardwood trees in a single operation...	$ 9.00	$ 9.00
Receipts (increased net value due to treatment):		
Thinning 10 years hence......................	8.00	4.47
Thinning 15 years hence......................	15.00	6.26
Final harvest 20 years hence.................	40.00	12.47
Total receipts............................	$63.00	$23.20
Net return...............................		$14.20

on the quality of the supporting data. In this respect, valuation can serve as a useful problem analysis by pointing out the kind and importance of specific information needs. Major emphasis is often placed on methods and costs, which tend to be specific and determinable, with inadequate attention given to returns. The latter are usually more difficult and uncertain to determine but equally necessary to evaluate the desirability of a particular forest practice.

USE OF BENEFIT-COST RATIOS AND UNIT COSTS

It often happens that one wishes to compare two or more alternative investments when the time periods involved are approximately equal. Different methods of site preparation, of low-value species removal, or of pruning, wherein the elapsed time between cost and return items and unit values of returns are the same or nearly so, are examples. In such situations, useful comparisons can be made directly by use of ratios or unit costs without use of compound interest. It is well to know something of the uses and limitations of such methods.

A simple generalized example will illustrate. Consider two alternative investments as follows:

1. A cost of $10 resulting in $50 of increased yield in 30 years (10 units at $5 each).
2. A cost of $14 resulting in $85 of increased yield in 30 years (17 units at $5 each).

The rate of return on these alternatives is accordingly

1. $10(1 + i)^{30} = \$50$, and $(1 + i)^{30} = 50/10$, or 5. By interpolation from interest tables, this ratio indicates a rate close to 5.5 percent.
2. By the same procedure, the rate is 6.2 percent.

On the basis of a compound rate, the comparison of alternative 2 is 6.2/5.5, or 1.13 times better than 1. On a simple rate, the comparison is 1.21.

Consider now some benefit-cost ratios and unit cost comparisons using the same data.

 a. A simple benefit-cost ratio.
 (1) $10 produces $50, giving a ratio of 5.000 and
 (2) $14 produces $85, and the ratio is 6.071.

The comparison is consequently 6.071/5, or 1.21.

 b. Ratio based on return per dollar expended.
 (1) $10 produces 10 units, so the return per dollar expended is 10/$10, or 1.000 units.
 (2) $14 produces 17 units, so the ratio is 17/$14, or 1.21 units.

The comparison is 1.21/1, or again 1.21. It is the same if the situation is reversed and the comparison made on the cost per additional unit produced.

   c. Discounted present worth benefit-cost ratio.
   (1) The discounted present worth of $50, assuming 5 percent (the rate assumed makes no relative difference) is $50/(1 + i)^{30}$, or $11.569. The benefit-cost ratio is accordingly 11.569/10, or 1.157.
   (2) By the same process, the present worth is $19.667, and the benefit-cost ratio 19.667/14, or 1.405.

The comparison is then 1.405/1.157, or 1.21 as before.

A little arithmetical reflection will indicate that ratios *a*, *b*, and *c* and the comparison based on a simple rate of interest have to be the same, because all are derived by multiplying or dividing by constants. They differ, however, from ratios between rates of compound interest because of the geometric nature of interest accumulation. For a time interval of 10 years, the interest rate ratio is a little more than the benefit-cost ratios regardless of the rate. At 20 years all ratios are about the same for interest rates beween about 4 and 7 percent. Over 20 years, the benefit-cost ratios increasingly exceed those between interest rates and consequently overestimate the differences between alternative investments in comparison to interest rate solutions, which are a more consistent basis. This points to the familiar fact that all ratio comparisons must be made with care and understanding.

marginal analysis applied to an uneven-aged stand

Analyses so far considered have dealt with the relationships between the actual cost of a single investment and the future results expected. Consider now the situation in a forest area managed on an uneven-aged basis (Chaps. 8 and 9). By definition, there is in general no beginning nor end in point of time to the timber on a particular area. Continuity of the forest must be assumed and annual carrying costs paid. There is no actual establishment cost. Returns resulting from a change in management practice, such as changing the average level of reserve growing stock, can, however, be compared to the present value of the growing stock. This assumes that the growing stock represents invested capital which can be converted into money by cutting and used elsewhere. The financial desirability of increasing or decreasing the growing stock is accordingly measured by the rate of return on the capital represented in the growing stock. In economic language, this is an opportunity cost, and the problem is to estimate a marginal rate of return which can be compared to an alternative rate for use of capital elsewhere (Duerr and Bond, 1952; Duerr, Fedkiw and Guttenberg, 1956; and Fedkiw and Yoho, 1960).

An illustration of desirable growing-stock level determination following this approach is given by Duerr and Bond (1952). It is assumed that the length of the cutting cycle is already established and that desirable tree diameter, species, and quality distribution of trees making up different reserve growing-stock levels will be properly determined. This leaves the volume of reserve growing stock as the variable to be investigated and the question is: What is financially the most desirable volume?

Various levels of reserve growing stock (the volume just after a cyclic cut) and estimated growth appropriate to a 5-year cutting cycle are shown in the first four columns of Table 20.3. Although volumes are here given in board feet, it would make no essential difference if cubic measure were used and products sold other than lumber included in the value estimates. Values are here expressed in terms of conversion surplus (product selling value less direct costs). They could be expressed in stumpage value or other

TABLE 20.3. ESTIMATED VALUE GROWTH PER ACRE FOR VARIOUS ASSUMED LEVELS OF RESERVE GROWING STOCK[a]

Reserve growing stock		Estimated 5-year growth		Average annual value growth, percent	Marginal increase in value of reserve growing stock	Marginal increase in value of 5-year growth	Annual marginal value growth, percent
Volume, bd ft	Value	Volume, bd ft	Value				
(1)	(2)	(3)	(4)	(5)	(6)	(7)	(8)
5,000	$210.00	2,340	$107.30	8.6			
6,000	257.30	2,670	125.00	8.3	$47.30	$17.70	6.6
7,000	306.50	2,960	141.00	7.9	49.20	16.00	5.8
8,000	357.40	3,190	155.30	7.5	50.90	14.30	5.1
9,000	410.10	3,380	167.70	7.1	52.70	12.40	4.3
10,000	464.70	3,520	178.10	6.7	54.60	10.40	3.5
11,000	521.00	3,610	186.30	6.3	56.30	8.20	2.8

[a] Data by Duerr and Bond (1952). Columns 1 to 4, assumed.

Column 5 calculated as follows: For 5,000 ft of reserve growing stock, the value at the end of 5 years is $210.00 + $107.30, or $317.30. Assuming a compound annual rate of growth, $(1 + i)^n = V_n/V_0$ (Formula 3, p. 337). Substituting values, $(1 + i)^5$ = $317.30/210.00 = 1.511. This indicates a value for i of 8.6 percent.

Column 6 gives the values of column 2 successively subtracted from the next smaller figure; for example, $257.30 - 210.00 = $47.30.

Column 7 gives the values of column 4 successively subtracted from the next smaller figure; for example, $125.00 - 107.30 = $17.70.

Column 8 is calculated from columns 6 and 7 in the same way as column 5. For example, $47.30 + 17.70 = $65.00. Then $(1 + i)^5$ = $65.00/47.30, or 1.374, and i = 6.6 percent. Note that the 5-year marginal growth percent is $17.70/47.30 × 100, or 37.4 percent. The 6.6 percent is the annual equivalent on a compound basis.

value base appropriate to the situation. The advantage of including only direct costs is that general costs, those fixed in total amount for the operation as a whole, do not affect relative choice and hence can be excluded in a comparative analysis.

The average annual growth percentages of column 5 show that throughout the range of reserve growing stock volumes studied a good rate of return is being made on the total capital investment as represented by the value of the reserve growing stock. If, for example, 6 percent is considered a satisfactory overall rate of return, it would appear desirable to build the reserve growing stock up to at least 11,000 ft per acre since such a rate of return is still being made at this level. This is indeed one way of looking at the matter.

The marginal growth percentages of column 8, calculated as explained in the table footnotes, tell a different story. These are based on marginal rather than total values and measure the change in rate of return associated with increments in reserve growing stock. As shown, they decrease more sharply as the volume of the reserve growing stock is increased than do the average growth percentages of column 5, which are based on the total stand. The marginal value growth rate is less than 6 percent for any reserve growing-stock level of more than 6,000 ft. The average return as indicated by the periodic annual growth percentages partially conceals the decreasing marginal return.

The significance of this is that if a forest owner has an alternate use for capital, he will make more in total by halting the building up of additional growing stock, which represents accumulated invested capital, at whatever he considers the marginal cost of capital to him. For example, if he considers 4 percent an alternative rate applicable to his situation, about 9,000 ft would be the optimum growing stock for him.[1] Since any *increase* in growing stock above this level will return less than this rate, the additional capital represented could better be used elsewhere. It can be shown that, for whatever alternative rate of return is assumed, maximum total return will be attained by stopping reserve growing-stock accumulation at a level corresponding to this alternative rate.

Alternative rates must, however, be used with discretion and within the capabilities of the forest. Suppose, for example, that an owner wants

[1] As Duerr and Bond (1952) point out, grouping by reserve growing-stock classes, of 1,000 ft in this instance, introduces some distortion into the calculation of the marginal percentages. They can be more precisely determined by graphical analysis, removing the grouping effect. Note also that the marginal figures of columns 6–8 apply to and are an average for a volume class (column 1). Strictly, therefore, they should be shown opposite the midpoint of the class. For example, the 6.6 percent figure in column 8 is an average for the 5,000- to 6,000-ft class and if plotted should be shown opposite 5,500 ft. Considering the various uncertainties to which this sort of analysis is subject, the refinement is of little significance in this instance.

7 percent. This would indicate (Table 20.3) that the reserve growing stock should be something less than 5,000 bd ft, which might fail to utilize fully the land and result in substantially decreased net annual value growth per unit of area.

As has been pointed out, a rate is a ratio and not a quantity. The rate is controlled by the relationship between the increment and its base. Marginal rates of growing-stock increment usually will maximize for very sparse stands; a few small trees with a low value or volume base can have a very high current rate of increase. Although general costs are fixed in total amount at a given time, it must be remembered that they *are* costs nonetheless. Since they are spread against a smaller base, a reduced growing stock in this instance, they increase costs per unit of area and consequently reduce net value. The land is the real base in timber production.

The same situation arises in using an alternative rate as an opportunity cost to determine when to cut or leave a tree. Application of an arbitrary rate above what most trees in the stand can sustain will seriously deplete the growing stock and decrease its value productivity per unit of area. To put it bluntly, if the forester demands too much, he will run out of trees to cut, which certainly is not utilizing the area, even if a few trees remaining individually are making, currently or prospectively, a high rate of return.

timber production schedule analysis

The forest manager is confronted with many timber production valuation questions that cannot be isolated as single factors but which must be appraised in the context of a timber-growing schedule. These questions are of many kinds: When should a particular stand be cut, and when should it be left to grow? What is the effect of a delay in regeneration on net returns? What is the result of a changing annual cost, or of regeneration or other costs, in a production schedule? Illustrative answers to a number of these questions are given in this section.

WHEN TO CUT AND WHEN TO LEAVE A STAND

A recurrent question is whether to cut or leave a stand at a particular time. An overall answer is given in Chap. 10 on determination of the rotation. For a particular production schedule applied to land of specified site quality, and at some acceptable rate of interest, the main stand becomes financially mature at rotation age, is cut, and another production cycle started. What about treatment of stands of intermediate age?

The issues can best be brought to practical focus by considering purchase of timberland to be managed on an even-aged basis. Several situations will be considered.

First, assume a tract is purchased at an average cost of $65 per acre. It has merchantable timber on it with a current stumpage value of $45. The stocking and timber quality is not good, however, and clearly much less in capability for future growth than could be attained through applying a timber-growing schedule established for lands of the same quality. Assume further that the schedule of production is that given in Table 17.1 (p. 360) where a 30-year pulpwood rotation is used based on a 5 percent rate of return (or opportunity cost).

In this situation, the answer, rather obviously, is to liquidate at once all current merchantable values and establish a new stand. As the purchase price was $65 and the liquidation value is $45, the land has, in effect, been purchased for $20 per acre. In comparison to the land or L_e value of $24.29 calculated from Table 17.1 for lands of this quality, a good purchase has been made.

Assume now that, for the same purchase price of $65 per acre, a tract was purchased having fairly good pine stocking about 10 years old but which is seriously overtopped by nonmerchantable hardwood species. Should the stand be cut or left? Full answer to this question can be given only through a production analysis. The current merchantable value of the pine is low; its value depends on future incomes expected. A sharp distinction must be made between currently merchantable values that can be captured through liquidation and future net income values. The whole timber-growing process is based on investments made in expectation of future returns.

Again following the production schedule given in Table 17.1, an income value for this particular stand is estimated in Table 20.4. As shown, the overtopping hardwoods will be killed by a poisoning operation costing $7 per acre. The normal 15-year thinning will have to be foregone; stand stocking is insufficient. Thinnings at 20 and 25 years can be made, but the volume cut will be somewhat reduced, as will the final harvest, in relation to what is expected from sites of similar quality. The net present value is estimated at $69.93, which in comparison to the cost value of $65 indicates that, at 5 percent, the stand should be kept and carried for at least 20 years to the end of the rotation established for the area. By interpolation, the rate is about 5.2 percent. The purchase price is sufficiently low to cover the reduced yields due to partial stocking and the cost of poisoning.

It should be noted that a land value is necessarily included as a receipt item. The value was that calculated for the production schedule established for the general area and was used as a good estimate of land value for continued timber production. However, any estimate of market value believed significant could be used. It is also true that the income value analysis does not necessarily have to be done in relation to any established timber production schedule. It is logical to do so, however, because in a timber production business any particular tract is likely to be considered in relation to timberlands of similar quality and character for which production information is available.

It is worth noting the relationship of this analysis to that given on p. 454 for an aerial spraying job to kill unmerchantable trees regarded as a single operation. There, no question was raised about keeping the stand, a land value, or continuing land management costs. The returns from the spraying were, however, estimated in the same way; all future receipts directly resulting from the operation were included. Such an analysis is sufficient if the situation is such that only this single operation need be considered. In this analysis, the effect of undesirable tree removal was considered in relation to a production schedule for the stand as a whole, giving a more complete and integrated answer.

One further possibility, based on the same simple example, should be explored. Suppose that the stand purchased has on it some currently merchantable growing stock that is making a good rate of growth. The stand cannot be identified by age in relation to a rotation, but there is a question as to whether or not it should be kept for a while before undertaking regeneration. It is estimated that in 10 years the present $45 worth of mer-

TABLE 20.4. INCOME VALUE PER ACRE OF STAND PURCHASED AT AGE 10
(THIRTY-YEAR ROTATION, INTEREST AT 5 PERCENT)

Item	Value per acre	Years to discount	Discount factor	Present value
Receipts:				
Thinning at age 15, none.......				
Thinning at age 20, 2.5 cords at $4.00.......................	$ 10.00	10	0.6139	$ 6.14
Thinning at age 25, 4 cords at $5.00.......................	20	15	0.4810	9.62
Harvest at age 30, 30 cords at $6.50.......................	195.00	20	0.3769	73.50
Land value at age 30[a]..........	24.29	20	0.3769	9.15
Total receipts...............	....	...	....	$98.41
Expenditures:				
Killing of overtopping hardwoods in year following purchase....	7.00	1	0.9524	6.67
Annual costs.................	1.75	20	12.4622	21.81
Total costs...	....	...	....	$28.48
Net present value.............	....	...	....	$69.93

[a] Land value established for production schedule assumed (derived from Table 17.1).

chantable growing stock per acre will increase to $80. Looking at these figures only, the rate of return is

$$\$45(1 + i)^{10} = \$80, \text{ and } (1 + i)^{10} = \frac{\$80}{\$40} = 2$$

which by interpolation from compound interest tables indicates a rate of 7.2 percent. According to this, and accepting 5 percent as an alternative rate, the stand certainly should be kept—and perhaps longer than 10 years. Let us now look at the situation in total production terms as follows:

	Present discounted value at 5 percent
Receipts:	
Cut 10 years hence of $80....................	$49.11
Land value 10 years hence of $24.29...........	14.91
Total......................................	$64.02
Expenditures:	
Annual cost for 10 years at $1.75 per acre......	13.51
Net worth...................................	$50.51

Compared to the purchase cost of $65 per acre, the investment as a whole is earning considerably less than 5 percent. By substitution of other rates and interpolation, the rate is 2.5 percent. Although the existing stand is earning a good rate of return, there is not enough of it *per acre* to cover annual costs plus the investment cost value. The point is that consideration of growing-stock values only does not measure the full investment. This again illustrates the limitations of using rate of return out of a complete production context.

One further question to be considered in this group of stand analyses is this: Suppose one is not dealing with a timberland purchase giving a definite cost value but with lands already owned on which similar problems arise? The valuation problem remains essentially the same. A single factor analysis can be made for a particular investment, if it can realistically be isolated and the valuation based directly on the costs and returns involved. If this cannot be done, and a production schedule analysis is necessary, then a present cost value must be estimated to compare with income values based on future costs and returns, following the general form of analysis illustrated in this section.

An almost endless number and variety of problems of this general type could be considered, but their general valuation pattern is recurrent.

EFFECT OF DELAY IN REGENERATION

The importance of avoiding a delay in getting a new stand regenerated was emphasized in Chaps. 7 and 10 in general terms. The purpose here

TABLE 20.5. COSTS AND RETURNS PER ACRE AND LAND VALUE FROM AN
EVEN-AGED STAND MANAGED ON A 30-YEAR CUTTING
AGE ROTATION WITH A 4-YEAR DELAY IN REGENERATION
(INTEREST AT 5 PERCENT)

Item	Value per acre	Years to accumulate	Value at rotation age
Receipts:			
Major harvest, age 30.......	$240.50	0	$240.50
Thinning, age 15............	6.00	15	12.47
Thinning, age 20............	14.00	10	22.80
Thinning, age 25............	35.00	5	44.67
Total receipts.............	....	...	$320.44
Expenditures:			
Site preparation, year 3......	20.00	31	90.76
Planting, year 4............	10.00	30	43.22
Annual costs..............	1.75	34	148.87
Total expenditures........	....	...	$282.85
Net value at rotation age......	....	...	$ 37.59

$$\text{Land expectation value} = \frac{\$37.59}{(1.05)^{34} - 1} = \frac{\$37.59}{4.2533} = \$8.84$$

is to show the high cost of such delay through a specific illustration. The
example is again based on the production schedule given in Table 17.1
(p. 360). Here it was assumed that complete regeneration was obtained
in the first year without loss of a growing season, so the regulatory and
cutting age rotations are the same. The timing is rather close, however,
and a complete stand often cannot be established immediately after cutting.
Assume here that the total regeneration cost remains $30 per acre but that
there are some delays so that $20 of it is spent in the third year and $10
in the fourth year (for the planting) when the new stand is fully established.
The regulatory rotation consequently becomes 34 years to get a 30-year
cutting age rotation, which is desired. Costs and returns are given in Table
20.5.

The effect of this delay in regeneration, all other items unchanged,
is shown below:

	Net value at rotation age	Land expectation value
No delay in regeneration (Table 17.1).......	$80.69	$24.29
4-year delay in regeneration (Table 20.5)....	37.59	8.84

As shown, the effect of what might seem a rather small change is drastic. The land value is reduced almost two-thirds (at a higher rate of interest, the difference would be greater). The reason is that the production period is lengthened to 34 years to get 30-year harvest age timber. Annual costs must be paid for this extra 4 years, and the net value at rotation age is necessarily capitalized for 34 years to give the L_e or land value (Davis, 1965). By the nature of interest accumulation, values increase at a geometric rate as the time period is lengthened. The effect of the 4-year delay at the beginning of the rotation is measured by the increase in total values with interest for the last 4 years of the rotation. As has been emphasized many times, valuations including interest, which is inescapable, are very sensitive to the rate of interest and the time periods involved. The practical point here is that delay in getting adequate regeneration is expensive, and every year lost counts rather heavily.

A PROGRESSIVE INCREASE IN ANNUAL COSTS

A common assumption regarding annual costs is that they do not change during the estimation period. This is often not true. Again using the production schedule of Table 17.1, assume that annual costs increase by what might seem the modest amount of 10 cents per year beginning with the second year. Consequently, the $1.75 initial cost will increase by $2.90 to a total of $4.65 in 30 years. What is the increased cost? The problem can be solved by use of formula 12, p. 338 as follows (interest at 5 percent). The value of the *increase* is

$$V_n = \$0.10 \frac{(1.05)^{30} - 30(0.05) - 1}{0.05^2}$$

$$= \$0.10 \frac{4.3219 - 1.5 - 1}{0.0025}$$

$$= \$72.88$$

This is the value of the increase only. To this must be added the accumulated value without increase. This latter value is

$$V_n = \$1.75 \frac{(1.05)^{30} - 1}{0.05}$$

$$= \$1.75 \ (66.4388)$$

$$= \$116.27$$

The total value at the end of the rotation V_n is accordingly $72.88 + 116.27$, or $189.15. In Table 17.1 the net income at rotation age is $80.69. This increased cost of $72.88 would obviously nearly wipe out a positive land value (it would reduce to $2.35!).

In reality, if annual costs increased, it is likely that timber values would too, so the net increase in cost might cancel out. This analysis does, however, show the sensitivity of annual costs in total to a small progressive change in the annual amount.

SOLUTION OF ROTATION LENGTH FOR THE MAXIMUM RATE OF RETURN

In Chap. 10 it was stated that a rotation of maximum L_e value could approach that of maximum mean annual increment, but no limit was defined. This limit can be simply given, and this is a good place to do so in relation to land values. As has been stated, a L_e calculation solves for a land value for a particular period of time, rate of interest, and timber-growing schedule assumed.

Basically, the rotation of maximum rate of return is defined by the market—or assumed—value of land. For example, if bare land is considered to be worth $30 per acre for timber production, an L_e rotation calculation that indicates a lower value cannot earn the rate used. Conversely, if the L_e value is greater, a higher rate could be earned by shortening the rotation. The problem, consequently, is to find an interest rate that will give an L_e value equal to whatever is assumed to be a meaningful land value. This relationship further underscores the basic importance of land values in timber production analysis.

It should be clear from the examples given in this and preceding sections that the effect of input-output changes in the production schedule on net returns can be analyzed separately and in combination. Such items as different regeneration methods and their timing, the use of genetically superior seed, the importance of the timing and weight of thinning, the effect of timber quality on product value, changes in annual costs and in product prices expected can all be analyzed to determine their effect on net return. The only limit in a particular situation is the range of practical alternatives possible. Extensive analyses of this nature, wherein the amount of arithmetic is usually voluminous, can be facilitated by programming and the use of electronic computers.

guides to profitable utilization

Alternative uses for different portions of a tree frequently exist. Sawtimber logs, veneer logs, pulp or chemical wood, and piling may all be obtainable from the boles of a group of trees. Not all these choices are likely to exist, but several of them often do. The value of these products, as measured in some common unit of volume as the cubic foot, usually varies substantially. To the extent that markets for several products are available, the total return from a given quantity of stumpage purchased is maximized by cutting the different portions of the tree stem into the most valuable products possible. The importance of recognizing log grades in appraising tree values was brought out in Chap. 19. The purpose here is to extend the analysis to alternative products and to consider further the effect of general and direct costs.

The problem of alternative uses can be narrowed down to the utilization of an individual tree and the issues involved seen most clearly (Guttenberg and Duerr, 1949; Duerr, Fedkiw, and Guttenberg, 1956). Consider an 18-in. southern pine tree with both a sawlog and pulpwood market available. If the tree has enough value to cover the cost of marking, felling, and any other joint costs applicable to the tree as a whole, it is worth cutting down. These costs are incurred if the tree is felled and their amount has no bearing on the subsequent utilization of the tree. The question then becomes: To what use should each part of the bole be put? It will pay to utilize any log the return from which will exceed the direct costs of conversion. Any such section will contribute something toward meeting general costs fixed in amount for the particular situation and, hence, will increase total profit. Applying the principle of marginal analysis, it follows that the most profitable utilization of the tree will result when each section is put to the use that will yield the greatest margin of selling value less direct costs of conversion. This margin is termed conversion surplus.

An analysis of this tree is given in Table 20.6. As shown, the conversion surplus for the first three logs is greatest when used as sawtimber. The fourth log is worth more for pulpwood, and the fifth one is merely a cull and

TABLE 20.6. BEST USE OF AN 18-IN. SOUTHERN PINE TREE
WHERE LUMBER AND PULPWOOD ARE ALTERNATIVE USES[a]

16-ft log section	Used for lumber			Used for pulpwood			Best use	
	Sale value[b]	Direct costs of conversion[c]	Conversion surplus	Sale value[d]	Direct costs of conversion[c]	Conversion surplus	Conversion surplus	Product
Butt........	$14.50	$7.00	$7.50	$3.35	$1.75	$1.60	$ 7.50	Sawtimber
Second......	8.75	5.00	3.75	2.65	1.50	1.15	3.75	Sawtimber
Third.......	6.00	4.00	2.00	2.10	1.25	0.85	2.00	Sawtimber
Fourth......	3.25	3.50	−0.25	1.75	1.00	0.75	0.75	Pulpwood
Fifth.......	......	.....	......	0.75	0.80	−0.05	......	Cull
Total.....	......	.....	......	.....	.....	......	$14.00	

[a] Data from Guttenberg and Duerr (1949).

[b] Based on finished lumber prices f.o.b. cars at mill.

[c] Cost of conversion is calculated as a total up to the stage in processing to which the sale value applies. Direct costs, as distinguished from general or fixed costs, include only those expenditures which are directly chargeable to the log in question and are incurred only if the log is utilized.

[d] Based on price of pulpwood f.o.b. cars.

should be left in the woods since it will not pay its way at all. The analysis can be continued diameter class by diameter class, or by tree classes, to uncover and determine negative conversion surpluses and determine most profitable use. The same sort of analysis can also be extended to situations where the key question is whether an operator should sell certain classes of material, as veneer logs, pulpwood, piling, and the like outright or process them himself.

Continuing the sawlog-pulpwood analysis, suppose a logger and saw-mill operator normally logs and saws about 10 million board feet a year and that his general or fixed costs, those that are incurred independently of whether any particular log is cut or not, are $70,000 a year. These costs include capital charges on invested capital, general administration, taxes, and similar items. Following the common practice of prorating general costs against the annual cut, the average charge is $70,000/10,000 M, or $7 per M. The timber averages three 16-ft logs per tree, and an analysis of direct costs shows that butt and second logs, making up 70 percent of the cut or 7 million feet, have on the average a $47 conversion surplus per M. The top logs, however, average only $5 per M in conversion surplus.

Since the top logs do not return their share of general costs by $2, the operator concludes that they are being handled at a loss and sells them for pulpwood at $3 per M as they lie in the woods. No effort is made to get additional logs to replace the volume of top logs sold. A comparison of the financial results after a year's operation under the two plans is as follows:

Present Plan		*Revised Plan*	
7 MM of butt and second logs at $47 per M	$329,000	7 MM butt and second logs at $47 per M	329,000
3 MM top logs at $5 per M	15,000	3 MM top logs sold as pulpwood at $3	9,000
Total surplus	$344,000	Total surplus	$338,000
Fixed costs	70,000	Fixed costs	70,000
Net return	$274,000	Net return	$268,000

When it is put in this form, it is clear that the operator was ill-advised to sell top logs for pulpwood. It cost him $6,000. His error was in failing to recognize that, while the top logs did not pay a full prorata share of general costs, they did pay $5 per M toward them, which is more than did selling them at $3 for pulpwood.

One important qualification or exception to analyses of this sort should be noted. They apply only when total volumes available and general costs remain fixed in total amount. Regarding supply, it was assumed in the case considered here that a fixed volume of timber was available over the year. Any tree or log with a positive conversion surplus will be worth taking out, since it contributes something to meeting general costs and their total amount has no bearing on this decision. In this case, if the top logs could have been sold for $6 per M, it would have been desirable to do so, since this amount exceeds their conversion surplus of $5 per M. If, however, there were no limitation on timber supply and sawmill and logging equipment could be operated to efficient capacity on timber of higher value, it would pay to sell the top logs in the woods for whatever they would bring and not take them to the sawmill.

Consequently, an analysis of most profitable utilization must be applied to a specific situation clearly defined. If the aim is to get the most total dollar return from a¹ particular body of timber available for cutting, then any tree or log that will return something over direct costs should be taken. If the aim is to get the greatest return per unit of volume handled, and supply is not a limiting factor, then some higher standard of the marginal tree or log would be set. It is erroneous to think that there is anything set and immutable about tree or log diameter marginal limits. They change with circumstances, and each operator must appraise his situation individually.

financial alternative analyses in review

The aim of this chapter has been to present a series of common financial alternative problems of concern to the forest manager in timber production. Other problems could have been included, and variations encountered in practice are almost endless. It is, in fact, easy to become confused by the specifics of a particular situation and fail to grasp the essentials of the valuation problem. Most such problems fall into a relatively few types, and it is of first importance to realize that this is so and learn to recognize recurrent patterns.

Timber production valuation problems all basically reduce to a comparison of inputs and outputs over time. The most difficult problem often is to identify and to quantify them. Single factor analyses are useful when the results of a particular input can realistically be isolated from the production framework. If this is not true, then the effect of one or more inputs or outputs must be analyzed in relation to a production schedule.

In utilization problems, such as briefly sketched in the preceding section, the time element drops out and the valuation problem usually focuses on current selection of alternatives that will maximize the return over direct costs.

There are many problems of financial management in a forestry enterprise that cannot be dealt with here but which rest in large part on principles presented in this book. They involve such matters as road construction programming, logging analyses, marketing, the scheduling of cutting to minimize transportation costs, and study of alternative timber production schedules. In such situations, and particularly when the computation job is heavy, as it often is, programming and use of electronic computers offer large possibilities (Curtis, 1962; Loucks, 1964; Chapelle and Nelson, 1964; Gould and O'Regan, 1965). A word of caution should be interposed, however. Enthusiasm for computers, linear programming, model building, and operations research generally should not outrun penetrating analysis of objectives and constraints, which condition the solution of real problems. The realities of the forest situation must be understood. The conclusion of the computer can be no better than the data used.

21
appraisal of forest damage

Forests may be damaged in many ways and by a multiplicity of causes, including fire, ice, floods, insects, disease, animals, and acts of man. Forest damage from the same causes may include damage to severed timber products in the forest, to watershed, recreation, wildlife, forage, real and personal property, and forest improvements related to the forest in some way. Values affected by forest damage consequently arise from timber products and from the many other goods and services the forest renders and influences.

Estimation of damage either to the forest or to something valuable associated with the forest is a problem in resource valuation. For example, the difference between appraising the effects of damage to a young timber stand by fire and applying some cultural measure to improve the stand is essentially that the first reduces and the second increases value. The basic valuation techniques are essentially the same. Timber damage resulting from fire is measured by the direct and indirect consequences of forest growing stock destroyed or damaged plus perhaps some injury to the soil. The value of the loss suffered is estimated following the same general procedures for determining timber and timberland values given in Chaps. 17 to 20. Similarly, evaluation of measures aimed to increase the watershed value of a forest area, either in terms of usable water produced or in flood damage averted or reduced, involves the same problems in estimating resource values as does determination of damage resulting from partial or complete destruction of the forest cover.

471

Damaging a forest is merely the reverse of building it up. In either case, the basic appraisal problem is to determine the value with and without treatment or damage. The difference is the value of the treatment or damage.

Damage appraisal should consequently be thought of as a special application of forest valuation procedures. Market, replacement or restoration, cost, and expectation value approaches are employed where appropriate, following the same general techniques employed for any forest value determination.

Forest damage does, however, introduce some special and often bafflingly difficult appraisal problems. These center around its unwanted, often peculiar, and usually unexpected nature, the legal questions that often enter in, and the frequent difficulty in identifying and measuring damages to values involved. These are the aspects that are emphasized in this chapter with special reference to timber values.

Damage appraisals are made for a number of purposes, principally:

1. To furnish managerial information. The owner or manager of a forest property normally wants to know, within the limits of accuracy that may affect operational decisions, the amount of forest damage suffered from whatever the cause. He needs this information, quite apart from any legal action that may be involved, to guide him in the effective management of the property. Salvage operations, changes in cutting schedules and silvicultural practices, need for capital investment, and maintenance of improvements may result from forest damage.

2. As a basis for economic resource valuation and analysis. Expenditures affecting forests, such as flood control projects, fire, insect, and disease control operations, and similar activities, depend for their justification largely on estimates of forest damage caused or expected that may be averted. For example, reasonable, uniform, consistent, and meaningful statistics on fire damage are badly needed to guide fire control effort and to evaluate more accurately the many effects of fire.

3. For taxation purposes. Particularly under Federal income taxation in the United States, a monetary estimate of damage is necessary to establish capital or other losses in obtaining tax relief.

4. For settlement of insurance claims.

5. To establish a factual basis for a legal claim against someone causing damage. Here, damage becomes a litigation matter and must be considered in relation to the framework of existing law. There is some tendency to think of damage primarily in connection with prosecuting or defending damage suits. In forestry, however, most damage is caused by what can be termed "acts of God" or by people either unable to pay or against whom it is either impractical or considered unwise to press suit. While damage suits are more or less spectacular and are important, they represent a small

proportion of total damage sustained. Large owners, such as corporations and public agencies, often suffer considerable damage from persons from whom they do not seek legal redress for reasons of public relations and general policy. The owner or society at large bears the loss.

Since forest damage may result from many causes, be of many kinds, and be estimated for several purposes, a first essential in considering damage is to be realistic and clear as to objectives. As with other appraisals, damage estimates of the same thing can vary widely according to the point of view and purpose. In appraising the results of a specific fire, an owner might make one estimate for his own information to get a measure of how much the fire really hurt his operations and another to use as a basis for court action. Still another estimate might be made from a general economic standpoint to appraise, in addition to direct timber and other property losses, damage that may result to watershed, wildlife, or recreation values for which a private owner may receive little or no direct return. Public agencies naturally consider these things differently than do private owners. All these estimates may be equally valid and meaningful when considered in terms of their purpose. A large element of judgment usually enters into damage estimates.

Estimates of monetary losses resulting from damage cannot realistically be considered apart from their specific economic setting as regards time, place, and circumstances. For example, if timber killed by insects could not have been marketed in the reasonably foreseeable future undamaged, it is not an economic loss but only a part of natural stand development. The monetary loss occasioned by insects, fire, and the like is directly controlled by the marketability, present or potential, of the timber damaged. For damage estimates to be meaningful, there has to be a loss *to* man's interests, whether to an individual or to a segment of society as a whole. There is no such thing as a monetary loss in the abstract; it has to be measured in relation to something. This fact becomes immediately apparent when the legal aspects of damage are considered.

legal aspects of damage

Since damage frequently involves questions of individual responsibility and indemnification for loss, some legal principles concerning damage should be understood. Much of the material given here is drawn from *Corpus Juris Secundum,* which gives a complete restatement of the entire American law as developed by all reported cases. Reference should also be made to Falk (1958) and to Kinney (1942). Only very general principles can be considered here.

Damage is defined as "loss, injury, or deterioration, caused by the negligence, design, or accident of one person to another, in respect to the latter's person or property" (25 CJS 441).[1] The fundamental principle or theory on which damages are based is just compensation or indemnity for the loss or injury sustained. This applies when the action is in connection with a contract or in tort. The latter means in general an act that in one way or another gives rise to a right of legal action otherwise than through breach of contract.

Under Anglo-Saxon common law, as it has developed, payment for damage is made in money as a compensation, or satisfaction, for a loss or injury sustained. While a court through injunction can require someone to desist in action that is causing or likely to cause damage, payment for damage sustained is measured in money and not in kind or by specific restorative action. In the case of a contract, "the person injured is, so far as it is possible to do so by a monetary award, to be placed in the position he would have been in had the contract been performed" (25 CJS 563). In torts, the intent is essentially the same but because of the frequent "impossibility of exactly fixing such compensation by a money standard its amount must be determined by the jury in the exercise of their sound discretion" (25 CJS 589).

KINDS AND MEASURE OF DAMAGES

The nature and circumstances of damage naturally affect their legal treatment. Three legally distinguishable classes or kinds of damages of frequent significance in appraisal of forest damage are termed compensatory, liquidated, and exemplary.

Compensatory Damages. Compensatory damages are awarded in tort actions to replace the loss caused by a wrong or injury. "A wrongdoer is liable to the person injured in compensatory damages for all of the natural and direct or proximate consequences of his wrongful act or omission" (25 CJS 471–472). A person is not liable for remote consequences. When the damage may have resulted from several causes and it is as probable that the defendant was responsible as not, no award can be made. Similarly, "uncertain, contingent or speculative damages may not be recovered" (25 CJS 489).

The measure of damages for injury to real property is usually the difference in the value of the property immediately before and after the injury. Losses arising from the destruction or depreciation of property and from the prevention of normal use of the property are elements of damage. It is both logical and proper in computing damages for injuries to a part of a land property to consider the effects on the property as a whole. That is, injury to a specific part of a property may affect its use as a whole

[1] *Corpus Juris Secundum,* Vol. 25, p. 441. Succeeding references to this source employ the same system of reference.

and cause damage in excess of that which might be apparent if only the part immediately affected is considered.

In the case of a forest property managed on a sustained-yield basis, damage to a part of it is most validly measured by the effect on the yield of the property as a whole. The problem is basically regulation of the cut. If portions or all of a particular age group or two in a forest managed on an even-aged basis are destroyed by fire, the management problem is to reregulate the forest, and the measure of damage is the reduction in annual cut resulting from regulatory readjustments necessary over a period of time to bridge the missing age classes. Damage estimated on this basis is difficult to establish in court because of general unfamiliarity with regulatory techniques, even though it is legally sound.

In computing damages, since they have to be expressed in money, a court favors measures that are as "real" and tangible as possible. "Where there is more than one method of estimating damages, that method which is most certain and definite should be adopted" (25 CJS 562). There must be some data and some assurance of their reality and validity of measurement; specific estimates and not mere guesses or opinion are necessary. Not only the plaintiff, but also the defendant must be protected, the former to give him reasonable compensation, and the latter to prevent excessive and unjust payment. It is natural for a plaintiff to overestimate loss and for a defendant to minimize it. It is the duty of the court or jury to reach an equitable decision in view of the evidence presented to it. Actual costs, restoration, or current market values are consequently favored where they can be established and are applicable. Profits, while not denied as a proper element of damage, are likely to be regarded as speculative if they are uncertain. If reasonably certain, they may be allowed.

While all reasonable expenses, present or future, consequent upon the wrong or injury may in theory be recovered, there is a tendency in practice to limit them to items rather directly connected with the damage. Interest on money specifically due but the payment of which is prevented by the tort may be allowed, usually on a simple interest basis. The use of interest, and especially compound interest, in computing damage is not looked upon with favor. Income values are difficult to establish for this reason. In general, a court does not favor mechanistic or mathematical formulas or procedures in determining damage unless their usage and applicability can be clearly established. In determining damage, the present or reasonably contemplated use by the owner is normally the basis. If an owner claimed that his present use was not a measure of a much more profitable use which he expected to make of the property, the burden of proof is on him to establish the point.

"As a general rule, sometimes expressed in statutory enactments, there can be no recovery for losses which might have been prevented by reasonable efforts on the part of the person injured" (25 CJS 499). An owner is never excused from taking reasonable care to protect his property, although determination of what is reasonable in a specific situation is often a difficult legal point. The general test is what a prudent man can be expected to do as measured by customary or ordinary practice. If a plaintiff reasonably could have prevented loss, all he is likely to recover is the reasonable cost of so doing.

As a practical matter, it should be observed that while the intent of the law is to give just compensation, a plaintiff seldom gets full recompense in fact because of these various limitations on the measure of damages. Bonbright (1937) points out several reasons for this, including:

1. Failure to allow full costs of litigation (attorney and court costs), time, anxiety, and all expenses involved.
2. Inadequate allowance of interest from time of injury to award.
3. Failure to allow for changes in the value of money.
4. Failure to allow for changes in the value of property.
5. General rule against allowance for sentimental values.
6. Doctrine against allowance for speculative damage.
7. Limitations on damage to that "reasonably contemplated" or "proximately caused," which may be overstrictly construed.

These items apply rather heavily in the case of timber damage. Literal restoration or replacement is impossible, and the damages suffered may be of long-time duration, difficult to measure, and have many ramifications. Damage to timber consequently tends to be uncertain and even speculative, and legal redress is consequently often incomplete and unsatisfactory. The amount of damage awarded is up to the jury (or judge) and is often arbitrarily determined with no specific basis given. Unless there is something patently in error about the determination of the amount, or fraud, corruption, or the like can be shown, courts will not overturn a decision rendered on the basis of amount awarded alone. This is particularly true if there was no precise way of measuring the amount of damage.

Liquidated Damages. Liquidated damages arise directly from breach of contract. "As a general rule, a contract may contain a provision fixing the amount to be paid in the event of a breach, where the damages are uncertain in nature and amount or difficult of ascertainment and the amount fixed is fair" (25 CJS 650). Such provisions are frequently included in contracts; building contracts are a notable example, for the purpose of agreeing upon and defining in advance what is to be paid for nonperformance of the contract in whole or in part. Such provisions are often inserted in Federal and other timber sale contracts relating to cutting of unauthorized trees, the leaving of high stumps, unnecessary damage to remaining trees, incomplete utilization, and the like. They avoid or minimize the necessity of court action under tort and attendant jury hazards, legal costs, and difficulties in determining damages. As long as the parties to the contract agree to its terms, no question of court action is involved. If, however, there is a breach of contract, a question as to the legal validity of a provision for liquidated damages may arise.

It should be noted that a provision for liquidated damages does not give an option to incur them at will in lieu of fulfilling the terms of a contract. For example, a consulting forester selling his business in an area and posting a bond against re-entering the business in the area for a stated period has no license deliberately to forfeit bond and set up shop again. Besides forfeiting his bond, he could be sued for compensatory damages. Similarly, a clause covering liquidated damages for leaving high stumps does not give license to so cut them merely by paying the stipulated damage rate.

A conflict between state laws sometimes arises concerning the validity of such provisions in a contract. Usually, state law at the place of performance governs unless the parties definitely had in mind some other law. Interest as a part of damages is similarly fixed by the law of the place of performance and is covered by applicable state law unless there is good reason for some other basis.

Two kinds of damage provisions, penalty and liquidated, may be included in contracts, and there is an important legal distinction between them. In general, a penalty damage is a threat or penalty stipulated to secure performance of a contract, while liquidated damage is a sum to be paid in lieu of performance. The two are difficult to tell apart in practice. If damage payments specified are not unreasonably high, courts will ordinarily allow them as liquidated damages but not as penalty damages. Courts do not like to mix liquidated or compensatory damages with exemplary (or punitive) damages upon which penalty clauses may verge. It is the duty of the court to determine whether an effort was made in good faith to estimate in advance a reasonable amount of damage that will follow a breach. If so, a liquidated damages clause will be enforced. If not, it will be regarded as a penalty and disallowed, regardless of the specific language employed in the contract. Merely calling a provision one of liquidated damages does not necessarily make it so in the eyes of the law, although the intent of the parties concerned carries considerable weight. As a generality, if the amount is reasonable, it will be considered a liquidated damage; if unreasonable, a penalty damage. The difficulty in measuring damages "is important in determining whether the provision is for liquidated damages or a penalty; ordinarily, if damages are difficult to ascertain, the provision will be construed as for liquidated damages. . . ." (25 CJS 666).

Exemplary Damages. Exemplary damages, also called punitive, are "imposed by way of punishment, and are given for that purpose in addition to compensation for a loss sustained" (25 CJS 455). Their award is rare in relation to compensatory and liquidated damages and usually rests entirely within the discretion of the jury. For exemplary damages to be allowed, it must be established that the damage was willful, grossly negligent, reckless, wanton, malicious, or fraudulent (Kinney, 1942). Multiple damages, that is, an amount of damage which is determined as a multiple of the direct or actual loss sustained, may be allowed as exemplary damages. Double or treble damages are not unusual. Multiple damages may also be regarded as liquidated damages when there is reason to claim that the total loss is something more than the directly measurable loss. Provisions for charging double stumpage for the cutting of unauthorized trees are sometimes included in timber sale contracts and regarded as liquidated damages.

timberland damage

There is an almost limitless number of ways in which timberland can be damaged or cause damage to other resources. The following classification will bring out the range of possibilities involved:

1. Damage to the timber stand itself.
    a. Complete. The existing stand may be completely wiped out as by fire, flood, hurricane, etc. Salvage, reestablishment, and related costs can often be estimated with a fair degree of accuracy.
    b. Partial. This is the more common and difficult situation. In addition to more or less directly observable effects in terms of trees killed, there may be many subsequent effects of indefinite duration difficult to measure. Greater susceptibility to insect, disease, or other damaging agencies, reduction in future growth due to reduced stocking, or an actual slowing of individual tree growth rates are examples. Some of these effects may be felt for many years after the initial damage.
2. Damage to the land itself. Excessively heavy cutting and fires, especially when severe or repeated, may cause damage to the soil lasting for many years, perhaps for one or more normal rotations. Such damage is logically expressed as a reduction in land expectation value.
3. Damage to nontimber resources within the forest. Values of the forest complex for fish and game, recreation, or grazing by domestic stock may be affected in one way or another by forest damage. Both plus and minus effects are involved. A fire may, for example, kill a lot of timber but improve big game conditions by increasing the supply of herbaceous vegetation.
4. Downstream damage. In areas subject to erosion or where water supplies are critical, the downstream effects of forest damage may be much more important than that to the stand itself. Moun-

tainous areas of Southern California or the Wasatch Mountains in Utah are good examples in the United States.

The financial effect of timberland damage can be felt in many ways. The loss may be immediate and expressible by an amount, as in the case of destruction of currently merchantable timber with no major time element involved. Salvage values must, of course, be deducted. The loss may also affect costs and returns over a period of time. The basic appraisal problem is to identify and evaluate all pertinent damages. Estimation of total values before and after damage may or may not be necessary. Estimates of total downstream values may be necessary to give a basis for estimation of damage to watersheds. In the case of mature timber, only the damage to it may need to be considered. Damage appraisal is resource evaluation from a particular point of view.

The purpose of the appraisal and exercise of good judgment must decide into what detail and how far into the future estimates of damage should be carried. From what has been said concerning legal aspects, estimates to support a suit must be definite and factually supportable. Estimates of forest damage for such a purpose are likely to be somewhat limited in scope. Effects of extended and often uncertain duration, and expectation values generally, are difficult to establish in court. The virtue of making damage estimates for managerial purposes depends upon what is to be gained from them. Detailed estimates of loss from severe damage by fire, wind, or some other cause just to get a dollar figure may be of little value, unless they are needed for income tax adjustment or related reasons. The managerial job is to face the situation as it is to replan operating schedules as may be necessary. This entails the application of regulatory techniques and general management planning going far beyond determination of damage. Estimates for statistical or analytical purposes are usually applied to many properties and situations and consequently are normally determined according to generalized and uniform procedures.

bibliography

CHAPTER 1

introduction to forest management: nature, purposes, development, status

AMERICAN FORESTRY ASSOCIATION, 1951. The progress of forestry, 1945 to 1950. Washington, D.C.

COMMITTEE ON HISTORY OF FORESTRY, R. K. WINTERS, CHAIRMAN, 1950. Fifty years of forestry in the U.S.A. Society of American Foresters, Washington, D.C.

DANA, S. T., 1951. The growth of forestry in the past half century. *J. Forestry,* **49**:86–92.

————, 1956. Forest and range policy. McGraw-Hill Book Company, New York.

————, and MYRON KRUEGER, 1958. California lands. The American Forestry Association, Washington, D.C.

————, J. H. ALLISON, and R. N. CUNNINGHAM, 1960. Minnesota lands. The American Forestry Association, Washington, D.C.

DANNECKER, KARL, 1939. The forest manager. American ed., translated by A. O. Weidelich. The American Forestry Association, Washington, D.C.

DAVIS, JOHN, A. L. BEST, P. E. LACHANCE, S. L. PRINGLE, J. M. SMITH, and D. A. WILSON, 1957. The outlook for the Canadian forest industries. Forestry Study Group: Royal Commission on Canada's Economic Prospects, W. L. Gordon, Chairman. Edmond Cloutier, Queen's Printer, Ottawa, Canada.

DAVIS, K. P., 1959. Forest fire: control and use. McGraw-Hill Book Company, New York.

FIFTH WORLD FORESTRY CONGRESS, 1960. University of Washington, Seattle.

GREELY, W. B., 1951. Forests and men. Doubleday & Company, Inc., Garden City, N.Y.

————, 1953. Forest policy. McGraw-Hill Book Company, New York.

HILEY, W. E., 1964. A forestry venture. Faber and Faber, Ltd., London.

KORSTIAN, C. F., 1944. Forestry on private lands in the United States. *Duke Univ. Forestry Bul. 8.*

LILLARD, R. G., 1947. The great forest. Alfred A. Knopf, Inc., New York.

PEPLER, W. A. E., 1953. The forestry situation in Canada—present and future. *Forestry Chronicle,* **29**:316–322.

PINCHOT, GIFFORD, 1947. Breaking new ground. Harcourt, Brace and World, Inc., New York.

ROTH, FILIBERT, 1925. Forest regulation, 2d ed. George Wahr Publishing Company, Ann Arbor, Mich.

SIXTH BRITISH COMMONWEALTH FORESTRY CONFERENCE, 1952. Edmond Cloutier, Queen's Printer, Ottawa, Canada.

SLOAN, G. McG., 1956. The forest resources of British Columbia, Report of the Commissioner. Don McDiarmid, Victoria, B.C.

SOCIETY OF AMERICAN FORESTERS, 1956. Forest practices developments in the United States, 1940 to 1955. Committee on Forest Practices, K. P. Davis, Chairman. Washington, D.C.

————, 1958. Forestry terminology, 3d ed., Washington, D.C.

————, 1960. American forestry, six decades of growth, Henry Clepper and Arthur B. Meyer, editors. Washington, D.C.

STODDARD, C. H., 1961. The small private forest in the United States. Resources for the Future, Inc. Washington, D.C.

TREVOR, C. G., and E. A. SMYTHIES, 1923. Practical forest management. Government Press, United Provinces, Allahabad, India.

U.S. DEPARTMENT OF AGRICULTURE, 1949. Trees: The Yearbook of Agriculture.

U.S. FOREST SERVICE, 1958. Timber resources for America's future. *U.S. Dept. Agr. Forest Serv., Forest Resource Rpt.* 14.

————, 1965. Timber trends in the United States. *U.S. Dept. Agr. Forest Serv., Forest Resource Rpt.* 17.

VAUX, H. J., 1952. Economic measures of forest conservation. *Biology Colloquium on Conservation,* Oregon State College, Corvallis.

WOODS, J. B., 1946. Report of the forest resource appraisal. *Am. Forests,* **52**(9):413–428.

ZIVNUSKA, J. A., 1949. Some aspects of the economic theory of forestry. *Land Economics,* **25**(2):165–172.

————, 1951. Future wood markets and forest management. *J. Forestry,* **49**:326–330.

CHAPTER 2

site, stocking, and spacing

ALLEN, J. C., 1960. Pine site index relationships in northwest Alabama and adjoining portions of Mississippi and Tennessee. Tennessee Valley Authority, Div. of Forestry Relations, Norris, Tenn.

AUSTIN, R. C., and D. H. BAISINGER, 1950. Manual for forest soils evaluation. Crown Zellerbach Corp., Portland, Ore.

AVERELL, J. L., 1945. Rules of thumb for thinning loblolly pine. *J. Forestry,* **43**:649–651.

BAKER, F. S., 1950. Principles of silviculture. McGraw-Hill Book Company, New York.

BICKFORD, C. A., 1957. Stocking normality and measurement of stand density. *J. Forestry*, **55**:99–104.

CARMEAN, W. H., 1956. Suggested modifications of the standard Douglas-fir site curves for certain soils in southwestern Washington. *Forest Sci.*, **2**:242–250.

CHISMAN, H. H., and F. X. SCHUMACHER, 1940. On the tree-area ratio and certain of its applications. *J. Forestry*, **38**:311–317.

COILE, T. S., 1940. Soil changes associated with the loblolly pine succession on abandoned agricultural land of the Piedmont plateau. *Duke Univ. Forestry Bul.* 5.

———, 1948. Relation of soil characteristics to site index of loblolly and shortleaf pines in the lower Piedmont Region of North Carolina. *Duke Univ. Forestry Bul.* 13.

———, 1952. Soil and the growth of forests. *Advan. in Agron.*, **4**:329–398.

———, and F. X. SCHUMACHER, 1953. Relation of soil properties to site index of loblolly and shortleaf pines in the Piedmont region of the Carolinas, Georgia, and Alabama. *J. Forestry*, **51**:739–744.

COWLIN, R. W., 1932. Sampling Douglas-fir reproduction stands by the stocked-quadrat method. *J. Forestry*, **30**:437–439.

DAVIS, K. P., 1935. A method of determining spacing in thinning. *J. Forestry*, **33**:80–81.

———, 1956. Determination of desirable growing stock—a central problem of forest management. *J. Forestry*, **54**:811–815.

DAY, B. B., 1937. A suggested method for allocating logging costs to log sizes. *J. Forestry*, **35**:69–71.

FOSTER, R. W., 1959. Relation between site indexes of eastern white pine and red maple. *Forest Sci.*, **5**:279–291.

GEVORKIANTZ, S. R., 1947. More about numerical expression of stocking in terms of height. *J. Forestry*, **45**:203.

——— and L. P. OLSEN, 1950. Growth and yield of upland balsam fir in the Lake States. *U.S. Forest Serv., Lake States Forest Expt. Sta. Paper* 22.

GRUSCHOW, G. F., and T. C. EVANS, 1959. The relation of cubic-foot volume growth to stand density in young slash pine stands. *Forest Sci.*, **5**:49–55.

HAIG, I. T., 1931. The stocked-quadrat method of sampling reproduction stands. *J. Forestry*, **29**:747–749.

———, 1932. Second-growth yield, stand, and volume tables for the western white pine type. *U.S. Dept. Agr. Tech. Bul.* 323.

HEIBERG, S. O., and D. P. WHITE, 1956. A site evaluation concept. *J. Forestry*, **54**:7–10.

LEXEN, B. R., 1943. Bole area as an expression of growing stock. *J. Forestry*, **41**:883–885.

———, 1939. Space requirement of ponderosa pine by tree diameter. *U.S. Forest Serv., Southwest. Forest and Range Expt. Sta. Note* 63.

LOWDERMILK, W. C., 1921. A unit of area as a unit of restocking. *U.S. Forest Serv., Missoula, Mont., Appl. Forestry Note* 17.

LUTZ, H. J., and R. F. CHANDLER, 1946. Forest soils. John Wiley & Sons, Inc., New York.

LYNCH, D. W., and F. X. SCHUMACHER, 1941. Concerning the dispersal of natural regeneration. *J. Forestry*, **39**:49–51.

MCARDLE, R. E., W. H. MEYER, and DONALD BRUCE, 1949. The yield of Douglas-fir in the Pacific Northwest, rev., October, 1949. *U.S. Dept. Agr. Tech. Bul.* 201.

MCLINTOCK, T. F., and C. A. BICKFORD, 1957. A proposed site index for red spruce in the northeast. *U.S. Forest Serv., Northeast. Forest Expt. Sta. Paper* 93.

MACKINNEY, A. L., and L. E. CHAIKEN, 1935. A method of determining density of loblolly pine stands. *U.S. Forest Serv., Appal. Forest Expt. Sta. Tech. Note* 15.

MEYER, W. H., 1937. Yield of even-aged stands of sitka spruce and western hemlock. *U.S. Dept. Agr. Tech. Bul.* 544.

——, 1938. Yield of even-aged stands of ponderosa pine. *U.S. Dept. Agr. Tech. Bul.* 630.

——, 1942. Yield of even-aged stands of loblolly pine in northern Louisiana. *Yale Univ., School Forestry Bul.* 51.

MITCHELL, H. C., 1943. Regulation of farm woodlands by rule of thumb. *J. Forestry,* **41**:243–248.

MULLOY, G. A., 1946. Rules of thumb in thinning. *J. Forestry,* **44**:735–737.

MUNGER, T. T., 1945. Stocked quadrats vs. number of trees as a basis for classifying reforesting land. *U.S. Forest Serv., Pacific Northwest Forest Expt. Sta. Forest Res. Note* 33.

RALSTON, C. W., 1951. Some factors related to the growth of longleaf pine in the Atlantic coastal plain. *J. Forestry,* **49**:408–412.

——, and C. F. KORSTIAN, 1962. Prediction of pulpwood yield of loblolly and shortleaf pine plantations. *Forest Sci.,* **8**:149–162.

REINEKE, L. H., 1933. Perfecting a stand-density index for even-aged forests. *J. Agr. Res.* **46**(7):627–638.

ROTH, FILIBERT, 1916. Concerning site. *Forestry Quart.,* **14**:3–13.

SCHNUR, G. L., 1937. Yield, stand, and volume tables for even-aged upland oak forests. *U.S. Dept. Agr. Tech, Bul.* 560.

SOCIETY OF AMERICAN FORESTERS, 1958. Forestry terminology, 3d ed. Washington, D.C.

SPURR, S. H., 1960. Photogrammetry and photo-interpretation. The Ronald Press Company, New York.

STONE, E. L., R. R. MORROW, and D. S. WELCH, 1954. A malady of red pine on poorly drained sites. *J. Forestry,* **52**:104–114.

U.S. FOREST SERVICE, 1929. Volume, yield, and stand tables for second-growth southern pines. *U.S. Dept. Agr. Misc. Pub.* 50.

WAKELEY, P. C., and JOSÉ MARRERO, 1958. Five-year intercept as site index in southern plantations. *J. Forestry,* **56**:332–336.

WELLNER, C. A., 1940. Relationships between three measures of stocking in natural reproduction of the western white pine type. *J. Forestry,* **38**:636–638.

WENGER, K. F., T. C. EVANS, T. LOTTI, R. W. COOPER, and E. V. BRENDER, 1958. The relation of growth to stand density in natural loblolly pine stands. *U.S. Forest Serv. Southeast. Forest Expt. Sta. Paper* 97.

WESTVELD, MARINUS, 1952. A method of evaluating forest site quality. *U.S. Forest Serv., Northeast. Forest Expt. Sta. Paper* 48.

WILSON, F. G., 1946. Numerical expression of stocking in terms of height. *J. Forestry,* **44:**758–761.

WINTERS, R. K., and J. G. OSBORNE, 1935. Growth and yield of second-growth red gum in fully stocked stands on alluvial lands in the south. *U.S. Forest Serv., South. Forest Expt. Sta. Occas. Paper* 54.

ZAHNER, ROBERT, 1957. Field procedures for soil-site classification of pine land in South Arkansas and North Louisiana. *U.S. Forest Serv., South. Forest Expt. Sta. Occas. Paper* 155.

———, 1958. Site-quality relationships of pine forests in southern Arkansas and northern Louisiana. *Forest Sci.,* **4:**162–176.

———, 1962. Loblolly pine site curves by soil groups. *Forest Sci.,* **8:**104–110.

CHAPTERS 3 AND 4

growth and yield

AREND, J. L., W. R. H. GUNDERSON, and A. F. MONROE, 1950. Growth of unmanaged oak-hickory woodlots in southern Michigan. *U.S. Forest Serv., Lake States Forest Expt. Sta. Tech. Note* 327.

ASSMANN, ERNST, 1961. Waldertragskunde. B L V Verlagsgesellschaft München, Bonn, Wien.

BEERS, THOMAS W., 1962. Components of forest growth. *J. Forestry,* **60:**245–248.

BICKFORD, C. A., F. R. LONGWOOD, and ROBERT BAIN, 1961. Average growth rates in the spruce-fir region of New England. *U.S. Forest Serv., Northeast. Forest Expt. Sta. Paper* 140.

BIOLLEY, H. E., 1920. L'aménagement des forêts par la méthode expérimentale et spécialement la méthode du contrôle. Attinger Frères, Neuchâtel and Paris.

BRENDER, E. V., 1960. Growth predictions for natural stands of loblolly pine in the lower Piedmont. *Georgia Forest Research Council Report* 6. Macon, Georgia.

BRIEGLEB, P. A., 1942. Progress in estimating trend of normality percentage in second-growth Douglas-fir. *J. Forestry,* **40:**785–793.

——— 1945. Calculating the growth of ponderosa pine forests. *U.S. Forest Serv., Pacific Northwest Forest and Range Expt. Sta.*

———, 1950. Growth of ponderosa pine. *J. Forestry,* **48:**349–352.

———, and J. W. GIRARD, 1943. New methods and results of growth measurements in Douglas fir. *J. Forestry,* **41:**196–201.

BROWN, R. M., and S. R. GEVORKIANTZ, 1934. Volume, yield, and stand tables for tree species in the Lake States, rev., 1934. *Univ. Minn., Agr. Expt. Sta. Tech. Bul.* 39.

BRUCE, DONALD, 1923. Preliminary yield tables for second-growth redwood. *Univ. Calif., Agr. Expt. Sta. Bul.* 361.

———, and F. X. SCHUMACHER, 1950. Forest mensuration, 3d ed. McGraw-Hill Book Company, New York.

CHAPELLE, D. E., and T. C. NELSON, 1964. Estimation of optimal stocking levels and rotation ages of loblolly pine. *Forest Sci,* **10:**471–502.

CHAPMAN, H. H., and W. H. MEYER, 1949. Forest mensuration. McGraw-Hill Book Company, New York.

DUERR, W. A., 1938. Comments on the general application of Gehrhardt's formula for approach toward normality. *J. Forestry,* 36:600–604.

———, and S. R. GEVORKIANTZ, 1938. Growth prediction and site determination in uneven-aged timber stands. *J. Agr. Res.,* 56:81–98.

DUNNING, DUNCAN, 1928. A tree classification for the selection forests of the Sierra Nevada. *J. Agr. Res.,* 36:755–771.

EYRE, F. H., and R. K. LEBARRON, 1944. Management of jack pine in the Lake States. *U.S. Dept. Agr.'Tech. Bul.* 863.

FLIGG, D. M., 1960. Empirical yield tables. *British Columbia Forest Serv., Forest Survey Note* 6.

GEHRHARDT, E., 1930. Ertragstafeln fur reine und gleichartige Hochwaldbestande von Eiche, Buche, Tanne, Fichte, Kiefer, gruner Douglasie und Larche. 2d. ed. Springer-Verlag, Berlin. Review by S. R. Gevorkiantz, *J. Forestry,* 32:487–488 (1934).

GEVORKIANTZ, S. R., 1927. A new growth per cent formula. *J. Forestry,* 25:44–49.

———, 1937. The approach of northern hardwood stands to normality. *J. Forestry,* 35:487–489.

——— and L. P. OLSEN, 1948. An improved increment-core method for predicting growth of forest stands. *U.S. Forest Serv., Lake States Forest Expt. Sta. Paper* 12.

HAIG, I. T., 1932. Second-growth yield, stand, and volume tables for the western white pine type. *U.S. Dept. Agr. Tech. Bul.* 323.

HEIBERG, S. O., and P. G. HADDOCK, 1955. A method of thinning and forecast of yield in Douglas-fir. *J. Forestry,* 53:9–18.

HERRICK, A. M., 1944. Multiple correlation in predicting growth of many-aged oak-hickory stands. *J. Forestry,* 42:812–817.

HORNIBROOK, E. M., 1940. A preliminary yield table for selectively cut lodgepole pine stands. *J. Forestry,* 38:641–643.

———, 1942. Yield of cut-over stands of Engelmann spruce. *J. Forestry,* 40:778–781.

HUBER, ALFRED, 1952. Examination of sustained yield management by the volume and increment control method. Trans. by Leif Holt. *Pulp Paper Mag.,* 53(1):104–113.

HUMMEL, F. C., and J. M. CHRISTIE, 1953. Revised yield tables for conifers in Great Britain. *Commission Forestry Record* 24. Her Majesty's Stationary Office, London.

HUSCH, BERTRAM, 1963. Forest mensuration and statistics. The Ronald Press Company, New York.

KEEN, F. P., 1943. Ponderosa pine tree classes redefined. *J. Forestry,* 41:249–253.

KIRBY, C. L., 1962. Growth and yield of white spruce-aspen stands in Saskatchewan. *Dept. of Natural Resources, Forestry Branch, Tech. Bul.* 4.

LEMMON, P. E., and F. X. SCHUMACHER, 1962. Volume and diameter growth of ponderosa pine trees as influenced by site index, density, age, and size. *Forest Sci.,* 8:236–249.

MADER, DONALD L., 1963. Volume growth measurement—an analysis of function and characteristics in site evaluation. *J. Forestry,* 61:193–198.

McArdle, R. E., W. H. Meyer, and Donald Bruce, 1930. The yield of Douglas fir in the Pacific Northwest, rev., October, 1949. *U.S. Dept. Agr. Tech. Bul.* 201.

McKeever, D. G., 1947. Empirical yield tables for Douglas fir, board feet Scribner rule by site and stocking classes. Weyerhaeuser Timber Co., Tacoma, Wash.

Meyer, H. A., 1935. A simplified increment determination on the basis of stand tables. *J. Forestry,* **33:**799–806.

———, 1936. Increment determination on the basis of stand tables. *J. Forestry,* **34:**948–950.

———, 1942. Methods of forest growth determination. *Pa. State Col., School Agr. Bul.* 435.

———, 1953. Forest mensuration. Penns Valley Publishers, Inc., State College, Pa.

Meyer, W. H., 1933. Approach of abnormally stocked forest stands of Douglas-fir to normal condition. *J. Forestry,* **31:**400–406.

———, 1934. Growth in selectively cut ponderosa pine forests of the Pacific Northwest. *U.S. Dept. Agr. Tech. Bull.* 407.

———, 1937. Yield of even-aged stands of sitka spruce and western hemlock. *U.S. Dept. Agr. Tech. Bul.* 544.

———, 1938. Yield of even-aged stands of ponderosa pine. *U.S. Dept. Agr. Tech. Bul.* 630.

———, 1942. Yield of even-aged stands of loblolly pine in northern Louisiana. *Yale Univ., School Forestry Bul.* 51.

Nelson, T. C., 1964. Diameter distribution and growth of loblolly pine. *Forest Sci.,* **10:**105–114.

——— and F. A. Bennett, 1965. A critical look at the normality concept. *J. Forestry,* **63:**107–109.

——— and E. V. Brender, 1963. Comparison of stand density measures for loblolly pine cubic-foot growth prediction. *Forest Sci.,* **9:**8–14.

———, T. Lotti, and E. V. Brender, 1961. Merchantable cubic-foot volume growth in natural loblolly pine stands. *U.S. Forest Serv. Southeas.. Forest Expt. Sta. Paper* 127.

Plonski, W. L., 1960. Normal yield tables. *Silvicultural Series Bul.* 2. Ontario Department of Lands and Forests, Toronto, Canada.

Reed, P. M., 1926. Red pine in central New England. *Harvard Univ., Harvard Forest Bul.* 9.

Rudolf, P. O., 1930. A comparison of several of the growth per cent methods of predicting growth. *J. Forestry,* **28:**28–33.

Salman, K. A., and J. W. Bongberg, 1942. Logging high risk trees to control insects in the pine stands of northeastern California. *J. Forestry,* **40:**533–539.

Schnur, G. L., 1937. Yield, stand, and volume tables for even-aged upland oak forests. *U.S. Dept. Agr. Tech. Bul.* 560.

Schumacher, F. X., 1926. Yield, stand, and volume tables for white fir in the California pine region. *Univ. Calif., Agr. Expt. Sta. Bul.* 407.

———, 1928. Yield, stand and volume tables for red fir in California. *Univ. Calif., Agr. Expt. Sta. Bul.* 456.

———, 1930. Yield, stand, and volume tables for Douglas fir in California. *Univ. Calif., Agr. Expt. Sta. Bul.* 491.

—— and T. S. COILE, 1960. Growth and yield of natural stands of the southern pines. T. S. Coile, Inc. Durham, N.C.

SPURR, S. H., 1952. Forest inventory. The Ronald Press Company, New York.

——, 1954. Simplified computation of volume and growth. *J. Forestry*, **52**:914–922.

STAEBLER, G. R., 1958. Some mensurational aspects of the level-of-growing stock problem in even-aged stands. *J. Forestry*, **56**:112–115.

——, 1959. Optimum levels of growing stock for managed stands. *Proc. Soc. Am. Foresters*, 1959.

TARBOX, E. E., 1924. Quality and growth of white pine as influenced by density, site and associated species. *Harvard Univ., Harvard Forest Bul.* 7.

U.S. FOREST SERVICE, 1929. Volume, yield, and stand tables for second-growth southern pines. *U.S. Dept. Agr. Misc. Pub.* 50.

WACKERMAN, A. E., RAPHAEL ZON, and F. G. WILSON, 1929. Yield of jack pine in the Lake States. *Univ. Wis., College Agr. Res. Bul.* 90.

WAHLENBERG, W. G., 1941. Methods of forecasting timber growth in irregular stands. *U.S. Dept. Agr. Tech. Bul.* 796.

WALKER, NAT, 1956. Growing stock volumes in unmanaged and managed forests. *J. Forestry*, **54**:378–383.

WARRACK, G. C., 1959. Forecast of yield in relation to thinning regimes in Douglas fir. British Columbia Forest Serv., Dept. of Lands and Forests.

WATERS, W. T., and J. M. CHRISTIE, 1958. Provisional yield tables for oak and beech in Great Britain. *Forestry Commission: Forest Record 36*. Her Majesty's Stationery Office, London.

WATT, R. F., 1950. Approach toward normal stocking in western white pine stands. *Northwest Sci.*, **24**:149–157.

WIEDEMANN, E., and R. SCHOBER, 1957. Ertragstafeln (Rev. by Schober). M. u. S. Schaper, Hannover, West Germany.

CHAPTERS 5, 6, 7, 8, 9, 10

methods of managing the forest

ARBORGAST, CARL, 1957. Marking guides for northern hardwoods under the section system. *U.S. Forest Serv., Lake States Forest Expt. Sta. Paper* 56.

BARNES, G. H., 1951. A new method of volume regulation. *J. Forestry*, **49**:272–277.

BAXTER, D. V., 1952. Pathology in forest practice, 2d ed. John Wiley & Sons, Inc., New York.

BEHRE, C. E., 1945. Growing stock, cutting age, and sustained yield. *J. Forestry*, **43**:477–483.

BENTLEY, W. A., and D. E. TEEGUARDEN, 1965. Financial maturity: a theoretical review. *Forest Sci.*, **11**:76–87.

BIOLLEY, H. E., 1920. L'aménagement des forêts par la méthode expérimentale et spécialement la méthode du contrôle. Attinger Frères, Neuchâtel and Paris.

BOYCE, J. S., 1961. Forest pathology, 3d ed. McGraw-Hill Book Company, New York.

CHAPMAN, H. H., 1942. Management of loblolly pine in the pine-hardwood region in Arkansas and in Louisiana west of the Mississippi River. *Yale Univ., School Forestry Bul.* 49.

DANA, S. T., 1951. The growth of forestry in the past half century. *J. Forestry,* 49:86–92.

DAVIS, K. P., 1942. Economic management of western white pine forests. *U.S. Dept. Agr. Tech. Bul.* 830.

———, 1965. A structural analysis of land, income, and cost values in timber production, *J. Forestry,* 63:446–451.

DUERR, W. A., JOHN FEDKIW, and SAM GUTTENBERG, 1956. Financial maturity: a guide to profitable timber growing. *U.S. Dept. Agr. Tech. Bul.* 1146.

DUKE UNIVERSITY, 1956. Second conference on southern industrial forest management. Proceedings, School of Forestry, Duke Univ.

EYRE, F. H., and PAUL ZEHNGRAFF, 1948. Red pine management in Minnesota. *U.S. Dept. Agr. Cir.* 778.

——— and W. M. ZILLGITT, 1953. Partial cuttings in northern hardwoods of the Lake States. *U.S. Dept. Agr. Tech. Bul.* 1076.

FAUSTMANN, MARTIN, 1849. Berechnung des Werthes, welchen Waldboden, sowie noch nicht haubare Holzbestande fur die Waldwirtschaft besitzen (Calculation of values for forest land and for immature stands used for timber production). Allgemeine Forst-und Jagd Zeitung, 25:441–455.

GEVORKIANTZ, S. R., and L. P. OLSEN, 1950. Growth and yield of upland balsam fir in the Lake States. *U.S. Forest Serv., Lake States Forest Expt. Sta. Paper* 22.

GILBERT, A. M., and V. S. JENSEN, 1958. A management guide for northern hardwoods in New England. *U.S. Forest Serv., Northeast. Forest Expt. Sta. Paper* 112.

GOODSPEED, A. W., 1945. Determination of the regulated empirical growing stock from field data. *J. Forestry,* 43:908–914.

GRAHAM, S. A., and F. B. KNIGHT, 1965. Forest entomology, 4th ed. McGraw-Hill Book Company, New York.

GROSENBAUGH, L. R., 1955. Better diagnosis and prescription in southern forest management. *U.S. Forest Serv., Southern Forest Expt. Sta. Occas. Paper* 145.

———, 1958. Allowable cut as a new function of growth and diagnostic tallies. *J. Forestry,* 56:727–730.

GROSS, L. S., 1950. Timber management plans on the National Forests. *U.S. Dept. Agr. Forest Serv.* (unnumbered).

GUILKEY, P. C., and S. R. GEVORKIANTZ, 1949. Allowable cut. *U.S. Forest Serv., Lake States Forest Expt. Sta. Misc. Rept.* 4.

HAIG, I. T., K. P. DAVIS, and R. H. WEIDMAN, 1941. Natural regeneration in the western white pine type. *U.S. Dept. Agr. Tech. Bul.* 767.

HALLIN, W. E., 1959. The application of unit area control in the management of ponderosa-Jeffrey pine at Blacks Mountain Experimental Forest. *U.S. Dept. Agr. Tech. Bul.* 1191.

HANZLIK, E. J., 1922. Determination of the annual cut on a sustained basis for virgin American forests. *J. Forestry,* 20:611–625.

HILEY, W. E., 1954. Woodland management. Faber and Faber Ltd., London.

HUBER, ALFRED, 1952. Examination of sustained yield management by the volume

490   bibliography

and increment control method. Trans. by Leif Holt. *Pulp Paper Mag.,* 53(1):104–113.

KIRKLAND, B. P., and A. J. F. BRANSTROM, 1936. Selective timber management in the Douglas-fir region. Charles Lathrop Pack Forestry Foundation, Washington, D.C.

KNUCHEL, HERMANN, 1953. Planning and control in the managed forest. Trans. by M. L. Anderson. Oliver and Boyd, Edinburgh.

KUUSELA, KULLERMO, 1959. Largest permanent allowable cut and a method for its calculation. Acta Forestalia Fennica 71.

———— and AARNE NYYSSÖNEN, 1962. The cutting budget for a desirable growing stock. Acta Forestalia Fennica 74.6.

LEAK, W. B., 1964. An expression of diameter distribution for unbalanced, uneven-aged stands and forests. *Forest Sci.,* 10:39–50.

LUTZ, J., and R. F. CHANDLER, 1946. Forest soils. John Wiley & Sons, Inc., New York.

MATTHEWS, D. M., 1935. Management of American forests. McGraw-Hill Book Company, New York.

MCCULLEY, R. D., 1950. Management of natural slash pine stands in the flatwoods of south Georgia and north Florida. *U.S. Dept. Agr. Cir.* 845.

MCKEEVER, D. G., 1947. Empirical yield tables for Douglas fir, board feet Scribner rule by site and stocking classes. Weyerhaeuser Timber Co., Tacoma, Wash.

MEYER, H. A., 1943. Management without rotation. *J. Forestry,* 41:126–132.

————, 1952. Structure, growth, and drain in balanced uneven-aged forests. *J. Forestry,* 50:85–92.

————, A. B. RECKNAGEL, D. D. STEVENSON, and R. A. BARTOO, 1961. Forest management 2d ed. The Ronald Press Company, New York.

MEYER, W. H., 1942. Yield of even-aged stands of loblolly pine in northern Louisiana. *Yale Univ., School Forestry Bul.* 51.

————, 1952. Regulation of cut in immature, understocked forests. *J. Forestry,* 50:934–939.

PEARSON, G. A., 1951. Management of ponderosa pine in the southwest. *U.S. Dept. Agr. Monograph* 6.

PUTNAM, J. A., 1951. The relationship of utilization to silvicultural management in bottomland hardwoods. *J. Forestry,* 49:783–786.

————, G. M. FURNIVAL, and J. S. MCKNIGHT, 1960. Management and inventory of southern hardwoods. *U.S. Dept. Agr. Handbook* 181.

RECKNAGEL, A. B., 1917. Theory and practice of working plans, 2d ed. John Wiley & Sons, Inc., New York.

REYNOLDS, R. R., 1947. Management of second-growth shortleaf–loblolly pine–hardwood stands. *J. Forestry,* 45:181–187.

————, 1952. Profit possibilities from intensive management of loblolly pine. *J. Forestry,* 50:294–296.

————, 1959. Eighteen years of selection timber management on the Crossett Experimental Forest. *U.S. Dept. Agr. Tech. Bul.* 1206.

ROTH, FILIBERT, 1925. Forest regulation, 2d ed. George Wahr Publishing Company, Ann Arbor, Mich.

SCHLICH, SIR WILLIAM, 1925. Manual of forestry, 5th ed., Vol. 3. Bradbury, Agnew and Co., Ltd., London.

SCHNUR, G. L., 1937. Yield, stand, and volume tables for even-aged upland oak forests. *U.S. Dept. Agr. Tech. Bul.* 560.

SMITH, D. M., 1962. The practice of silviculture, 7th ed. John Wiley & Sons, Inc., New York.

SOCIETY OF AMERICAN FORESTERS, 1958. Forestry Terminology, 3d ed. Society of American Foresters, Washington, D.C.

TRIMBLE, G. R., JR., 1961. Managing mountain hardwoods—a ten-year appraisal. *U.S. Forest Serv., Northeastern Forest Expt. Sta. Paper* 143.

U.S. FOREST SERVICE, 1958. Report of the allowable cut task force, A. A. Hasel, Chairman. U.S. Dept. Agr. Forest Serv., Washington, D.C.

——, 1962. Determination of allowable annual timber cut on forty-two western national forests. Report of the Board of Review, K. P. Davis, Chairman. U.S. Dept. of Agr., Forest Serv., Washington D.C.

VAUX, H. J., 1954. Economics of the young-growth sugar pine resource. *Univ. Calif. Agr. Expt. Sta. Bul.* 738.

WEBSTER, H. H., 1960. Timber management opportunities in Pennsylvania. *U.S. Forest Serv., Northeast. Forest Expt. Sta. Paper* 137.

WEST COAST FORESTRY PROCEDURES COMMITTEE, 1950. Recommended forest practices and techniques. Western Forestry and Conservation Association, Portland, Ore.

CHAPTERS 11, 12, 13

forest organization, inventory, timber management planning and plans

ANONYMOUS, 1934. Working plans. *Punjab Forest Leaflet* 11. Issued by C. G. Trevor, Chief Conservator of Forests, Superintendent of Government Printing, Lahore, Punjab, Pakistan.

BAKER, R. D., and E. V. HUNT, JR., 1960. Continuous forest inventory with punch card machines for a small property. Dept. Forestry, Stephen F. Austin State College, Nacogdoches, Texas.

BENTLEY, A. W., 1953. Forest practice on privately-owned and privately-operated public lands in Canada. *Forestry Chronicle,* 29:53–63.

BERNSTEIN, D. A., 1962. Use of aerial photography in unit area control management. *J. Forestry,* 60:191–195.

BEST, A. L., 1954. Economics of forest management. *Dept. of Northern Affairs and National Resources, Forestry Branch, Economics Section, Bul.* 112. Ottawa, Canada.

BICKFORD, C. A., 1954. The place of individual-tree data in estimating growth. *J. Forestry,* 52:423–426.

BIOLLEY, H. E., 1920. L'aménagement des forêts par la méthode expérimentale et spécialement la méthode du contrôle. Attinger Frères, Paris and Neuchâtel.

BRITISH COLUMBIA FOREST SERVICE, 1952. Forest management licenses. *British Columbia Forest Serv. Pub.* B 37.

Bruce, Donald, and F. X. Schumacher, 1950. Forest mensuration, 3d ed. McGraw-Hill Book Company, New York.

Chapman, C. S., 1905. A working plan for forest lands in Berkeley County, South Carolina. *U.S. Dept. Agr. Bur. Forestry Bul.* 56.

Chapman, H. H., 1950. Forest management. The Hildreth Press, Bristol, Conn.

Cochran, W. G., 1953. Sampling techniques. John Wiley & Sons, Inc. New York.

Davis, K. P., 1959. Forest fire: control and use. McGraw-Hill Book Company, New York.

————, 1960. Progress in forest management. American Forestry: Six Decades of Growth, Henry Clepper and A. B. Meyer, Editors. Society of American Foresters, Washington, D.C.

————, 1960. Developments in planning and control on managed forests in the United States and Canada. Proc. Fifth World Forestry Congress, Univ. of Washington, Seattle.

Georgia, University of, 1959. Continuous inventory control in forest management, proceedings. School of Forestry and Center for Continuing Education, Athens, Georgia.

Graves, H. S., 1899. Practical forestry in the Adirondacks. *U.S. Dept. Agr. Div. Forestry Bul.* 26.

Gross, L. S., 1950. Timber management plans on the national forests. *Forest Serv., U.S. Dept. of Agr.* (unnumbered).

————, 1952. Management planning on the national forests. *J. Forestry,* **50:**618–622.

Hall, O. F., 1959. The contribution of remeasured sample plots to the precision of growth estimates. *J. Forestry,* **57:**807–811.

Hallin, W. E., 1951. Unit area control in California forests. *U.S. Forest Serv., Calif. Forest and Range Expt. Sta. Forest Res. Note* 77.

Hosmer, R. S., and E. S. Bruce, 1901. A forest working plan for township 40. *U.S. Dept. Agr., Div. Forestry Bul.* 30.

Huber, Alfred, 1952. Examination of sustained yield management by the volume and increment control method. Trans. by Leif Holt. *Pulp Paper Mag.,* **53:**104–113.

Knuchel, Hermann, 1953. Planning and control in the managed forest. Trans. by M. L. Anderson. Oliver and Boyd Ltd., Edinburgh and London.

Lachance, P. E., 1949. Sustained-yield management in Quebec. *Forestry Chronicle,* **25:**305–310.

Matthews, D. M., 1935. Management of American forests. McGraw-Hill Book Company, New York.

Mahan, N. P., 1934. Revised working plan for the forests of the Hoshiarpur forest division, 2 vols. Superintendent of Government Printing, Lahore, Punjab, Pakistan.

Meyer, W. H., 1960. Impressions of industrial forestry in southeastern United States. *J. Forestry,* **58:**179–187.

Moore, Barrington, 1915. Working plans: past history, present situation and future development. *Soc. Am. Foresters Proc.,* **10:**217–258.

Morriss, Donald J., 1962. Trends in timber management planning on the national forests. *J. Forestry* **60:**301–305.

Olmstead, F. E., 1902. A working plan for forest lands near Pine Bluff, Ark. *U.S. Dept. Agr., Bur. Forestry Bul.* 32.

ORCHARD, C. D., 1949. Forest management. *British Columbia Forest Serv. Publ. B.* 40, Vancouver.

——, 1953. Sustained yield forest management in British Columbia. *Forestry Chronicle,* **29**:45–54.

——, 1959. Preposterous prognosis (or the future of tree farm licences, public working circles, and sustained yield units in British Columbia). *Forestry Chronicle,* **35**:275–281.

OSBORNE, J. G., 1960. Influence of intended use of forest data on sample plot layout. Proc. Forest Management Control Conference, Purdue University, Ind.

PINCHOT, GIFFORD, 1898. The Adirondack spruce. The Critic Co., New York.

——, 1947. Breaking new ground. Harcourt, Brace and World, Inc., New York.

PURDUE UNIVERSITY, 1960. Forest management control conference, proc. Dept. of Forestry and Cons., Lafayette, Ind.

RECKNAGEL, A. B., 1913. Theory and practice of working plans. John Wiley & Sons, Inc., New York.

REED, F. W., 1905. A working plan for forest lands in central Alabama. *U.S. Dept. Agr., Forest Serv. Bul.* 68.

ROTH, FILIBERT, 1925. Forest regulation, 2d ed. George Wahr Publishing Company, Ann Arbor, Mich.

SAMLER, W. H. G., 1935. Revised working plan for the Kulu forests, 1934–35 to 1973–74. Superintendent of Government Printing, Lahore, Punjab, Pakistan.

SCHUMACHER, F. X., and R. A. CHAPMAN, 1948. Sampling methods in forestry and range management, rev. ed. *School Forestry, Duke University Bul.* 7.

SHERRARD, T. H., 1903. A working plan for forest lands in Hampton and Beaufort counties, South Carolina. *U.S. Dept. Agr., Bur. Forestry Bul.* 43.

SOCIETY OF AMERICAN FORESTERS, 1958. Forestry terminology, 3d ed. Washington, D.C.

SPURR, S. H., 1952. Forest inventory. The Ronald Press Company, New York.

——, 1960. Photogrammetry and photo-interpretation, 2d ed. The Ronald Press Company, New York.

UNITED STATES DEPARTMENT OF AGRICULTURE, 1949. Trees: The Yearbook of Agriculture.

WARE, K. D., and TIBERIUS CUNIA, 1962. Continuous forest inventory with partial replacement of samples. *Forest Sci., Monograph* 3.

WOOLSEY, T. S., 1922. American forest regulation. The Tuttle, Morehouse and Taylor Co. New Haven, Conn.

CHAPTERS 14, 15, 16, 17, 18, 19, 20

valuation

ACKOFF, R. L., 1962. Scientific method optimizing applied research decisions. John Wiley & Sons, Inc., New York.

ANDERSON, I. V., 1935. Application of selective logging to a ponderosa pine operation in western Montana. *Mont. Univ. Studies* 2, Missoula.

ANDERSON, W. C., 1961. A method of appraising pine sawtimber in South Carolina. *U.S. Forest Serv., Southeast. Forest Expt. Sta. Paper* 122.

BEERS, T. W., 1962. Components of forest growth. *J. Forestry*, 60:245–248.

BENTLEY, W. A., and D. E. TEEGUARDEN, 1965. Financial maturity: a theoretical review. *Forest Sci.*, 11:76–87.

BONBRIGHT, J. C., 1937. The valuation of property, Vol. 1, Part 1. McGraw-Hill Book Company, New York.

BRUNDAGE, M. R., M. E. KRUEGER, and DUNCAN DUNNING, 1933. The economic significance of tree size in western Sierra lumbering. *Univ. Calif., Agr. Expt. Sta. Bul.* 549.

BURKLE, J. L., and SAM GUTTENBERG, 1952. Marking guides for oaks and yellow-poplar in the southern uplands. *U.S. Forest Serv., South. Forest Expt. Sta. Occas. Paper* 125.

CAMPBELL, R. A., 1951. Tree grades, yields and values for some Appalachian hardwoods. *U.S. Forest Serv., South. Forest Expt. Sta. Paper* 8.

———, 1955. Tree grades and economic maturity for some Appalachian hardwoods. *U.S. Forest Serv., Southeast. Forest Expt. Sta. Paper* 53.

———, 1959. Tree grades give accurate estimate of second-growth yellow-poplar values. *U.S. Forest Serv., Southeast. Forest Expt. Sta. Paper* 108.

CHAPELLE, D. E., and T. C. NELSON, 1964. Estimation of optimal stocking levels and rotation ages of loblolly pine. *Forest Sci.*, 10:471–502.

CHAPMAN, H. H., and W. H. MEYER, 1947. Forest valuation. McGraw-Hill Book Company, New York.

COAN, NORMAN, 1962. "ROI" cash flow. *Pulp & Paper*, 36(10):112–115.

CORPUS JURIS SECUNDUM, Vol. 25, 1941. The American Law Book Co., Brooklyn, New York.

CURTIS, F. H., 1962. Linear programming the management of a forest property. *J. Forestry*, 60:611–616.

DAVIS, K. P., 1942. Economic management of western white pine forests. *U.S. Dept. Agr. Tech. Bul.* 830.

———, 1965. A structural analysis of land, income, and cost values in timber production. *J. Forestry*, 63:446–451.

DOWDLE, BARNEY, 1962. Investment theory and forest management planning. *Yale Univ., School of Forestry Bul.* 67.

DUERR, W. A., 1951. Guides to profitable forest management. *J. Forestry*, 49:771–773.

——— and W. E. BOND, 1952. Optimum stocking of a selection forest. *J. Forestry*, 50:12–16.

———, JOHN FEDKIW, and SAM GUTTENBERG, 1956. Financial maturity: a guide to profitable timber growing. *U.S. Dept. Agr. Tech. Bul.* 1146.

DUKE UNIVERSITY, SCHOOL OF FORESTRY, 1956. Second conference on southern industrial forest management.

———, 1958. Third conference on southern industrial forest management.

DUNNING, DUNCAN, 1928. A tree classification for the selection forests of the Sierra Nevada. *J. Agr. Res.*, 36:755–771.

FALK, H. W., JR., 1958. Timber and forest products law. Howell-North, Berkeley, California.

FEDKIW, JOHN, and J. G. YOHO, 1956. Financial maturity—what's it good for? *J. Forestry*, 54:587–590.

———, and ———, 1960. Economic models for thinning and reproducing even-aged stands. *J. Forestry,* **58**:26–34.

FENDER, D. E., and G. A. BROCK, 1963. Point center extension: a technique for measuring current economic growth and yield of merchantable forest stands. *J. Forestry,* **61**:109–114.

FLORA, D. F., 1964. Uncertainty in forest investment decisions. *J. Forestry,* **62**:376–380.

FOREST PRODUCTS LABORATORY, 1953. Hardwood lumber grades for standard lumber. *U.S. Forest Serv., Forest Products Lab. Rpt.* D1737.

GAFFNEY, M. M., 1957. Concepts of financial maturity of timber and other assets. A. E. Information Series 62, North Carolina State College, Raleigh.

GARVER, R. D., and R. H. MILLER, 1933. Selective logging in the shortleaf and loblolly pine forests of the Gulf States region. *U.S. Dept. Agr. Tech. Bul.* 375.

GILBERT, A. M., 1959. Sampling the quality of hardwood trees. *U.S. Forest Serv., Northeast. Forest Expt. Sta. Paper* 114.

GOULD, E. M. JR., and W. G. O'REGAN, 1965. Simulation, a step toward better forest planning. *Harvard Forest Papers* 13. Petersham, Mass.

GRANT, E. L., and W. G. IRESON, 1960. Principles of engineering economy, 4th ed. The Ronald Press Company, New York.

GROSENBAUGH, L. R., 1958. Allowable cut as a new function of growth and diagnostic tallies. *J. Forestry,* **56**:727–730.

GUTTENBERG, SAM, 1950. The rate of interest in forest management. *J. Forestry,* **48**:3–7.

——— and W. A. DUERR, 1949. A guide to profitable tree utilization. *U.S. Forest Serv., South. Forest Expt. Sta. Occas. Paper* 114.

——— and J. A. PUTNAM, 1951. Financial maturity of bottomland red oaks and sweetgum. *U.S. Forest Serv., South. Forest Expt. Sta. Occas. Paper* 117.

HAGENSTEIN, P. R., 1964. Factors affecting the location of wood-using plants in the northern Appalachians. *U.S. Forest Serv., Northeast. Forest Expt. Sta. Res. Paper* NE-16.

——— and BARNEY DOWDLE, 1962. A theoretical model for examining forest land use alternatives. *J. Forestry,* **60**:187–191.

HEIBERG, S. O., 1942. Cutting based upon economic increment. *J. Forestry,* **40**:645–651.

HENDERSON, J. D., 1931. Real estate appraising. The Bankers Publishing Company, Boston.

HENMAN, D. W., 1963. Pruning conifers for the production of quality timber. *Forestry Comm. Bul.* 35. Her Majesty's Stationery Office, Edinburgh.

HERRICK, A. M., 1946. Grade yields and overrun from Indiana hardwood sawlogs. *Purdue Univ., Agr. Expt. Sta. Bul.* 516.

———, 1948. Accuracy in estimating overrun. *South. Lumberman,* **177**(2):57–58.

———, 1956. The quality index in hardwood sawtimber management. *Purdue Univ., Agr. Expt. Sta. Bul.* 632.

HILEY, W. E., 1930. The economics of forestry. Clarendon Press, Oxford.

———, 1956. Economics of Plantations. Faber & Faber, Ltd., London.

HOLSOE, TORKEL, 1950. Profitable tree forms of yellow-poplar. *West Va. Univ. Agr. Expt. Sta. Bul.* 341.

HUTCHISON, S. B., 1951. A yardstick for judging public forestry projects. *J. Forestry*, **49**:99–101.

JAMES, L. M., 1946. Logging and milling studies in the southern Appalachian region. *U.S. Forest Serv., South. Forest Expt. Sta. Tech. Notes* 62, 63, 64 and 65.

———, 1949. Time study technique. *J. Forestry*, **47**:708–712.

JILES, R. A., JR., and J. W. LEHMAN, 1960. Hardwood logging methods and costs in the Tennessee Valley. *T.V.A. Div. of Forestry Rept.*, 232–60.

JOSEPHSON, H. R., 1941. Factors affecting income from second-growth forests in the western Sierra Nevada. *Univ. Calif., Agr. Expt. Sta. Bul.* 658.

KALMAR, L. F., 1958. The economy of intensive management of forest lands as it applies to site preparation and land regeneration. *J. Forestry*, **56**:489–491.

KEEN, F. P., 1943. Ponderosa pine tree classes redefined. *J. Forestry*, **41**:249–253.

KING, W. W. 1959. Quality control in circular sawmill operation. *T.V.A. Div. of Forestry Relations Rept.*, 226–259.

KINNEY, J. P., 1942. The essentials of American timber law, rev. ed., 1942. John Wiley & Sons, Inc., New York.

LEBARRON, R. K., 1958. What is unit area control? *J. Forestry*, **56**:662–663.

LOCKARD, C. R., J. A. PUTNAM, and R. D. CARPENTER, 1950. Log defects in southern hardwoods. *U.S. Dept. Agr. Handbook* 4.

LOUCKS, D. P., 1964. The development of an optimal program for sustained yield management. *J. Forestry*, **62**:485–490.

LUNDGREN, A. L., 1962. A graphical method of compounding and discounting for use in forest valuation problems. *J. Forestry*, **60**:136–138.

MARQUIS, R. W., 1939. Economics of private forestry. McGraw-Hill Book Company, New York.

———, 1951. Dollar signs and social values. *J. Forestry*, **49**:107–108.

MARTY, ROBERT, 1964. Analyzing uncertain timber investments. *U.S. Forest Serv. Northeast. Forest Expt. Sta. Res. Paper* NE-23.

MATTHEWS, D. M., 1935. Management of American forests. McGraw-Hill Book Company, New York.

———, 1942. Cost control in the logging industry. McGraw-Hill Book Company, New York.

MCLEAN, JOHN, G., 1958. How to evaluate new capital investments. *Harvard Business Review*, **36**(6):59–69.

MERTENS, JACOB, JR., (rev. by PHILIP ZIMET), 1958. The law of Federal income taxation, Vol. 10:59.01. Callaghan and Company, Mundelein, Illinois.

NORTHEASTERN FOREST EXPERIMENT STATION, 1963. A guide to hardwood log grading. *U.S. Forest Serv. Northeast. Forest Expt. Sta.*

PATON, W. A., ed., 1949. Accountant's handbook. The Ronald Press Company, New York.

RAPRAEGER, E. F., 1938. Results and application of a logging and milling study in the western white pine type of northern Idaho. *Univ. Idaho Bul.* 16.

REUL, R. I., 1957. Profitability index for investments. *Harvard Business Review*, **35**(4):116–132.

REYNOLDS, R. R., W. E. BOND, and B. P. KIRKLAND, 1944. Financial aspects of selective cutting in the management of second-growth pine-hardwood forests west of the Mississippi river. *U.S. Dept. Agr. Tech. Bul.* 861.

ROTHERY, J. E., 1941. Some interesting factors. *J. Forestry,* **39**:680–684.

———, 1945. Some aspects of appraising standing timber. *J. Forestry,* **43**:490–498.

———, 1952. A study of forest taxation in the Pacific Northwest. Industrial Forestry Association, Portland, Ore.

SCHICK, S. M., and G. L. FRASER, 1946. Fire prevention and the doctrine of tort. Eureka, Calif.

SHAW, E. W., and G. R. STAEBLER, 1950. Financial aspects of pruning. *U.S. Forest Serv., Pacific Northwest Forest and Range Expt. Sta.*

——— and ———, 1952. An analysis of investments in pruning. *J. Forestry,* **50**:819–823.

SMITH, J. H. G., 1954. The economics of pruning. *Forestry Chronicle,* **30**:197–214.

SOCIETY OF AMERICAN FORESTERS, 1924. What interest to use in forestry. Report of the committee on interest. *J. Forestry,* **22**(6):84–88.

TENNESSEE VALLEY AUTHORITY, 1956. Comparative results of circular sawmill surveys in the Tennessee valley. *T.V.A. Div. of Forestry Relations Rept.,* 215–56.

THOMSON, R. B., 1942. An examination of basic principles of comparative forest valuation. *Duke Univ. Forestry Bul.* 6.

U.S. FOREST SERVICE, n.d. Forest service handbook title 2400, timber management, Chapter 2420. Timber appraisal (national), Chapter 2425 (supplemental instructions and procedures separately by Regions 1–10). U.S. Forest Service, Washington, D.C.

———, 1922. Instructions for appraising stumpage on national forests. *U.S. Dept. Agr.(rev.)* 1922.

———, 1963. A general review of U.S. Forest Service timber appraisal policies and procedures. Report of Timber Appraisal Review Committee, A. C. Worrell, chairman. U.S. Dept. of Agr., Forest Service, Washington, D.C.

VAUX, H. J., 1949. Some economic goals in forest policy. *J. Forestry,* **47**:612–617.

———, 1951. Comments on a yardstick for judging public forestry projects. *J. Forestry,* **49**:101–103.

———, 1952. Economic measures of forest conservation. *Biology Colloquium on Conservation,* Oregon State College, Corvallis.

WEBSTER, H. H., 1960. Timber management opportunities in Pennsylvania. *U.S. Forest Serv. Northeast. Forest Expt. Sta. Paper* 137.

———, 1963. Timber management and economic analyses: a case study. *U.S. Forest Serv., Northeast. Forest Expt. Sta. Res. Paper* NE-14.

——— and P. R. HAGENSTEIN, 1963. Economic analysis of watershed management decisions—what sort of guides for land managers? *J. Forestry,* **61**:631–634.

———, R. J. MARTY, and R. A. SKOK, 1963. Forestry practice, biological research, and economic analysis. *J. Forestry,* **61**:754–759.

WEINTRAUB, SIDNEY, 1958. An examination of some economic aspects of Forest Service stumpage prices and appraisal policies. U.S. Forest Service, Washington, D.C.

WORRELL, A. C., 1953. A discussion of financial maturity. *J. Forestry,* **51**:711–714.

———, 1959. Economics of American forestry. John Wiley & Sons, Inc., New York.

WORTHINGTON, N. P., and JOHN FEDKIW, 1964. Economic consideration in the management of Douglas-fir growing stock. *U.S. Forest Serv. Pacific Northw. Forest and Range Expt. Sta. Res. Paper* PNW-12.

YALE UNIVERSITY, SCHOOL OF FORESTRY, 1960. Financial management of large forest ownerships. *Bul.* 66.

ZIVNUSKA, J. A., 1949. Some aspects of economic theory of forestry. *Land Economics,* **25**(2):165–172.

ZON, RAPHAEL, and R. D. GARVER, 1930. Selective logging in the northern hardwoods of the Lake States. *U.S. Dept. Agr. Tech. Bul.* 164.

appendix a   AREAS OF CIRCLES IN SQUARE FEET
CORRESPONDING TO DIAMETERS IN INCHES

Diam-eter, inches	Diameter, tenths of an inch									
	0.0	0.1	0.2	0.3	0.4	0.5	0.6	0.7	0.8	0.9
	Area, square feet									
1	0.006	0.007	0.008	0.009	0.011	0.012	0.014	0.016	0.018	0.020
2	0.022	0.024	0.026	0.029	0.031	0.034	0.037	0.040	0.043	0.046
3	0.049	0.052	0.056	0.059	0.063	0.067	0.071	0.075	0.079	0.083
4	0.087	0.092	0.096	0.101	0.106	0.111	0.115	0.121	0.126	0.131
5	0.136	0.142	0.147	0.153	0.159	0.165	0.171	0.177	0.184	0.190
6	0.196	0.203	0.210	0.216	0.223	0.230	0.238	0.245	0.252	0.260
7	0.267	0.275	0.283	0.291	0.299	0.307	0.315	0.323	0.332	0.340
8	0.349	0.358	0.367	0.376	0.385	0.394	0.403	0.413	0.422	0.432
9	0.442	0.452	0.462	0.472	0.482	0.492	0.503	0.513	0.524	0.535
10	0.545	0.556	0.568	0.579	0.590	0.601	0.613	0.625	0.636	0.648
11	0.660	0.672	0.684	0.697	0.709	0.721	0.734	0.747	0.760	0.772
12	0.785	0.799	0.812	0.825	0.839	0.852	0.866	0.880	0.894	0.908
13	0.922	0.936	0.950	0.965	0.979	0.994	1.009	1.024	1.039	1.054
14	1.069	1.084	1.100	1.115	1.131	1.147	1.163	1.179	1.195	1.211
15	1.227	1.244	1.260	1.277	1.294	1.310	1.327	1.344	1.362	1.379
16	1.396	1.414	1.431	1.449	1.467	1.485	1.503	1.521	1.539	1.558
17	1.576	1.595	1.614	1.632	1.651	1.670	1.689	1.709	1.728	1.748
18	1.767	1.787	1.807	1.827	1.847	1.867	1.887	1.907	1.928	1.948
19	1.969	1.990	2.011	2.032	2.053	2.074	2.095	2.117	2.138	2.160
20	2.181	2.204	2.226	2.248	2.270	2.292	2.315	2.337	2.360	2.383
21	2.405	2.428	2.451	2.475	2.498	2.521	2.545	2.568	2.592	2.616
22	2.640	2.664	2.688	2.712	2.737	2.761	2.786	2.810	2.835	2.860
23	2.885	2.910	2.936	2.961	2.986	3.012	3.038	3.064	3.089	3.115
24	3.142	3.168	3.194	3.221	3.247	3.275	3.301	3.328	3.355	3.382

Diam-eter, in.	Area, sq ft	Diam-eter, in.	Area, sq ft	Diam-eter, in.	Area, sq ft	Diam-eter, in.	Area, sq ft	Diam-eter, in.	Area, sq ft
25	3.41	32	5.59	39	8.30	46	11.54	53	15.32
26	3.69	33	5.94	40	8.73	47	12.05	54	15.90
27	3.98	34	6.30	41	9.17	48	12.57	55	16.50
28	4.28	35	6.68	42	9.62	49	13.10	56	17.10
29	4.59	36	7.07	43	10.08	50	13.64	57	17.72
30	4.91	37	7.47	44	10.56	51	14.19	58	18.35
31	5.24	38	7.88	45	11.04	52	14.75	59	18.99

appendix b   COMPOUND INTEREST TABLES
VALUES OF $(1+i)^n$

Years	Where $i^a =$									
n	0.1	0.2	0.3	0.4	0.5	0.6	0.7	0.8	0.9	1.0
1	1.001	1.002	1.003	1.004	1.005	1.006	1.007	1.008	1.009	1.010
2	1.002	1.004	1.006	1.008	1.010	1.012	1.014	1.016	1.018	1.020
3	1.003	1.006	1.009	1.012	1.015	1.018	1.021	1.024	1.027	1.030
4	1.004	1.008	1.012	1.016	1.020	1.024	1.028	1.032	1.036	1.041
5	1.005	1.010	1.015	1.020	1.025	1.030	1.035	1.041	1.046	1.051
6	1.006	1.012	1.018	1.024	1.030	1.037	1.043	1.049	1.055	1.062
7	1.007	1.014	1.021	1.028	1.036	1.043	1.050	1.057	1.065	1.072
8	1.008	1.016	1.024	1.032	1.041	1.049	1.057	1.066	1.074	1.083
9	1.009	1.018	1.027	1.037	1.046	1.055	1.065	1.074	1.084	1.094
10	1.010	1.020	1.030	1.041	1.051	1.062	1.072	1.083	1.094	1.105
11	1.011	1.022	1.033	1.045	1.056	1.068	1.080	1.092	1.104	1.116
12	1.012	1.024	1.037	1.049	1.062	1.074	1.087	1.100	1.114	1.127
13	1.013	1.026	1.040	1.053	1.067	1.081	1.095	1.109	1.124	1.138
14	1.014	1.028	1.043	1.057	1.072	1.087	1.103	1.118	1.134	1.149
15	1.015	1.030	1.046	1.062	1.078	1.094	1.110	1.127	1.144	1.161
16	1.016	1.032	1.049	1.066	1.083	1.100	1.118	1.136	1.154	1.173
17	1.017	1.035	1.052	1.070	1.088	1.107	1.126	1.145	1.165	1.184
18	1.018	1.037	1.055	1.075	1.094	1.113	1.134	1.154	1.175	1.196
19	1.019	1.039	1.059	1.079	1.099	1.120	1.142	1.163	1.186	1.208
20	1.020	1.041	1.062	1.083	1.105	1.127	1.150	1.173	1.196	1.220
21	1.021	1.043	1.065	1.087	1.110	1.134	1.158	1.182	1.207	1.232
22	1.022	1.045	1.068	1.092	1.116	1.141	1.166	1.192	1.218	1.245
23	1.023	1.047	1.071	1.096	1.122	1.148	1.174	1.201	1.229	1.257
24	1.024	1.049	1.075	1.101	1.127	1.154	1.182	1.211	1.240	1.270
25	1.025	1.051	1.078	1.105	1.133	1.161	1.190	1.220	1.251	1.282
26	1.026	1.053	1.081	1.109	1.138	1.168	1.199	1.230	1.262	1.295
27	1.027	1.055	1.084	1.114	1.144	1.175	1.207	1.240	1.274	1.308
28	1.028	1.058	1.087	1.118	1.150	1.182	1.216	1.250	1.285	1.321
29	1.029	1.060	1.091	1.123	1.156	1.189	1.224	1.260	1.297	1.334
30	1.030	1.062	1.094	1.127	1.161	1.197	1.233	1.270	1.308	1.348
35	1.036	1.072	1.111	1.150	1.191	1.233	1.277	1.322	1.368	1.417
40	1.041	1.083	1.127	1.173	1.221	1.270	1.322	1.375	1.431	1.489
45	1.046	1.094	1.144	1.197	1.252	1.309	1.369	1.431	1.497	1.565
50	1.051	1.105	1.162	1.221	1.283	1.349	1.417	1.490	1.565	1.645
55	1.057	1.116	1.179	1.246	1.316	1.390	1.468	1.550	1.637	1.729
60	1.062	1.127	1.197	1.271	1.349	1.432	1.520	1.613	1.712	1.817
65	1.067	1.139	1.215	1.296	1.383	1.475	1.574	1.679	1.790	1.909
70	1.072	1.150	1.233	1.322	1.418	1.520	1.630	1.747	1.872	2.007
75	1.078	1.162	1.252	1.349	1.454	1.566	1.687	1.818	1.958	2.109
80	1.083	1.173	1.271	1.376	1.490	1.614	1.747	1.892	2.048	2.217
85	1.089	1.185	1.290	1.404	1.528	1.663	1.809	1.969	2.142	2.330
90	1.094	1.197	1.309	1.432	1.567	1.713	1.874	2.049	2.240	2.449
95	1.100	1.209	1.329	1.461	1.606	1.765	1.940	2.132	2.342	2.574
100	1.105	1.221	1.349	1.491	1.647	1.819	2.009	2.219	2.450	2.705
110	1.116	1.246	1.390	1.551	1.731	1.931	2.154	2.402	2.680	2.988
120	1.127	1.271	1.433	1.615	1.819	2.050	2.310	2.602	2.931	3.300

a Here i is expressed in percentage form.

VALUES OF $(1+i)^n$

Years n	Where $i =$									
	1.1	1.2	1.3	1.4	1.5	1.6	1.7	1.8	1.9	2.0
1	1.011	1.012	1.013	1.014	1.015	1.016	1.017	1.018	1.019	1.020
2	1.022	1.024	1.026	1.028	1.030	1.032	1.034	1.036	1.038	1.040
3	1.033	1.036	1.040	1.043	1.046	1.049	1.052	1.055	1.058	1.061
4	1.045	1.049	1.053	1.057	1.061	1.066	1.070	1.074	1.078	1.082
5	1.056	1.061	1.067	1.072	1.077	1.083	1.088	1.093	1.099	1.104
6	1.068	1.074	1.081	1.087	1.093	1.100	1.107	1.113	1.120	1.126
7	1.080	1.087	1.095	1.102	1.110	1.118	1.125	1.133	1.141	1.149
8	1.091	1.100	1.109	1.118	1.126	1.135	1.144	1.153	1.163	1.172
9	1.103	1.113	1.123	1.133	1.143	1.154	1.164	1.174	1.185	1.195
10	1.116	1.127	1.138	1.149	1.161	1.172	1.184	1.195	1.207	1.219
11	1.128	1.140	1.153	1.165	1.178	1.191	1.204	1.217	1.230	1.243
12	1.140	1.154	1.168	1.182	1.196	1.210	1.224	1.239	1.254	1.268
13	1.153	1.168	1.183	1.198	1.214	1.229	1.245	1.261	1.277	1.294
14	1.166	1.182	1.198	1.215	1.232	1.249	1.266	1.284	1.302	1.319
15	1.178	1.196	1.214	1.232	1.250	1.269	1.288	1.307	1.326	1.346
16	1.191	1.210	1.230	1.249	1.269	1.289	1.310	1.330	1.352	1.373
17	1.204	1.225	1.246	1.267	1.288	1.310	1.332	1.354	1.377	1.400
18	1.218	1.240	1.262	1.284	1.307	1.331	1.355	1.379	1.403	1.428
19	1.231	1.254	1.278	1.302	1.327	1.352	1.378	1.404	1.430	1.457
20	1.245	1.269	1.295	1.321	1.347	1.374	1.401	1.429	1.457	1.486
21	1.258	1.285	1.312	1.339	1.367	1.396	1.425	1.455	1.485	1.516
22	1.272	1.300	1.329	1.358	1.388	1.418	1.449	1.481	1.513	1.546
23	1.286	1.316	1.346	1.377	1.408	1.441	1.474	1.507	1.542	1.577
24	1.300	1.331	1.363	1.396	1.429	1.464	1.499	1.535	1.571	1.608
25	1.315	1.347	1.381	1.416	1.451	1.487	1.524	1.562	1.601	1.641
26	1.329	1.364	1.399	1.435	1.473	1.511	1.550	1.590	1.631	1.673
27	1.343	1.380	1.417	1.456	1.495	1.535	1.576	1.619	1.662	1.707
28	1.358	1.397	1.436	1.476	1.517	1.560	1.603	1.648	1.694	1.741
29	1.373	1.413	1.454	1.497	1.540	1.585	1.631	1.678	1.726	1.776
30	1.388	1.430	1.473	1.518	1.563	1.610	1.658	1.708	1.759	1.811
35	1.467	1.518	1.572	1.627	1.684	1.743	1.804	1.867	1.932	2.000
40	1.549	1.611	1.676	1.744	1.814	1.887	1.963	2.041	2.123	2.208
45	1.636	1.710	1.788	1.869	1.954	2.043	2.135	2.232	2.333	2.438
50	1.728	1.816	1.908	2.004	2.105	2.211	2.323	2.440	2.563	2.692
55	1.825	1.927	2.035	2.148	2.268	2.394	2.527	2.668	2.816	2.972
60	1.928	2.046	2.171	2.303	2.443	2.592	2.750	2.917	3.094	3.281
65	2.036	2.171	2.315	2.469	2.632	2.806	2.991	3.189	3.399	3.623
70	2.151	2.305	2.470	2.646	2.835	3.038	3.254	3.486	3.734	4.000
75	2.272	2.446	2.635	2.837	3.055	3.289	3.541	3.811	4.103	4.416
80	2.399	2.597	2.810	3.041	3.291	3.560	3.852	4.167	4.508	4.875
85	2.534	2.756	2.998	3.260	3.545	3.854	4.191	4.556	4.952	5.383
90	2.677	2.926	3.198	3.495	3.819	4.173	4.559	4.981	5.441	5.943
95	2.827	3.106	3.411	3.746	4.114	4.518	4.960	5.446	5.978	6.562
100	2.986	3.296	3.639	4.016	4.432	4.891	5.396	5.954	6.568	7.245
110	3.331	3.714	4.140	4.615	5.144	5.732	6.387	7.116	7.928	8.831
120	3.717	4.185	4.711	5.303	5.969	6.718	7.560	8.506	9.570	10.77

VALUES OF $(1 + i)^n$

Years n	Where $i =$									
	2.1	2.2	2.3	2.4	2.5	2.6	2.7	2.8	2.9	3.0
1	1.021	1.022	1.023	1.024	1.025	1.026	1.027	1.028	1.029	1.030
2	1.043	1.045	1.047	1.049	1.051	1.053	1.055	1.057	1.059	1.061
3	1.064	1.068	1.071	1.074	1.077	1.080	1.083	1.086	1.090	1.093
4	1.087	1.091	1.095	1.100	1.104	1.108	1.113	1.117	1.121	1.126
5	1.110	1.115	1.120	1.126	1.131	1.137	1.140	1.148	1.154	1.159
6	1.133	1.140	1.146	1.153	1.160	1.167	1.173	1.180	1.187	1.194
7	1.157	1.165	1.173	1.181	1.189	1.197	1.205	1.213	1.222	1.230
8	1.181	1.190	1.200	1.209	1.218	1.228	1.238	1.247	1.257	1.267
9	1.206	1.216	1.227	1.238	1.249	1.260	1.271	1.282	1.293	1.305
10	1.231	1.243	1.255	1.268	1.280	1.293	1.305	1.318	1.331	1.344
11	1.257	1.271	1.284	1.297	1.312	1.326	1.341	1.355	1.370	1.384
12	1.283	1.299	1.314	1.329	1.345	1.361	1.377	1.393	1.409	1.426
13	1.310	1.327	1.344	1.361	1.379	1.396	1.414	1.432	1.450	1.468
14	1.338	1.356	1.375	1.394	1.413	1.433	1.453	1.472	1.492	1.513
15	1.366	1.386	1.407	1.427	1.448	1.470	1.492	1.513	1.536	1.558
16	1.395	1.417	1.439	1.462	1.485	1.508	1.532	1.556	1.580	1.605
17	1.424	1.448	1.472	1.497	1.522	1.547	1.573	1.599	1.626	1.653
18	1.454	1.480	1.506	1.533	1.560	1.587	1.615	1.644	1.673	1.702
19	1.484	1.512	1.541	1.569	1.599	1.629	1.659	1.690	1.721	1.753
20	1.515	1.545	1.576	1.607	1.639	1.671	1.704	1.737	1.771	1.806
21	1.547	1.579	1.612	1.646	1.680	1.714	1.750	1.786	1.823	1.860
22	1.580	1.614	1.649	1.685	1.722	1.759	1.797	1.836	1.876	1.916
23	1.613	1.650	1.687	1.726	1.765	1.805	1.846	1.887	1.930	1.974
24	1.647	1.686	1.726	1.767	1.809	1.852	1.895	1.940	1.986	2.033
25	1.681	1.723	1.766	1.809	1.854	1.900	1.947	1.995	2.044	2.094
26	1.717	1.761	1.806	1.853	1.900	1.949	1.999	2.050	2.103	2.157
27	1.753	1.800	1.848	1.897	1.948	2.000	2.053	2.108	2.164	2.221
28	1.790	1.839	1.890	1.943	1.997	2.052	2.109	2.167	2.227	2.288
29	1.827	1.880	1.934	1.989	2.046	2.105	2.165	2.227	2.291	2.357
30	1.865	1.921	1.978	2.037	2.098	2.160	2.224	2.290	2.358	2.427
35	2.070	2.142	2.216	2.294	2.373	2.456	2.541	2.629	2.720	2.814
40	2.296	2.388	2.483	2.581	2.685	2.792	2.903	3.017	3.138	3.262
45	2.548	2.663	2.782	2.907	3.038	3.174	3.316	3.465	3.620	3.782
50	2.827	2.969	3.117	3.274	3.437	3.609	3.789	3.978	4.176	4.384
55	3.136	3.310	3.493	3.686	3.889	4.103	4.329	4.567	4.818	5.082
60	3.480	3.690	3.913	4.150	4.400	4.665	4.946	5.243	5.558	5.892
65	3.861	4.115	4.385	4.672	4.978	5.304	5.650	6.019	6.412	6.830
70	4.284	4.587	4.912	5.260	5.632	6.030	6.455	6.911	7.397	7.918
75	4.753	5.115	5.504	5.923	6.372	6.856	7.375	7.934	8.534	9.179
80	5.273	5.703	6.167	6.668	7.210	7.795	8.426	9.109	9.845	10.64
85	5.850	6.358	6.909	7.508	8.157	8.862	9.627	10.46	11.35	12.34
90	6.491	7.089	7.741	8.452	9.229	10.06	11.00	12.01	13.10	14.30
95	7.702	7.904	8.673	9.517	10.44	11.46	12.57	13.78	15.12	16.58
100	7.991	8.812	9.718	10.72	11.81	13.02	14.36	15.82	17.44	19.22
110	9.836	10.83	12.20	13.58	15.12	16.60	18.74	20.86	23.21	25.83
120	12.11	13.62	15.31	17.21	19.36	21.76	24.46	27.49	30.89	34.71

VALUES OF $(1+i)^n$

Years	Where $i =$									
n	3.1	3.2	3.3	3.4	3.5	3.6	3.7	3.8	3.9	4.0
1	1.031	1.032	1.033	1.034	1.035	1.036	1.037	1.038	1.039	1.040
2	1.063	1.065	1.067	1.070	1.071	1.073	1.075	1.077	1.080	1.082
3	1.096	1.100	1.102	1.106	1.109	1.112	1.115	1.118	1.122	1.125
4	1.130	1.134	1.139	1.143	1.148	1.152	1.157	1.161	1.165	1.170
5	1.165	1.171	1.176	1.182	1.188	1.194	1.199	1.205	1.211	1.217
6	1.201	1.208	1.215	1.222	1.229	1.236	1.244	1.251	1.258	1.265
7	1.238	1.247	1.255	1.264	1.272	1.281	1.290	1.298	1.307	1.316
8	1.277	1.287	1.297	1.307	1.317	1.327	1.337	1.348	1.358	1.369
9	1.316	1.328	1.339	1.351	1.363	1.375	1.387	1.399	1.411	1.423
10	1.357	1.370	1.384	1.397	1.411	1.424	1.438	1.452	1.466	1.480
11	1.399	1.414	1.429	1.445	1.460	1.476	1.491	1.507	1.523	1.539
12	1.443	1.459	1.476	1.494	1.511	1.529	1.547	1.565	1.583	1.601
13	1.487	1.506	1.525	1.545	1.564	1.584	1.604	1.624	1.644	1.665
14	1.533	1.554	1.576	1.597	1.619	1.641	1.663	1.686	1.709	1.732
15	1.581	1.604	1.628	1.651	1.675	1.700	1.725	1.750	1.775	1.801
16	1.630	1.655	1.681	1.707	1.734	1.761	1.788	1.816	1.844	1.873
17	1.680	1.708	1.737	1.766	1.795	1.824	1.855	1.885	1.916	1.948
18	1.733	1.763	1.794	1.826	1.857	1.890	1.924	1.957	1.991	2.026
19	1.786	1.819	1.853	1.888	1.923	1.958	1.994	2.031	2.069	2.107
20	1.842	1.878	1.915	1.952	1.990	2.029	2.068	2.108	2.149	2.191
21	1.899	1.938	1.978	2.018	2.059	2.102	2.145	2.189	2.233	2.279
22	1.958	2.000	2.043	2.087	2.132	2.177	2.224	2.272	2.320	2.370
23	2.018	2.064	2.110	2.158	2.206	2.256	2.306	2.358	2.411	2.465
24	2.081	2.130	2.180	2.231	2.283	2.337	2.392	2.448	2.505	2.563
25	2.145	2.198	2.252	2.307	2.363	2.421	2.480	2.541	2.603	2.666
26	2.212	2.268	2.326	2.385	2.446	2.508	2.572	2.637	2.704	2.772
27	2.280	2.341	2.403	2.467	2.532	2.599	2.667	2.737	2.810	2.883
28	2.351	2.416	2.482	2.550	2.620	2.692	2.766	2.841	2.919	2.999
29	2.424	2.493	2.564	2.637	2.712	2.789	2.868	2.949	3.033	3.119
30	2.499	2.573	2.649	2.727	2.807	2.889	2.974	3.061	3.151	3.243
35	2.911	3.012	3.115	3.223	3.334	3.448	3.567	3.689	3.815	3.946
40	3.391	3.525	3.664	3.809	3.959	4.115	4.277	4.445	4.620	4.801
45	3.951	4.127	4.310	4.502	4.702	4.911	5.129	5.357	5.594	5.841
50	4.602	4.830	5.070	5.321	5.585	5.861	6.151	6.455	6.776	7.107
55	5.361	5.654	5.964	6.290	6.633	6.995	7.376	7.778	8.201	8.646
60	6.245	6.619	7.015	7.434	7.878	8.348	8.846	9.373	9.930	10.52
65	7.275	7.748	8.251	8.784	9.357	9.963	10.61	11.29	12.02	12.80
70	8.473	9.069	9.706	10.39	11.11	11.89	12.78	13.59	14.56	15.57
75	9.872	10.62	11.42	12.28	13.20	14.19	15.26	16.40	17.63	18.95
80	11.50	12.43	13.43	14.51	15.68	16.94	18.29	19.76	21.34	23.05
85	13.40	14.56	15.80	17.15	18.62	20.21	21.94	23.81	25.84	28.04
90	15.61	17.03	18.58	20.27	22.11	24.12	26.31	28.69	31.29	34.12
95	18.18	19.93	21.85	23.96	26.26	28.79	31.55	34.58	37.89	41.51
100	21.16	23.33	25.71	28.32	31.19	34.36	37.83	41.66	45.87	50.50
110	28.74	31.97	35.57	39.56	44.00	48.93	54.41	60.50	67.25	74.76
120	39.00	43.81	49.21	55.27	62.06	69.69	78.25	87.84	98.59	110.7

VALUES OF $(1 + i)^n$

Years	Where $i =$									
n	4.1	4.2	4.3	4.4	4.5	4.6	4.7	4.8	4.9	5.0
1	1.041	1.042	1.043	1.044	1.045	1.046	1.047	1.048	1.049	1.050
2	1.083	1.086	1.088	1.090	1.092	1.094	1.096	1.098	1.100	1.103
3	1.128	1.131	1.135	1.138	1.141	1.145	1.148	1.151	1.154	1.158
4	1.174	1.179	1.184	1.188	1.193	1.197	1.202	1.206	1.211	1.216
5	1.223	1.228	1.234	1.240	1.246	1.252	1.258	1.264	1.270	1.276
6	1.273	1.280	1.287	1.295	1.302	1.310	1.317	1.325	1.333	1.340
7	1.325	1.334	1.343	1.352	1.361	1.370	1.379	1.389	1.398	1.407
8	1.379	1.390	1.401	1.411	1.422	1.433	1.444	1.455	1.466	1.478
9	1.436	1.448	1.461	1.473	1.486	1.499	1.512	1.532	1.539	1.551
10	1.495	1.509	1.524	1.539	1.553	1.568	1.583	1.598	1.614	1.629
11	1.556	1.573	1.589	1.610	1.623	1.640	1.657	1.675	1.693	1.710
12	1.620	1.638	1.657	1.677	1.696	1.716	1.735	1.755	1.776	1.796
13	1.686	1.707	1.729	1.750	1.772	1.794	1.817	1.840	1.863	1.886
14	1.755	1.779	1.803	1.827	1.852	1.877	1.902	1.928	1.954	1.980
15	1.827	1.854	1.881	1.908	1.935	1.963	1.992	2.020	2.050	2.079
16	1.902	1.932	1.961	1.992	2.022	2.054	2.085	2.117	2.150	2.183
17	1.980	2.013	2.046	2.079	2.113	2.148	2.183	2.219	2.255	2.292
18	2.061	2.097	2.134	2.171	2.208	2.247	2.286	2.326	2.366	2.407
19	2.146	2.185	2.225	2.266	2.308	2.350	2.393	2.437	2.482	2.527
20	2.234	2.277	2.321	2.366	2.412	2.458	2.506	2.554	2.603	2.653
21	2.325	2.373	2.421	2.459	2.520	2.571	2.624	2.677	2.731	2.786
22	2.421	2.472	2.525	2.579	2.634	2.690	2.747	2.805	2.865	2.925
23	2.520	2.576	2.634	2.692	2.752	2.813	2.876	2.940	3.005	3.072
24	2.623	2.684	2.747	2.811	2.876	2.943	3.011	3.081	3.152	3.225
25	2.731	2.797	2.865	2.934	3.005	3.078	3.153	3.229	3.307	3.386
26	2.843	2.915	2.988	3.064	3.141	3.220	3.301	3.384	3.469	3.556
27	2.959	3.037	3.117	3.198	3.282	3.368	3.456	3.546	3.639	3.733
28	3.081	3.164	3.251	3.339	3.430	3.523	3.618	3.716	3.817	3.920
29	3.207	3.297	3.390	3.486	3.584	3.685	3.788	3.895	4.004	4.116
30	3.338	3.436	3.536	3.640	3.745	3.854	3.967	4.082	4.200	4.322
35	4.081	4.221	4.365	4.514	4.667	4.826	4.990	5.160	5.335	5.516
40	4.989	5.185	5.387	5.598	5.816	6.043	6.279	6.523	6.777	7.040
45	6.099	6.369	6.650	6.943	7.248	7.567	7.900	8.246	8.608	8.985
50	7.257	7.823	8.208	8.611	9.033	9.475	9.939	10.43	10.93	11.47
55	9.116	9.610	10.13	10.68	11.26	11.87	12.51	13.18	13.89	14.64
60	11.15	11.81	12.51	13.25	14.03	14.86	15.73	16.66	17.64	18.68
65	13.62	14.50	15.44	16.43	17.48	18.60	19.79	21.06	22.41	23.84
70	16.66	17.81	19.05	20.37	21.78	23.29	24.90	26.63	28.46	30.43
75	20.36	21.88	23.52	25.27	27.15	29.17	31.33	33.66	36.16	38.83
80	24.84	26.88	29.03	31.34	33.93	36.52	39.42	42.55	45.93	49.56
85	30.43	33.02	35.82	38.86	42.16	45.73	49.60	53.79	58.33	63.25
90	37.20	40.56	44.22	48.20	52.54	57.26	62.41	68.00	74.10	80.73
95	45.48	49.82	54.58	59.78	65.47	71.70	78.51	85.97	94.12	103.0
100	55.60	61.20	67.37	74.14	81.59	89.78	98.78	108.7	119.6	131.5
110	83.10	92.35	102.6	114.0	126.7	140.8	156.4	173.7	192.9	214.2
120	124.2	139.4	156.4	175.4	196.8	220.7	247.5	277.5	311.2	348.9

VALUES OF $(1 + i)^n$

Years n	Where $i =$									
	5.1	5.2	5.3	5.4	5.5	5.6	5.7	5.8	5.9	6.0
1	1.051	1.052	1.053	1.054	1.055	1.056	1.057	1.058	1.059	1.060
2	1.105	1.107	1.109	1.111	1.113	1.115	1.117	1.119	1.122	1.124
3	1.161	1.164	1.168	1.171	1.174	1.178	1.181	1.184	1.188	1.191
4	1.220	1.226	1.230	1.234	1.239	1.244	1.248	1.253	1.258	1.262
5	1.282	1.289	1.295	1.301	1.307	1.313	1.319	1.326	1.332	1.338
6	1.348	1.356	1.363	1.371	1.379	1.387	1.395	1.403	1.411	1.419
7	1.417	1.423	1.436	1.445	1.455	1.464	1.474	1.484	1.494	1.504
8	1.489	1.500	1.512	1.523	1.535	1.547	1.558	1.570	1.582	1.594
9	1.565	1.578	1.592	1.604	1.619	1.633	1.647	1.661	1.675	1.689
10	1.645	1.660	1.676	1.692	1.708	1.724	1.741	1.757	1.774	1.791
11	1.729	1.747	1.765	1.783	1.802	1.821	1.840	1.859	1.879	1.898
12	1.817	1.837	1.859	1.880	1.901	1.923	1.945	1.967	1.990	2.012
13	1.909	1.933	1.957	1.981	2.006	2.031	2.056	2.081	2.107	2.133
14	2.007	2.033	2.061	2.088	2.116	2.144	2.173	2.202	2.231	2.261
15	2.109	1.139	2.170	2.201	2.233	2.265	2.297	2.330	2.363	2.397
16	2.216	2.250	2.285	2.320	2.355	2.391	2.428	2.465	2.502	2.540
17	2.329	2.367	2.406	2.445	2.485	2.525	2.566	2.608	2.650	2.693
18	2.448	2.491	2.534	2.577	2.621	2.667	2.712	2.759	2.806	2.854
19	2.573	2.620	2.668	2.716	2.766	2.815	2.867	2.919	2.972	3.026
20	2.704	2.756	2.809	2.863	2.918	2.974	3.030	3.088	3.147	3.207
21	2.842	2.900	2.958	3.018	3.078	3.140	3.203	3.267	3.383	3.400
22	2.987	3.050	3.115	3.181	3.248	3.316	3.386	3.457	3.530	3.604
23	3.136	3.209	3.280	3.352	3.426	3.502	3.579	3.657	3.738	3.829
24	3.300	3.376	3.454	3.533	3.615	3.698	3.783	3.870	3.958	4.049
25	3.468	3.551	3.637	3.724	3.813	3.905	3.998	4.094	4.192	4.292
26	3.645	3.736	3.830	3.925	4.023	4.124	4.226	4.332	4.439	4.550
27	3.831	3.930	4.033	4.137	4.245	4.354	4.467	4.583	4.701	4.822
28	4.026	4.135	4.246	4.361	4.478	4.598	4.722	4.850	4.978	5.112
29	4.231	4.350	4.471	4.596	4.724	4.856	4.993	5.130	5.272	5.418
30	4.447	4.576	4.708	4.844	4.984	5.128	5.275	5.427	5.583	5.744
35	5.703	5.896	6.095	6.301	6.514	6.734	6.960	7.195	7.436	7.686
40	7.313	7.596	7.891	8.197	8.513	8.842	9.184	9.537	9.905	10.29
45	9.378	9.788	10.22	10.66	11.13	11.61	12.12	12.64	13.19	13.77
50	12.03	12.61	13.23	13.87	14.54	15.25	15.99	16.76	17.57	18.42
55	15.42	16.25	17.02	18.04	19.01	20.02	21.09	22.23	23.40	24.65
60	19.78	20.94	22.17	23.47	24.84	26.29	27.83	29.45	31.17	32.99
65	25.36	26.98	28.70	30.52	32.46	34.53	36.72	39.05	41.52	44.14
70	32.52	34.76	37.15	39.71	42.43	45.34	48.15	51.76	55.30	59.08
75	41.71	44.79	48.10	51.65	55.46	59.54	63.92	68.62	73.66	79.06
80	53.48	57.71	62.27	67.18	72.48	78.18	84.33	90.96	98.10	105.8
85	68.59	74.36	80.62	87.38	94.73	102.7	111.3	120.6	130.6	141.6
90	87.95	95.81	104.4	113.7	123.8	134.8	146.8	159.9	174.0	189.5
95	112.8	123.4	135.1	147.9	161.8	177.0	193.7	211.9	231.8	253.5
100	144.6	159.1	174.9	192.3	211.5	232.5	249.8	280.9	305.8	339.3
110	237.9	264.1	293.2	325.4	361.2	400.9	444.9	493.7	547.7	607.6
120	391.1	438.4	491.4	550.7	617.0	691.3	788.7	867.5	971.7	1,088

VALUES OF $(1+i)^n$

Years n	Where $i =$									
	6.2	6.4	6.6	6.8	7.0	7.2	7.4	7.6	7.8	8.0
1	1.062	1.064	1.066	1.068	1.070	1.072	1.074	1.076	1.078	1.080
2	1.127	1.132	1.136	1.141	1.145	1.149	1.154	1.158	1.162	1.166
3	1.198	1.205	1.211	1.218	1.225	1.232	1.239	1.246	1.253	1.260
4	1.272	1.282	1.291	1.301	1.311	1.321	1.331	1.341	1.351	1.361
5	1.351	1.364	1.377	1.390	1.403	1.416	1.429	1.442	1.456	1.469
6	1.435	1.451	1.467	1.484	1.501	1.518	1.535	1.552	1.569	1.587
7	1.524	1.544	1.564	1.585	1.606	1.627	1.648	1.670	1.692	1.714
8	1.618	1.643	1.668	1.693	1.718	1.744	1.770	1.797	1.824	1.851
9	1.718	1.748	1.778	1.808	1.839	1.870	1.901	1.933	1.966	1.999
10	1.825	1.860	1.895	1.931	1.967	2.004	2.042	2.080	2.119	2.159
11	1.938	1.979	2.020	2.062	2.105	2.149	2.193	2.238	2.285	2.326
12	2.058	2.105	2.153	1.202	2.252	2.303	2.355	2.409	2.463	2.518
13	2.186	2.240	2.295	2.352	2.407	2.469	2.530	2.592	2.655	2.720
14	2.321	2.383	2.447	2.512	2.579	2.647	2.716	2.789	2.862	2.938
15	2.465	2.535	2.608	2.683	2.759	2.838	2.918	3.001	3.085	3.172
16	2.618	2.698	2.781	2.865	2.952	3.042	3.133	3.229	3.326	3.426
17	2.781	2.870	2.964	3.060	3.159	3.261	3.366	3.474	3.585	3.700
18	2.953	3.055	3.160	3.268	3.380	3.496	3.615	3.738	3.865	3.996
19	3.136	3.250	3.368	3.490	3.617	3.747	3.882	4.022	4.166	4.316
20	3.330	3.458	3.590	3.728	3.870	4.017	4.170	4.328	4.491	4.661
21	3.537	3.679	3.827	3.981	4.141	4.306	4.478	4.657	4.842	5.034
22	3.756	3.915	4.080	4.252	4.431	4.616	4.810	5.010	5.219	5.437
23	3.989	4.165	4.349	4.541	4.741	4.949	5.165	5.391	5.627	5.872
24	4.236	4.432	4.636	4.850	5.072	5.305	5.548	5.801	6.065	6.341
25	4.499	4.716	4.942	5.180	5.428	5.687	5.958	6.213	6.538	6.849
26	4.778	5.018	5.269	5.532	5.807	6.096	6.399	6.716	7.048	7.396
27	5.074	5.339	5.616	5.908	6.214	6.535	6.873	7.227	7.598	7.988
28	5.389	5.680	5.987	6.310	6.649	7.005	7.381	7.776	8.191	8.627
29	5.723	6.044	6.382	6.739	6.794	7.510	7.927	8.367	8.830	9.317
30	6.078	6.431	6.803	7.197	7.612	8.051	8.514	9.003	9.518	10.06
35	8.210	8.769	9.365	10.00	10.68	11.40	12.17	12.99	13.86	14.79
40	11.09	11.96	12.89	13.90	14.98	16.14	17.39	18.73	20.17	21.73
45	14.98	16.31	17.75	19.31	21.00	22.85	24.84	27.01	29.37	31.92
50	20.24	22.24	24.43	26.82	29.46	32.34	35.50	38.96	42.75	46.90
55	27.34	30.33	33.62	37.28	41.32	45.79	50.73	56.19	62.24	68.92
60	36.94	41.35	46.29	51.79	57.95	64.82	72.49	81.05	90.60	101.3
65	49.90	56.39	63.71	71.97	81.27	91.76	103.5	116.4	131.9	149.1
70	67.41	76.90	87.70	100.0	114.0	129.9	148.0	168.6	192.0	218.6
75	91.06	104.9	120.7	139.0	159.9	183.9	211.5	243.2	279.5	321.2
80	123.0	143.0	166.2	193.1	224.2	260.4	302.2	350.7	406.9	472.0
85	166.2	195.0	228.8	268.3	314.5	368.6	431.9	505.8	592.4	693.5
90	224.5	265.9	314.9	372.8	441.1	521.8	617.1	729.6	862.4	1,019
95	303.3	362.6	433.5	517.9	618.7	738.8	881.9	1,052	1,256	1,497
100	409.7	494.5	596.7	719.7	867.7	1,046	1,260	1,518	1,828	2,200

VALUES OF $(1 + i)^n$

Years n	Where $i =$									
	8.2	8.4	8.6	8.8	9.0	9.2	9.4	9.6	9.8	10
1	1.082	1.084	1.086	1.088	1.090	1.092	1.094	1.096	1.098	1.100
2	1.171	1.175	1.179	1.184	1.188	1.193	1.197	1.201	1.206	1.210
3	1.267	1.274	1.281	1.288	1.295	1.302	1.309	1.317	1.324	1.331
4	1.371	1.381	1.391	1.401	1.412	1.422	1.432	1.443	1.454	1.464
5	1.483	1.497	1.510	1.525	1.539	1.552	1.567	1.582	1.596	1.611
6	1.605	1.623	1.641	1.659	1.677	1.696	1.714	1.733	1.752	1.772
7	1.736	1.759	1.782	1.805	1.828	1.852	1.876	1.900	1.924	1.949
8	1.878	1.907	1.935	1.964	1.993	2.022	2.052	2.082	2.113	2.144
9	2.033	2.067	2.101	2.136	2.172	2.208	2.245	2.282	2.320	2.358
10	2.199	2.240	2.282	2.324	2.367	2.411	2.456	2.501	2.547	2.594
11	2.380	2.429	2.478	2.529	2.581	2.633	2.687	2.741	2.797	2.853
12	2.575	2.632	2.691	2.751	2.813	2.875	2.939	3.004	3.071	3.139
13	2.786	2.854	2.923	2.994	3.066	3.133	3.125	3.293	3.372	3.452
14	3.014	3.093	3.174	3.257	3.337	3.429	3.518	3.609	3.702	3.798
15	3.262	3.353	3.447	3.544	3.643	3.744	3.848	3.955	4.065	4.177
16	3.529	3.635	3.744	3.855	3.970	4.089	4.210	4.334	4.463	4.595
17	3.818	3.940	4.066	4.195	4.328	4.465	4.606	4.751	4.901	5.055
18	4.131	4.271	4.415	4.564	4.717	4.875	5.038	5.207	5.381	5.560
19	4.470	4.630	4.795	4.965	5.142	5.324	5.512	5.707	5.908	6.116
20	4.837	5.019	5.207	5.402	5.605	5.814	6.030	6.254	6.487	6.728
21	5.233	5.440	5.655	5.878	6.109	6.349	6.597	6.855	7.123	7.400
22	5.662	5.897	6.141	6.395	6.659	6.933	7.217	7.513	7.821	8.140
23	6.127	6.393	6.669	6.958	7.258	7.571	7.896	8.235	8.587	8.954
24	6.629	6.930	7.243	7.570	7.911	8.267	8.638	9.025	9.429	9.850
25	7.173	7.512	7.866	8.236	8.623	9.028	9.450	9.892	10.35	10.84
26	7.761	8.143	8.542	8.961	9.399	9.858	10.34	10.84	11.37	11.92
27	8.397	8.827	9.277	9.750	10.25	10.77	11.31	11.88	12.48	13.11
28	9.086	9.568	10.08	10.61	11.17	11.76	12.37	13.02	13.71	14.42
29	9.831	10.37	10.94	11.54	12.17	12.84	13.54	14.27	15 05	15.86
30	10.64	11.24	11.88	12.56	13.27	14.03	14.81	15.64	16.52	17.45
35	15.78	16.83	17.95	19.14	20.41	21.77	23.21	24.73	26.37	28.10
40	23.39	25.19	27.11	29.19	31.41	33.80	36.37	39.12	42.08	45.26
45	34.69	37.70	40.96	44.49	48.33	52.48	56.99	61.87	67.16	72.89
50	51.45	56.43	61.87	67.83	74.36	81.50	89.30	97.84	107.2	117.4
55	76.30	84.45	93.46	103.3	114.4	126.6	140.0	154.7	171.1	189.1
60	113.2	126.4	141.2	157.7	176.0	196.5	219.3	244.7	273.0	304.5
65	167.8	189.2	213.3	240.4	270.8	305.1	343.7	387.0	435.7	490.4
70	248.8	283.2	322.2	366.5	416.7	473.8	538.5	612.0	695.3	798.8
75	369.0	423.8	486.7	558.7	641.2	735.7	843.9	967.8	1,110	1,272
80	547.3	634.4	735.2	851.8	986.6	1,142	1,323	1,531	1,771	2,048

index

index